Calculus
Concepts and Applications
Second Edition

Instructor's Resource Book

Paul A. Foerster

Key Curriculum Press
Innovators in Mathematics Education

Project Editor: Josephine Noah

Consulting Editor: Christopher David

Project Administrator: Shannon Miller

Project Contributors: Stu Schwartz, Scott Steketee

Accuracy Checker: Dudley Brooks

Production Director: Diana Jean Ray

Production Editor: Christine Osborne

Copyeditor: Margaret Moore

Production Coordinator: Michael Hurtik

Text and Cover Designer: Jenny Somerville

Art Editor: Jason Luz

Art and Design Coordinator: Kavitha Becker

Technical Art: Jason Luz

Cover Photo Credit: Alec Pytlowaney/Masterfile

Compositor and Prepress: Interactive Composition Corporation

Printer: Von Hoffmann Corporation

Executive Editor: Casey FitzSimons

Publisher: Steve Rasmussen

Key Curriculum Press
1150 65th Street
Emeryville, CA 94608
editorial@keypress.com
www.keypress.com

Printed in the United States of America

10 9 8 7 6 5 4 3 2 1   11 10 09 08 07 06 05 04

ISBN 1-55953-656-X

Contents

Contents

Guide to the *Instructor's Resource Book*

This table is designed to assist you in locating the resources that can be found in this volume.
The number of checks in each column indicates the number of resources available for a particular lesson.
Note that the checks in the Test column indicate the last section of a chapter that the test covers.
Checks in the final section indicate Chapter Tests or Cumulative Tests.

Lesson	Blackline Master	Exploration Master	Test
1-1		✓	
1-2	✓	✓	
1-3		✓	
1-4		✓	
1-5			
1-6	✓		✓✓✓
2-1		✓	
2-2	✓	✓	
2-3		✓✓	✓
2-4		✓	
2-5		✓	
2-6			
2-7		✓✓	✓✓
3-1			
3-2	✓	✓	
3-3	✓	✓✓	
3-4	✓	✓	✓
3-5	✓	✓✓	
3-6		✓	
3-7		✓	
3-8		✓	✓
3-9		✓	✓
3-10	✓		✓✓
4-1			
4-2		✓	
4-3	✓	✓	
4-4			
4-5		✓	✓
4-6		✓✓	
4-7	✓	✓	
4-8	✓	✓✓	✓✓
4-9			✓
4-10	✓		✓
5-1			
5-2		✓✓	
5-3			
5-4		✓	✓
5-5		✓	
5-6		✓✓	
5-7	✓	✓	✓
5-8	✓	✓	
5-9		✓✓	
5-10		✓✓	✓
5-11	✓		✓
6-1			
6-2	✓	✓✓	
6-3		✓✓	
6-4		✓	✓
6-5		✓	
6-6		✓	✓✓
6-7	✓		
6-8	✓		✓✓✓

Lesson	Blackline Master	Exploration Master	Test
7-1			
7-2		✓	
7-3		✓	✓
7-4	✓	✓✓	
7-5	✓	✓	
7-6	✓	✓✓✓	✓
7-7	✓		
7-8	✓		✓
8-1		✓	
8-2	✓	✓✓	
8-3		✓✓	✓
8-4		✓✓	✓
8-5		✓	
8-6		✓	
8-7	✓	✓✓✓	✓
8-8	✓		✓
9-1			
9-2			
9-3		✓	
9-4		✓	✓
9-5		✓✓	
9-6		✓	
9-7	✓	✓	
9-8		✓	✓
9-9		✓✓	
9-10		✓	✓
9-11		✓	
9-12			
9-13	✓		✓
10-1			
10-2		✓	
10-3	✓	✓	
10-4		✓	
10-5			✓
10-6	✓	✓✓✓	✓
10-7	✓		✓
11-1	✓		
11-2		✓	
11-3		✓	
11-4		✓✓✓	
11-5		✓	
11-6		✓	
11-7			✓
12-1			
12-2		✓	
12-3		✓	
12-4		✓	
12-5		✓✓	✓
12-6		✓✓	
12-7		✓✓	
12-8		✓✓	
12-9			
12-10	✓		✓✓✓✓

Overview

Calculus: Concepts and Applications is designed to be used by instructors with a wide spectrum of teaching styles. It is possible for you to use the text in a lecture-and-note-taking mode, but the text is most effective in a cooperative learning environment in which you and the students interact during class and in which students are expected to arrive at conclusions on their own. Your role in this mode is to provide guidance and to follow up and reinforce what the students discover. The *Instructor's Resource Book* and accompanying CD contain the materials to help you do the job. All of the material in this text may be reproduced for direct classroom use with your students.

- The Blackline Masters are enlarged, reproducible copies of graphs that are needed to complete examples and problems in the student text. Also included are reproducible copies of special kinds of graph paper.

- The Exploration Masters enable you to help students learn mathematical concepts by exploring them before reading the material in the text. Often the Explorations are intended for cooperative groups. Complete solutions to each exploration are also provided.

- The Assessment Suggestions are based on the National Council of Teachers of Mathematics' *Assessment Standards for School Mathematics*. This section provides supplementary materials to meet these standards, as well as specific suggestions and examples from the author's classroom on how to use the text.

- The Tests include up to five tests for each chapter. Each Section Test covers material from one or more sections, and the Chapter Test covers material from the whole chapter. Several Cumulative Tests are also provided, covering Chapters 1–3, Chapters 1–6, Chapters 7–12, and Chapters 1–12. Complete solutions to each test are provided.

- The Calculator Programs include the programs called for in specific places in the student text.

- The Technology Projects for The Geometer's Sketchpad, Fathom, and CBL include fifteen technology-enhanced projects that cover various topics of the textbook.

Note on the *Calculus: Concepts and Applications* Instructor's Resource CD-ROM

The CD that accompanies this volume contains electronic files for the Exploration Masters and Solutions; Section, Chapter, and Cumulative Tests and Solutions; Calculator Programs; and Technology Projects and Solutions. The files on this CD are provided in these formats:

- Exploration Masters and Solutions: PDF (Postscript Document File)

- Section, Chapter, and Cumulative Tests and Solutions: PDF and Microsoft® Word

- Calculator Programs: TI-Connect™ program files

- Technology Projects and Solutions: PDF (Postscript Document File), The Geometer's Sketchpad®, Fathom

To access the contents on the CD, you'll need Adobe® Acrobat® Reader®, Microsoft Word 97 or later for the PC *or* Word 5.1 or later for the Macintosh, TI-Connect Software, The Geometer's Sketchpad, and Fathom.

Blackline Masters

The Blackline Masters provide an important tool for whichever mode of instruction you use. At the beginning, for easy accessibility, are reproducible copies of special kinds of graph paper.

- *Centimeter graph paper,* on which students can plot accurate figures. This graph paper may also be duplicated on heavier stock (index card weight is good) and used for problems such as the Open Box Project in Problem Set 8-3, in which students cut out boxes of various sizes, seeking to maximize the volume.

- *Dot graph paper* that students will find useful for sketching graphs they have plotted on their graphers, particularly if they have used the GRID ON option. The six grids on each sheet have the same proportions as the screen of a typical graphing calculator. The dot graph paper is particularly effective for accurate plotting of vectors in Section 10-6, where the lines on regular graph paper might obscure the picture.

- *Polar coordinate paper* is useful for students as they sketch polar graphs that they have plotted on their graphers. There are six polar grids per sheet, making them large enough to see easily, but not so large that students have difficulty drawing on them.

Many of the problems in the text call for students to draw accurately on a photocopy of a graph that appears in the text. The graphs in the Blackline Masters section are grouped according to the problem set in which they appear. For instance, if students are working on the slope fields in Problem Set 7-4, all of the graphs they need are on the same sheet or sheets. You can photocopy these sheets and distribute them to the students as you assign the particular problem set. Students find that these graphs assist their work and reduce the incentive to mark in their textbooks.

The Blackline Masters may also be used to make transparencies of the graphs that you wish to present to the class. For instance, in Problem Set 8-2 students learn to sketch the graph of a function from number-line graphs of its first and second derivatives. The number lines are reproduced in the Blackline Masters to Problem Set 8-2, along with axes on which to sketch the function graphs. You can use a transparency of the master not only to show on the overhead how to do one of the problems, but also for presentation of homework problems in class the following day.

Name: _____ Group Members: _____

Centimeter Graph Paper

Date: _____

Dot Graph Paper

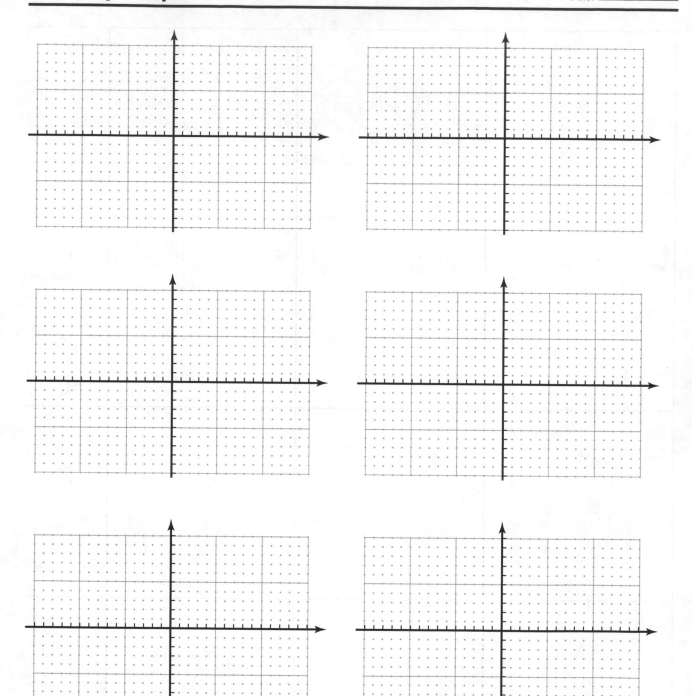

Polar Coordinate Paper

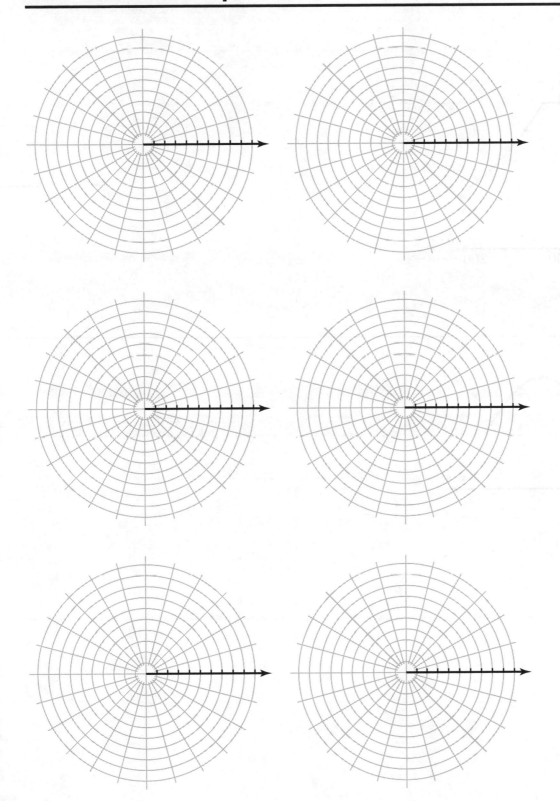

Problem Set 1-2/Page 12

11a.

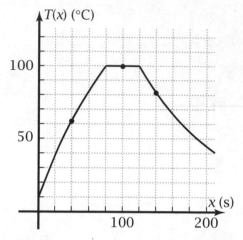

Figure 1-2i

12a.

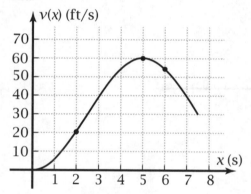

Figure 1-2j

Problem Set 1-6/Pages 28–29

C3.

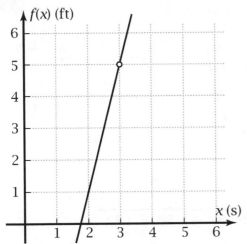

Figure 1-6d

T5.

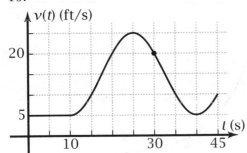

Figure 1-6e

13. $x = 3$, $\varepsilon = 0.5$

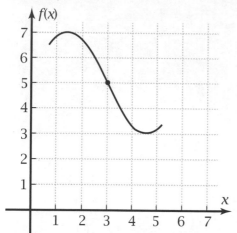

14. $x = 2$, $\varepsilon = 0.5$

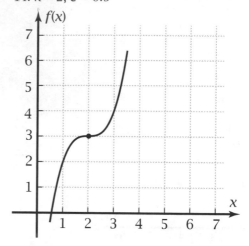

15. $x = 6$, $\varepsilon = 0.7$

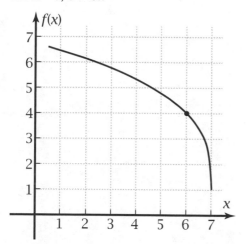

16. $x = 4$, $\varepsilon = 0.8$

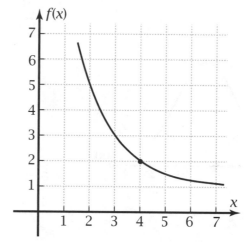

17. $x = 5$, $\varepsilon = 0.3$

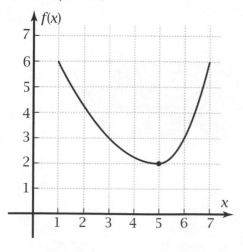

18. $x = 3$, $\varepsilon = 0.4$

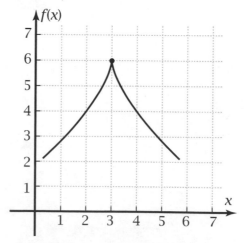

Calculus: Concepts and Applications Instructor's Resource Book
©2005 Key Curriculum Press

Problem Set 3-2/Pages 77–78

19.

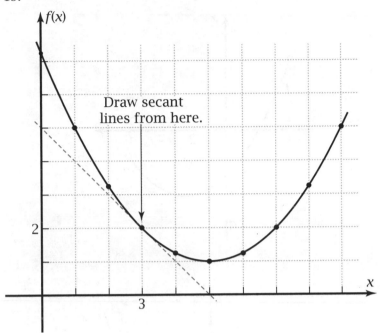

Draw secant lines from here.

Figure 3-2f

20.

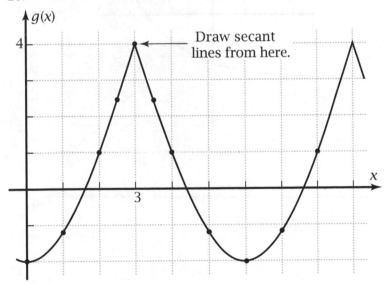

Draw secant lines from here.

Figure 3-2g

7.

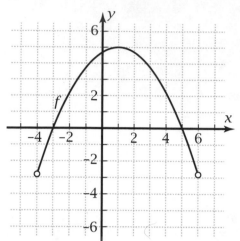

8.

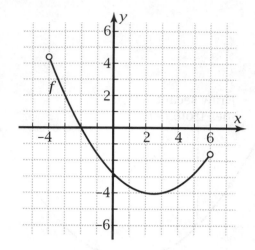

9.

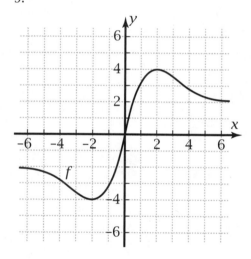

10.

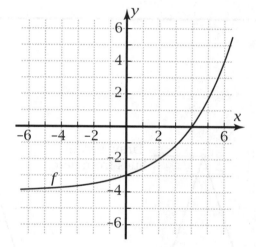

25.

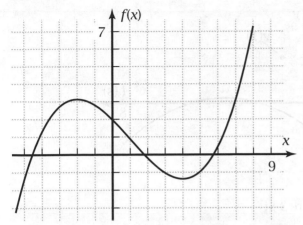

26.

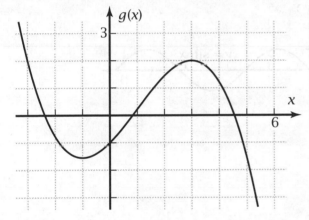

Problem Set 3-5/Pages 98–100

10a.

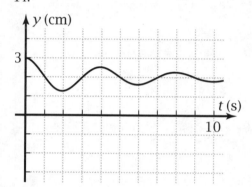

Figure 3-5h

11.

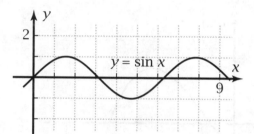

$v(1) = 2$

Figure 3-5i

14.

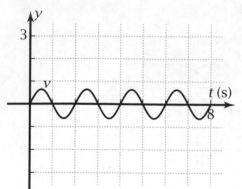

Figure 3-5j

21.

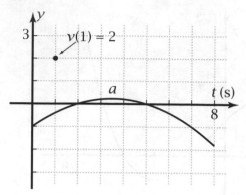

$y = \sin x$

22.

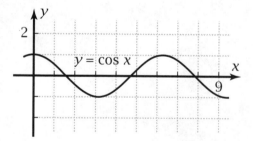

$y = \cos x$

Calculus: Concepts and Applications Instructor's Resource Book
©2005 Key Curriculum Press

Problem Set 3-10/Page 124

R4i.

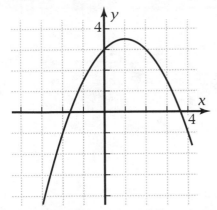

Figure 3-10a

R5d.

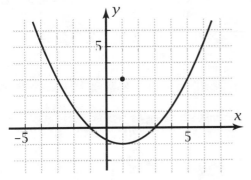

Figure 3-10b

Problem Set 4-3/Page 141

32.

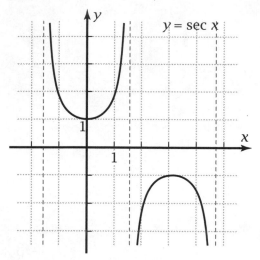

Figure 4-3c

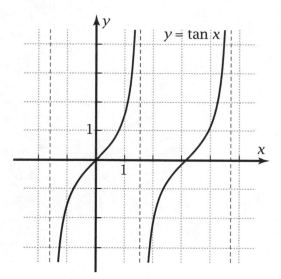

Figure 4-3d

Calculus: Concepts and Applications Instructor's Resource Book
©2005 Key Curriculum Press

Problem Set 4-7/Pages 165–166

5c.

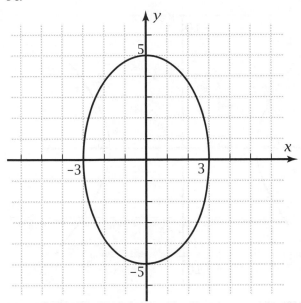

Figure 4-7g

6c.

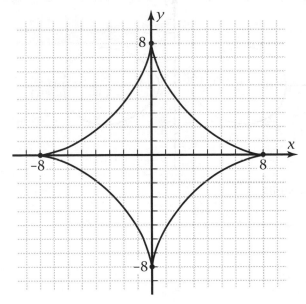

Figure 4-7h

25.

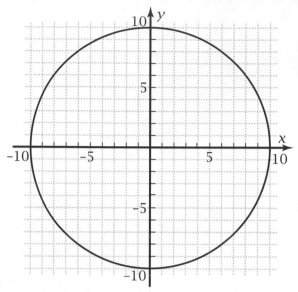

Figure 4-8d

26.

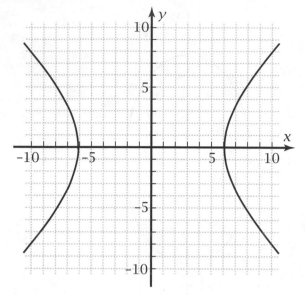

Figure 4-8e

27.

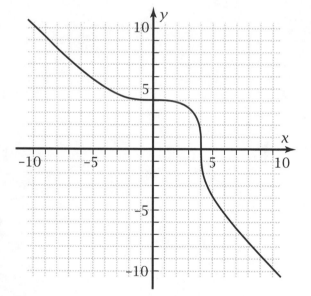

Figure 4-8f

28.

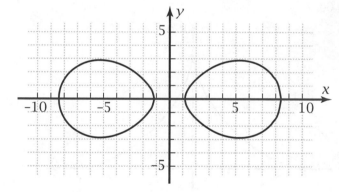

Figure 4-8g

R8.

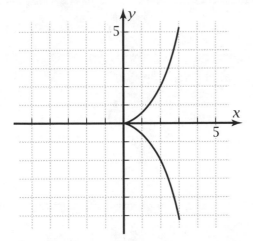

Figure 4-10c

T16.

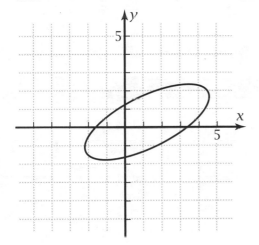

Figure 4-10g

Problem Set 5-7/Pages 232–233

37.

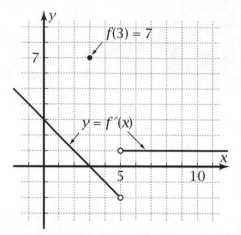

Figure 5-7h

38.

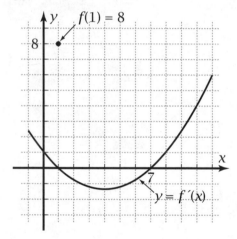

Figure 5-7i

Problem Set 5-8/Pages 237–239

1.

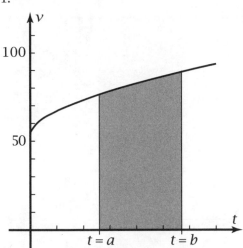

Figure 5-8e

3.

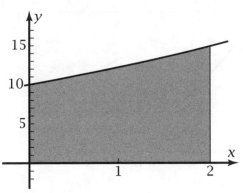

Figure 5-8f

7.

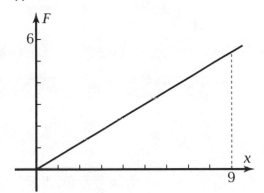

Figure 5-8h

9.

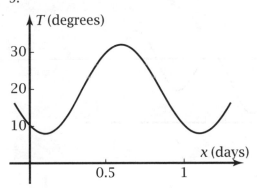

Figure 5-8i

Problem Set 5-11/Page 265

T5.

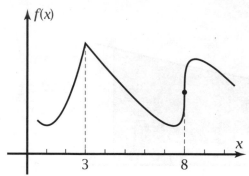

Figure 5-11h

T7.

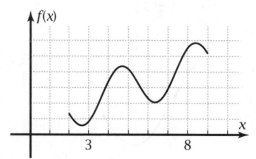

Figure 5-11i

Problem Set 6-2/Page 278

57.

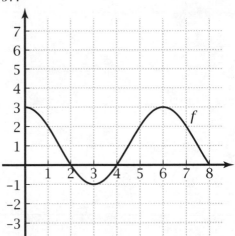

Figure 6-2j

58.

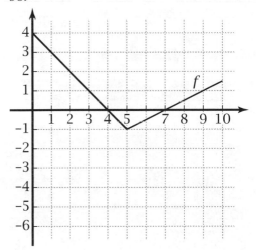

Figure 6-2k

R2e.

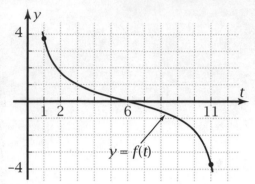

Figure 6-7a

T18a.

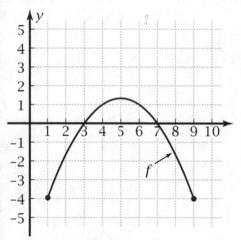

Figure 6-7g

Problem Set 6-8/Pages 313–314

9.

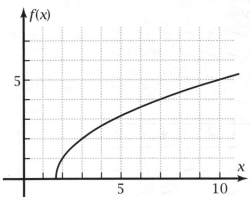

Figure 6-8b

23.

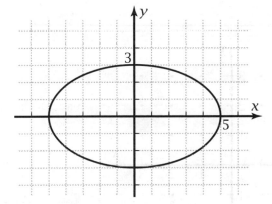

Figure 6-8c

Problem Set 7-4/Pages 336–341

1.

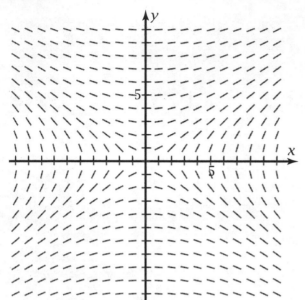

Figure 7-4g

2.

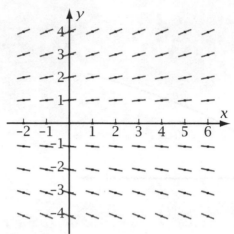

Figure 7-4h

3.

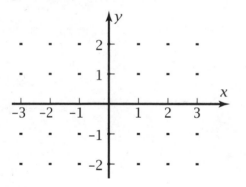

Figure 7-4i

4.

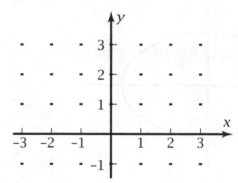

Figure 7-4j

(Over)

Calculus: Concepts and Applications Instructor's Resource Book
©2005 Key Curriculum Press

5.

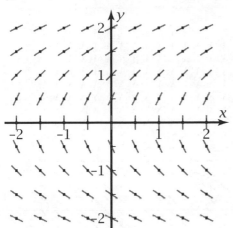

6.

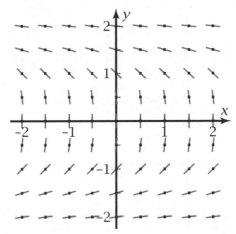

7.

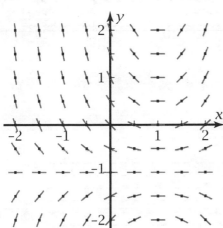

8.

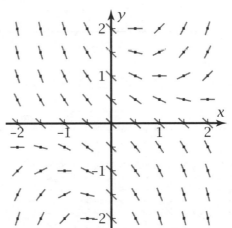

9.

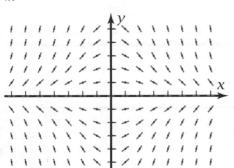

Figure 7-4k

Problem Set 7-4 *continued*/Pages 336–341

10.

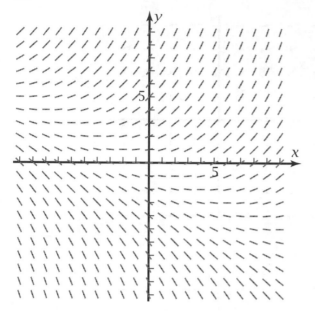

Figure 7-4l

11.

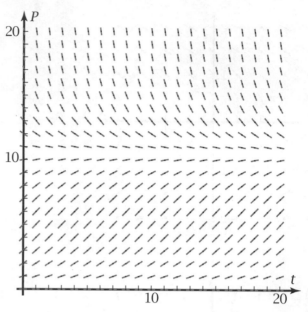

Figure 7-4m

12.

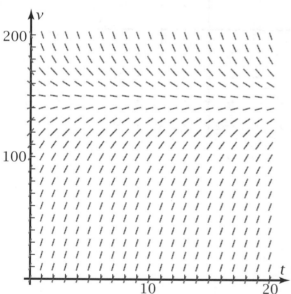

Figure 7-4n

13.

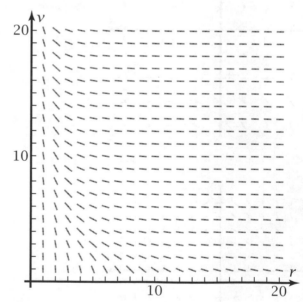

Figure 7-4o

Problem Set 7-5/Pages 346–347

7.

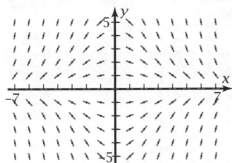

Figure 7-5g

8.

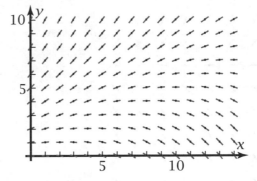

Figure 7-5h

9.

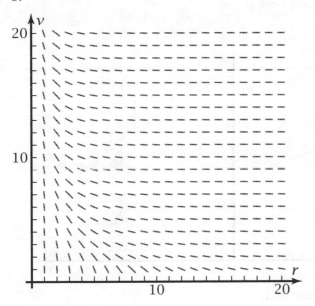

Figure 7-5i

10.

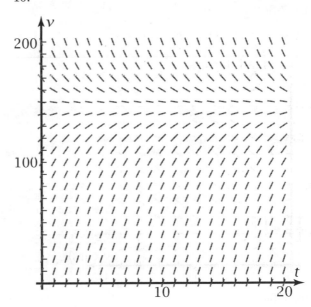

Figure 7-5j

Problem Set 7-6/Pages 353–358

1.

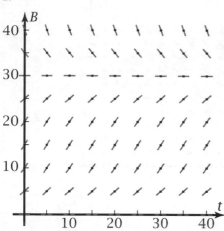

Figure 7-6c

2.

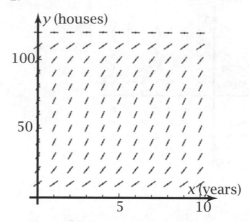

Figure 7-6d

5.

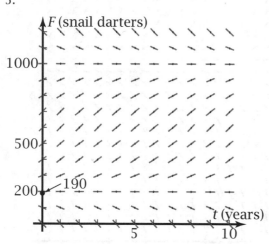

Figure 7-6e

7.

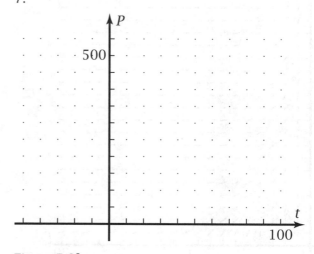

Figure 7-6f

(Over)

Problem Set 7-6 *continued*/Pages 353–358

14.

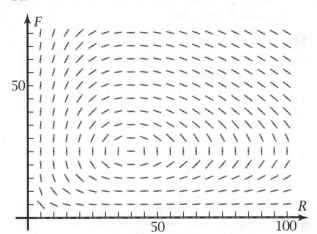

Figure 7-6g

18.

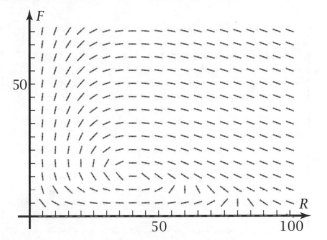

Figure 7-6h

21.

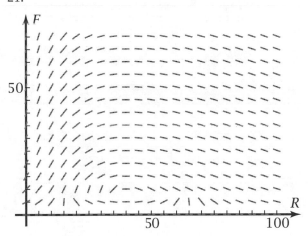

Figure 7-6i

R4.

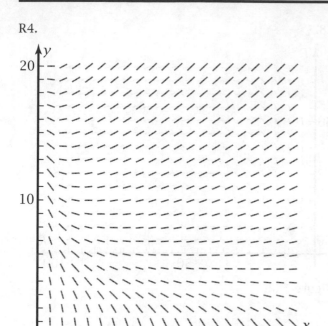

Figure 7-7b

R6a.

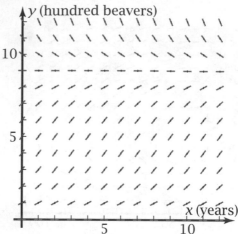

Figure 7-7c

R6e.

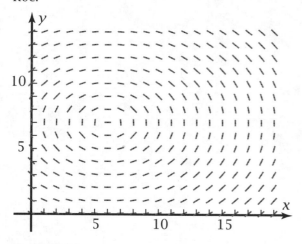

Figure 7-7d

(Over)

T4.

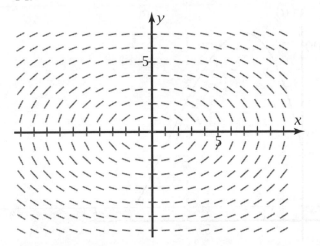

Figure 7-7f

T11.

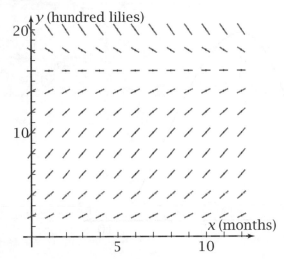

Figure 7-7g

T12.

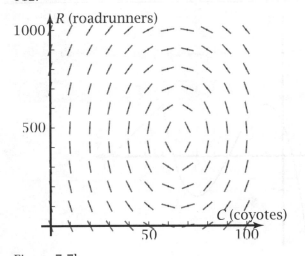

Figure 7-7h

Problem Set 7-8/Pages 365–368

1.

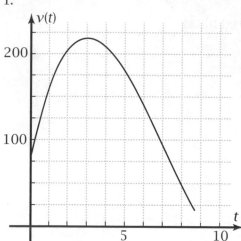

Figure 7-8a

5.

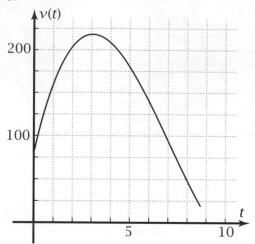

Figure 7-8a

13.

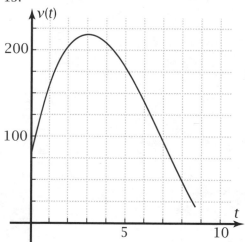

Figure 7-8a

29.

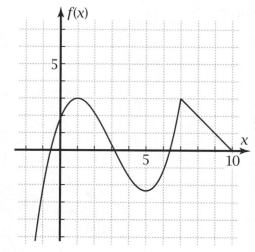

Figure 7-8c

34–35.

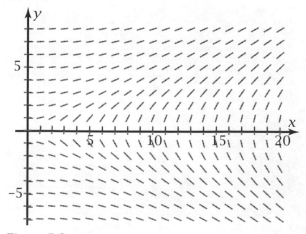

Figure 7-8e

11.

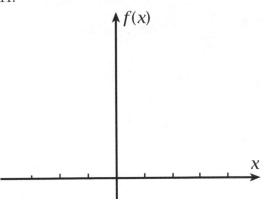

$f'(x)$	+	0	–		0	+	0	–
x		–2			1		3	

$f''(x)$		–	0	+		0	–
x			–1			2	

12.

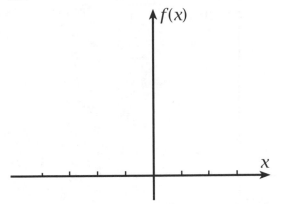

$f'(x)$	–	0	+	0		+		0 –
x		–3		–1				3

$f''(x)$		+	0 –	0		+		0	–
x			–2 –1					2	

13.

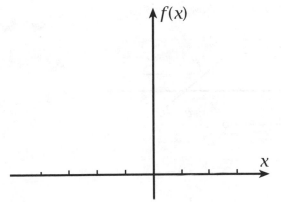

$f'(x)$	+	∞	–	0	–
x		–2		1	

$f''(x)$	+	∞	+	0	–
x		–2		1	

14.

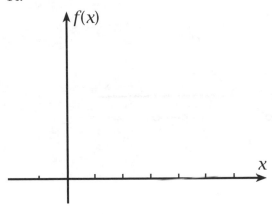

$f'(x)$	–	0	+	∞	+	0	–
x		2		3		4	

$f''(x)$		+	∞	–
x			3	

(Over)

15.

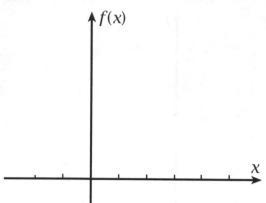

$f'(x)$	e.p.	+	0←zero→0	–	e.p.
x	-1		1 3		5

$f''(x)$	e.p.	–	0←zero→0	–	e.p.
x	-1		1 3		5

16.

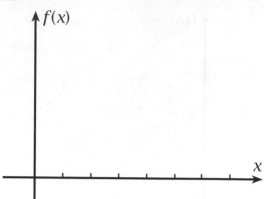

$f'(x)$	e.p.+ 0	–	0 + e.p.
x	1 2		6 7

$f''(x)$	e.p.	–	0←zero→0	+	e.p.
x	1		3 5		7

17.

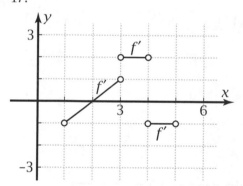

18.

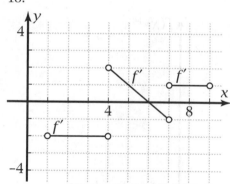

19.

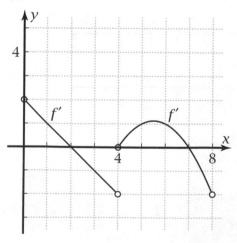

20.

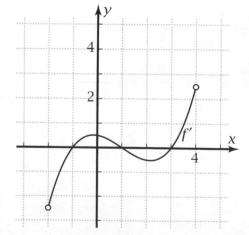

22.

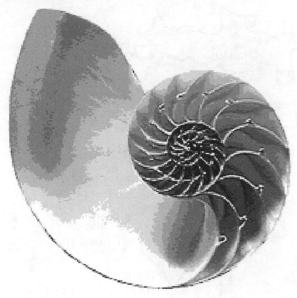

Problem Set 8-8/Pages 424–427

R2b.

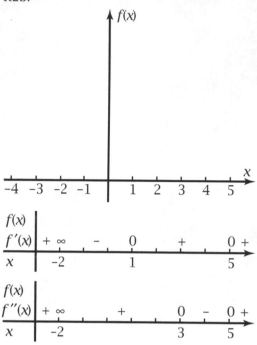

Figure 8-8b

C5.

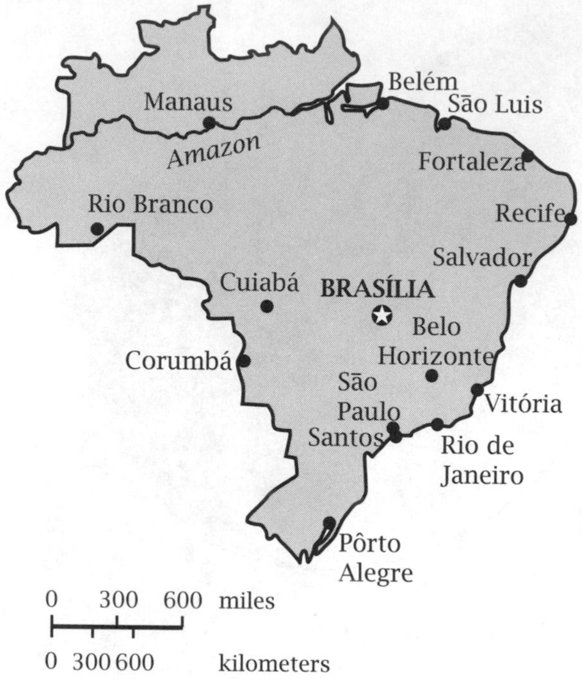

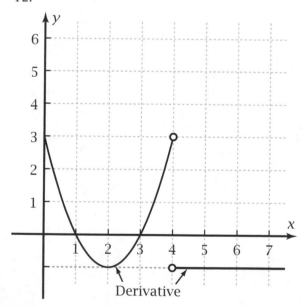

Figure 8-8g

T1.

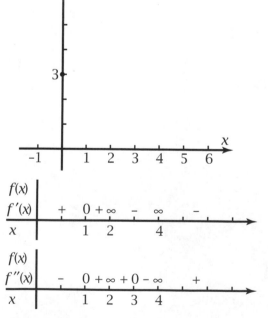

Figure 8-8j

T2.

Figure 8-8k

19.

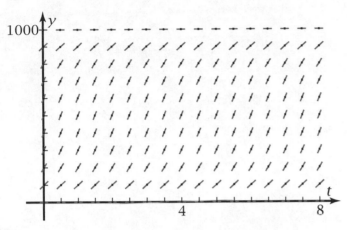

Figure 9-7a

Problem Set 9-9/Page 478

26.

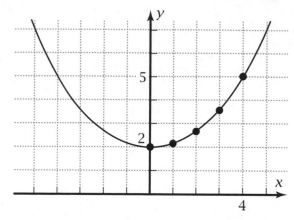

Figure 9-9h

Calculus: Concepts and Applications Instructor's Resource Book
©2005 Key Curriculum Press

Problem Set 9-13/Page 497

R7e.

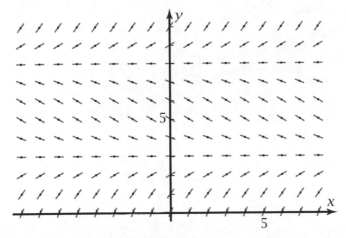

Figure 9-13b

15.

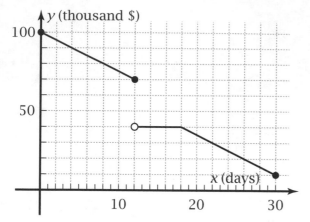

Figure 10-3e

16.

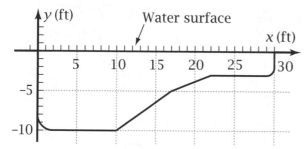

Figure 10-3f

Problem Set 10-6/Pages 533–538

1.

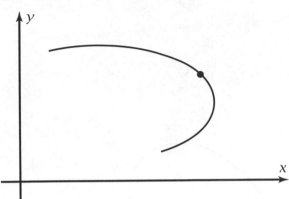

Figure 10-6o

5.

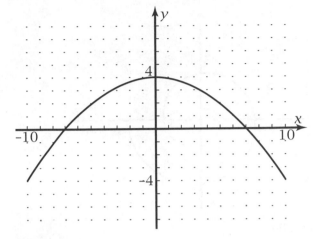

Figure 10-6q

6.

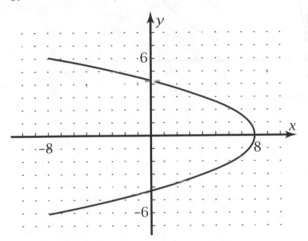

Figure 10-6r

7.

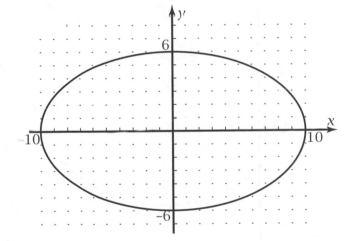

Figure 10-6s

(Over)

Problem Set 10-6 *continued*/**Pages 533–538**

8.

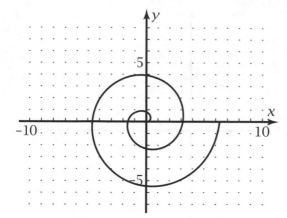

Figure 10-6t

10.

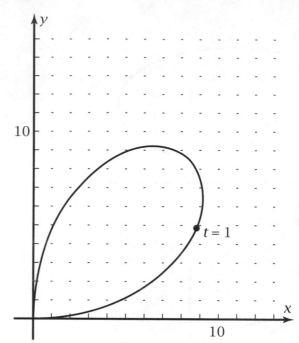

Figure 10-6u

17.

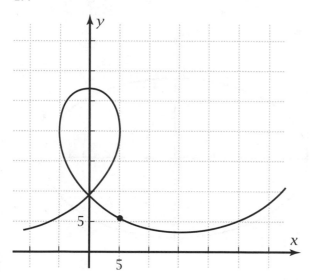

Figure 10-6y

Calculus: Concepts and Applications Instructor's Resource Book
©2005 Key Curriculum Press

Problem Set 10-7/Pages 542–545

R6.

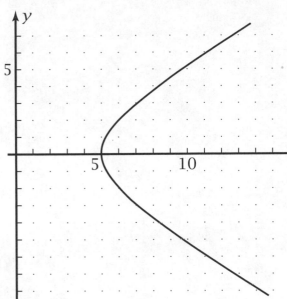

Figure 10-7c

T4.

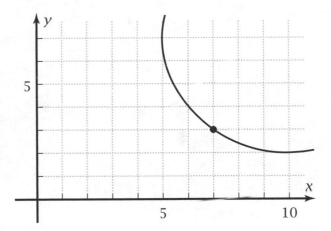

Figure 10-7i

T3.

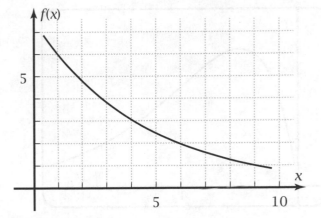

Figure 10-7h

T12–T14.

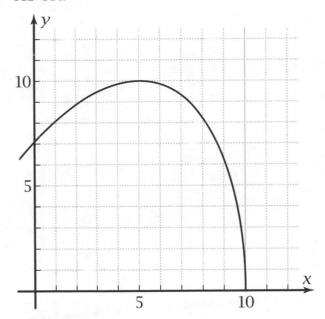

Figure 10-7j

Problem Set 11-1/Page 549

1.

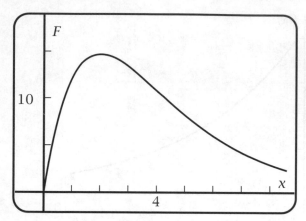

Figure 11-1b

5.

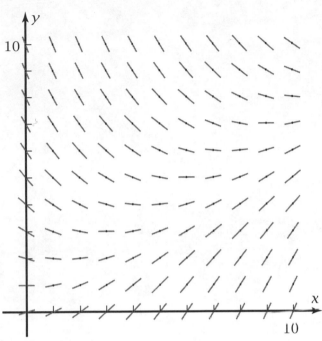

Figure 12-10a

25.

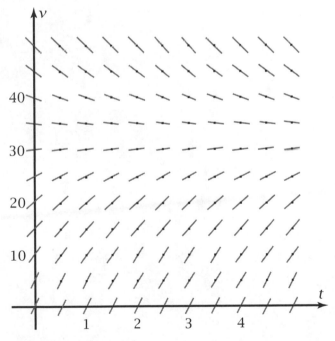

Figure 12-10d

Exploration Masters

The materials in this section are activities for students to do in class. Individual Explorations can be reproduced and distributed to students. Most are single sheets. Space is provided for work to be done right on the sheet. This feature is particularly important when something must be drawn on an accurate graph.

Most of the Explorations are intended to be worked in cooperative groups. The students discover something about the material in a given section of the text by working on their own, with input from one another and minimal guidance from the instructor. Before the students leave class, you should spend five or ten minutes summarizing what it is they have learned to make sure that they haven't "discovered" something wrong! The Explorations may also be used as directed discovery exercises, in which students work the problems one at a time, on their own or in groups, with answers and discussion after each problem. After following up on one problem, you may give students an instruction such as "Okay, you have 3 minutes to do Problem 5." The materials in the Explorations can even be used as a basis for your lecture on that particular text section.

Students often catch on to the fact that the Explorations refer to material in the given text section. They do the work with their texts open, often finishing before students in the surrounding groups. They think that they have outsmarted you. But really *you* have outsmarted *them* by getting them to read the text!

The last question in an Exploration is often "What did you learn as a result of doing this Exploration that you did not know before?" You will find it interesting to read these comments. Sometimes you will learn surprising things about your students or about their insights into mathematics. Often they have something mixed up. Sometimes the comments include personal information that is helpful for you to know. Occasionally you will learn something about calculus that you did not realize yourself!

The title "Exploration" has been picked deliberately. Students are learning things by exploring them on their own, without having read the materials in the text. You should avoid calling the Explorations "worksheets" or "reviews." These names have unpleasant or boring connotations in most students' minds. Some instructors call them games, alluding to the fact that there is some sport involved, and to the idea that they are not necessarily done for a grade. ("It is not whether you win or you lose. It is how you play the *game*!")

Exploration 1-1a: Instantaneous Rate of Change of a Function

Objective: Explore the instantaneous rate of change of a function.

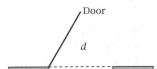
Door

d

The diagram shows a door with an automatic closer. At time $t = 0$ s, someone pushes the door. It swings open, slows down, stops, starts closing, then slams shut at time $t = 7$ s. As the door is in motion, the number of degrees, d, it is from its closed position depends on t.

1. Sketch a reasonable graph of d versus t.

2. Suppose that d is given by the equation

   $d = 200t \cdot 2^{-t}$

   Plot this graph on your grapher. Sketch the results here.

3. Make a table of values of d for each second from $t = 0$ through $t = 10$. Round to the nearest 0.1°.

t	d
0	
1	
2	
3	
4	
5	
6	
7	
8	
9	
10	

4. At time $t = 1$ s, does the door appear to be opening or closing? How do you tell?

5. What is the average rate at which the door is moving for the time interval [1, 1.1]? Based on your answer, does the door seem to be opening or closing at time $t = 1$? Explain.

6. By finding average rates using the time intervals [1, 1.01], [1, 1.001], and so on, make a conjecture about the *instantaneous* rate at which the door is moving at time $t = 1$ s.

7. In calculus you will learn by four methods:
   • algebraically,
   • numerically,
   • graphically,
   • verbally (talking and writing).

   What did you learn as a result of doing this Exploration that you did not know before?

8. Read Section 1-1. What do you notice?

Exploration 1-2a: Graphs of Familiar Functions

Objective: Recall the graphs of familiar functions, and tell how fast the function is changing at a particular value of x.

For each function:

a. Without using your grapher, sketch the graph on the axes provided.

b. Confirm by grapher that your sketch is correct.

c. Tell whether the function is increasing, decreasing, or not changing when $x = 1$. If it is increasing or decreasing, tell whether the rate of change is slow or fast.

1. $f(x) = 3^{-x}$

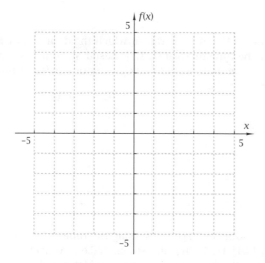

2. $f(x) = \sin \frac{\pi}{2} x$

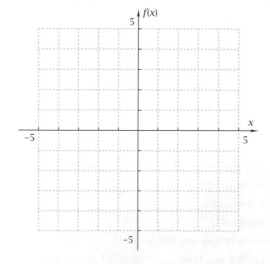

3. $f(x) = x^2 + 2x - 2$

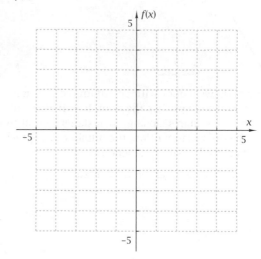

4. $f(x) = \sec x$

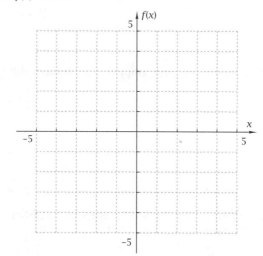

5. $f(x) = \frac{1}{x}$

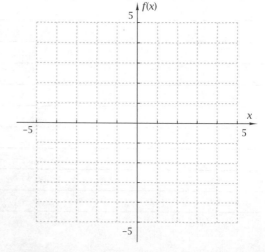

Exploration 1-3a: Introduction to Definite Integrals

Objective: Find out what a definite integral is by working a real-world problem that involves the speed of a car.

As you drive on the highway you accelerate to 100 ft/s to pass a truck. After you have passed, you slow down to a more moderate 60 ft/s. The diagram shows the graph of your velocity, $v(t)$, as a function of the number of seconds, t, since you started slowing.

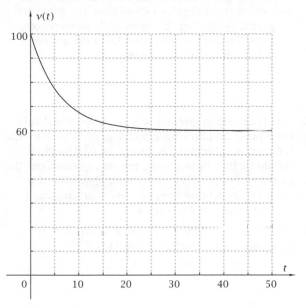

1. What does your velocity seem to be between $t = 30$ and $t = 50$ s? How far do you travel in the time interval [30, 50]?

2. Explain why the answer to Problem 1 can be represented as the area of a *rectangular* region of the graph. Shade this region.

3. The distance you travel between $t = 0$ and $t = 20$ can also be represented as the area of a region bounded by the (curved) graph. Count the number of squares in this region. Estimate the area of parts of squares to the nearest 0.1 square space. For instance, how would you count this partial square?

4. How many feet does each small square on the graph represent? How far, therefore, did you go in the time interval [0, 20]?

5. Problems 3 and 4 involve finding the product of the x-value and the y-value for a function where y may *vary* with x. Such a product is called the **definite integral** of y with respect to x. Based on the units of t and $v(t)$, explain why the definite integral of $v(t)$ with respect to t in Problem 4 has feet for its units.

6. The graph shows the cross-sectional area, y, in in.^{2}, of a football as a function of the distance, x, in in., from one of its ends. Estimate the definite integral of y with respect to x.

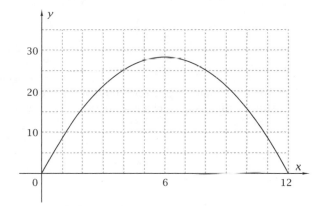

7. What are the units of the definite integral in Problem 6? What, therefore, do you suppose the definite integral represents?

8. What did you learn as a result of doing this Exploration that you did not know before?

Exploration 1-4a: Definite Integrals by Trapezoidal Rule

Objective: Estimate the definite integral of a function numerically rather than graphically by counting squares.

Rocket Problem: Ella Vader (Darth's daughter) is driving in her rocket ship. At time $t = 0$ min, she fires her rocket engine. The ship speeds up for a while, then slows down as Alderaan's gravity takes its effect. The graph of her velocity, $v(t)$, in miles per minute, is shown below.

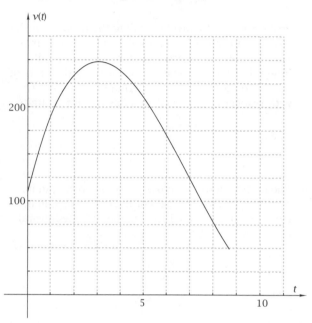

1. What mathematical concept would you use to estimate the distance Ella goes between $t = 0$ and $t = 8$?

2. Estimate the distance in Problem 1 graphically.

3. Ella figures that her velocity is given by

    $v(t) = t^3 - 21t^2 + 100t + 110$

    Plot this graph on your grapher. Does the graph confirm or refute what Ella figures? Tell how you arrive at your conclusion.

4. Divide the region under the graph from $t = 0$ to $t = 8$, which represents the distance, into four vertical strips of equal width. Draw four trapezoids whose areas approximate the areas of these strips and whose parallel sides extend from the x-axis to the graph. By finding the areas of these trapezoids, estimate the distance Ella goes. Does the answer agree with the answer to Problem 2?

5. The technique in Problem 4 is the **trapezoidal rule.** Put a program into your grapher to use this rule. The function equation may be stored as y_1. The input should be the starting time, the ending time, and the number of trapezoids. The output should be the value of the definite integral. Test your program by using it to answer Problem 4.

6. Use the program from Problem 5 to estimate the definite integral using 20 trapezoids.

7. The *exact* value of the definite integral is the *limit* of the estimates by trapezoids as the width of each trapezoid approaches zero. By using the program from Problem 5, make a conjecture about the exact value of the definite integral.

8. What is the fastest Ella went? At what time was that?

9. Approximately what was Ella's rate of change of velocity when $t = 5$? Was she speeding up or slowing down at that time?

10. Based on the equation in Problem 3, there are positive values of time t at which Ella is stopped. What is the first such time? How did you find your answer?

11. What did you learn as a result of doing this Exploration that you did not know before?

Exploration 2-1a: Introduction to Limits

Objective: Find the limit of a function that approaches an indeterminate form at a particular value of x and relate it to the definition.

1. Plot on your grapher the graph of this function.

$$f(x) = \frac{x^3 - 7x^2 + 17x - 15}{x - 3}$$

Use a friendly window with $x = 3$ as a grid point, but with the grid turned off. Sketch the results here. Show the behavior of the function in a neighborhood of $x = 3$.

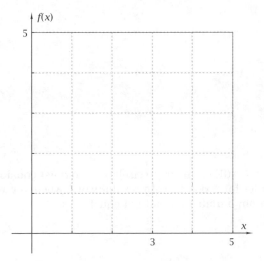

2. Substitute 3 for x in the equation for $f(x)$. What form does the answer take? What name is given to an expression of this form?

3. The graph of f has a **removable discontinuity** at $x = 3$. The y-value at this discontinuity is the **limit** of $f(x)$ as x approaches 3. What number does this limit equal?

4. Make a table of values of $f(x)$ for each 0.1 unit change in x-value from 2.5 through 3.5.

x	$f(x)$
2.5	
2.6	
2.7	
2.8	
2.9	
3.0	
3.1	
3.2	
3.3	
3.4	
3.5	

5. Between what two numbers does $f(x)$ stay when x is kept in the open interval (2.5, 3.5)?

6. Simplify the fraction for $f(x)$. Solve numerically to find the two numbers close to 3 between which x must be kept if $f(x)$ is to stay between 1.99 and 2.01.

7. How far from $x = 3$ (to the left and to the right) are the two x-values in Problem 6?

8. For the statement "If x is within _____ units of 3 (but not equal to 3), then $f(x)$ is within 0.01 unit of 2," write the largest number that can go in the blank.

9. The formal definition of limit is

$$L = \lim_{x \to c} f(x) \text{ if and only if}$$

- for any positive number ε (no matter how small)
- there is a positive number δ such that
- if x is within δ units of c, but not equal to c,
- then $f(x)$ is within ε units of L.

The four numbers L, c, ε, and δ all appear in Problem 8. Which is which?

10. What did you learn as a result of doing this Exploration that you did not know before?

Exploration 2-2a: The Definition of Limit

Objective: Interpret graphically and algebraically the definition of limit.

Let f be the function whose graph is shown here.

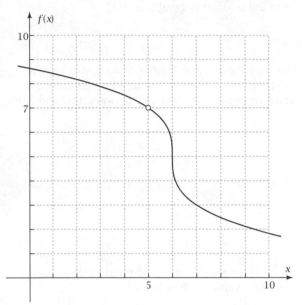

1. The limit of $f(x)$ as x approaches 5 is equal to 7. Write the definition of limit as it applies to f at this point.

2. Let $\varepsilon = 1$. From the graph, estimate how close to 5 on the left side x must be kept in order for $f(x)$ to be within ε units of 7.

3. From the graph, estimate how close to 5 on the right side x must be kept in order for $f(x)$ to be within $\varepsilon = 1$ unit of 7.

4. For $\varepsilon = 1$, approximately what must δ equal in the definition of limit in order for $f(x)$ to be within ε units of 7 whenever x is within δ units of 5 (but not equal to 5)?

5. The equation of the function graphed is

$$f(x) = 5 - 2(x - 6)^{1/3}, \text{ for } x \neq 5$$

Calculate precisely the value of δ from Problem 4.

6. If $\varepsilon = 0.01$, calculate precisely what δ must equal in order for $f(x)$ to be within ε units of 7 whenever x is within δ units of 5 (but not equal to 5).

7. Substitute $(7 - \varepsilon)$ for $f(x)$ and $(5 + \delta)$ for x. Solve for δ in terms of ε. Use the result to show that there is a *positive* value of δ for any $\varepsilon > 0$, no matter how small ε is.

8. What did you learn as a result of doing this Exploration that you did not know before?

Exploration 2-3a: Limit of a Sum, Epsilon and Delta Proof

Objective: Prove by ε-δ techniques that the limit of a sum of two functions equals the sum of the two limits.

1. Write the definition of limit using ε and δ.

For Problems 2–5,

Let $y_1 = 5x + 1$.

Let $y_2 = x^2$.

Let $y_3 = y_1 + y_2$.

2. Find

$$L_1 = \lim_{x \to 2} y_1 = \text{_____} \quad \text{and} \quad L_2 = \lim_{x \to 2} y_2 = \text{_____}$$

3. Let $\varepsilon = 0.1$. Find δ_1 such that y_1 is within $\varepsilon/2$ unit of L_1 on the positive side by substituting $(L_1 + 0.05)$ for y_1 and $(2 + \delta_1)$ for x.

4. Using $\varepsilon = 0.1$ as in Problem 3, find δ_2 such that y_2 is within $\varepsilon/2$ units of L_2 on the positive side by substituting $(L_2 + 0.05)$ for y_2 and $(2 + \delta_2)$ for x.

5. Add $L_1 + L_2$ to get $L = \lim_{x \to 2} y_3$.

Let $\delta = \min\{\delta_1, \delta_2\}$, which means that δ is the smaller of δ_1 and δ_2. Make a table of values of y_3 for several values of x between 2 and $(2 + \delta)$. Does the table show that y_3 is within $\varepsilon = 0.1$ unit of L whenever x is within δ units of 2 on the positive side?

For Problems 6 and 7,

Let $f(x) = g(x) + h(x)$.

Let $L_1 = \lim_{x \to c} g(x)$.

Let $L_2 = \lim_{x \to c} h(x)$.

6. Suppose that someone has chosen a number $\varepsilon > 0$. Because L_1 is the limit of $g(x)$ as x approaches c, you can keep $g(x)$ as close as you like to L_1 just by keeping x close enough to c. Thus, there is a number δ_1 such that $g(x)$ can be kept within $\varepsilon/2$ units of L_1. That is,

$$L_1 + e/2 < g(x) < L_1 + \varepsilon/2$$

Similarly, you can keep $h(x)$ within $\varepsilon/2$ units of L_2 just by keeping x within δ_2 units of c. Write an inequality for $h(x)$ if x is within δ_2 units of c.

7. Let $\delta = \min\{\delta_1, \delta_2\}$. Thus, both inequalities in Problem 6 will be true. By appropriate operations on these inequalities, show that $f(x)$ is within ε units of $(L_1 + L_2)$, and thus that $(L_1 + L_2)$ is the limit of $f(x)$ as x approaches c.

8. State the property of the limit of a sum verbally.

9. What did you learn as a result of doing this Exploration that you did not know before?

Exploration 2-3b: Extension of the Limit Theorems by Mathematical Induction

Objective: Prove that the limit of a sum property is true for the sum of *any* finite number of terms.

Suppose that $f_n(x)$ is the sum of n other functions,

$$f_n(x) = g_1(x) + g_2(x) + g_3(x) + \cdots + g_n(x)$$

and that $g_1(x), g_2(x), g_3(x), \ldots, g_n(x)$ have limits $L_1, L_2, L_3, \ldots, L_n$, respectively, as x approaches c. Prove that

$$\lim_{x \to c} f_n(x) = L_1 + L_2 + L_3 + \cdots + L_n$$

for *all* integers $n \geq 2$.

Proof: (You supply the details!)

1. Explain how you know that the property is true for $n = 2$. (This fact is called the **anchor** of the proof.)

2. Assume that the property is false. What does this assumption tell you about values of n?

3. Let j be a value of n for which the property is not true. Let T be the set of values of n for which the property *is* true, and let F be the set of values of n for which the property is *false*. On the Venn diagram below, show a value of n that is in T and a value of n that is in F.

 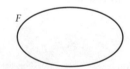

4. By a clever use of the associative property for addition, you can turn a sum of three terms into a sum of two terms. By doing this, show that the property is true for $n = 3$. You may write "lim" as an abbreviation for limit as $x \to c$. Write 3 in T.

5. Suppose you assume that the property is true for $n = 5$. Show how you could prove that it is also true for $n = 6$.

6. The **well-ordering axiom** states that any nonempty set of positive integers has a *least* element. How do you know that set F is a nonempty set of positive integers?

7. Let l be the least element of F. How do you know that $l - 1$ is a *positive* integer? In which set is $l - 1$? Show l and $l - 1$ in the Venn diagram of Problem 3.

8. Write a statement about the limit of $f_{l-1}(x)$ and a statement about the limit of $f_l(x)$ as x approaches c.

9. By the definition of $f_n(x)$,

$$f_l(x) = g_1(x) + g_2(x) + g_3(x) + \cdots + g_{l-1}(x) + g_l(x)$$

By clever use of the associative property, as in Problem 5, associate the right side of this equation into a sum of *two* terms.

(Over)

Calculus: Concepts and Applications Instructor's Resource Book
©2005 Key Curriculum Press

Exploration 2-3b: Extension of the Limit Theorems
by Mathematical Induction *continued*

10. Take the limit of both sides of the equation in Problem 9. Use the anchor to write the right side of the equation as a sum of *two* limits.

11. Use the equation for the limit of $f_{l-1}(x)$ from Problem 8 to simplify the equation in Problem 10.

12. Explain why the simplified equation in Problem 11 contradicts what you wrote about the limit of $f_l(x)$ in Problem 8.

13. The only place in the steps above that could account for the contradiction in Problem 12 is the assumption in Problem 2 that the property was *not* true for all integers $n \geq 2$. What can you conclude about this assumption? What can you conclude about the property?

The proof process in Problems 1 through 13 can be shortened if you realize that all you need to do is (a) find an anchor and (b) show that if the property is true for some integer $n = k$, then it is also true for the next integer, $n = k + 1$. This shortened process is called **mathematical induction.** Complete the following for the property of the limit of a sum.

Proof:

Anchor:

Induction hypothesis: Assume the property is true for $n = k > 2$.

Verification for $n = k + 1$:

Conclusion:

Q.E.D.

14. What did you learn as a result of doing this Exploration that you did not know before?

Exploration 2-4a: Continuous and Discontinuous Functions

Objective: Given a function specified by two different rules, make the function continuous at the boundary between the two branches.

Let f be the piecewise function defined by

$$f(x) = \begin{cases} x + 1, & \text{if } x < 2 \\ k(x - 5)^2, & \text{if } x \geq 2 \end{cases}$$

where k stands for a constant.

1. Plot the graph of f for $k = 1$. Sketch the result.

2. Function f is **discontinuous** at $x = 2$. Tell what it means for a function to be discontinuous.

3. Find $\lim_{x \to 2^-} f(x)$ and $\lim_{x \to 2^+} f(x)$. (The second limit will be in terms of k.) What must be true of these two limits for f to be **continuous** at $x = 2$?

4. Find the value of k that makes f continuous at $x = 2$. Sketch the graph of f for this value of k.

5. The graph in Problem 4 has a **cusp** at $x = 2$. What is the origin of the word *cusp*, and why is it appropriate to use in this context?

6. Suppose someone asks, "Is $f(x)$ increasing or decreasing at $x = 2$ with k as in Problem 4?" How would you have to answer that question? What, then, can you conclude about the derivative of a function at a point where the graph has a cusp?

7. What did you learn as a result of doing this Exploration that you did not know before?

Exploration 2-5a: Limit As *x* Approaches Infinity

Objective: Discover what it means for a function to approach a limit as *x* approaches infinity.

A pendulum is pulled away from its rest position and let go. As it swings back and forth, its distance, $d(x)$, in cm from the wall, is given by the equation

$$d(x) = 50 + 30(0.9)^x \cdot \cos \pi x$$

where *x* is time in seconds since it was let go. The graph of function *d* shows that friction decreases the amplitude of the swings as time goes on.

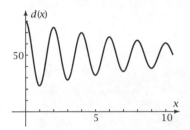

1. Plot $y_1 = d(x)$ on your grapher using the window shown. Does the graph agree with the figure?

2. The number 50 is the **limit of** $d(x)$ **as** *x* **approaches infinity.** Plot lines $y_2 = 52$ and $y_3 = 48$. If *x* is large enough, the graph stays within these two lines. By experimenting with the window, find the smallest possible number *D* for which $d(x)$ stays within 2 units of 50 for *all* values of $x > D$.

3. The quantity $30(0.9)^x$ in the equation for $d(x)$ is the **amplitude** of the cosine function. Plot $y_4 = 50 + 30(0.9)^x$. Is this graph really an upper bound for $d(x)$?

4. Find a new value of $x = D$ that makes $30(0.9)^D = 2$. Change the window so that *x* goes from about 5 below this value to about 5 above. Use a *y*-range of [45, 55]. Sketch the result. Does $d(x)$ really stay within 2 units of 50 for all $x > D$ for this value of *D*?

5. Find quickly a value of $D > 0$ such that $d(x)$ stays within 0.1 unit of 50 whenever $x > D$. Show how you get your answer.

Because infinity is not a number, you cannot make *x* close to infinity. So the limit as *x* approaches infinity must be modified to say that *x* is kept far enough away from zero. Here is a formal definition.

$L = \lim_{x \to \infty} f(x)$ if and only if

• for any $\varepsilon > 0$ (no matter how small)

• there is a number $D > 0$ such that

• if $x > D$,

• then $f(x)$ is within ε units of *L*.

6. For the function *d* in this Exploration, explain why this statement is false: "The larger *x* gets, the closer $d(x)$ gets to 50." Explain how the words "stays within" in the definition of limit avoid the misconception that $d(x)$ is always getting closer to the limit.

7. Tell the real-world meaning of the limit 50 for the function *d* in this Exploration.

8. What did you learn as a result of doing this Exploration that you did not know before?

Exploration 2-7a: Partial Rehearsal for Test on Limits   Date: _____

Objective: Make sure you understand the epsilon-delta definition of limit and how to use it to calculate a derivative.

1. Let $f(x) = x^3$. Find $\lim_{x \to 2} f(x)$.

   How close must x be kept to 2 in order to make $f(x)$ stay within 0.1 unit of $f(2)$? How close must x be kept to 2 in order to make $f(x)$ stay within ε units of $f(2)$? How does your answer to this question show that $f(2)$ really *is* the limit of $f(x)$ as x approaches 2?

2. Let $g(x) = \sin \pi x$. Evaluate $g(0.5)$. Sketch the graph of g, showing at least one full cycle. How close must x be kept to 0.5 in order to make $g(x)$ stay within 0.01 unit of $g(0.5)$? Show that there is a positive number δ for any $\varepsilon > 0$ such that if x is within δ units of 0.5 (but not equal to 0.5), then $g(x)$ is within ε units of $g(0.5)$.

3. Let $h(x) = 2^{x-3} + 5$. Find $h(3)$. How close must x be kept to 3 in order to make $h(x)$ stay within ε units of $h(3)$?

4. Let $r(x) = \dfrac{\sin \pi x - 0.5}{x - 1/6}$.

   What form does $r(1/6)$ take? What name is given to forms like this? See if you can figure out the limit of $r(x)$ as x approaches 1/6. See if you can figure out what key(s) to press on your calculator to find this number.

(Over)

Calculus: Concepts and Applications Instructor's Resource Book
©2005 Key Curriculum Press

Exploration 2-7a: Partial Rehearsal for
Test on Limits *continued*

5. Let $p(x) = 3 + 2(0.95^x) \sin x$, graphed here.

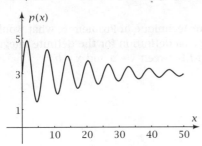

Explain why $p(x)$ is within 0.2 unit of 3 whenever $x > D$, where D is the value of x that makes $2(0.95^x) = 0.2$. Find this value of D. Plot these graphs using a window with about $D - 5$ to $D + 5$ for x and [2.7, 3.3] for y. Sketch the result.

$y_1 = p(x)$

$y_2 = 3.2$

$y_3 = 2.8$

$y_4 = 2(0.95^x)$

6. Show that for any $\varepsilon > 0$, there is a $D > 0$ such that if $x > D$, then $p(x)$ is within ε units of 3. What does this fact allow you to conclude about the number 3? Why does the line $y = 3$ satisfy the definition of a horizontal asymptote, even though the graph of p crosses the line an infinite number of times?

7. Let $T(x) = \tan \frac{\pi}{2}x$. Find $\lim_{x \to 1^-} T(x)$ and $\lim_{x \to 1^+} r(x)$.

Sketch the graph of function T in the neighborhood of $x = 1$. Why can't you say that $\lim_{x \to 1} T(x) = \infty$? Why can you say that $\lim_{x \to 1} T(x)$ is infinite?

8. For function T in Problem 7, how close to 1 on the negative side must you keep x in order for $T(x)$ to be greater than 1000? Show that for any positive number E, no matter how large, there is a number $\delta > 0$ such that if x is within δ units of 1 on the left (but not equal to 1), then $T(x) > E$.

9. What did you learn as a result of doing this Exploration that you did not know before?

Exploration 2-7b: One-Problem Summary of Calculus So Far

Date: _____

Objective: Find approximate values of definite integrals and approximate and exact values of derivatives (Chapters 1 and 2).

In this Exploration you will operate on the function graphed here.

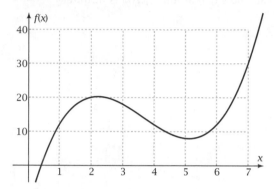

1. Estimate the definite integral of $f(x)$ from $x = 1$ to $x = 7$ by counting squares.

2. Estimate the derivative of $f(x)$ at $x = 1$ by drawing a line tangent to the graph at that point and measuring its slope.

3. The equation of f is $f(x) = x^3 - 11x^2 + 34x - 12$. Confirm on your grapher that this equation really produces the above graph. (The GRID ON feature will help.)

4. Estimate the derivative of $f(x)$ at $x = 1$ by using $f(1.01)$ and $f(0.99)$. Did the answer come fairly close to the one you got in Problem 2?

5. Estimate the definite integral of $f(x)$ from $x = 1$ to $x = 7$ using the trapezoidal rule with $n = 6$ increments. Did the answer come fairly close to the one you got in Problem 1?

6. The exact value of the integral in Problem 5 happens to be an *integer*. By an appropriate technique, find out what that integer is.

7. Based on your technique in Problem 6, what would you propose as a definition for the definite integral of a function f between $x = a$ and $x = b$?

8. Write a difference quotient for the average rate of change of $f(x)$ from $x = 1$ to $x = x$. Plot the difference quotient on your grapher with the grid turned off. Use a friendly window that includes $x = 1$. Sketch the graph here.

9. Do the appropriate algebra to simplify the difference quotient in Problem 8. Then find the exact value of the derivative at $x = 1$ by finding the limit of the simplified difference quotient. Name the limit theorem(s) you use at each step.

10. What did you learn as a result of doing this Exploration that you did not know before?

Calculus: Concepts and Applications Instructor's Resource Book
©2005 Key Curriculum Press

Exploration 3-2a: Exact Value of a Derivative

Objective: Use the definition of derivative to find the exact value of the derivative of a function at a given point.

The figure shows the graph of

$$f(x) = x^3 - 4x^2 - 9x + 46$$

In this Exploration you will use the definition of derivative to find the *exact* value of $f'(4)$.

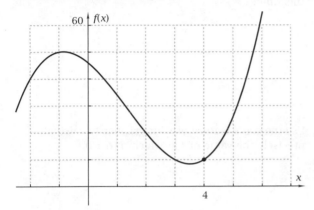

1. Find $f(4)$. Show that your answer agrees with the graph.

2. Write the definition of derivative as it applies to f at $x = 4$.

3. Substitute the values of $f(x)$ and $f(4)$ into the definition in Problem 2. Then simplify the resulting rational expression, and take the limit.

4. Plot a line on the graph at $(4, f(4))$ that has slope $f'(4)$. Observe the different scales on the two axes. Tell how the line confirms that the derivative is correct.

5. Find the exact value of $f'(2)$ using the same procedure you used for $f'(4)$. How can you tell quickly that your answer is reasonable?

6. What did you learn as a result of doing this Exploration that you did not know before?

Exploration 3-3a: Numerical Derivative by Grapher

Objective: Plot the numerical derivative of a function and make connections between the derivative graph and the function graph.

In Section 1-1, you explored the function

$$d(t) = 200t \cdot 2^{-t}$$

where t is the number of seconds since you pushed open a door and $d(t)$ is the number of degrees the door is from its rest position. The figure below is an accurate graph of function d. In this Exploration you will use the numerical derivative feature of your grapher to calculate values of $d'(t)$, the instantaneous rate at which the door is opening.

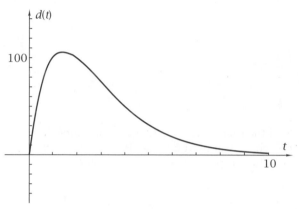

1. Confirm that the graph shown is correct by plotting the equation as y_1 on your grapher. Use a friendly x-window of about [0, 10].

2. Use a symmetric difference quotient with $\Delta t = 0.001$ to find an estimate of $d'(1)$.

3. Use the numerical derivative feature of your grapher to find an estimate of $d'(1)$. Does the answer agree with that in Problem 2?

4. Estimate $d'(2)$ numerically. In what way do the values of $d'(1)$ and $d'(2)$ correspond to the graph? What do the signs of $d'(1)$ and $d'(2)$ tell you about the motion of the door?

5. Plot the numerical derivative, $d'(t)$, as y_2. Have your instructor check your graph. _____

6. What is true about the graph of d at the point where $d'(t) = 0$? What is happening to the door's motion at this time?

7. Use the SOLVE feature of your grapher to calculate precisely the value of t at which $d'(t) = 0$.

8. Use the MINIMUM feature of your grapher to find precisely the value of t at which $d'(t)$ is a minimum. What does $d(t)$ equal at this value of t? Put a dot at this point on the graph on this sheet.

9. The point in Problem 8 is called a **point of inflection.** Why do you suppose this name is used?

10. What did you learn as a result of doing this Exploration that you did not know before?

Exploration 3-3b: Derivative Graphs from Function Graphs

Objective: Given the graph of a function, sketch the graph of the derivative function.

For each function given, sketch the graph of the derivative function. Locate *x*-intercepts on the derivative graph by recalling that the derivative is zero if the tangent line is horizontal and has a high point or a low point where the derivative is steepest. Show the behavior of the derivative graph where the given function graph has a cusp or a discontinuity.

1.

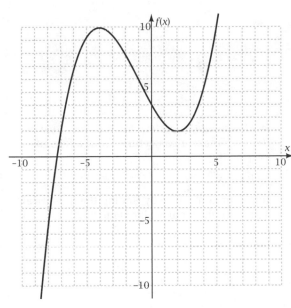

2.

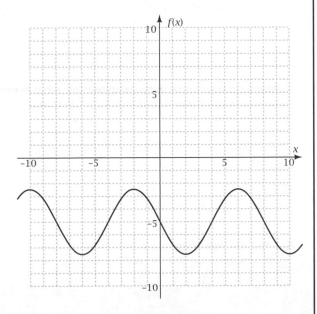

3.

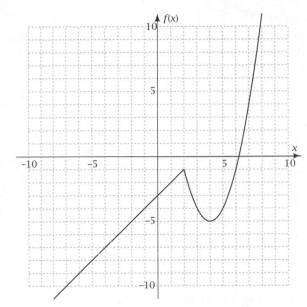

4.

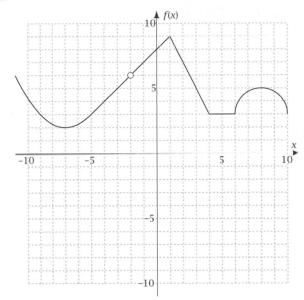

5. What did you learn as a result of doing this Exploration that you did not know before?

Exploration 3-4a: Algebraic Derivative of a Power Function

Objective: Find an equation for the derivative of a power function.

The graph below shows the power function

$$f(x) = x^5$$

In this Exploration you will find a formula for $f'(c)$, the derivative at $x = c$, and from the answer figure out a way to find a formula for $f'(x)$ for *any* power function.

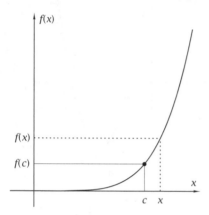

1. By the definition of derivative,

$$f'(c) = \lim_{x \to c} \frac{f(x) - f(c)}{x - c}$$

Substitute for $f(x)$ and for $f(c)$.

2. The numerator of the fraction in Problem 1 is $x^5 - c^5$. Use what you have learned in previous courses about a difference of two like powers to factor this expression. Then use the result to simplify the equation for $f'(c)$ in Problem 1, and take the limit.

3. Use the formula in Problem 2 to find the *exact* value of $f'(3)$. Confirm the answer by estimating $f'(3)$ numerically on your grapher.

4. By observing the pattern for the derivative of $f(x) = x^5$, make a conjecture about a formula for $f'(c)$ if

$$f(x) = x^{10}$$

Test your conjecture by finding the numerical derivative for a particular value of $x = c$.

5. Based on your work in this Exploration, what seems to be a formula for $f'(x)$ if $f(x) = x^n$, where n is *any* positive integer?

6. What did you learn as a result of doing this Exploration that you did not know before?

Exploration 3-5a: Velocity and Acceleration Reading

Objective: Learn about velocity and acceleration by reading Section 3-5.

1. What is the difference between **displacement** of an object from a given point and the **distance** it travels while it is in motion?

2. What is the difference between the **velocity** of a moving object and the **speed** at which it is going?

3. If the displacement of a moving object from a fixed point is given by $y = f(t)$, where t is time, write three different symbols for the velocity, v.

4. If the velocity of a moving object is given by $v = g(t)$, write three different symbols for the acceleration, a.

5. The acceleration, a, is the **second derivative** of the displacement, $y = f(t)$. Write three different symbols for the acceleration as a second derivative.

6. True or false: "If the acceleration of a moving object is negative, then the object is slowing down." Justify your answer.

7. A particle moves along the x-axis with a displacement x feet from the origin given as a function of t seconds by
$$x = t^3 - 9t^2 + 23t - 15$$
What is meant by a "particle"?

8. Write an equation for the velocity of the particle in Problem 7 as a function of t.

9. With your grapher in parametric mode, plot x as a function of t with $y = 1$. Use a t-domain of $[0, 7]$ and a window with $[-20, 20]$ for x and $[0, 2]$ for y. Set the grapher for path style. Describe the motion you see.

10. At $t = 2$, what are the velocity and acceleration of the particle? Is the particle speeding up or slowing down at this time? At what rate? Justify your answer.

11. What did you learn as a result of doing this Exploration that you did not know before?

Exploration 3-5b: Deriving Velocity and Acceleration from Displacement Data

Objective: Find a regression equation from displacement data, and use the equation to find velocity and acceleration.

A bullet is fired from a rifle. The table shows the bullet's (horizontal) displacement from the rifle at various times after it was fired.

t s	$x(t)$ ft
0.3	1000
0.6	1900
0.9	2700
1.2	3400
1.5	4000
1.8	4500
2.1	4900

1. Find the particular equation (the **regression equation**) for the best-fitting power function,

   $$x(t) = at^b$$

   where a and b represent constants. What does the correlation coefficient equal?

2. On your grapher, make a scatter plot of the data. On the same screen, plot the regression equation from Problem 1. Does the equation seem to fit the data reasonably well?

3. The **velocity** of the bullet is the instantaneous rate of change of displacement. Write an equation for the velocity as a function of time.

4. Use the equation in Problem 3 to calculate the velocity at $t = 0.9$ s.

5. Confirm your answer to Problem 4 by estimating the velocity directly from the data.

6. The **acceleration** of the bullet is the instantaneous rate of change of the velocity. Write an equation for the acceleration as a function of time.

7. The equations you have derived in this Exploration are advantageous because they can be used at values of t that are *not* in the data table. Calculate the displacement, velocity, and acceleration at $t = 1$.

8. Finding a value of displacement *between* two data points is called **interpolation.** Finding a value *beyond* the data is called **extrapolation.** Suppose you use the equation in Problem 1 to extrapolate to 1 minute. Do you think the answer would match the actual displacement reasonably well? Explain.

9. What did you learn as a result of doing this Exploration that you did not know before?

Exploration 3-6a: Derivative of the Sine of a Function   Date: _____

Objective: Find the derivative of the sine function if the argument is a *function* of x.

The figure shows the graphs of

$y_1 = \sin x$
$y_2 = \cos x$
y_3 = numerical derivative of y_1 (thick style)

As you can see, there is strong graphical evidence that the derivative of sin x is cos x. Assuming that this is true, you are to investigate derivatives of **composite functions** of the form y = sin (function of x).

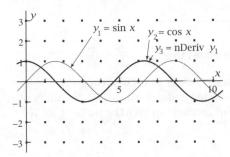

1. Duplicate this figure on your grapher. Use the window shown. Turn on the grid to help you see the critical points. Does the derivative of sin x really seem to be cos x? _____

2. Let $g(x) = \sin 3x$. Change y_1 to sin 3x. Deactivate y_2 and y_3. Plot the graph of y_1 and sketch the result here.

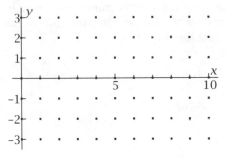

3. Without actually plotting the graphs, make a conjecture about what function $g'(x)$ equals.

   Conjecture: $g'(x) = $ _____

4. Plot the three graphs

   $y_1 = \sin 3x$
   y_2 = your conjecture in Problem 3
   y_3 = numerical derivative of y_1

   Was your conjecture correct? If so, indicate this fact. If not, change your conjecture and replot the graphs until your conjecture matches the numerical derivative graph. Write the final answer here.

   $g(x) = \sin 3x$

   Actual $g'(x) = $ _____

   Was your original $g'(x)$ conjecture correct? _____

5. Enter $y_1 = h(x) = \sin x^2$ on your grapher. Deactivate y_2 and y_3. Change the window as shown here. Sketch the resulting graph.

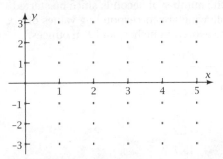

6. Make a conjecture about what an equation for $h'(x)$ might be. Then verify (or refute!) your conjecture by appropriate graphing on your grapher. If your conjecture was wrong, figure out a correct equation for $h'(x)$.

   $h(x) = \sin x^2$

   Original conjecture: $h'(x) = $ _____

   Final answer: $h'(x) = $ _____

7. What operation could you perform on the original equation, $h(x) = \sin x^2$, to get the actual derivative you found in Problem 6?

8. Reset the window as in Problem 1. Plot the graph of $y_1 = t(x) = \sin x^{0.7}$. Sketch the result below. Make conjectures about the derivative function until you have found an equation for y_2 that matches the derivative graph in y_3. Write the result here.

   $t(x) = \sin x^{0.7}$

   $t'(x) = $ _____

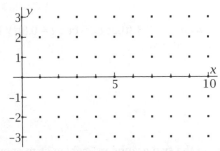

9. Look up the **chain rule** in your text. On the back of this sheet, tell what you learned about how to find the derivative of a composite function using the chain rule.

Exploration 3-7a: Rubber-Band Chain Rule Problem

Date: _____

Objective: Given data for a composite function, demonstrate that the chain rule gives correct answers.

Calvin pulls back a rubber band and shoots it at Phoebe. He figures that the force, *F*, with which he pulls is a function of *x*, the length of the rubber band, and *x* is a function of *t*, the number of seconds since he started pulling. The following are corresponding values of *t*, *x*, and *F*, with *x* measured in inches, and *F* in ounces.

t s	*x* in.	*F* oz
0	3.0	0
0.2	4.8	4.4
0.4	6.1	8.2
0.6	6.9	11.2
0.8	7.3	13.7
1.0	7.7	14.4
1.2	7.9	15.6
1.4	8.0	16.0
1.6	8.0	16.0
1.8	3.0	0

1. Plot the graphs of *F* versus *x* and *x* versus *t*. Connect the dots with smooth curves.

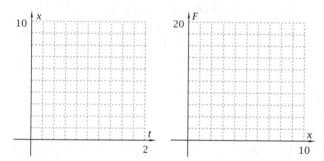

2. Estimate *dx/dt* at *t* = 0.8. What are the units of *dx/dt*?

3. Estimate *dF/dx* at *x* = 7.3 (that is, when *t* = 0.8). What are the units of *dF/dx*?

4. Draw lines on the two graphs in Problem 1 to show graphically that the answers to Problems 2 and 3 are correct. Observe the different scales on the axes.

5. Plot the graph of *F* versus *t*.

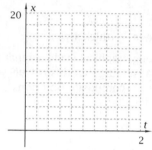

6. The **chain rule** states that $\dfrac{dF}{dt} = \dfrac{dF}{dx} \cdot \dfrac{dx}{dt}$.

Find an estimate of *dF/dt* at *t* = 0.8 using the answers to Problems 2 and 3. Show how the units of *dF/dx* and *dx/dt* combine to give the units of *dF/dt*.

7. Find *dF/dt* at *t* = 0.8 directly from *t* and *F* data in the table. How does the answer compare with the one you got using the chain rule?

8. How can you show graphically that your answers to Problems 6 and 7 are correct?

9. What did you learn as a result of doing this Exploration that you did not know before?

Exploration 3-8a: Algebraic Derivative of Sine Problem

Objective: Confirm algebraically that $\frac{d}{dx}(\sin x) = \cos x$, a property that was discovered graphically.

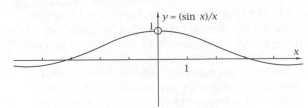

1. The graph of $y = (\sin x)/x$, shown above, seems to approach $y = 1$ at the discontinuity at $x = 0$. Give numerical evidence to confirm this observation.

2. The figure below shows an angle of x radians cutting off an arc x units long on a unit circle. From the figure it appears that $\sin x < x < \tan x$. Give numerical evidence to show that this is true if positive x is kept close to zero.

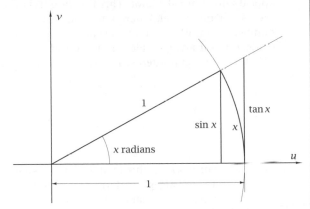

3. Transform the inequality in Problem 2 to show that for small positive values of x,

$$1 < \frac{x}{\sin x} < \sec x$$

4. The **squeeze theorem** states that if $f(x)$ is between $g(x)$ and $h(x)$ for all x in a neighborhood of c, and $g(x)$ and $h(x)$ both approach L for a limit as x approaches c, then the limit of $f(x)$ as x approaches c is also equal to L. Use the squeeze theorem to prove that $(\sin x)/x$ approaches 1 as x approaches 0 from the right.

5. $\frac{d}{dx}(\sin x) = \lim\limits_{\Delta x \to 0} \dfrac{\sin(x + \Delta x) - \sin x}{\Delta x}$

Use the appropriate properties to show that the limit equals $\cos x$.

6. The property you proved in Problem 4 can be called a **lemma** for proving the property in Problem 5. What is meant by a lemma?

7. What did you learn as a result of doing this Exploration that you did not know before?

Exploration 3-9a: Introduction to Exponential Function Calculus

Objective: Find a pattern that allows you to differentiate an exponential function.

Compound Interest Problem: When money is left in an account such as an IRA (individual retirement account), it earns interest at a certain *annual percentage rate* (abbreviated APR). Suppose that you invest $1000 in an IRA that pays 9% per year APR. From previous mathematics courses, you recall that the amount $M(x)$ in the account after x years is given by the exponential function

$$M(x) = 1000(1.09^x)$$

1. Enter $M(x)$ as y_1 in your grapher. Use the LIST feature to make a list containing three columns:

   L_1 with integer values of x from 0 through 5

   L_2 with values of $M(x)$ corresponding to L_1

   L_3 with ΔList(L_2)

   The third list contains the amount of interest earned for the first through fifth years. How do you explain the fact that these amounts are increasing?

2. Enter the numerical derivative of $M(x)$ as y_2. Enter the ratio y_2/y_1 as y_3. Use the TABLE feature of your grapher to make a table of values of y_1, y_2, and y_3. What do you notice about the ratio of the derivative to the function value? Make a conjecture about how you could calculate $M'(x)$ from $M(x)$.

3. By the definition of derivative,

   $$M'(x) = \lim_{h \to 0} \frac{M(x + h) - M(x)}{h}$$

   Substitute for M, then use the properties of exponents and limits to show that $M'(x)$ equals $M(x)$ times the limit of a fraction involving h. Show numerically that this fraction approaches the factor you found in Problem 2.

4. Your calculator has a built-in exponential function, e^x, called the **natural exponential function.** Let $f(x) = e^x$. Use the definition of derivative as you did in Problem 3 to write $f'(x)$ as e^x times a limit involving h. What does the limit appear to equal? What is true about the natural exponential function that makes it important enough to deserve its own key on your calculator?

5. Find the value of e on your grapher. Write the answer to as many decimal places as your calculator gives you.

6. The **natural logarithmic function,** $y = \ln x$, also appears on your calculator. This function uses e as the base. Find $\ln 1.09$. Where have you seen this number recently? Based on your answer, write a conjecture for an algebraic formula for $M'(x)$, where M is the compound interest function in Problem 1.

7. Based on your work on this Exploration, make a conjecture for the algebraic derivative of $f(x) = b^x$, where b is a positive constant not equal to 1. Test your conjecture by plotting

   $y_4 = 2^x$

   $y_5 =$ your conjecture for the derivative

   $y_6 =$ numerical derivative of y_4 (thick style)

   Does your conjecture agree with the numerical derivative?

8. What did you learn as a result of doing this Exploration that you did not know before?

Exploration 4-2a: Derivative of a Product

Objective: Make a conjecture about an algebraic formula for the derivative of a product of two functions.

1. Let $g(x) = x^7$ and let $h(x) = x^{11}$.
   Let $f(x) = g(x) \cdot h(x)$.
   Find $g'(x)$ and $h'(x)$.

2. Write an equation for $f(x)$ as a single power of x.
   Then find an equation for $f'(x)$.

3. Show that $f'(x)$ does *not* equal $g'(x) \cdot h'(x)$.

4. It is possible to get the correct answer for $f'(x)$ by a clever combination of the equations for $g(x)$, $h(x)$, $g'(x)$, and $h'(x)$. For instance, you might notice that the 18 in $18x^{17}$ is the *sum* of the 7 and 11 in $7x^6$ and $11x^{10}$. Figure out what this combination is.

5. Make a conjecture about what $f'(x)$ equals in terms of $g(x)$, $h(x)$, $g'(x)$, and $h'(x)$.

6. Assume that your conjecture in Problem 5 is true for any product of two functions. If $f(x) = x^2 \sin x$, what would $f'(x)$ equal?

7. Plot on the same screen the graphs of $f(x)$, the numerical derivative of $f(x)$, and the equation for $f'(x)$ that you wrote in Problem 6. If the graphs refute your conjecture in Problem 5, change your conjecture and try again.

8. What did you learn as a result of doing this Exploration that you did not know before?

Exploration 4-3a: Derivative of a Quotient—Do-It-Yourself!

Objective: Derive, without looking at the text, an algebraic formula for the derivative of a quotient of two functions.

1. Let $f(x) = \dfrac{x^3}{\sin x}$.

   Estimate $f'(1)$ numerically using your grapher.

2. Show that $f'(1)$ is definitely *not* equal to the quotient of the derivatives of the numerator and the denominator.

3. Let $y = \dfrac{u}{v}$, where u and v stand for differentiable functions of x and where $v \neq 0$. What does $y + \Delta y$ equal in terms of u, v, Δu, and Δv?

4. Use the answer to Problem 3, and the appropriate form of the definition of derivative, to write the value of $\frac{dy}{dx}$.

5. Transform the complex fraction from Problem 4 so that the numerator no longer contains fractions.

6. Transform the fraction in Problem 5 in such a way that the quantities $\Delta u/\Delta x$ and $\Delta v/\Delta x$ appear in an appropriate way.

7. By taking the limit in Problem 6, get a formula for $\frac{dy}{dx}$ that does *not* involve the limit symbol.

8. Verify that your formula in Problem 7 produces the *correct* answer for $f'(1)$ in Problem 1.

9. Write the formula in Problem 7 as a *procedure* (i.e., as a series of things you *do* to get the derivative of a quotient of two functions).

10. What did you learn as a result of doing this Exploration that you did not know before?

Exploration 4-5a: Derivatives of Inverse Trig Functions Date: _____

Objective: Derive algebraic formulas for derivatives of inverse trig functions.

1. You recall that if $y = \sin^{-1} x$, then $x = \sin y$. With your grapher in parametric mode, plot the graph of $y = \sin^{-1} x$ by plotting

   $x = \sin t$
   $y = t$

   Use equal scales on the two axes, with an x-window of about $[-10, 10]$ and a y-window of about $[-6, 6]$. Let t go from -10 to 10. Sketch the result here.

2. On the same screen, plot the graph of $y = \sin x$ by using parametric mode with

   $x = t$
   $y = \sin t$

   How are the two graphs related to each other?

3. If $y = \sin^{-1} x$, and you want to find y', you could start with the definition of derivative. However, this new problem can be transformed to an old problem by using $x = \sin y$. In this form, both sides of the equation are functions of x, but the right side is a composite function, with y as the inside function. If two functions are equal, then their derivatives are equal. Use this fact to differentiate both sides of $x = \sin y$. Solve the resulting equation for y'.

4. It is possible to get the answer to Problem 3 as an *algebraic* function (involving square roots). The figure shows y as an angle (radians) in standard position in a uv-coordinate system. Use the fact that $\sin y = (x/1)$ to write x and 1 on two sides of the reference triangle. Use the Pythagorean theorem to write the length of the third side. Then write y' as an algebraic function of x.

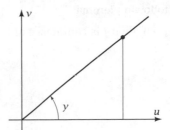

5. Demonstrate that your formula in Problem 4 gives reasonable results by plotting a line through the point $(0.5, \sin^{-1} 0.5)$ with slope calculated by the formula.

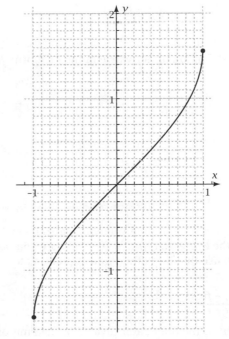

6. Derive algebraic formulas for the derivatives of $\tan^{-1} x$ and $\sec^{-1} x$. Use the back of this sheet.

7. What did you learn as a result of doing this Exploration that you did not know before?

Date: _____

Exploration 4-6a: Differentiability Implies Continuity

Objective: Prove that if *f* is differentiable at *x* = *c*, then *f* is continuous there.

1. Write the definition of continuity at *x* = *c*.

2. Use the definition of continuity and the properties of limits to prove the following **lemma:**

   If $\lim_{x \to c} [f(x) - f(c)] = 0$, then *f* is continuous at *x* = *c*.

3. Write the definition of derivative in the $f'(c)$ form.

4. The definition of derivative you wrote in Problem 3 contains the expression [*f*(*x*) − *f*(*c*)]. Why are you *not* allowed to use the limit of a quotient property to write

   $$\lim_{x \to c} \frac{f(x) - f(c)}{x - c}$$

   as the limit of the numerator divided by the limit of the denominator?

5. Starting with $\lim_{x \to c} [f(x) - f(c)]$, do transformations that lead to $f'(c) \cdot 0$.

6. If *f* is differentiable at *x* = *c*, then $f'(c)$ is a real number. Thus the last expression in Problem 5 is equal to zero. Explain how this fact leads to the **theorem:** "If *f* is differentiable at *x* = *c*, then *f* is continuous at *x* = *c*."

7. Give an example which shows that the converse of the theorem in Problem 6 is *false*.

8. What is meant by a *lemma* for a theorem? What word is used to describe a property that can be proved as an easy consequence of a previously proved theorem?

9. What did you learn as a result of doing this Exploration that you did not know before?

Calculus: Concepts and Applications Instructor's Resource Book
©2005 Key Curriculum Press

Exploration 4-6b: Differentiability and Continuity at a Point

Objective: Find the constants in a piecewise function that make it differentiable where the rule changes.

Let $f(x) = \begin{cases} ax^2, & \text{if } x \le 3 \\ bx - 2, & \text{if } x > 3 \end{cases}$

1. Write a piecewise equation for $f'(x)$. Explain why neither piece of the f' equation contains $x = 3$.

2. Find the one-sided limits of $f'(x)$ as x approaches 3. Write the answers in terms of a and b.

3. Show that $\lim_{x \to 3^-} f'(x) = \lim_{x \to 3^+} f'(x)$ if $a = 1$ and $b = 6$.

4. Plot the graph of f using $a = 1$ and $b = 6$ as in Problem 3. Sketch the result.

5. Tell why it is *not* sufficient to prove that a function is differentiable just by showing that the one-sided limits of the derivative are equal.

6. Find the one-sided limits of $f(x)$ in terms of the constants a and b. Then combine the results with the results of Problem 2 to find the values of a and b that make f differentiable at $x = 3$.

7. Plot the graph of f using the values of a and b from Problem 6. Sketch the graph here. Check your graph with your instructor.   _____

8. What did you learn as a result of doing this Exploration that you did not know before?

Exploration 4-7a: Parametric Function Graphs— The Adam Ant Problem

Objective: Analyze the motion of an object whose path is given parametrically.

1. As Adam Ant crawls along the xy-plane, his position (x, y) is given by

   $$x = 0.4t \cos t$$
   $$y = 0.3t + 2 \sin 2t$$

   Plot the path on your grapher. Use a square window of about −5 to 5 in the x-direction and −2 to 5 in the y-direction. Use a t-range of 0 to 4π. Have your instructor check your graph.

2. Find equations for dx/dt and dy/dt. Evaluate the two derivatives at $t = 6$.

3. Use the answers to Problem 2 in an appropriate way to find the slope of the path at $t = 6$. Offer an explanation, based on the graph, why your answer is reasonable.

4. Use the CALCULATE feature of your grapher to find the answer to Problem 3 numerically.

5. Adam starts out at the origin and goes to the "northeast" for a while. At approximately what value of t does he turn around and start coming back?

6. Reset the t-range to go from 0 to the time Adam first arrives back at $y = 0$. Use a t-step of 0.01 to get a fairly accurate graph. Sketch the result here.

7. Find precisely by calculation the value of t at which y first stops increasing and starts decreasing.

8. At the time in Problem 7, is Adam stopped, or is he still moving? Justify your answer.

9. Use the ZOOM BOX feature to zoom in on the point in Problem 8. How does your answer confirm (or refute!) your conclusion in that problem?

10. What did you learn as a result of doing this Exploration that you did not know before?

Exploration 4-8a: Implicit Relation Derivatives

Objective: Find the derivative of a function specified implicitly, and confirm by graphing.

The following is the graph of the implicit relation

$$x^2 - 4xy + 4y^2 + x - 12y - 10 = 0$$

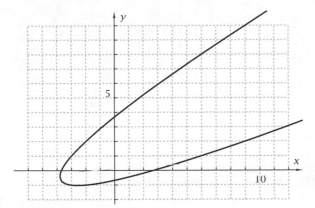

1. Tell why this relation is not a function.

2. Confirm that the graph is reasonable by calculating the values of y when $x = 6$ and by showing that the corresponding points are on the graph.

3. Find an equation for y' by differentiating implicitly with respect to x. The answer will be in terms of x and y. Observe the product rule and the chain rule!

4. Use the equation from Problem 3 to calculate the values of y' at the two points you found in Problem 1. Show on the graph that the two answers are reasonable.

5. What does the formula for y' give you if you substitute (1, 3) for (x, y)? Why does the answer have no meaning for this problem?

6. Find an equation for y explicitly in terms of x. Then tell why it is easier to find y' by implicit differentiation than it would be to find it directly from the explicit equation.

7. How can you tell algebraically that the graph in this exercise is a parabola?

8. What did you learn as a result of doing this Exploration that you did not know before?

Exploration 4-8b: Ovals of Cassini Project

Objective: Use implicit differentiation to analyze the ovals of Cassini.

The figure shows the **ovals of Cassini,**

$$[(x - 6)^2 + y^2][(x + 6)^2 + y^2] = 1200$$

In 1680, Giovanni Domenico Cassini used these figures to describe the relative motions of Earth and the Sun. In this project you will find dy/dx by implicit differentiation and show graphically that your answers are reasonable. You may use the back of this sheet if necessary.

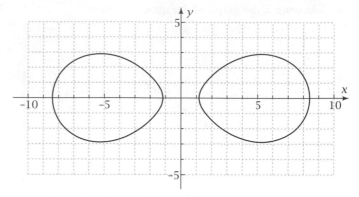

1. Expand the powers and products to get a polynomial equation with terms involving powers of x and y. Differentiate the resulting equation implicitly to find an equation for dy/dx in terms of x and y.

2. Find the two points on the graph at which $x = 8$. Find the two values of dy/dx when $x = 8$. Show that the answers are reasonable.

3. What does dy/dx seem to be at the four x-intercepts? Confirm your conclusion by finding the precise value of the largest x-intercept algebraically or numerically and substituting it into the dy/dx equation.

4. Starting with the polynomial equation in Problem 1, use the quadratic formula to find an equation for y^2 explicitly in terms of x. Then solve for y. Use this equation to duplicate the figure on your grapher.

5. Replace the number 1200 in the original equation with 1400, then plot the graph. In what way(s) is the graph different from the one shown above?

6. Show that for any point on the graph, the *product* of its distances from (6, 0) and (−6, 0) is constant. How does this property compare with the two-focus property of ellipses? (Search on the Internet for ovals of Cassini. For instance, see a dynamic version at *http://new.math.uiuc.edu/eggmath/Shape/cassini.html*.)

7. What did you learn as a result of doing this Exploration that you did not know before?

Exploration 5-2a: Differentials, and Linearization of a Function

Objective: Find the equation of the linear function that best fits the graph of a given function at a given point.

The figure shows the graph of the function

$f(x) = \sec x$

In this Exploration you will find the equation of the linear function that best fits the graph of f when x is kept close to 1.

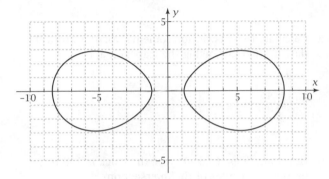

1. You recall the point-slope form, $y - y_0 = m(x - x_0)$, of the linear function equation. In this equation, m is the slope and (x_0, y_0) is a point on the graph. If the linear function is to fit function f when x is close to 1, then m should equal the slope of f at $x = 1$, and y_0 should equal $f(1)$. Thus the best-fitting linear function has an equation of the form

    $y = f(1) + f'(1)(x - 1)$

    Find the particular equation of the best-fitting linear function.

2. Plot the graph of f and the graph of the linear function on the same screen. Sketch the linear function on the graph above. Is the linear function tangent to the graph of f at $x = 1$?

3. Zoom in on the point (1, sec 1). What words describe the fact that the graph looks more and more like the tangent line as you zoom?

4. The quantity $(x - 1)$ in Problem 1 is called the **differential of** x and is abbreviated dx. The quantity $f'(1)(x - 1)$ is called the **differential of** y, abbreviated dy. Let $dx = 0.4$. Draw lines on the graph showing what dx and dy mean.

5. What "interesting" quantity does the ratio $dy \div dx$ equal?

6. Tell how dx and dy are related to Δx and Δy, the changes in x and $f(x)$ as x goes from 1 to 1.4.

7. The quantity $\Delta y - dy$ is the **error** involved in using y in Problem 1 as an approximation for $f(x)$. Explain why this quantity is equal to $f(x) - y$. Then, on your grapher, make a table of values of the error for each 0.01 unit of x from $x = 0.97$ to $x = 1.03$. What happens to the error as x gets closer to 1?

8. How close to 1 should x be kept in order for the error in Problem 7 to be less than 0.001?

9. What did you learn as a result of doing this Exploration that you did not know before?

Exploration 5-2b: A Motion Antiderivative Problem

Date: _____

Objective: Given an equation for the velocity of a moving object, find equations for the displacement and acceleration.

Tay L. Gates wants to determine the characteristics of his new pickup truck. With special instruments he records its velocity at 2-second intervals as he starts off from a traffic light.

t s	Velocity, ft/s
0	0
2	4.5
4	6.9
6	8.8
8	10.4
10	11.9

1. Show that the power function

   $$v(t) = 3t^{0.6}$$

   fits these data closely.

2. Write an equation for Tay's acceleration, $a(t)$. Is the acceleration getting larger or smaller as time goes on? Tell how you figured this out.

3. Velocity is the derivative of displacement. Thus, displacement is the **antiderivative** of velocity. Write an equation for $x(t)$, the truck's displacement from the middle of the intersection. Use the fact that the truck was initially at $x(0) = -50$ ft from the center of the intersection at $t = 0$ when the light turned green.

4. Use the equation in Problem 3 to predict where Tay's truck was 10 s after he started accelerating.

5. Calculate the answer to Problem 4 directly from the data in the table, using the trapezoidal rule.

6. How long does it take before the truck is 100 ft beyond the center of the intersection?

7. What did you learn as a result of doing this Exploration that you did not know before?

Calculus: Concepts and Applications Instructor's Resource Book
©2005 Key Curriculum Press

Exploration 5-4a: Riemann Sums for Definite Integrals Date: _____

Objective: Find an alternative to the trapezoidal rule for estimating a definite integral.

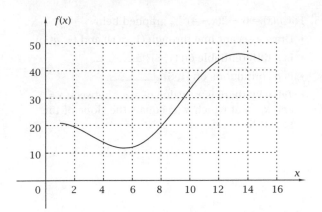

1. The symbol $\int_a^b f(x)\, dx$ stands for the definite integral of $f(x)$ from $x = a$ to $x = b$.

   By counting squares, find an approximation of $\int_2^{14} f(x)\, dx$ for the function graphed above.

2. Find an estimate of $f(c)$ for these values of $x = c$.

c	$f(c)$
3	_____
5	_____
7	_____
9	_____
11	_____
13	_____

3. On the figure above, draw rectangles between vertical grid lines with altitudes equal to $f(c)$, starting at $x = 2$ and ending at $x = 14$. Tell why the sum of the areas of these rectangles is an estimate of $\int_2^{14} f(x)\, dx$.

4. The sum of the areas of the rectangles mentioned in Problem 3 is called a **midpoint Riemann sum.** Evaluate this sum. How close does the answer come to the estimate of $\int_2^{14} f(x)\, dx$ you got by counting squares in Problem 1?

5. Find an estimate of $f(c)$ for these values of c.

c	$f(c)$
2	_____
4	_____
6	_____
8	_____
10	_____
12	_____

6. The values of c in Problems 2 and 5 are called **sample points** for a Riemann sum. Find an estimate of $\int_2^{14} f(x)\, dx$ using the sample points in Problem 5.

7. Tell how estimating an integral using a Riemann sum is related to doing it by trapezoidal rule.

8. What did you learn as a result of doing this Exploration that you did not know before?

Exploration 5-5a: The Mean Value Theorem

Objective: Without looking at the text, discover the hypotheses and conclusion of the mean value theorem.

1. For $f(x) = -0.1x^3 + 1.2x^2 - 3.6x + 5$, graphed below, there is a value of $x = c$ between 3 and 7 at which the tangent to the graph is parallel to the secant line through $(3, f(3))$ and $(7, f(7))$.

   • Draw the secant line and the tangent line.

   • From the graph, $c \approx$ _____

   • Is f differentiable on $(3, 7)$? _____

   • Is f continuous on $[3, 7]$? _____

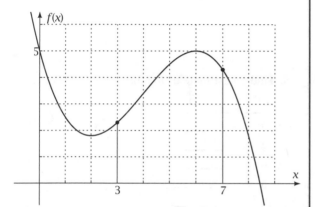

2. Function f from Problem 1 has *two* values of $x = c$ between $x = 1$ and $x = 7$ at which $f'(c)$ equals the slope of the corresponding secant line. (That is, the tangent line parallels the secant line.)

   • Draw the secant and tangents on the graph below.

   • From the graph, $c \approx$ _____ and $c \approx$ _____

   • Is f differentiable on $(1, 7)$? _____

   • Is f continuous on $[1, 7]$? _____

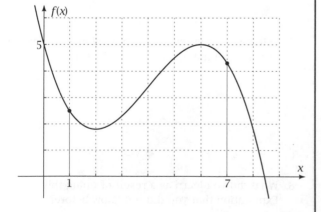

3. For $g(x) = 6 - 2(x - 4)^{2/3}$, graphed below,

   • Draw a secant line through $(1, g(1))$ and $(5, g(5))$.

   • Is g differentiable on $(1, 5)$? _____

   • Is g continuous on $[1, 5]$? _____

   • Tell why there is *no* value of $x = c$ between $x = 1$ and $x = 5$ at which $g'(c)$ equals the slope of the secant line.

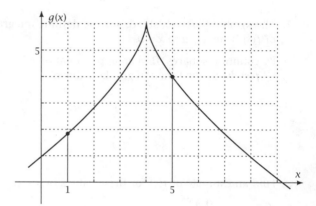

4. Function g from Problem 3 *does* have a value $x = c$ in $(1, 4)$ for which $g'(c)$ equals the slope of the secant line through $(1, g(1))$ and $(4, g(4))$.

   • Draw the secant line and tangent line, below.

   • From the graph, $c \approx$ _____

   • Is g differentiable on $(1, 4)$? _____

   • Is g continuous on $[1, 4]$? _____

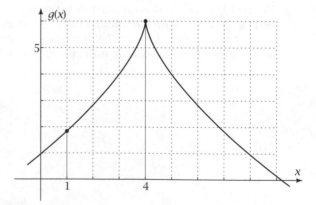

(Over)

Calculus: Concepts and Applications Instructor's Resource Book
©2005 Key Curriculum Press

Exploration 5-5a: The Mean Value Theorem *continued*   Date: _____

5. Piecewise function *h* is defined by

$$h(x) = \begin{cases} 0.2(x-2)^2 + 2.2, & \text{if } x \le 5 \\ 0.3(x-5)^2 + 1, & \text{if } x > 5 \end{cases}$$

- Draw a secant line through $(5, h(5))$ and $(7, h(7))$.
- Is *h* differentiable on $(5, 7)$? _____
- Is *h* continuous on $[5, 7]$? _____
- Why is there *no* value $x = c$ in $(5, 7)$ for which $h'(c)$ equals the slope of the secant line?

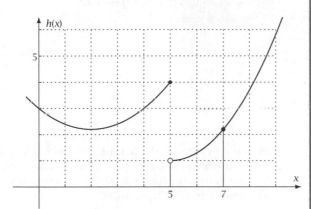

6. The graph below is function *h* from Problem 5.
- Draw a secant line through $(5, h(5))$ and $(9, h(9))$.
- Is *h* differentiable on $(5, 9)$? _____
- Is *h* continuous on $[5, 9]$? _____
- There *is* a point $x = c$ in $(5, 9)$ where $h'(c)$ equals the slope of the secant line. Draw the tangent line. Estimate the value of *c*. _____

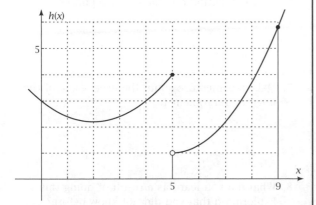

7. The graph below is function *h* from Problem 5.
- Draw a secant line through $(1, h(1))$ and $(5, h(5))$.
- Show that there is a point $x = c$ in $(1, 5)$ where $h'(c)$ equals the slope of the secant line.
- Is *h* differentiable on $(1, 5)$? _____
- Explain why *h* is continuous on $[1, 5]$, even though there is a step discontinuity at $x = 5$.

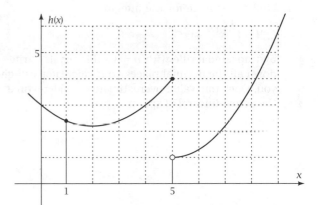

8. The mean value theorem states:
If *f* is differentiable on (a, b) and
f is continuous on $[a, b]$,
then there is a number *c* in (a, b) such that

$$f'(c) = \frac{f(b) - f(a)}{b - a} \qquad \text{i.e., the secant's slope}$$

For which problem(s) are
- the hypotheses and conclusion true? _____
- the hypotheses and conclusion not true? _____
- the conclusion true, but not the hypotheses? _____

9. The number $x = c$ in the above problems is the "mean" value referred to in the name "mean value theorem." Explain why the hypotheses are **sufficient** conditions for the conclusion, but *not* **necessary** conditions.

10. What did you learn as a result of doing this Exploration that you did not know before?

Exploration 5-6a: Some Very Special Riemann Sums   Date: _____

Objective: Calculate Riemann sums for given sets of sample points and reach a conclusion about how the sample points were chosen.

The figure shows the graph of $f(x) = x^{1/2}$. In this Exploration you will integrate $f(x)$ from $x = 1$ to 4.

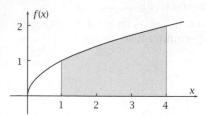

1. Find an estimate for the integral

$$I = \int_1^4 x^{1/2}\, dx$$

by trapezoidal rule with $n = 3$ subintervals. Write down all the decimal places your calculator will give you. Does this value overestimate or underestimate the actual integral? Explain.

2. Find a midpoint Riemann sum for integral I in Problem 1. Use $n = 3$ increments. Show that this sum is *not* equal to the value by trapezoidal rule. Does the midpoint sum overestimate or underestimate the actual integral? Explain.

3. Find a Riemann sum for integral I using the subintervals in Problem 1, but using the following sample points. (k stands for the subinterval number.)

k	$x = c$
1	1.4858425557
2	2.4916102607
3	3.4940272163

How does this sum compare with the answers to Problem 1 and Problem 2?

4. Find a Riemann sum for I using six subintervals of equal width, and these sample points:

k	$x = c$
1	1.2458051304
2	1.7470136081
3	2.2476804000
4	2.7481034438
5	3.2483958519
6	3.7486100806

How does the integral by this Riemann sum compare with other values in this Exploration?

5. Let $g(x) = \frac{2}{3}x^{3/2}$. Find the point in the open interval $(1, 1.5)$ at which the conclusion of the mean value theorem is true for function g. Where have you seen this number in this Exploration?

6. How is function g related to function f?

7. Make a conjecture about the *exact* value of the integral in Problem 1.

8. What did you learn as a result of doing this Exploration that you did not know before?

Calculus: Concepts and Applications Instructor's Resource Book
©2005 Key Curriculum Press

Exploration 5-6b: The Fundamental Theorem of Calculus

Objective: Prove that a definite integral can be calculated *exactly*, using an indefinite integral.

1. Write the definition of $\int_a^b f(x)\,dx$.

2. Write the definition of $g(x) = \int f(x)\,dx$.

3. How can you be sure that the mean value theorem applies to function g?

4. The figure shows function g in Problem 2. Write the conclusion of the mean value theorem as it applies to g on the interval from $x = a$ to $x = x_1$, and illustrate the conclusion on the graph.

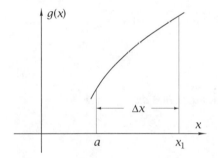

5. The figure in the next column shows the graph of $f(x)$ from Problem 2. Let $c_1, c_2, c_3, \ldots, c_n$ be sample points determined by the mean value theorem as in Problem 4. Write a Riemann sum R_n for $\int_a^b f(x)\,dx$ using these sample points and equal Δx values. Show the Riemann sum on the graph.

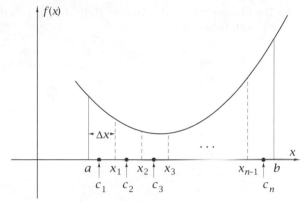

6. By the mean value theorem, $g'(c_1) = \frac{g(x_1) - g(a)}{\Delta x}$, and so on. By the definition of indefinite integral, $g'(c_1) = f(c_1)$. By appropriate substitutions, show that R_n from Problem 5 is equal to $g(b) - g(a)$.

7. R_n from Problem 6 is *independent* of n, the number of increments. Use this fact, and the fact that $L_n \le R_n \le U_n$, to prove that

$$\int_a^b f(x)\,dx = g(b) - g(a)$$

8. The conclusion in Problem 7 is called the **fundamental theorem of calculus.** Show that you understand what it says by using it to find the *exact* value of $\int_1^4 x^{1/2}\,dx$. Use the back of this page if needed.

Exploration 5-7a: Some Properties of Definite Integrals

Objective: Illustrate by graph or by the fundamental theorem of calculus that certain properties of definite integrals are true.

1. The graph shows $f(x) = 19 - x^2$. Tell why f is called an **even function.**

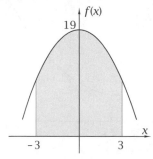

2. Use the fundamental theorem to calculate

$$\int_{-3}^{3} (19 - x^2)\, dx \quad \text{and} \quad \int_{0}^{3} (19 - x^2)\, dx$$

Explain why the first integral is *twice* the second.

3. The graph shows $g(x) = x^3$. Explain why g is called an **odd function.**

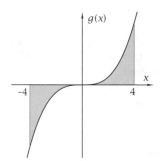

4. Use the fundamental theorem to calculate $\int_{-4}^{4} x^3\, dx$. Explain why the answer equals zero.

5. The graph shows $h(x) = 0.4x^3 - 3x^2 + 5x + 5$.

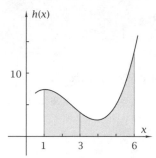

Use the fundamental theorem to calculate

$$\int_{1}^{3} h(x)\, dx \quad \text{and} \quad \int_{3}^{6} h(x)\, dx$$

6. Quick! Calculate $\int_{1}^{6} h(x)\, dx$.

7. Given:

$$\int_{2}^{7} u(x)\, dx = 29,\ \int_{2}^{7} v(x)\, dx = 13,\ \int_{2}^{4} v(x)\, dx = 8$$

a. Find $\int_{2}^{7} [u(x) + v(x)]\, dx$.

b. Find $\int_{4}^{7} v(x)\, dx$.

8. What did you learn as a result of doing this Exploration that you did not know before?

Exploration 5-8a: Applications of Definite Integrals   Date: _____

Objective: Without looking at the text, learn an interpretation of $f(x)\, dx$ in a definite integral.

Spaceship Velocity and Displacement Problem: A spaceship is fired into orbit. As the last stage of the booster rocket is fired, the spaceship is going 3000 ft/s (a bit under 2000 mi/h). Its velocity, $v(t)$, at t s since the booster was fired is given by

$$v(t) = 3000 + 18t^{1.4}$$

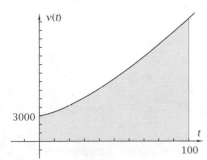

1. On the graph, pick a sample point, t, somewhere on the t-axis between 0 and 100. Show the corresponding point $(t, v(t))$ on the graph.

2. Draw a narrow vertical strip of the region in such a way that the ordered pair $(t, v(t))$ is within the strip. Label the width of the strip dt.

3. If the strip is narrow (i.e., dt is small), the velocity throughout the time interval dt is not much different from the velocity $v(t)$ at the sample point. Explain why the distance traveled in this time interval is approximately equal to $v(t) \cdot dt$.

4. Write a Riemann sum that represents, approximately, the total distance the spaceship goes between $t = 0$ and $t = 100$.

5. Explain why the Riemann sum in Problem 4 is between the corresponding lower sum and upper sum. Based on this fact, why can you conclude that the limit of the Riemann sum is *exactly* equal to $\int_0^{100} v(t)\, dt$?

6. Find the distance traveled by the spaceship by evaluating the integral in Problem 5 using the fundamental theorem of calculus.

7. In order to orbit, the spaceship must be going at least 26,000 ft/s (about 17,500 mi/h). To the nearest second, at what time is it going that fast?

8. How far does the spaceship go from the time the last stage fires till it reaches orbital velocity?

9. Based on what you observed while doing this Exploration, why do you suppose integrals are written in *differential* form, $\int f(x)\, dx$, instead of simply in derivative form, $\int f(x)$?

Exploration 5-9a: Volume by Plane Disk Slices

Objective: Calculate exactly the volume of a solid of variable cross-sectional area.

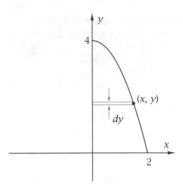

Draw the region.
Slice a strip perpendicular to the
axis of rotation.

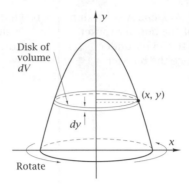

Rotate the region and the strip to
form a solid. The rotating strip forms
a flat disk.

The region in Quadrant I bounded by the parabola

$$y = 4 - x^2$$

is rotated about the y-axis to form a solid paraboloid, as shown above.

1. A representative slice of the region is shown in the figure at left. As the slice turns, it generates a **plane disk,** as shown in the figure at right. Let (x, y) be a sample point on the graph within the slice. Find the volume, dV, of the slice in terms of the coordinates of the sample point.

2. By appropriate algebra, transform dV so that it is in terms of y alone.

3. Find, exactly, the volume V of the solid by adding the volumes of the slabs and taking the limit as the thickness of the slabs goes to zero (i.e., integrate).

4. As a rough check on your answer, compare it with the volume of a circumscribed cylinder and with the volume of an inscribed cone.

5. Based on your answer to Problem 4, make a conjecture about the volume of a paraboloid in relation to the volume of the circumscribed cylinder.

6. What did you learn as a result of doing this Exploration that you did not know before?

Exploration 5-9b: Volume by Plane Washer Slices

Objective: Find the volume of a solid of revolution that has a hole in it.

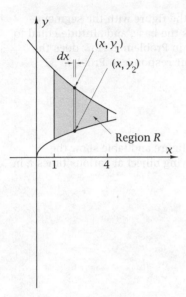

Region R

1. Write the area of the circular ring as a function of y_1 and y_2. Use the result to write the volume, dV, of the washer.

2. Transform the equation for dV so that it is in terms of x alone.

3. Find V by adding up the dV values and taking the limit (i.e., integrate). Use the fundamental theorem to evaluate the integral *exactly*.

The figure above shows the region R that is bounded above and below by the graphs of

$$y_1 = 6e^{-0.2x} \quad \text{and} \quad y_2 = \sqrt{x}$$

and on the left and right by the lines $x = 1$ and $x = 4$. The figure below shows the solid generated by rotating R about the x-axis. A strip of width dx generates a **plane washer** of thickness dx whose cross section is a **circular ring** of outer radius y_1 and inner radius y_2.

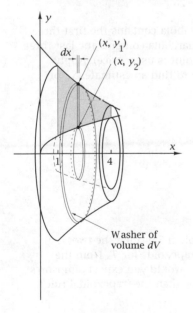

Washer of
volume dV

4. Get a decimal approximation for the volume you found in Problem 3.

5. Evaluate the integral in Problem 3 numerically. Show that the answer is (virtually) the same as in Problem 4.

6. Check your answer with Example 3 in Section 5-9 of the text.

7. What did you learn as a result of doing this Exploration that you did not know before?

Exploration 5-10a: Introduction to Simpson's Rule

Objective: Calculate Riemann sums for given sets of sample points and reach a conclusion about how the sample points were chosen.

Simpson's rule enables you to approximate the value of a definite integral of a function by replacing the graph with sections of parabolas. In this Exploration you will learn how this is done, prior to proving Simpson's rule algebraically.

For Problems 1–4, the figure shows the parabola

$$y = -x^2 + 11x - 16$$

1. Find the area of the region under the graph from $x = 3$ to $x = 7$ using the fundamental theorem.

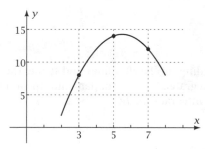

2. Find the y-values at $x = 3$, 5, and 7. Then find the *weighted average* of these values, using the first one, four times the middle one, and the last one.

x	y	**Weighted y**
3		
5		
7		

3. Multiply the weighted average from Problem 2 by the distance between $x = 3$ and $x = 7$. What do you notice about the answer? The result is an example of Simpson's rule.

4. Draw a rectangle on the figure with the segment from $x = 3$ to $x = 7$ as the base, and altitude equal to the weighted average in Problem 2. How does the rectangle confirm your response in Problem 3?

For Problems 5 and 6, the figure and table show the velocity, v, in ft/s, of a moving object at various times t, in seconds.

t	v
6	10
11	7
16	12
21	19
26	22

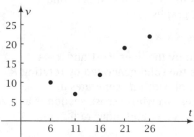

5. Assume that one parabola contains the first three points and another parabola contains the last three points (the middle point is used twice). Apply Simpson's rule twice to find an estimate, S_4, of $\int_6^{26} v \, dt$.

6. On the figure in Problem 5, sketch the two parabolas, and the trapezoids for T_4 from the trapezoidal rule. Why would you expect Simpson's rule to have less error than the trapezoidal rule?

(Over)

Calculus: Concepts and Applications Instructor's Resource Book
©2005 Key Curriculum Press

Exploration 5-10a: Introduction
to Simpson's Rule *continued*

7. Look up Simpson's rule in the text. Write the formula for Simpson's rule. Explain how the formula is consistent with your work in Problem 5.

8. Write or download two programs, one to calculate an integral by Simpson's rule from a set of data as in Problem 5, and another to calculate an integral by Simpson's rule from an equation. Test the first program using the data from Problem 5. Does the program give the same answer you calculated?

9. Use the second program from Problem 8 to find a Simpson's rule approximation, S_{10} (with $n = 10$ increments), for

$$\int_0^\pi \sin x \, dx$$

Use the trapezoidal rule to find another approximation, T_{10}, for the integral. Which approximation is closer to the exact answer, 2?

10. Look up the proof of Simpson's rule in your text. Do you understand how the formula is derived?

11. What did you learn as a result of doing this Exploration that you did not know before?

Exploration 5-10b: Simpson's Rule Demonstration

Date: _____

Objective: Verify Simpson's rule by actually finding the equations of the parabolas and integrating algebraically.

The graph shows the following points for a function f.

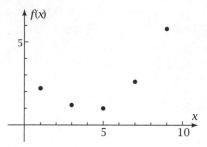

1. Find $\int_1^9 f(x)\,dx$ approximately, using Simpson's rule with $n = 4$ increments. Show your work.

x	$f(x)$	Factor	$f(x) \cdot$ Factor
1	2.2		
3	1.2		
5	1.0		
7	2.6		
9	5.8		

2. Let h be the piecewise function with graphs being the two parabolas in Simpson's rule. Find the particular equations for the two branches of h, one for the first three points and one for the last three points. You may use quadratic regression.

3. Plot the given data points and the two branches of h. Use Boolean variables to restrict the domains of the branches. Sketch the results on the given figure. Is h continuous at $x = 5$? Is h differentiable at $x = 5$? Use one-sided limits to justify your answers.

4. Find $\int_1^9 h(x)\,dx$. Does the result agree with Simpson's rule for $\int_1^9 f(x)\,dx$ from Problem 1?

5. Draw something on the given figure to show why you would expect Simpson's rule to give an answer closer to the actual integral of f than the trapezoidal rule would.

6. What did you learn as a result of doing this Exploration that you did not know before?

Calculus: Concepts and Applications Instructor's Resource Book
©2005 Key Curriculum Press

Exploration 6-2a: Another Form of the Fundamental Theorem

Objective: Find the derivative of a definite integral from a fixed lower limit to a variable upper limit.

1. Let $f(x) = \int_1^x t^{1/2} \, dt$. Evaluate $f(9)$.

2. Sketch the graph of $y = t^{1/2}$. Show on the graph the geometrical meaning of $f(x)$.

3. Evaluate the integral to find an equation for $f(x)$ that does not involve the integral sign.

4. Differentiate both sides of the equation in Problem 3 to find an equation for $f'(x)$. Then tell how you could get $f'(x)$ quickly, in one step, simply by looking at the definition of $f(x)$ in Problem 1.

5. Let $g(x) = \int_3^x t^3 \, dt$. Quick! Find $g'(x)$.

6. Let $h(x) = \int_2^{x^3} \cos t \, dt$. Evaluate the integral to find an equation for $h(x)$ that does not involve the integral sign.

7. Find $h'(x)$ using your answer in Problem 6. Observe the chain rule!

8. By observing the pattern in Problems 6 and 7, evaluate the following derivative *quickly*.

$$\frac{d}{dx} \left[\int_0^{\sin x} \tan^3 (t^5) \, dt \right]$$

9. As a result of your work in Problems 1 through 8, you should be able to understand the **fundamental theorem of calculus in the derivative of an integral form,** specifically:

If $g(x) = \int_a^x f(t) \, dt$, where a stands for a constant, then $g'(x) = f(x)$.

Use this theorem to find $L'(x)$ quickly if

$$L(x) = \int_1^x \frac{1}{t} \, dt$$

10. Explain why $L(x)$ in Problem 9 cannot be evaluated directly by the fundamental theorem in the $g(b) - g(a)$ form using the power rule for antiderivatives.

Exploration 6-2b: Integral of the Reciprocal Function

Date: _____

Objective: Learn why $\int (1/x)\, dx = \ln |x| + C$.

1. $\int \frac{1}{x}\, dx$ can be written as $\int x^{-1}\, dx$.

   Explain why the power rule for integrals *cannot* be used to evaluate this integral.

2. Let $f(x) = 1/x$ and let $g(x) = \ln x$. Write an equation for $g'(x)$. Explain why functions f and g meet the statement of the definition of indefinite integral.

3. Write the definition of $\ln x$ as a definite integral.

4. The figure shows the graph of $y = 1/t$ as a function of t. On the graph, illustrate the meaning of $\ln 5$. What is the difference in meaning between the t and the x in the definition of $\ln x$ in Problem 3?

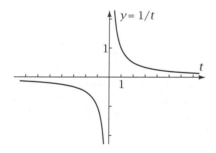

5. Use numerical integration to show that

   $$\int_3^7 \frac{1}{x}\, dx = \ln 7 - \ln 3$$

6. Explain why your calculator gives you an error message if you evaluate this integral numerically.

   $$\int_2^{-5} \frac{1}{t}\, dt$$

7. Shade the region that represents this integral. Explain why your calculator *does* give you an answer if you evaluate this integral numerically, even though both $\ln (-2)$ and $\ln (-5)$ are undefined. Explain why the answer is *positive,* even though the integrand, $1/t$, is negative for all t in $[-5, -2]$.

   $$\int_{-2}^{-5} \frac{1}{t}\, dt$$

8. Given $\int 1/x\, dx$, where x is a negative number. Let $u = -x$ so that u is a positive number. What does dx equal in terms of u? Substitute for x and dx in the integral. Then explain why the integral equals $\ln u + C$. Substitute x back into the answer.

9. The integral $\int 1/x\, dx$ can be written as the piecewise function

   $$\int \frac{1}{x}\, dx = \begin{cases} \ln x + C, & \text{if } x > 0 \\ \ln (-x) + C, & \text{if } x < 0 \end{cases}$$

   Explain why the integral can also be written $\ln |x| + C$.

10. What did you learn as a result of doing this Exploration that you did not know before?

Calculus: Concepts and Applications Instructor's Resource Book
©2005 Key Curriculum Press

Exploration 6-3a: Natural Logs and the Uniqueness Theorem

Objective: Prove algebraically that ln has the properties of logarithms.

1. Write the definition of ln x.

2. Let $f(x) = \ln 3x$.
   Let $g(x) = \ln 3 + \ln x$.

   Show numerically that $f(7) = g(7)$.

3. Show *algebraically* that $f(1) = g(1)$.

4. Show that f and g meet the differentiability hypothesis of the mean value theorem on any interval $(1, b)$ where $b > 0$.

5. Tell why f and g in Problem 4 meet the continuity hypothesis of the mean value theorem on $[1, b]$.

6. Let $h(x) = f(x) - g(x)$. Explain why h meets the hypotheses of the mean value theorem on $[1, b]$.

7. What does $h(1)$ equal? What does the mean value theorem allow you to conclude about function h on the interval $(1, b)$?

8. Assume that there is a number $x = b > 0$ such that $\ln 3b \neq \ln 3 + \ln b$. Let c be the value of x in the conclusion of the mean value theorem for function h on the interval $(1, b)$. What does this assumption tell you about $h'(c)$?

9. In Problem 4, you should have found $f'(x)$ and $g'(x)$. What does $h'(x)$ equal for all $x > 0$? What, specifically, does $h'(c)$ equal? What can you say about the assumption made in Problem 8? As a result, what must be true about $\ln 3x$ and $\ln 3 + \ln x$ for *all* $x > 0$?

10. Problems 2 through 9 constitute a proof by example of the **uniqueness theorem for derivatives.** Write the statement of this theorem.

11. What did you learn as a result of doing this Exploration that you did not know before?

Exploration 6-3b: Properties of Logarithms

Objective: Use the uniqueness theorem to show that ln x, defined as an integral, has the properties of logarithms.

1. You have defined the natural logarithm as

$$\ln x = \int_1^x \frac{1}{t}\, dt$$

Based on this definition, explain why ln 1 = 0 and why ln′ x = 1/x.

2. Let $f(x) = \ln 7x$.
   Let $g(x) = \ln 7 + \ln x$.

   Use the uniqueness theorem to prove that $f(x) = g(x)$ for all $x > 0$.

3. Let $p(x) = \ln 7 - \ln x$.
   Let $q(x) = \ln \frac{7}{x}$.

   Use the uniqueness theorem to prove that $p(x) = q(x)$ for all $x > 0$.

4. Let $h(x) = \ln (x^5)$.
   Let $j(x) = 5 \ln x$.

   Use the uniqueness theorem to prove that $h(x) = j(x)$ for all $x > 0$.

5. You recall that for any permissible base b,

   $$\log_b 1 = 0$$

   Use this fact and the uniqueness theorem to prove that $\log_e x = \ln x$ for all $x > 0$.

6. You recall that for any permissible base b,

   $$\log_b b = 1$$

   Set the integral in Problem 1 equal to 1, and solve numerically to find the value of x that makes the integral equal to 1. Show that the answer is equal to e, to a large number of decimal places.

7. What did you learn as a result of doing this Exploration that you did not know before?

Exploration 6-4a: A Compound Interest Problem

Objective: Use a base-*e* exponential function as a mathematical model of the money in a savings account as a function of time.

When Max de Monet started high school, his parents invested $10,000 in a savings account to help pay for his college education. Exactly 4 years later when he graduated, the account had $15,528.08 in it. Max knows that since the account pays interest compounded continuously, the general equation for $M(t)$, the number of dollars *t* years after the investment, is

$$M(t) = ae^{kt}$$

where *a* and *k* stand for constants and *e* is the base of natural logarithms.

1. By substituting the two given ordered pairs into the general equation, find the particular values of *a* and *k* for Max's account.

2. At what instantaneous rate is the amount in Max's account changing when the money was first invested at *t* = 0? At what rate was it changing when he graduated at *t* = 4?

3. Find the rate of change of Max's money as a percentage of the amount in the account at *t* = 0 and at *t* = 4. What do you notice about the two answers?

4. Show algebraically that if $M(t) = ae^{kt}$, then

$$\frac{\frac{d}{dt}[M(t)]}{M(t)}$$

is a constant. Where does this constant appear in the general equation?

5. Suppose that Max gets a scholarship and is able to leave the money in the account until he graduates from college at *t* = 8 yr. How much money would be there at that time?

6. Max anticipates getting a good job after college and wants to keep the money in the savings account until he retires at time *t* = 50 yr. How much money would he have then? Surprising?!

7. How long does it take for Max's money to double what it was when it was first invested?

8. What did you learn as a result of doing this Exploration that you did not know before?

Exploration 6-4b: Definition of an Exponential for Any Real Exponent

Objective: Discover a definition for the quantity b^x that applies to any positive number b and any real exponent x.

1. Show that you know the algebraic definitions of powers with various kinds of exponents by writing the meanings of the following expressions.

   • Positive integer exponents: $b^3 =$ _____

   • Reciprocal exponents: $b^{1/3} =$ _____

   • Rational exponents: $b^{2/3} =$ _____

   • Negative exponents: $b^{-2/3} =$ _____

2. Explain why a power with an irrational exponent, such as b^π, cannot be expressed exactly using any of the definitions of powers in Problem 1.

3. Write the definition of $\ln y$. Explain why $\ln y$ is well defined for any positive real value of y, rational or irrational.

4. Even though the function $f(y) = \ln y$, graphed here, increases more slowly as y increases, it is unbounded above. Prove by contradiction that this is true by assuming that there is an upper bound, M, such that $\ln y \le M$ for all values of y, and showing that if $y = e^{M+1}$, then $\ln y > M$.

5. Prove that $\ln y$ is unbounded below using reasoning similar to that in Problem 4.

6. The **image theorem** (Problem 14 in Section 2-6) states that if f is continuous on a given interval, then f takes on all values between the minimum and the maximum. Explain how you know that the image theorem applies to $f(y) = \ln y$, and thus the image of the ln function is all real numbers.

7. If $x = \ln y$, then $y = e^x$. Explain how you know from the results of Problem 6 that the domain of e^x is all real numbers.

8. Any positive number b can be written as $e^{\ln b}$. Explain why b^x can be written as $e^{x \ln b}$, and thus b^x is well defined for any real number x, positive, negative, rational, or irrational.

9. Show numerically that 5^π and $e^{\pi \ln 5}$ are equal.

10. What did you learn as a result of doing this Exploration that you did not know before?

Exploration 6-4c: Derivative of an Exponential Function

Objective: Use implicit differentiation to find the derivative of an exponential function.

1. Let $y = 5^x$. Find the numerical derivative of y if $x = 2$.

2. Show that the power rule for derivatives does *not* give the correct answer for y' in Problem 1.

3. Take the ln of both sides of the equation in Problem 1. Differentiate both sides of this implicit relation, observing the chain rule. Do the necessary algebra to solve the resulting equation for y' explicitly in terms of x.

4. Does your equation in Problem 3 give the correct answer for y' if $x = 2$? If not, go back and correct your work in Problem 3.

5. Generalize the pattern in Problem 3 to find a formula for $f'(x)$ if $f(x) = b^x$, where b stands for a positive constant.

6. The figure below shows an accurate graph of

   $$f(x) = 5(0.6^x)$$

   Find $f'(1)$. Demonstrate geometrically on the graph that your answer is correct.

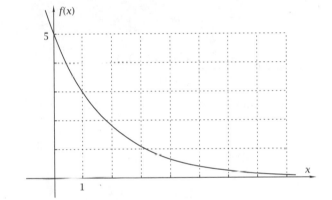

7. By observing the pattern for the derivative of an exponential function, you should be able to write the antiderivative. Find

   $$\int 5^x \, dx$$

8. What did you learn as a result of doing this Exploration that you did not know before?

Exploration 6-5a: Introduction to l'Hospital's Rule

Date: _____

Objective: Find the number that dy/dx approaches if both dy/dt and dx/dt approach zero at a particular value of t.

1. Plot $f(x) = \dfrac{x^3 - 8x^2 + 21x - 14}{\ln x}$.

   Use a friendly window that includes $x = 1$ as a grid point. Sketch the graph.

2. Explain why $f(1)$ is undefined. What does the limit of $f(x)$ seem to be as x approaches 1?

3. Find $\lim\limits_{x \to 1} \dfrac{\frac{d}{dx}(x^3 - 8x^2 + 21x - 12)}{\frac{d}{dx}(\ln x)}$.

   What do you notice?

4. Look up **l'Hospital's rule** in your text. Write the statement of l'Hospital's rule.

5. What form does $\lim_{x \to \infty} x^2 e^{-x}$ take? Tell why this form is indeterminate.

6. L'Hospital's rule also works for the form ∞/∞. Transform the limit in Problem 5 to this form.

7. Use l'Hospital's rule to evaluate the limit in Problem 6.

8. Show that l'Hospital's rule applies to

   $$\lim_{x \to 2} \frac{1 - \cos 3(x - 2)}{(x - 2)^2}$$

   Use the rule to find the limit.

9. Confirm your answer to Problem 8 graphically.

10. Confirm your answer to Problem 8 by table.

11. What did you learn as a result of doing this Exploration that you did not know before?

Calculus: Concepts and Applications Instructor's Resource Book
©2005 Key Curriculum Press

Exploration 6-6a: Derivative, Integral, and Limit Practice

Objective: Demonstrate that you know how to evaluate simple algebraic derivatives, integrals, and limits.

Find the derivative, integral, or limit.
No calculators allowed.

1. $\dfrac{d}{dx}(e^{2x})$

2. $\displaystyle\int e^{2x}\,dx$

3. $\dfrac{d}{dx}(3^{2x})$

4. $\displaystyle\int 3^{2x}\,dx$

5. $\dfrac{d}{dx}(x^3)$

6. $\displaystyle\int x^3\,dx$

7. $\dfrac{d}{dx}[(5x+1)^4]$

8. $\displaystyle\int (5x+1)^4\,dx$

9. $\displaystyle\int (x^5+1)^2 x^4\,dx$

10. $\displaystyle\int (x^5+1)^2\,dx$

11. $\dfrac{d}{dx}[(x-3)^{-1}]$

12. $\displaystyle\int (x-3)^{-1}\,dx$

13. $\displaystyle\int (x-3)^{-2}\,dx$

14. $\displaystyle\int (3-x)^{-1}\,dx$

15. $\displaystyle\int \dfrac{3}{x-1}\,dx$

16. $\displaystyle\int \dfrac{3}{(x-1)^2}\,dx$

17. $\displaystyle\int (x^2+6x+7)^5(x+3)\,dx$

18. $\displaystyle\int (x^2+6x+7)\,dx$

19. $\displaystyle\lim_{x\to 4} \dfrac{\sin(5x-20)}{x-4}$

20. $\displaystyle\lim_{x\to 0} \dfrac{e^{3x}-1}{\sin 5x}$

21. What did you learn as a result of doing this Exploration that you did not know before?

Exploration 7-2a: Differential Equation for Compound Interest

Objective: Write and solve a differential equation for the amount of money in a savings account as a function of time.

When money is left in a savings account, it earns interest equal to a certain percent of what is there. The more money you have there, the faster it grows. If the interest is *compounded continuously,* the interest is added to the account the instant it is earned.

1. For continuously compounded interest, the instantaneous rate of change of money is directly proportional to the amount of money. Define variables for time and money, and write a **differential equation** expressing this fact.

2. **Separate the variables** in the differential equation in Problem 1, then integrate both sides with respect to t. Transform the integrated equation so that the amount of money is expressed explicitly in terms of time.

3. The integrated equation from Problem 2 will contain e raised to a power containing *two* terms. Write this power as a product of two different powers of e, one that contains the time variable and one that contains no variable.

4. You should have the expression e^C in your answer to Problem 3. Explain why e^C is always positive.

5. Replace e^C with a new constant, C_1. If C_1 is allowed to be positive or negative, explain why you no longer need the $\pm$ sign that appeared when you removed the absolute value in Problem 2.

6. Suppose that the amount of money is $1000 when time equals zero. Use this **initial condition** to evaluate C_1.

7. If the interest rate is 5% per year, then $d(\text{money})/d(\text{time}) = 0.05(\text{money})$ in dollars per year. What, then, does the proportionality constant in Problem 1 equal?

8. How much money will be in the account after 1 year? 5 years? 10 years? 50 years? 100 years? Do the computations in the most time-efficient manner.

9. How long would it take for the amount of money to double its initial value?

10. What did you learn as a result of doing this Exploration that you did not know before?

Exploration 7-3a: Differential Equation for Memory Retention

Objective: Write and solve a differential equation for the number of names remembered as a function of time.

Ira Member is a freshman at a large university. One evening he attends a reception at which there are many members of his class whom he has not met. He wants to predict how many new names he will remember at the end of the reception.

1. Ira assumes that he meets people at a constant rate of R people per hour. Unfortunately, he forgets names at a rate proportional to y, the number he remembers. The more he remembers, the faster he forgets! Let t be the number of hours he has been at the reception. What does dy/dt equal? (Use the letter k for the proportionality constant.)

2. The equation in Problem 1 is a **differential equation** because it has differentials in it. By algebra, separate the variables so that all terms containing y appear on one side of the equation and all terms containing t appear on the other side.

3. Integrate both sides of the equation in Problem 2. You should be able to make the integral of the reciprocal function appear on the side containing y.

4. Show that the solution in Problem 3 can be transformed into the form

   $$ky = R - Ce^{-kt}$$

   where C is a constant related to the constant of integration. Explain what happens to the absolute value sign that you got from integrating the reciprocal function.

5. Use the initial condition $y = 0$ when $t = 0$ to evaluate the constant C.

6. Suppose that Ira meets 100 people per hour, and that he forgets at a rate of 4 names per hour when $y = 10$ names. Write the particular equation expressing y in terms of t.

7. How many names will Ira have remembered at the end of the reception, $t = 3$ h?

8. What did you learn as a result of doing this Exploration that you did not know before?

Exploration 7-4a: Introduction to Slope Fields

Objective: Find graphically a particular solution of a given differential equation, and confirm it algebraically.

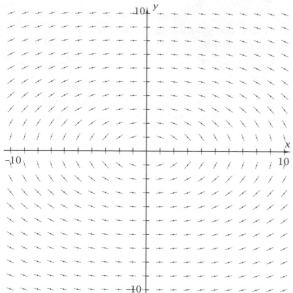

The figure above shows the **slope field** for the differential equation

$$\frac{dy}{dx} = -\frac{0.36x}{y}$$

1. From the differential equation, find the slope at the points $(-5, -2)$ and $(-8, 9)$. Mark these points on the figure. Tell why the slopes are reasonable.

2. Start at the point $(0, 6)$. Draw a graph representing the particular solution of the differential equation which contains that point. The graph should be "parallel" to the slope lines and be some sort of average of the slopes if it goes between lines. Go both to the right and to the left. Where does the graph seem to go after it touches the x-axis? What geometric figure does the graph seem to be? Why should you not continue below the x-axis?

3. Start at the point $(-5, -2)$ from Problem 1 and draw another particular solution of the differential equation. How is this solution related to the one in Problem 2?

4. Solve the differential equation algebraically. Find the particular solution that contains $(0, 6)$. Verify that the graph really *is* the figure you named in Problem 2.

5. What did you learn as a result of doing this Exploration that you did not know before?

Exploration 7-4b: Slope Field Practice

Objective: Solve a differential equation graphically, using its slope field, and make interpretations about various particular solutions.

1. The figure shows the slope field for the vertical displacement, y, in feet, as a function of x, in seconds, since a ball was thrown upward with a particular initial velocity. Sketch y as a function of x if the ball starts at $y = 5$ ft when $x = 0$. Approximately when will the ball be at its highest? Approximately when will it hit the ground? If the ball is thrown starting at $y = -20$ when $x = 0$, at approximately what two times will it be at $y = 0$?

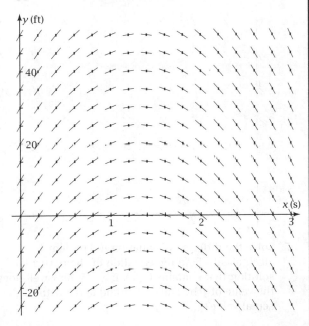

2. Sketch the particular solutions for these initial conditions: $(-7, 2)$, $(-5, -1)$, and $(8, -4)$. Describe the difference in the patterns.

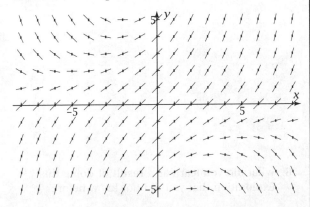

3. The figure shows the slope field for bacteria count, y, in thousands, as a function of time, x, in hours. At $x = 0$, $y = 15$. At $x = 6$, a treatment reduces y to 4. At $x = 20$, another treatment reduces y to 2. Sketch the three branches of the particular solution. Tell what eventually happens to the number of bacteria and what would have happened without the treatments.

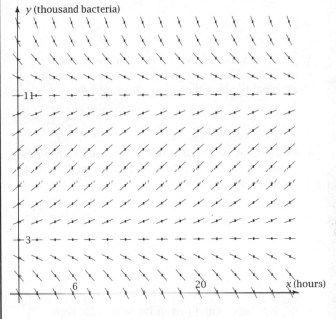

4. Plot the slope field for $\frac{dy}{dx} = \frac{x}{y}$ at the grid points. On the slope field, plot the particular solutions for the initial conditions $(2, 1)$, $(0, -1)$, and $(-2, -1)$.

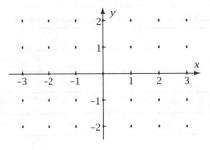

5. What did you learn as a result of doing this Exploration that you did not know before?

Exploration 7-5a: Introduction to Euler's Method

Objective: Given a differential equation, find an approximation to a particular solution by a numerical method.

For the differential equation

$$\frac{dy}{dx} = 0.3y$$

1. Write an equation for the differential dy.

2. Find dy at the point (1, 2) if $dx = 0.5$.

3. Add this value of dy to 2 to estimate the value of y at $x = 1.5$. Plot (1, 2) and (1.5, y) on the figure in Problem 6. Show the values of dx and dy.

4. Estimate the value of y at $x = 2$ by finding dy at the point (1.5, y) from Problem 3 and adding it to that (approximate) y-value.

5. Repeat the calculations in Problem 4 for each 0.5 unit of x up to $x = 6$. Record the y-values in this table. This technique is called **Euler's method** for solving differential equations numerically.

x	y	dy
1	2	0.3
1.5	2.3	0.345
2	2.645	
2.5		
3		
3.5		
4		
4.5		
5		
5.5		
6		

6. The figure shows the slope field for this differential equation. Plot the y-values from Problem 5 on the slope field. Connect the points with line segments. Show dx and dy for $x = 5.5$ to $x = 6$.

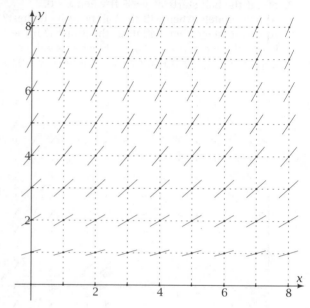

7. Solve the differential equation in Problem 1 algebraically. Find the equation of the particular solution that contains (1, 2). If $x = 5$, how well does the value of y by Euler's method agree with the actual value?

8. What did you learn as a result of doing this Exploration that you did not know before?

Exploration 7-6a: Logistic Function—
The Roadrunner Problem

Objective: Analyze a logistic population growth problem graphically, numerically, and algebraically.

The figure shows the slope field for the differential equation

$$\frac{dP}{dt} = 0.05(P - 4)(12 - P)$$

where P is the population of roadrunners (in hundreds) in a particular region at time t, in years.

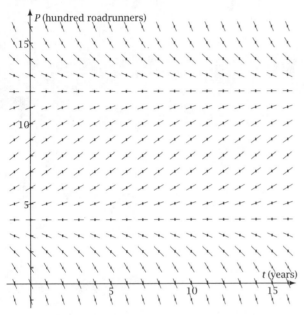

1. Show algebraically that P is
   • Increasing, if $P = 5$.
   • Decreasing, if $P = 3$ or $P = 15$.
   • Not changing ("stable") if $P = 4$ or $P = 12$.

   Does the slope field agree with the calculations?

2. Assume that $P = 5$ when $t = 0$. Using $dt = 0.1$, show the steps in the Euler's method estimation of P when $t = 0.1$ and $t = 0.2$.

3. Use Euler's method with $dt = 0.1$ to estimate P for these values of t, using the initial condition $(0, 5)$. Round to one decimal place.

t	P
2	
4	
6	
8	
10	
12	
14	
16	

4. Plot the values from Problem 3 on the given figure and connect with a smooth curve. Does the curve follow the slope lines?

(Over)

Exploration 7-6a: Logistic Function—
The Roadrunner Problem *continued*

5. This copy of the given slope field shows the particular solution in Problem 4 up to time $t = 8$. Suppose that at this time the Game and Wildlife Commission brings 600 more roadrunners into the region to help increase the population. Use $P(8)$ from Problem 3 to get a new initial condition. Sketch the graph on this slope field. What actually happens to the roadrunner population?

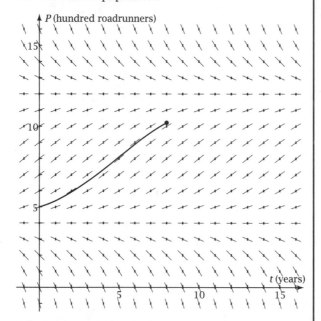

6. Suppose that P had been 3.99 (399 roadrunners) at $t = 0$. Use Euler's method with $dt = 1$ to estimate the year in which the roadrunners become extinct.

7. Estimate the extinction year again, using $dt = 0.1$. Sketch this solution on the slope field. Based on what you know about Euler's method, why is the predicted extinction earlier than in Problem 6?

8. Suppose that 300 roadrunners had been introduced at $t = 8$, using the initial condition in Problems 6 and 7. Sketch and describe the particular solution.

9. Separating the variables and integrating gives

$$\frac{1}{8} \ln \left| \frac{P - 4}{12 - P} \right| = 0.05t + C$$

as you will learn when you study partial fractions. Use the initial condition (0, 5), as in Problem 2, to get the algebraic solution for P as a function of t. How close does the Euler's solution at $t = 8$ in Problem 3 come to the algebraic solution for $P(8)$?

10. What did you learn as a result of doing this Exploration that you did not know before?

Exploration 7-6b: A Predator-Prey Problem

Objective: Analyze the slope field for a differential equation modeling the populations of predatory coyotes and their deer prey.

The figure shows the slope field for a differential equation that represents the relative populations of deer, D, and coyotes, C, that prey on the deer. The slope at any point represents

$$\frac{dC}{dD} = \frac{dC/dt}{dD/dt}$$

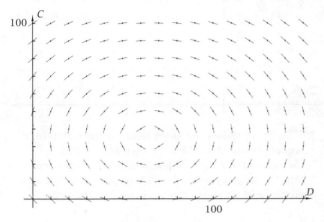

1. At the point (80, 20), there are relatively few coyotes. Would you expect the deer population to be increasing or decreasing at this point? Which way, then, would the graph of the solution start out under this condition?

2. Sketch the graph of the solution to the differential equation subject to the initial condition (80, 20). Describe what you expect to happen to the two populations under this condition.

3. Suppose that the initial number of deer is increased to 120, with the same 20 coyotes. Sketch the graph. What unfortunate result do you predict to happen under this condition?

4. Suppose that the initial deer population had been 140, with the same 20 coyotes. Sketch the graph. What other unfortunate thing would you expect to happen under this condition?

5. At the point (100, 35), what seems to be happening to the two populations? What seems to be happening at the point (65, 80)?

6. Does there seem to be an "equilibrium" condition for which neither population changes? Explain.

7. What did you learn as a result of doing this Exploration that you did not know before?

Exploration 7-6c: U.S. Population Project

Objective: Use actual census data to make a mathematical model of U.S. population as a function of time.

Year	t	Millions
1940	0	131.7
1950	10	151.4
1960	20	179.3
1970	30	203.2
1980	40	226.5
1990	50	248.7

1. The table shows the U.S. population in millions. For 1950, 1960, 1970, and 1980, find symmetric difference quotients, $\Delta P/\Delta t$, and record them in the table. Then calculate $(\Delta P/\Delta t)/P$, the fractional increase in population, for these years. Store P in L1 and $(\Delta P/\Delta t)/P$ in L2.

2. By regression, find the best-fitting linear function for $(\Delta P/\Delta t)/P$ as a function of P. Assuming that the instantaneous rate of change of population, $(dP/dt)/P$, follows the same linear function, write a differential equation for dP/dt. What special name is given to a differential equation of this form?

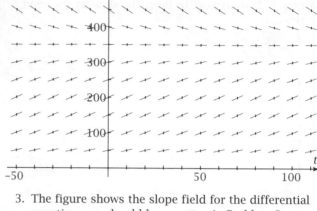

3. The figure shows the slope field for the differential equation you should have gotten in Problem 2. Accounting for the unequal scales on the two axes, are the slope lines for $P = 200$ reasonable? Plot this slope field on your grapher. Does it agree?

4. Use Euler's method with $dt = 1$ to calculate the population for each 10 years from $t = -50$ through $t = 100$. Use 1940 as the initial condition. Plot the points on the graph and connect them with a smooth curve.

t	P		t	P
−50			30	
−40			40	
−30			50	
−20			60	
−10			70	
0	131.7*		80	
10			90	
20			100	

5. How well do the Euler's method numbers agree with the given data points?

(Over)

Exploration 7-6c: U.S. Population Project *continued*

6. According to this mathematical model, what is the maximum sustainable population of the United States? Show how you can calculate this from the differential equation.

7. Suppose that in the year 2010, immigration brings 200 million more people to the United States. Use Euler's method to predict the populations each 10 years for the next 40 years, using $dt = 1$ y. What seems to be happening?

8. Plot the results of Problem 7 on this copy of the slope field and connect the points with a smooth curve. Does the curve follow the slope lines?

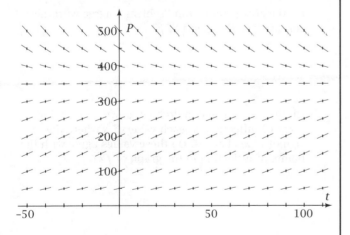

9. On the Internet, find U.S. Census data for 1900 through 1930. Tell the URL of the Web site you used. How well do the predicted figures agree with the actual census? Think of some reasons for any discrepancies.

10. What did you learn as a result of doing this Exploration that you did not know before?

Exploration 8-1a: Number-Line Graphs for Derivatives

Date: _____

Objective: Relate the signs of the first and second derivatives to the graph of a function.

The graph shows the quartic function

$$f(x) = 3x^4 - 52x^3 + 300x^2 - 672x + 900$$

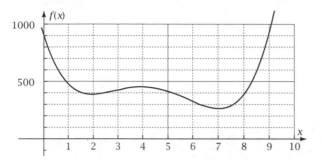

1. Find an equation for $f'(x)$. Factor the expression for $f'(x)$ into three linear factors. Use the result to write all values of x for which $f'(x) = 0$.

2. The values of x in Problem 1 determine **critical points** of the graph of f. On this number line, put a short vertical arrow pointing down to each of these x-values. Write 0 above each arrow, in the row corresponding to $f'(x)$.

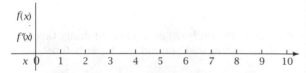

3. The arrows in Problem 2 divide the number line into four intervals. In the $f'(x)$ row for each interval, put + if $f'(x)$ is positive in that interval or − if $f'(x)$ is negative. In the $f(x)$ row, put diagonal arrows pointing upward if there is a + in the $f'(x)$ row or downward if there is a − in the $f'(x)$ row, like this:

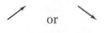 or

4. From the arrows you drew in Problem 3, you can tell whether the critical point is a maximum or a minimum. Write "max" or "min" in the $f(x)$ row. Do these agree with the graph of f at the beginning of this Exploration?

5. Find an equation for $f''(x)$, the second derivative. Find the two values of x that make $f''(x) = 0$. Mark these on this number line the way you marked the critical points in Problem 2, putting 0 in the $f''(x)$ row. Put + or − in the $f''(x)$ row for intervals where $f''(x)$ is positive or negative. Put arcs in the $f(x)$ row, opening up if you put + for $f''(x)$ or down if you put −, like this:

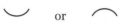 or

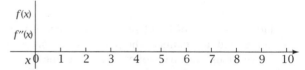

6. Do the arcs you drew in Problem 5 agree with the concavity of the graph of f?

7. On the number line in Problem 5, write "p.i." (for point of inflection) at each value of x where the sign of $f''(x)$ changes. Do these values agree with the points of inflection in the graph of f?

(Over)

Calculus: Concepts and Applications Instructor's Resource Book
©2005 Key Curriculum Press

Exploration 8-1a: Number-Line Graphs
for Derivatives *continued*

8. Demonstrate that you understand the relationships among $f'(x)$, $f''(x)$, and the graph of f by sketching the graph of a continuous function that has the features indicated on these number lines.

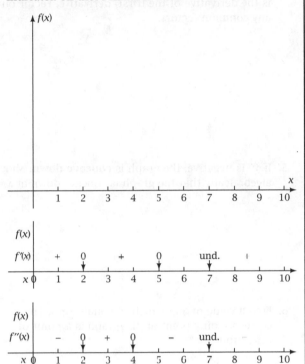

9. What did you learn as a result of doing this Exploration that you did not know before?

Exploration 8-2a: Maxima, Minima, and Points of Inflection

Objective: Find the first and second derivatives for a function, and show how values of these correspond to the graph.

The figure shows the graph of

$$y = 5x^{2/3} - x^{5/3}$$

as it might appear on your grapher. In this Exploration you will make connections between the graph and the first and second derivatives.

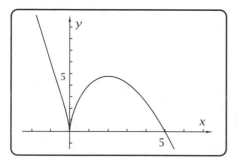

1. Find an equation for y'. Factor out any common factors, including $x^{-1/3}$ (the lowest power of x).

2. What value of x makes y' equal zero? What is true about the graph of y at that value of x?

3. You realize that zero raised to a negative power is infinite because it involves dividing by zero. What value of x makes y' infinite? What is true about the graph at this value of x?

4. Find an equation for the second derivative, y''. This is the derivative of the (first) derivative. Factor out any common factors.

5. If y'' is negative, the graph is **concave down.** Show algebraically that the graph is concave down at $x = 1$.

6. Find a value of x at which y'' equals zero. The corresponding point on the graph is a **point of inflection.**

7. By picking a value of x on either side of the point of inflection in Problem 6, show that the graph is really concave up on one side and concave down on the other, even though the graph appears to be straight in a neighborhood of this x-value.

8. What did you learn as a result of doing this Exploration that you did not know before?

Exploration 8-2b: Derivatives and Integrals from Given Graphs

Objective: Given the graph of a function, sketch the graph of its derivative function or its integral function.

1. The graph below shows a function *h*. On the same axes, sketch the graph of the derivative function, *h'*. At the cusp, *h'*(1) is undefined. Make sure your graph accounts for this fact.

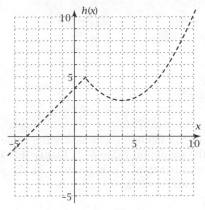

2. For *h* in Problem 1, is it also correct to say that *h'*(1) is infinite? Explain.

3. For Problem 1, is *h* *continuous* at *x* = 1? Is *h* *differentiable* at *x* = 1?

4. The graph below shows the *derivative, g'*, of function *g*. On the same axes, sketch the graph of *g*, using as an initial condition *g*(0) = 3.

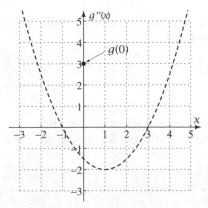

5. The graph below shows a function *y*. On the same axes, sketch the graph of the derivative, *y'*.

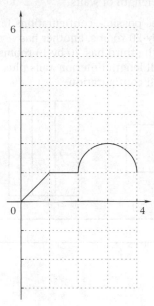

6. The graph shows the derivative of a function, *y'*. On the same axes, sketch the graph of the function if (0, 0) is on the graph of *y*.

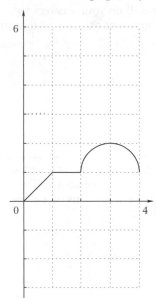

7. What did you learn as a result of doing this Exploration that you did not know before?

Exploration 8-3a: Minimum-Cost Motel Three Problem Date: _____

Objective: Find an equation for a function, and use the equation to find the minimum value of that function.

Developers plan to build motels units with three rooms in a row. Each room must have 400 square feet of floor space. To lower construction costs, they want each unit to have the minimum total length of walls.

1. The figure shows three possible configurations for a motel. One has 20-by-20 rooms, another has 10-by-40 rooms, and the third has 40-by-10 rooms. Calculate the total wall length (interior walls plus exterior walls) for each configuration.

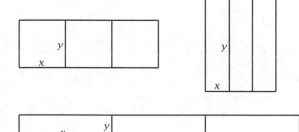

2. Let x be the breadth of each room and let y be the depth of each room. Based on your answers to Problem 1, sketch the graph of the total wall length, L, as a function of x.

3. Write an equation for L as a function of x and y. Use the fact that each room must have area 400 to transform the equation for L in terms of x alone.

4. Plot the graph of L as a function of x. Sketch the result. Use MINIMUM on your grapher to find the minimum value of L and the value of x at which this occurs. Show this point on your sketch.

5. Use derivatives to calculate algebraically the value of x that gives the minimum value of L. Justify that this is a minimum rather than a maximum. Does the answer agree with Problem 4?

6. Write the overall dimensions of the motel with the minimum value of L.

7. What did you learn as a result of doing this Exploration that you did not know before?

Calculus: Concepts and Applications Instructor's Resource Book
©2005 Key Curriculum Press

Exploration 8-3b: Maximal Cylinder in a Cone Problem

Objective: Find an equation for a function, and maximize the function.

The figures show cylinders inscribed in a cone. The cone has radius 4 in. and altitude 12 in. If the cylinder is tall and skinny as in the figure at left, the volume is small because the radius is small. If the cylinder is short and fat as in the figure at right, the volume is small because the altitude is small. In this Exploration you will learn how to find the dimensions that give the inscribed cylinder its *maximum* volume.

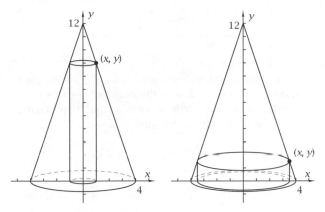

1. Calculate the volumes of cylinders for which the radius, x, equals 0, 1, 2, 3, and 4 units.

2. Write the volume of the cylinder in terms of the sample point (x, y) on an element of the cone. Then transform the equation so that the volume is in terms of x alone. You may find it useful to determine the equation of the line in Quadrant I that the sample point lies on.

3. Differentiate both sides of the volume equation in Problem 2 with respect to x.

4. As x increases the volume increases, reaches a maximum, then decreases again. At the maximum point its rate of change will be zero. Set dV/dx from Problem 3 equal to zero and solve for x.

5. Plot the graph of V. Sketch the graph here. Show on the graph that the maximum volume occurs at the value of x you found algebraically in Problem 4.

6. Find the radius, altitude, and volume of the maximum-volume cylinder.

7. Summarize the steps you went through in Problems 2 through 6 in order to find the maximum-volume cylinder.

8. What did you learn as a result of doing this Exploration that you did not know before?

Exploration 8-4a: Volume by Cylindrical Shells

Objective: Find the volume of a solid of revolution by slicing the rotated region *parallel* to the axis of rotation.

The left-hand figure below shows the region under the graph of $y = 4x - x^2$ from $x = 0$ to $x = 3$. The right-hand figure shows the solid formed when this region is rotated about the y-axis.

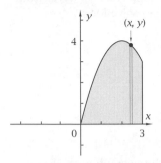 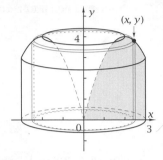

1. As the region rotates, the strip parallel to the y-axis generates a **cylindrical shell** as shown below. The volume, dV, of this shell equals the circumference at the sample point (x, y), times the altitude of the shell, times the thickness of the shell, dx. Write an equation for dV in terms of x, y, and dx.

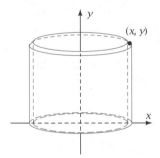

2. Substitute for y to get dV in terms of x and dx alone.

3. Calculate the volume of the solid by adding up all the dV's and taking the limit (i.e., integrate). Tell why the limits of integration are 0 to 3, not −3 to 3.

4. Demonstrate that you understand slicing a solid into cylindrical shells by using the technique to find the volume of the solid shown below.

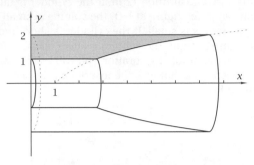

In this solid, the region bounded by the y-axis, the lines $y = 1$ and $y = 2$, and the graph of $y = \ln x$ is rotated about the x-axis to form a solid. (For clarity, only the back side of the solid is shown.)

5. What did you learn as a result of doing this Exploration that you did not know before?

Exploration 8-4b: Volumes by Shells or Washers

Objective: Find volumes of revolution by appropriate calculus.

The figure shows the region R in Quadrant I bounded by the graphs of $y_1 = e^{0.4x}$ and $y_2 = 4 - x^2$.

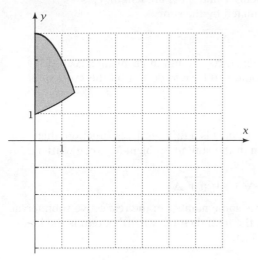

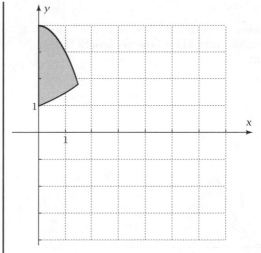

1. In doing calculus with this region, tell why it would be more convenient to slice the region vertically rather than horizontally.

2. Find numerically the value of $x = b$ in Quadrant I where the two graphs intersect.

3. On the figure above, sketch the solid generated by rotating R about the line $x = 3$. Write an integral equal to its volume. Evaluate the integral numerically.

4. On the figure above, sketch the solid formed by rotating R around the x-axis. Write an integral equal to its volume. Evaluate the integral numerically.

5. What is the main difference between finding the volume of a solid of revolution by cylindrical shells and finding the volume by washers as you have done earlier?

6. What did you learn as a result of doing this Exploration that you did not know before?

Exploration 8-5a: Length of a Plane Curve (Arc Length)

Date: _____

Objective: Calculate the arc length of a plane curve approximately by geometry and exactly by calculus.

The figure shows the graph of $y = x^2$ from $x = -1$ to $x = 2$. In this Exploration you will find the **arc length** of this graph segment.

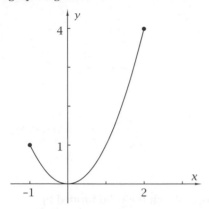

1. Draw line segments connecting (consecutively) the points on the graph where x is -1, 0, 1, and 2. Estimate the length of the graph by calculating the lengths of these segments. Does this overestimate or underestimate the arc length?

2. Find an estimate of the length using segments connecting the points on the graph where x is -1, -0.5, 0, 0.5, 1, 1.5, and 2. Explain why this estimate is better than the one in Problem 1.

3. In Problems 1 and 2 the arc length, L, is approximated by the sum

$$L \approx \sum \sqrt{\Delta x^2 + \Delta y^2}$$

In Problem 1, $\Delta x = 1$ and in Problem 2, $\Delta x = 0.5$. What would you have to do to find the *exact* value of L?

4. If $y = f(x)$, and f is a differentiable function, then any term in the sum in Problem 3 can be written exactly as

$$\Delta L = \sqrt{1 + [f'(c)]^2}\, \Delta x$$

where c is some number in the respective subinterval. Consult the text, then tell what theorem is the basis for this fact.

5. Explain why, in the limit, ΔL can be written as

$$dL = \sqrt{dx^2 + dy^2}$$

6. Find dL for $y = x^2$. Then write L exactly as a definite integral.

7. Find a decimal approximation for the exact arc length by evaluating the integral in Problem 6 numerically. (You can consult Section 9-6 to see how to do the integrating exactly, by trigonometric substitution.)

8. What did you learn as a result of doing this Exploration that you did not know before?

Calculus: Concepts and Applications Instructor's Resource Book
©2005 Key Curriculum Press

Exploration 8-6a: Area of a Surface of Revolution

Objective: Calculate exactly the area of a doubly-curved surface of revolution.

If a line segment is rotated about an axis coplanar with it, a *singly*-curved surface is formed (a cone or cylinder). Such a surface can be rolled out flat and its area found by calculus or geometry techniques you have learned before. If a plane curve is rotated about an axis coplanar with it, a *doubly*-curved surface is formed. Spheres, ellipsoids, paraboloids, and so on, are examples. Because such a surface *cannot* be flattened without distortion, its area must be found without first flattening. The figure below shows a doubly-curved surface formed by rotating a graph about the *x*-axis.

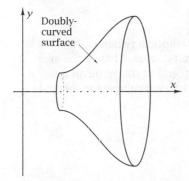

Rotate a curved graph,
get a doubly-curved surface.

In the problems below, you will turn the new problem of finding the area of a doubly-curved surface into the old problem of finding areas of many singly-curved surfaces. Then you will add the areas of these surfaces and take the limit (i.e., integrate).

1. Suppose that a curve in the figure above has been sliced into curved segments by partitioning the *x*-axis into subintervals of equal length. Show on the diagram how rotating one of these segments gives a surface that resembles a frustum of a cone.

2. Prove that the lateral area of a cone is πRL, where R is the radius of the cone's base and L is the slant height of the cone.

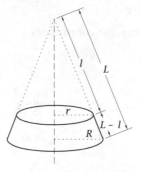

3. The diagram above shows a frustum of a cone with base radii and slant heights R and r, and L and l. Prove that the lateral area of the frustum equals the circumference at the *average* radius multiplied by the slant height of the frustum.

4. The slice you drew in Problem 1 has a slant height approximately equal to dL, the differential of arc length. Write an equation for dS, the differential of surface area.

5. The graph of $y = x^3$ from $x = 0$ to $x = 1$ is rotated about the *x*-axis to form a surface. Find its area.

6. What did you learn as a result of doing this Exploration that you did not know before?

Exploration 8-7a: Area of an Ellipse in Polar Coordinates

Date: _____

Objective: Find the area of an ellipse from its polar equation, then compare with the area found by familiar geometry.

The figure shows the **ellipse** in polar coordinates

$$r = \frac{10}{3 - 2\cos\theta}$$

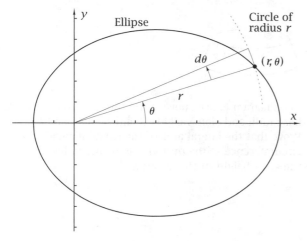

1. Set your grapher to POLAR mode and plot the graph. Use equal scales on both x- and y-axes. Does your graph agree with the figure above?

2. The sample point (r, θ) shown in the figure is at $\theta = 0.3$ radian. Calculate r, x, and y for this point. Show that all three agree with the graph.

3. The area of a wedge-shaped piece of the elliptical region bounded by the graph is approximately equal to the area of the sector of a circle. Calculate the area of the sector shown in the figure above, if $\theta = 0.3$ radian and $d\theta = 0.1$ radian.

4. Show that in general, the area dA of the sector is

$$dA = \frac{1}{2}r^2\,d\theta$$

5. The exact area of the elliptical region is the *limit* of the *sum* of the sectors' areas. That is, the area equals the definite integral of dA. Write an integral representing the exact area. Evaluate the integral numerically.

6. The x-radius, a, of the ellipse shown is 6 units. Measure or calculate the y-radius, b. Then confirm that the answer you got by integration in Problem 5 agrees with the answer you get using the ellipse area formula $A = \pi ab$.

7. What did you learn as a result of doing this Exploration that you did not know before?

Exploration 8-7b: Polar Coordinate Area, Length, and Intersection Problem

Objective: Find the area and arc length of a region bounded by graphs in polar coordinates, and find intersections of polar curves.

This problem concerns the region in Quadrant I outside the circle $r_1 = 4$ and inside one "leaf" of the **four-leaved rose** $r_2 = 6 \sin 2\theta$.

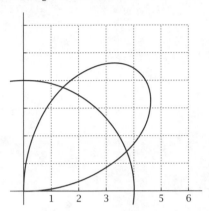

1. Plot the entire graph (one revolution) on your grapher. Use equal scales on the two axes. (Using SIMULTANEOUS mode will reveal some things you need to know later in this problem.) Does your grapher confirm what is shown in the figure above? _____

2. Find the values of θ in Quadrant I at which the two graphs cross. You may do this algebraically or numerically. Store the answers, without round-off, as a and b, respectively.

3. Find the area of the region between the two graphs.

4. Confirm from the given figure that your answer to Problem 3 is reasonable.

5. Find the area of the entire leaf in Quadrant I. Is the answer an "interesting" multiple of π?

6. Find the length of the boundary of the leaf in Quadrant I. Is the answer an "interesting" multiple of π?

7. The two graphs seem to intersect at two points in Quadrant II. Explain why *neither* of these points is a true intersection point. (Tracing the graph may help.)

8. What did you learn as a result of doing this Exploration that you did not know before?

Exploration 8-7c: Comet Polar Coordinates Problem

Objective: Find the area and arc length of a region bounded by graphs in polar coordinates.

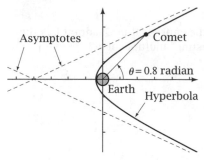

When a comet approaches Earth, it is drawn into a more and more curved path by gravity as it gets closer and closer. If the velocity is high enough, the comet follows a hyperbolic path with Earth's center at one focus as shown in the figure. (When the comet is far away, its path is close to one of the two asymptotes of the hyperbola.) Assume that a comet is on a path whose polar equation is

$$r = 84(10 - 11 \cos \theta)^{-1}$$

where distances are in thousands of miles.

1. Plot the path on your grapher. Use a window with [−55, 55] for x and equal scales on the two axes. Does your graph agree with the figure?

2. How far is the comet from Earth's center at the point shown in the figure where $\theta = 0.8$ radian?

3. Find the area swept out by the line segment from Earth's center to the comet from the time $\theta = 0.8$ to the time $\theta = 5.5$. Show your work.

4. How far does the comet travel along its curved path from the time $\theta = 0.8$ to the time $\theta = 5.5$? Show your work.

5. Perform a quick check to show that the distance you calculated in Problem 4 is reasonable.

6. What did you learn as a result of doing this Exploration that you did not know before?

Exploration 9-3a: Integration by Parts Practice

Objective: Integrate by parts to find antiderivatives quickly.

Find the integral. Show the steps you take.

1. $\displaystyle\int x^2 \sin 3x \, dx$

2. $\displaystyle\int x^5 \ln 4x \, dx$

3. $\displaystyle\int e^{5x} \cos 6x \, dx$

4. $\displaystyle\int x(\ln x)^3 \, dx$

5. $\displaystyle\int \sin^{10} x \cos x \, dx$ (Be clever!)

6. $\displaystyle\int \sin^{10} x \, dx$, in terms of $\displaystyle\int \sin^8 x \, dx$

7. What did you learn as a result of doing this Exploration that you did not know before?

Exploration 9-4a: Reduction Formulas

Objective: Integrate by parts to find a reduction formula, and use that formula in a volume problem.

1. Integrate by parts to find a formula for $\int \sin^{10} x \, dx$ in terms of $\int \sin^8 x \, dx$.

2. Based on the pattern you observe in the answer to Problem 1, write a formula for $\int \sin^n x \, dx$ in terms of $\int \sin^{n-2} x \, dx$. Check with Section 9-4 to make sure your formula is correct.

3. The graph shows $y = \sin^3 x$. Find numerically the volume of the solid generated by rotating about the x-axis the region under this graph from $x = 0$ to $x = \pi$.

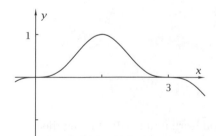

4. Problem 3 involves $\int \sin^6 x \, dx$. Use the reduction formula to evaluate this indefinite integral. Use the result to find the volume of the solid algebraically, using the fundamental theorem. Does the result agree with the answer to Problem 3?

5. What did you learn as a result of doing this Exploration that you did not know before?

Exploration 9-5a: Integrals of Special Powers of Trig Functions

Objective: Integrate odd powers of sine and cosine, and even powers of secant and cosecant.

1. Integrate $\int \cos^7 x \sin x \, dx$ as a power.

2. Explain why $\int \cos^7 x \, dx$ cannot be integrated as a power.

3. Associate all but one of the cosines in the integral in Problem 2, change them to sines using the Pythagorean properties, then evaluate the integral as a *sum* of *powers*.

4. Explain why $\int \cos^6 x \, dx$ cannot be integrated by the method of Problem 3.

5. Integrate $\int \tan^5 x \sec^2 x \, dx$ as a power.

6. Explain why $\int \sec^8 x \, dx$ cannot be integrated as a power.

7. Associate all but two of the secants in the integral in Problem 6, change them to tangents using the Pythagorean properties, then evaluate the integral as a *sum of powers*.

8. Explain why $\int \sec^7 x \, dx$ cannot be integrated by the method of Problem 7.

9. What did you learn as a result of doing this Exploration that you did not know before?

Exploration 9-5b: Other Special Trigonometric Integrals

Objective: Find the antiderivatives $\int \sin^2 x\, dx$ and $\int \cos^2 x\, dx$ and $\int \cos ax \sin bx\, dx$.

1. You recall that

$$\cos(A + B) = \cos A \cos B - \sin A \sin B$$

Use this property to write the double-argument property for $\cos 2x$.

2. Transform the double-argument property so that $\cos 2x$ is expressed in terms of $\cos x$ alone.

3. Transform the double-argument property so that $\cos 2x$ is expressed in terms of $\sin x$ alone.

4. Transform the properties in Problems 2 and 3 so that $\cos^2 x$ is expressed in terms of $\cos 2x$ and so that $\sin^2 x$ is expressed in terms of $\cos 2x$.

5. Use the results of Problem 4 to find the integrals $\int \cos^2 x\, dx$ and $\int \sin^2 x\, dx$.

6. Products of sine and cosine with two different arguments can be integrated by parts. Integrate $\int \cos 7x \sin 5x\, dx$.

7. Use the result of Problem 6 to write a formula for $\int \cos ax \sin bx\, dx$.

8. What did you learn as a result of doing this Exploration that you did not know before?

Exploration 9-6a: Introduction to Integration by Trig Substitution

Objective: Integrate a square root of a quadratic by making a rationalizing substitution.

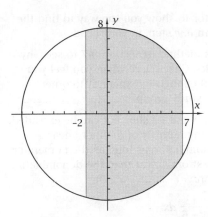

1. The diagram above shows the circle for which

   $$y = \pm\sqrt{64 - x^2}$$

   Use the most time-efficient method to find the area of the zone of this circle from $x = -2$ to $x = 7$.

2. In Problem 1, you evaluated the definite integral

   $$\int_{-2}^{7} \sqrt{64 - x^2}\ dx$$

   numerically. Although the radical can be written as $(64 - x^2)^{1/2}$, explain why the indefinite integral cannot be found using the power rule.

3. The radical in Problems 1 and 2 looks like the third side of a right triangle (diagram below) with one leg x, hypotenuse 8, and θ in standard position.

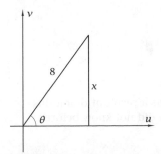

Write the integral in Problem 2 in terms of trig functions of θ.

4. Using the techniques you have learned for integrating powers of trig functions, evaluate the integral in Problem 3 algebraically.

5. Do the reverse substitution to get the answer in Problem 4 into terms of x.

6. Use the answer to Problem 5 to find *exactly* the area of the zone in Problem 1. Show that a decimal approximation of this exact answer agrees with the answer found numerically.

7. What did you learn as a result of doing this Exploration that you did not know before?

Exploration 9-7a: Integrals of Rational Functions by Partial Fractions

Date: _____

Objective: Integrate algebraically a function of the form (polynomial)/(polynomial).

1. The integral

$$\int \frac{10x - 32}{x^2 - 4x - 5} \, dx$$

has an integrand that is a **rational algebraic function.** It can be transformed to

$$\int \frac{10x - 32}{(x - 5)(x + 1)} \, dx$$

The integrand can then be broken up into two **partial fractions,**

$$\frac{A}{x - 5} + \frac{B}{x + 1}$$

Find the constants A and B.

2. The integral in Problem 1 can be evaluated as a sum of two terms, each of which has the form of the **reciprocal function.** Find the indefinite integral.

3. Ask your instructor to show you the way to find the partial fractions in *one* step, in your head.

4. Study Heaviside's method in Section 9-7 to see why the shortcut works. Check here when you feel you understand it well enough to explain it to other members of your study group. _____

5. Heaviside's method and its shortcut can be extended to integrals with any number of distinct linear factors in the denominator, as long as the numerator is of degree at least one lower than the denominator. Do this integration:

$$\int \frac{11x^2 - 22x - 13}{x^3 - 2x^2 - 5x + 6} \, dx$$

6. What did you learn as a result of doing this Exploration that you did not know before?

Calculus: Concepts and Applications Instructor's Resource Book
©2005 Key Curriculum Press

Exploration 9-8a: Integrals of Inverse Trigonometric Functions

Objective: Use integration by parts to learn how to integrate an inverse trigonometric function.

For Problems 1 and 2, let $I = \int \sin^{-1} x\, dx$.

1. The integral I can be written as a product in two different ways:

$$\int (1)(\sin^{-1} x\, dx) \quad \text{or} \quad \int (\sin^{-1} x)(1\, dx)$$

Why is the first form not useful for integration by parts, while the second form is?

2. Evaluate the integral to find I. Check your answer with the answer in the text. If it does not agree, go back and find the source of your differences.

3. Find $I = \int \sec^{-1} x\, dx$. Assume that $x > 0$. To do this, you will have to recall $\int \sec x\, dx$ and integration by trigonometric substitution, as well as integration by parts.

4. What did you learn as a result of doing this Exploration that you did not know before?

Exploration 9-9a: Introduction to Hyperbolic Functions Date: _____

Objective: Starting with two combinations of exponential functions, show that they have properties similar to those of trigonometric functions.

For this exploration, let

$$u = \frac{1}{2}(e^x + e^{-x}) \quad \text{and} \quad v = \frac{1}{2}(e^x - e^{-x})$$

1. On the same screen, plot the graphs of $y_1 = u$, $y_2 = v$, and $y_3 = (1/2)e^x$ using a window with $[-2, 2]$ for x and $[-4, 4]$ for y. Sketch the results. Tell how the graphs of u and v are related to the graph of $(1/2)e^x$.

2. Show that $u' = v$, $u'' = u$, $u''' = v$, and $u^{(4)} = v$, where u''' and $u^{(4)}$ are the **third derivative** and the **fourth derivative** of u, respectively. How do these derivatives compare to the first four derivatives of $y = \cos x$?

3. Functions u and v are *parametric functions* of x. Eliminate the parameter x by finding $u^2 - v^2$.

4. The equation $u^2 - v^2 = 1$ that you found in Problem 3 plots as a **unit equilateral hyperbola** in a uv-coordinate system, as shown here. Use the two parametric equations to find $u(1.3)$ and $v(1.3)$. Show that the point (u, v) is on the hyperbola.

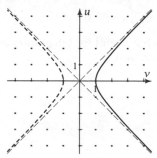

5. Tell why the branch of the hyperbola for negative values of u is extraneous.

6. The figure shows the **unit circle** in a uv-coordinate system. Show that the point $(u, v) = (\cos 1.3, \sin 1.3)$ is on this unit circle.

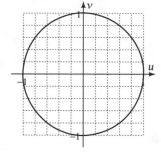

7. Why do you suppose that cosine and sine are called **circular functions** and u and v at the beginning of this Exploration are called **hyperbolic functions**?

8. What did you learn as a result of doing this Exploration that you did not know before?

Exploration 9-9b: Chain Experiment

Date: _____

Objective: Find the particular equation for a hanging chain, and verify it by actual measurement.

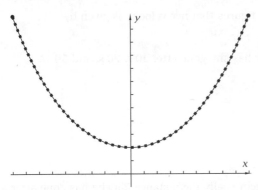

1. Hang a chain from the frame around the chalkboard, as shown in the diagram. Let x be the horizontal distance (cm) from the vertex to a point on the chain, and let y be the vertical distance (cm) from the chalk tray to the point. Measure x and y for the vertex and for the two endpoints.

   Vertex: _____

   Ends: Left: _____   Right: _____

2. From Problem Set 9-9, you found that the general equation for a hanging chain is

   $$y = \frac{h}{w}\cosh\frac{w}{h}x + C$$

   where h is the horizontal tension in the chain and w is the weight of the chain per unit length. Let $k = h/w$. Calculate the constants k and C. Show your work. Store the answers in your grapher.

3. Weigh and measure the chain. Use the results to find values of h and w.

4. Calculate y for each 20 cm from the vertex, from the left end to the right end of the chain. Use a time-efficient method. Round to one decimal place.

x	y		x	y

5. Remove the chain from the board. Plot the data on the board as accurately as you can. Then hang the chain again. How closely do the calculated data fit the shape of the actual chain?

6. Use the equation to calculate the length of the chain between the two endpoints. Then measure the chain to see how close your calculated value is to the actual value.

7. On the back of this sheet, derive the equation

   $$y = \frac{h}{w}\cosh\frac{w}{h}x + C$$

   using the fact that the tension in the chain is equal to the vector sum of the horizontal tension (of magnitude h) and the vertical tension, and is always directed along the chain.

8. What did you learn as a result of doing this Exploration that you did not know before?

Exploration 9-10a: Introduction to Improper Integrals

Objective: Find the limit of a definite integral as the upper limit of integration becomes infinite.

Calvin is driving at 80 ft/s (about 55 mi/h). At time $t = 0$ s, he lifts his foot from the accelerator and coasts. His velocity decreases as shown in the graph.

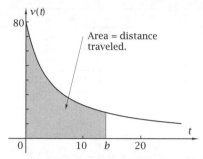

1. Calvin figures that his velocity is given by
   $$v(t) = 320(t + 4)^{-1}$$
   How far has he gone after 10 s, 20 s, and 50 s?

2. Find algebraically the distance Calvin has gone after $t = b$ s. Use the result to find out how long it will take him to go a distance of 1000 ft.

Phoebe does the same thing Calvin did. Her velocity-time graph is shown below.

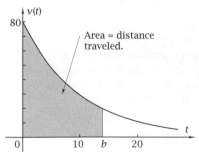

3. Phoebe figures that her velocity is given by
   $$v(t) = 80e^{-0.1t}$$
   How far has she gone after 10 s, 20 s, and 50 s?

4. Find algebraically the distance Phoebe has gone after $t = b$ s. Use the result to find out how long it will take her to go a distance of 1000 ft.

5. Show that Phoebe's distance approaches a limit as b approaches infinity, but Calvin's distance does *not*.

6. How do you reconcile the fact that Phoebe's distance approaches a limit, and the fact that her velocity never reaches zero?

7. What did you learn as a result of doing this Exploration that you did not know before?

Calculus: Concepts and Applications Instructor's Resource Book
©2005 Key Curriculum Press

Exploration 9-11a: Miscellaneous Integration Practice!

Objective: Evaluate an antiderivative when the particular technique is not specified.

1. $\int \tan^5 4x \, dx$

2. $\int \sqrt{1 + t^2} \, dt$

3. $\int \tanh x \, dx$

4. $\int_1^\infty x^3 e^{-x} \, dx$

5. $\int \dfrac{x}{(x-2)(x-3)(x-4)} \, dx$

(Over)

Exploration 9-11a: Miscellaneous Integration
Practice! *continued*

6. $\int \sin^5 x \, dx$

7. $\int (x^4 + 2)^3 \, dx$

8. $\int x^2 e^{x^3} \, dx$

9. $\int e^{ax} \cos bx \, dx$

10. $\int \sin^{-1} ax \, dx$

11. What did you learn as a result of doing this Exploration that you did not know before?

Exploration 10-2a: Finding Distance from Acceleration Data

Objective: Given data for the acceleration of a moving object, find its displacement at various times.

The following table shows acceleration of a moving object, in (m/s)/s.

t	a
0	5
10	12
20	11
30	−4
40	−13
50	−20
60	0

1. Assume that the acceleration changes linearly in each 10-s time interval and that the velocity at time $t = 0$ is 3 m/s. Show how the velocity may be calculated at time $t = 10$.

2. In the table above, put in a column showing the velocity at the end of each 10-s time interval.

3. Assume that the average velocity in each time interval is the average of the velocity at the beginning and the velocity at the end of the interval. Assume also that the displacement is zero when $t = 0$. Show how the displacement may be calculated at time $t = 10$ s.

4. In the table, put in a column that shows the displacement at the end of each 10-s time interval.

5. Explain how you can tell that sometime between $t = 0$ and $t = 60$ the object stops and begins going backward.

6. Does the object go far enough backward to go back beyond its starting point? Explain.

7. What did you learn as a result of doing this Exploration that you did not know before?

Exploration 10-3a: Average Velocity

Objective: Given an equation for the velocity of a moving object, calculate the average velocity over a given time interval.

Rhoda accelerates her motorcycle from one stop sign, then slows down at the next stop sign. She figures that her velocity is given by

$$v(t) = 6t - 0.3t^2$$

where t is in seconds and $v(t)$ is in feet per second. The velocity-time graph is shown below.

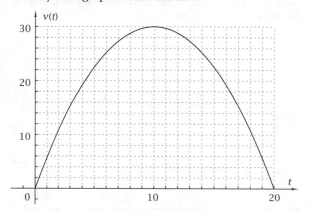

1. Find Rhoda's velocity at $t = 1$ and $t = 17$. Show that the graph agrees with these numbers.

2. Find Rhoda's displacement from $t = 1$ to $t = 17$.

3. Rhoda's **average velocity** in the interval [1, 17] is her displacement for that interval divided by the number of seconds in that interval. Find her average velocity.

4. Does the average velocity over the interval [1, 17] equal the average of $v(1)$ and $v(17)$?

5. Shade lightly the region under the graph that represents Rhoda's displacement.

6. Draw a horizontal line across the graph at the average velocity you calculated in Problem 3. Then draw a rectangle bounded by this line, the t-axis, and the lines $t = 1$ and $t = 17$. How does the area of this rectangle compare with the area of the region you shaded in Problem 5?

7. Make another conclusion about the areas of various regions in the figure that results from Problem 6.

8. Show that you understand the conclusions you have made above by estimating graphically the average velocity for this function over [0, 10].

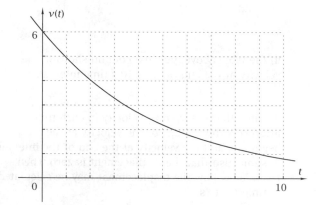

9. What did you learn as a result of doing this Exploration that you did not know before?

Exploration 10-4a: Introduction to Minimal Path Problems

Date: _____

Objective: Find out how to construct a road of minimal cost between points in different regions.

Anita Hammer builds a cabin in the woods. She wants to make a road to the cabin starting at the gate, going through the clearing along the edge of the woods, and then cutting through the woods to the cabin (see figure).

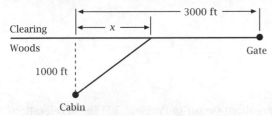

1. The distance from the cabin to the point on the edge of the clearing closest to the cabin is 1000 ft. The distance from the gate to this closest point is 3000 ft. Building the roadway costs $20 per foot through the clearing and $30 per foot through the woods. Let x be the number of feet from the closest point to the point where the road will cut off. Write an equation expressing cost, C, of the road in terms of x.

2. Plot the graph of cost versus x. Sketch the result here.

3. At what value of x does the cost seem to be a minimum?

4. Differentiate to find dC/dx algebraically. Set the derivative equal to zero and solve for x. Why does the answer tell you where the minimum value of C is?

5. What is the minimum cost of the road? How much more would the road cost if Anita built it from the cabin to the closest point on the edge of the clearing and then to the gate? How much more would it cost if she built it directly from the gate to the cabin?

6. What did you learn as a result of doing this Exploration that you did not know before?

Exploration 10-6a: Introduction to Calculus of Vectors   Date: _____

Objective: Find the derivative function for an object moving in two dimensions.

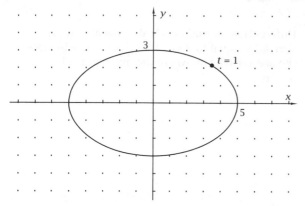

1. The graph above shows the path of a pendulum moving in both the *x*- and *y*-directions. The position (in feet) at any time *t* seconds is given by the parametric equations

$$x = 5 \cos 0.8t$$

$$y = 3 \sin 0.8t$$

Find dx/dt and dy/dt when $t = 1$.

2. The derivatives in Problem 1 are the velocity of the pendulum in the *x*- and *y*-directions. On the figure, construct vectors of lengths dx/dt and dy/dt in the *x*- and *y*-directions, respectively, starting at the point on the graph where $t = 1$.

3. On the figure, construct the vector sum of the two vectors in Problem 1. What relationship does this vector have to the graph?

4. The vector sum in Problem 3 is the velocity vector of the pendulum. How fast is the pendulum moving at time $t = 1$?

5. Find the second derivatives of *x* and *y* with respect to *t* at time $t = 1$. On the figure, construct vectors of these lengths in the *x*- and *y*-directions, respectively, starting at the point on the graph where $t = 1$. Construct the resultant of these vectors.

6. The resultant vector in Problem 5 is the acceleration of the pendulum. Based on your work, is the pendulum speeding up or slowing down at $t = 1$? How can you tell?

7. Just for fun, see if you can figure out the *rate* at which the pendulum is speeding up or slowing down when $t = 1$.

8. What did you learn as a result of doing this Exploration that you did not know before?

Calculus: Concepts and Applications Instructor's Resource Book
©2005 Key Curriculum Press

Exploration 10-6b: Derivatives of a Position Vector Date: _____

Objective: Given the vector equation for motion in two dimensions, find velocity and acceleration as functions of time.

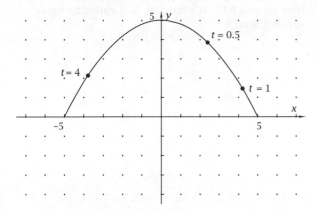

The graph above shows the path traced by a moving object with position vector $\vec{r}(t)$ given by

$$\vec{r}(t) = (5 \sin t)\vec{i} + (5 \cos^2 t)\vec{j}$$

Distances x and y are in feet and time t is in seconds.

1. Confirm that the points shown at $t = 0.5$ and $t = 1$ are correct.

2. On the graph above, construct the position vectors $\vec{r}(0.5)$ and $\vec{r}(1)$.

3. Calculate the difference $\Delta\vec{r} = (\vec{r}(1) - \vec{r}(0.5))$ by subtracting the respective components. Construct $\Delta\vec{r}$ with its tail at the head of $\vec{r}(0.5)$. Where is the head of $\Delta\vec{r}$?

4. The **average velocity** vector of the object for interval $[0.5, t]$ is the difference quotient

$$\vec{v}_{av} = \frac{\vec{r}(t) - \vec{r}(0.5)}{t - 0.5}$$

Find the average velocities for $[0.5, 1]$ and $[0.5, 0.6]$. Construct these vectors starting at the head of the position vector $\vec{r}(0.5)$.

5. Find the (instantaneous) velocity vector, $\vec{v}(0.5)$. Construct it starting at the end of $\vec{r}(0.5)$. How does $\vec{v}(0.5)$ relate to the graph? How do the average velocity vectors in Problem 4 relate to $\vec{v}(0.5)$?

6. Find the speed of the object at time $t = 0.5$.

7. Write vector equations for the velocity vector, $\vec{v}(t)$, and the acceleration vector, $\vec{a}(t)$.

(Over)

Exploration 10-6b: Derivatives of a Position Vector *continued*

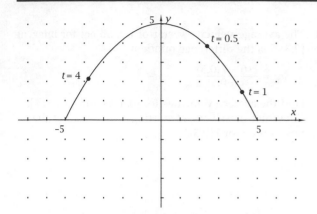

8. On this copy of the graph, construct the position vector $\vec{r}(4)$. Calculate the vectors $\vec{v}(4)$ and $\vec{a}(4)$. From the head of $\vec{r}(4)$, construct the velocity and acceleration vectors.

9. How fast is the object going at time $t = 4$?

10. Compute $\vec{a}_t(4)$, the **tangential component** of the acceleration (parallel to the path). Construct this vector starting at the position of the object at time $t = 4$, thus showing that it really is tangent.

11. Is the object speeding up or slowing down at $t = 4$? How do you tell? At what rate is it speeding up or slowing down?

12. Compute $\vec{a}_n(4)$, the **normal component** of acceleration (perpendicular to the path). Construct this vector starting at the position of the object at time $t = 4$, thus showing that it really is perpendicular to the path.

13. Toward which side of the path does $\vec{a}_n(4)$ point? What effect does this component have on the motion of the object?

14. What did you learn as a result of doing this Exploration that you did not know before?

Exploration 10-6c: Hypocycloid Vector Problem

Objective: Given the vector equation for motion in two dimensions, find velocity and acceleration as functions of time.

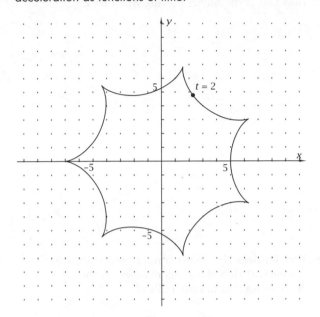

The graph above shows a **hypocycloid of seven cusps.** The graph is the path traced by a point on a circle that rolls on the inside of another circle that has 7 times the radius. The position vector $\vec{r}(t)$ is given by

$$\vec{r}(t) = (6\cos 0.5t - \cos 3t)\vec{i} + (6\sin 0.5t + \sin 3t)\vec{j}$$

Distances x and y are in feet and time t is in seconds,

1. Plot the path of the object on your grapher. Does the graph agree with the one shown here?

2. Write equations for $\vec{v}(t)$ and for $\vec{a}(t)$, the velocity and acceleration vectors.

3. Find $\vec{v}(2)$ and $\vec{a}(2)$. Round to two places.

4. Construct $\vec{v}(2)$ and $\vec{a}(2)$ on the graph above, starting at the head of $\vec{r}(2)$.

5. Geometrically, does the object seem to be speeding up or slowing down when $t = 2$? How do you tell?

6. Find the scalar projection of $\vec{a}(2)$ on $\vec{v}(2)$.

7. Algebraically, is the object speeding up or slowing down when $t = 2$? How do you tell?

8. Calculate the tangential component of acceleration at $t = 2$.

9. Calculate the normal component of acceleration at $t = 2$.

10. Construct the tangential and normal components of acceleration on the graph shown.

(Over)

Exploration 10-6c: Hypocycloid
Vector Problem *continued*

11. Tell the physical effects of the tangential and normal components of acceleration at $t = 2$.

12. There is a cusp at the point with approximate coordinates (6, 3). What must be true of dx/dt and dy/dt at this point?

13. Find by appropriate numerical techniques the value of t at the cusp near (6, 3). Leave a "trail" so that the reader can tell how you did this.

14. Find a point close to (6, 3) where $dy/dt = 0$ but $dx/dt \neq 0$. What is the value of t at that point?

15. How fast is the object moving when $t = 2$?

16. How far does the object travel in one complete revolution? How does this number compare with a circle of an appropriate radius?

17. What did you learn as a result of doing this Exploration that you did not know before?

Exploration 11-2a: Pumping Work Problem

Objective: Find the work done in pumping a liquid from a container to a point above the container.

Treadwell Winery has a vat on the ground floor where they store wine. They pump the wine up to the second floor, 15 ft above the bottom of the vat, where it is put into bottles. The vat is the shape of a truncated cone with base radius 6 ft and top radius 8 ft. The vat is 10 ft deep. Mr. Treadwell calls on you to find out how much work is done in pumping a full vat of wine up to the second floor.

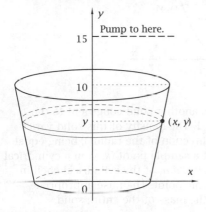

1. The work done by a pump in lifting a horizontal "slice" of the wine from y ft up to 15 ft equals the force needed to lift the slice multiplied by the distance the slice is lifted. The force equals the weight of the slice, which is equal to its volume times its density. Write dW, the work needed to lift the slice, in terms of the sample point (x, y) shown in the figure. Assume that the wine weighs 63 pounds per cubic foot, about the same as water.

2. To get a relationship between x and y, observe that (x, y) is a point on a line in the xy-plane. Use this information to write dW in terms of y alone.

3. By appropriate calculus, find the work done in pumping all of the wine from the vat up to the second floor.

4. What did you learn as a result of doing this Exploration that you did not know before?

Exploration 11-3a: Mass of a Variable-Density Solid   Date: _____

Objective: Find the mass of a solid of revolution if its density varies axially or radially.

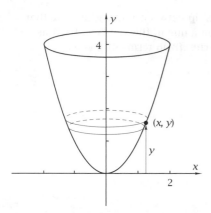

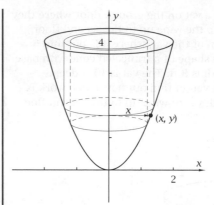

1. The figure shows the paraboloid formed by rotating about the *y*-axis the region above the graph of $y = x^2$, below $y = 4$, and to the right of the *y*-axis, where *x* and *y* are in centimeters. Assume that the density of the solid varies **axially** (in the direction of the axis of the solid), being equal to $3y^{1/2}$ g/cm^3 at a sample point (x, y) in a horizontal disk. Find the mass, *dm*, of the disk in terms of the sample point. Then use appropriate calculus to find the mass of the entire solid.

2. The figure shows another solid congruent to the solid in Problem 1. The density of this solid varies **radially** (in the direction of the radius), being equal to $x + 5$ g/cm^3 at a sample point (x, y) in a cylindrical shell. Find the mass, *dm*, of the cylindrical shell in terms of the sample point. Then use appropriate calculus to find the mass of the entire solid.

3. What did you learn as a result of doing this Exploration that you did not know before?

Calculus: Concepts and Applications Instructor's Resource Book
©2005 Key Curriculum Press

Exploration 11-4a: Moment of Volume, and Centroid   Date: _____

Objective: Find the first moment of volume of a solid, and find the solid's geometric center (centroid).

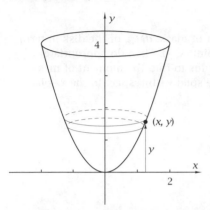

1. The figure shows the paraboloid formed by rotating about the y-axis the region above the graph of $y = x^2$, below $y = 4$, and to the right of the y-axis, where x and y are in centimeters. Find the volume, V, of the solid. (You may do this quickly!)

2. The **first moment of volume** of the solid with respect to the xz-plane is defined to be the volume of the solid times the displacement of the solid from the xz-plane. (The z-axis comes straight out of the page.) Unfortunately, different parts of the solid are at different displacements from the plane. Explain why the (first) moment of the horizontal disk shown in the figure can be found approximately by multiplying the volume of the disk by the y-coordinate of the sample point.

3. Find the moment, dM_{xz}, of the disk in terms of the sample point (x, y). Then do appropriate algebra and calculus to find the moment, M_{xz}, of the entire solid with respect to the xz-plane.

4. The **centroid** (which means "centerlike") of the solid is at the point $\bar{y}$ (pronounced "y bar") on the y-axis for which

    $$M_{xz} = \bar{y} \cdot V$$

    Find $\bar{y}$. Mark this point on the figure given. Explain why it is *more* than halfway up the solid.

5. What did you learn as a result of doing this Exploration that you did not know before?

Exploration 11-4b: Moment of Mass and Center of Mass

Objective: Learn the meaning of moment of mass and center of mass.

The figure shows the paraboloid formed by rotating about the y-axis the region above the graph of $y = x^2$, below $y = 4$, and to the right of the y-axis, where x and y are in centimeters. Assume that the density of the solid varies **axially** (in the direction of the axis of the solid), being equal to $3y^{1/2}$ g/cm^3 at a sample point (x, y) in a horizontal disk.

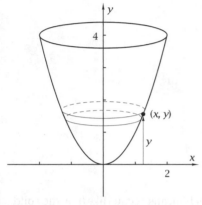

1. Find the mass of the solid. If you have worked Exploration 11-3a, you may use the results of that exploration.

2. The **first moment of mass** of the solid with respect to the xz-plane is defined to be the mass of the solid times the displacement of the solid from the xz-plane. (The z-axis comes straight out of the page.) Unfortunately, different parts of the solid are at different displacements from the plane. Explain why the (first) moment of mass of the horizontal disk shown in the figure can be found approximately by multiplying the mass of the disk by the y-coordinate of the sample point.

3. Find the moment of mass, dM_{xz}, of the disk in terms of the sample point (x, y). Then do appropriate algebra and calculus to find the moment of mass, M_{xz}, of the entire solid with respect to the xz-plane.

4. The **center of mass** of the solid is the point at which the mass could be concentrated to produce the same moment of mass with respect to any plane. It is at the point $\bar{y}$ on the y-axis for which

$$M_{xz} = \bar{y} \cdot m$$

Find $\bar{y}$. Mark this point on the figure given.

5. In Exploration 11-4a, you may have found that the **centroid** (center of volume) is at $y = 8/3$, which is *not* the same point as the center of mass. Under what condition would the center of mass be at the centroid?

6. What did you learn as a result of doing this Exploration that you did not know before?

Exploration 11-4c: Second Moment of Mass

Objective: Learn the meaning of second moment of mass and of radius of gyration.

The figure below shows an aluminum solid. It is in the shape of the paraboloid formed by rotating about the y-axis the region above the graph of $y = x^2$, below $y = 4$, and to the right of the y-axis, where x and y are in centimeters. Its density is 2.7 g/cm^3.

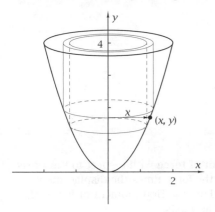

1. Find the mass, m, of the solid. (You may do this quickly!)

2. The **second moment of mass** of the solid with respect to the y-axis is defined to be the mass of the solid times the *square* of its distance from the y-axis. This quantity is sometimes called the **moment of inertia.** It measures how difficult it is to change the angular velocity of the solid as it rotates about the y-axis. Explain why it is appropriate to slice the solid into cylindrical shells in order to find dM_{2y}, the differential of second moment.

3. Find the second moment of mass, dM_{2y}, of a cylindrical shell in terms of the sample point (x, y). Then do appropriate algebra and calculus to find the second moment of mass, M_{2y}, of the entire solid with respect to the y-axis.

4. The **radius of gyration** of the solid is the distance from the y-axis at which the mass could be concentrated to produce the same second moment. That is, it is the distance $\bar{r}$ for which

$$M_{2y} = \bar{r}^2 m$$

Find the radius of gyration.

5. Suppose that a weight on a string is being rotated around its axis of rotation. If the weight is moved three times as far from the axis as it had been, by what factor is the second moment of mass changed?

6. What did you learn as a result of doing this Exploration that you did not know before?

Exploration 11-5a: Force Exerted by a Variable Pressure

Objective: Find the force exerted on a surface if the pressure is different at various places on the surface.

Dam Problem: A dam is to be built across a gully. The back face of the dam (where the water will be) is the shape of the parabolic region bounded below by the graph of $y = 0.03x^2$ and above by the line $y = 12$, where x and y are in feet (see figure). The **force** the water will exert on the dam face equals the water pressure (pounds per square foot) times the area of the dam face. Unfortunately, the pressure gets higher as the water gets deeper, so the force cannot be found by simple multiplication.

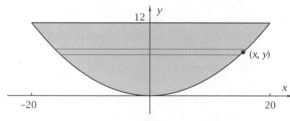

1. The pressure, p, equals the depth of the water times the weight density of water, 62.4 lb/ft^3. Find the pressure at the sample point (x, y) shown in the figure when the water is all the way to the top of the dam, $y = 12$ ft.

2. The pressure acting at any point in a horizontal strip such as the one shown in the figure is approximately equal to the pressure at the sample point. Find the force, dF, acting on the strip in terms of the sample point (x, y).

3. By appropriate algebra and calculus, find the total force, F, acting on the back face of the dam.

4. The **first moment of force** with respect to the x-axis is defined to be the force times the displacement from the x-axis. Find the first moment of force, M_x, with respect to the x-axis.

5. The **center of pressure** is the point at which the entire force could be concentrated to produce the same first moment with respect to the x-axis. Its y-coordinate, $\bar{y}$, is given by

$$M_x = \bar{y} \cdot F$$

Find the y-coordinate of the center of pressure.

6. What did you learn as a result of doing this Exploration that you did not know before?

Calculus: Concepts and Applications Instructor's Resource Book
©2005 Key Curriculum Press

Exploration 11-6a: Spindletop Oil Well Problem

Objective: Estimate the amount of oil that flowed from the Spindletop gusher in 1901.

On January 10, 1901 (the 10th day of the 20th century), as a culmination of work by Pattillo Higgins and Anthony Lucas, the first oil well gusher blew at a place called Spindletop close to Beaumont, Texas. The flow from the well was estimated initially to be 100,000 barrels per day, more than half the entire oil production of all other wells in the United States at that time. The well gushed for 9 days before it was finally controlled. In this Exploration you will make assumptions about the flow rate as a function of time, then use the assumptions to estimate the total amount of oil that flowed from the well in the 9-day period.

1. Assume that the flow rate decreased exponentially with time, dropping to half its original value at the end of the 9 days. Write an equation expressing barrels per day as a function of time.

2. By appropriate calculus, find the total number of barrels of oil that flowed from the well in the 9 days.

3. The oil that gushed from Spindletop in those 9 days was contained by building lakes using earthen dams. But most of it was lost. At today's oil prices, how much would that oil have been worth?

4. A barrel of oil is 42.5 gal. A railroad tank car 60 ft long can hold 44,000 gal of oil. How long a train of tank cars would it take to hold all the oil that flowed from Spindletop in those 9 days?

5. For a fascinating account of the events preceding and following the Spindletop gusher, see *Pattillo Higgins and the Search for Texas Oil,* by Robert W. McDaniel with Henry C. Dethloff, Texas University Press, 1989.

6. What did you learn as a result of doing this Exploration that you did not know before?

Exploration 12-2a: Two Geometric Series

Objective: Use geometric series as mathematical models of real-world phenomena that vary discretely rather than continuously.

Drug Dosage Problem: A patient takes a 30-mg (milligram) antibiotic capsule every hour. At the end of any one hour, the amount of antibiotic remaining in her body is only 90% of the amount at the beginning of that hour. Your objective is to predict the total amount in her body after many hours.

1. The first 30-mg dose is taken at time $t = 0$ h. How much of this dose remains at the end of 1 h? 2 h? 3 h? 4 h?

2. Starting with the last dose, the amounts remaining from the first 5 doses ($t = 4$ h) can be written

    $$30, 30(0.9), 30(0.9)^2, 30(0.9)^3, 30(0.9)^4$$

    These numbers are part of a **geometric sequence.** The next term in the sequence is formed by multiplying the preceding term by 0.9, the **common ratio.** The total amount in the patient's body after these 5 doses is a **partial sum** of a **geometric series,**

    $$30 + 30(0.9) + 30(0.9)^2 + 30(0.9)^3 + 30(0.9)^4$$

    How many milligrams of the antibiotic are in her body after these 5 doses?

3. You can use the SUM and SEQUENCE commands on your grapher to compute partial sums of any series. Write the appropriate commands to sum the formula $30(0.9)^n$ from $n = 0$ to $n = t$. Check your commands by showing that you get the same sum as in Problem 2 when $t = 4$ h.

4. Find the 11th partial sum ($t = 10$) and the 21st partial sum ($t = 20$).

5. The partial sums for this series **converge** to a limit. What does this limit appear to be? What implications does the convergence of this series have for the patient in this problem?

Regular Savings Problem: Ernest Lee Dunn puts $800 into his IRA each year. The money earns 10% per year interest (APR), which means that at the end of any year the amount in the IRA is 1.1 times the amount at the beginning of that year.

6. The amount in the account at the beginning of year t is the sum of the worths of each deposit. Starting with the worth of the last deposit, the total is a partial sum of this geometric series:

    $$800 + 800(1.1) + 800(1.1)^2 + \cdots + 800(1.1)^t$$

    Find the totals in the account when $t = 10$ yr, 20 yr, and 30 yr.

7. Do the totals in Problem 6 seem to be **converging** to a finite limit or **diverging** toward infinity?

8. What did you learn as a result of doing this Exploration that you did not know before?

Calculus: Concepts and Applications Instructor's Resource Book
©2005 Key Curriculum Press

Exploration 12-3a: A Power Series for a Familiar Function

Objective: Learn what a power series is, and how it can fit closely a particular function.

Let $P(x)$ be defined by

$$P(x) = 1 + x + \frac{1}{2!}x^2 + \frac{1}{3!}x^3 + \cdots + \frac{1}{n!}x^n + \cdots$$

The letter P is used because the right side of the equation is a **power series.** It is also appropriate because the expression looks like a **polynomial,** except that it has an infinite number of terms. In this Exploration you will calculate and plot values of $P(x)$ and try to figure out which familiar function P represents.

1. Calculate $P(0.6)$ three times, using 3, 4, and 5 terms of the series ($n = 2, 3,$ and 4).

2. The values of $P(0.6)$ in Problem 1 are **partial sums** of the series. Use the SUM and SEQUENCE commands on your grapher to enter an equation into y_1 that will calculate $P(0.6)$ for $n = x$. Then make a table of values of $P(0.6)$ using $n = 5, 6, 7, 8, 9,$ and 10. What limit do the partial sums seem to be approaching as x increases?

3. Change the equation in y_1 so that it calculates the 11th partial sum ($n = 10$) of the series for $P(x)$. Then plot the graph using a friendly x-window of about $[-5, 5]$ and a y-window of $[-1, 10]$. Sketch the result here.

4. Find the 11th partial sum ($n = 10$) as in Problem 3 for $P(1)$. What familiar number does the answer resemble?

5. Make a conjecture about which one of the elementary functions on your grapher fits the series for $P(x)$ when x is not too far from zero. Give numerical or graphical evidence that your conjecture is correct.

6. Show that the 11th partial sum for this series is *not* close to the function you conjectured in Problem 5 at $x = 10$.

7. What did you learn as a result of doing this Exploration that you did not know before?

Exploration 12-4a: Power Series by Equating Derivatives

Objective: Find a power series for a given function by equating derivatives.

1. The general **Maclaurin series** (power series) is

$$P(x) = c_0 + c_1 x + c_2 x^2 + c_3 x^3 + c_4 x^4 + c_5 x^5 + c_6 x^6 + \cdots$$

Write the first five derivatives of $P(x)$.

$P'(x) =$ _____

$P''(x) =$ _____

$P'''(x) =$ _____

$P^{(4)}(x) =$ _____

$P^{(5)}(x) =$ _____

2. Evaluate the function and each of the derivatives in Problem 1 at $x = 0$. Rewrite each one using factorials. Based on the pattern you observe, write the kth derivative at $x = 0$.

$P(0) =$ _____ = _____

$P'(0) =$ _____ = _____

$P''(0) =$ _____ = _____

$P'''(0) =$ _____ = _____

$P^{(4)}(0) =$ _____ = _____

$P^{(5)}(0) =$ _____ = _____

. . .

$P^{(k)}(0)$ (using factorials) = _____

3. Let $f(x) = \sin x$. Write the first five derivatives. Evaluate the function and the derivatives at $x = 0$.

$f(x) = \sin x$ $\Rightarrow f(0) =$ _____

$f'(x) =$ _____ $\Rightarrow f'(0) =$ _____

$f''(x) =$ _____ $\Rightarrow f''(0) =$ _____

$f'''(x) =$ _____ $\Rightarrow f'''(0) =$ _____

$f^{(4)}(x) =$ _____ $\Rightarrow f^{(4)}(0) =$ _____

$f^{(5)}(x) =$ _____ $\Rightarrow f^{(5)}(0) =$ _____

4. In order for $P(x)$ to fit $f(x)$ well at $x = 0$, $P(0)$ and all of its derivatives at $x = 0$ must equal $f(0)$ and the corresponding derivatives. Use this information to find values of c_0 through c_5. Write the answers in terms of factorials.

$c_0 =$ _____ $c_1 =$ _____ $c_2 =$ _____ $c_3 =$ _____ $c_4 =$ _____ $c_5 =$ _____

5. Write the first six nonzero terms of the Maclaurin series for $\sin x$. Use the information from Problem 4 for as many terms as you can, then follow the pattern you observe to get the rest.

$\sin x =$

(Over)

Exploration 12-4a: Power Series
by Equating Derivatives *continued*

6. The equation below specifies in **sigma notation** the power series for sin x that you wrote in Problem 5.

$$f(x) = \sum_{n=0}^{\infty} (-1)^n \frac{1}{(2n+1)!} x^{2n+1}$$

Write out the first three terms of this series by substituting 0, 1, and 2 for n. Show that you get the same terms as in Problem 5.

7. Use the SUM and SEQUENCE commands on your grapher to enter the sixth partial sum ($n = 5$) as y_1 on your grapher. Enter the target function, $y_2 = \sin x$. Plot both graphs on the same screen. Use a window with $[-10, 10]$ for x and $[-3, 3]$ for y. Sketch the resulting graphs. For what interval of x-values does the partial sum graph seem to fit the target function well?

8. Find the difference between the partial sum and the value of sine at $x = 2$ by finding $y_2(4) - y_1(4)$. Is the partial sum reasonably close to the target function for this value of x?

9. Show numerically that the partial sum is quite different from the target function if $x = 8$.

10. Change y_1 so that it calculates the 11th partial sum ($n = 10$). Plot the partial sum and the target function on the same screen as you did in Problem 7. Sketch the result. For what interval of x-values does the 11th partial sum seem to fit the target function well?

11. Show numerically that the 11th partial sum at $x = 4$ is much closer to the target function than the 6th partial sum in Problem 8.

12. What did you learn as a result of doing this Exploration that you did not know before?

Exploration 12-5a: Power Series
from Given Derivatives

Objective: Write a power series using given numerical values for the first few derivatives.

For Problems 1 and 2, function f has derivatives of all orders for all real numbers x. Assume that $f(3) = -2$, $f'(3) = 7$, $f''(2) = 0.8$, and $f'''(2) = -2.4$.

1. Write the third-degree Taylor polynomial for f about $x = 3$, and use it to approximate $f(2.5)$.

2. Write the fourth-degree Taylor polynomial, $P(x)$, for $g(x) = f(x^2 + 3)$ about $x = 0$. Use P to explain why g must have a relative minimum at $x = 0$.

For Problems 3–6, let f be a function that has derivatives of all orders for all real numbers. Assume that $f(0) = 3$, $f'(0) = -2$, $f''(0) = 1.2$, and $f'''(0) = 3$.

3. Write the third-degree Maclaurin polynomial for f and use it to approximate $f(0.4)$.

4. Write the fourth-degree Maclaurin polynomial for g, where $g(x) = f(x^2)$.

5. Write the third-degree Maclaurin polynomial for h, where $h(x) = \int_0^x f(t)\, dt$.

6. Let h be defined as in Problem 5. Given that $f(0.7) = 5$, either find the exact value of $h(0.7)$ or explain why it cannot be determined.

7. What did you learn as a result of doing this Exploration that you did not know before?

Exploration 12-5b: A Power Series for a Definite Integral

Objective: Write a power series for the integrand in a definite integral, then evaluate the integral.

The figure shows the solid formed by rotating about the y-axis the region under the graph of $y = x \sin x$ from $x = 0$ to $x = \pi$. In this Exploration you will find the volume of the solid several ways.

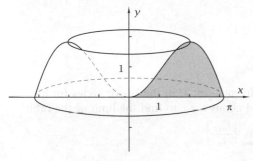

1. Using cylindrical shells, write an integral representing the volume of this solid.

2. The integrand in Problem 1 involves the expression $x^2 \sin x$. Write this expression as a Maclaurin series, taking advantage of the fact that you already know the series for $\sin x$.

3. Substitute the series in Problem 2 into the integral for the volume. Evaluate the integral (algebraically) and substitute the limits of integration. Use the sixth partial sum ($n = 5$) of the resulting series to find an estimate of the volume.

4. Evaluate the integral in Problem 1 directly, using the fundamental theorem. How close does the estimate in Problem 3 come to the actual volume?

5. What did you learn as a result of doing this Exploration that you did not know before?

Exploration 12-6a: Introduction to the Ratio Technique Date: _____

Objective: Find an interval of values of x for which the Taylor series for $\ln x$ converges.

1. Write the first five terms of the Taylor series for $\ln x$ expanded about $x = 1$. Use this fifth partial sum, S_5, to find an estimate of $\ln 1.6$. How close is S_5 to the value of $\ln 1.6$ by calculator?

The following numbers are the absolute values, $|t_n|$, of the $\ln 1.6$ series. Below them are the ratios, $|t_{n+1}/t_n|$, the numbers you could multiply $|t_n|$ by to get $|t_{n+1}|$.

$$|t_n|: 0.6 + 0.18 + 0.072 + 0.0324 + 0.015552 + \cdots$$

Ratio: $\times 0.3$ $\times 0.4$ $\times 0.45$ $\times 0.48$ $\cdots$

2. Enter $y_1 = |t_x|$ and $y_2 = |y_1(x + 1)/y_1(x)|$ into your grapher. Make a table starting at $x = 1$. Does the table confirm these values and ratios?

3. Scroll down your table of y_2 values to show that the ratio is approaching 0.6 from below. Show algebraically why this is true.

4. This table shows the absolute values of the terms in the tail of the series, starting at $|t_6|$. Put a column in the table showing terms of the geometric series with first term equal to $|t_6|$ and common ratio 0.7.

n	$|t_n|$	Geom. Series
6	0.007776	0.007776
7	0.0039990...	
8	0.0020995...	
9	0.0011197...	
10	0.0006046...	

5. How do the given term values in Problem 4 compare with the geometric series term values? To what number does the geometric series converge? What can you conclude about the sum of the given values of $|t_n|$ as n approaches infinity?

6. Use the formula for t_n in the Taylor series for $\ln x$ expanded about $x = 1$ to find the limit of the ratio

$$L = \lim_{n \to \infty} \left| \frac{t_{n+1}}{t_n} \right|$$

7. The tail of the series converges if $L < 1$ because then you could find a convergent geometric series with common ratio between L and 1 that is an upper bound for the $\ln$ series. Set $L < 1$ and solve the resulting inequality to find the (open) interval of convergence. This technique of finding the interval of convergence is called the **ratio technique.**

8. What did you learn as a result of doing this Exploration that you did not know before?

Calculus: Concepts and Applications Instructor's Resource Book
©2005 Key Curriculum Press

Exploration 12-6b: Inverse Tangent Series

Objective: Find the Maclaurin series for $f(x) = \tan^{-1} x$, and its interval of convergence.

1. Try to find the Taylor series expanded about $x = 0$ (i.e., the Maclaurin series) for $f(x) = \tan^{-1} x$ by equating derivatives. Explain why this process would be very tedious.

2. Recall that $\dfrac{d}{dx}(\tan^{-1} x) = \dfrac{1}{1 + x^2}$.

   Thus, $\tan^{-1} x = \displaystyle\int_0^x \dfrac{1}{1 + t^2} dt$.

   Write a Maclaurin series for the integrand. This can be done relatively easily by writing the geometric series for $1/(1 - u)$, then substituting $-t^2$ for u. Then do the integrating to find the first four terms and the general term of the series for $\tan^{-1} x$.

3. Plot the fourth partial sum, S_3, for the series in Problem 2, along with $y_2 = \tan^{-1} x$. Sketch the result. Then plot S_4 and sketch the result. From the graphs, make a conjecture about the interval of convergence of the inverse tangent series.

4. Use the ratio technique to find algebraically the interval of convergence you conjectured graphically in Problem 3.

5. What did you learn as a result of doing this Exploration that you did not know before?

Exploration 12-7a: Improper Integrals to Test for Convergence

Objective: Prove that a *p*-series converges by comparing the tail of the series with a convergent improper integral.

The *p*-series $1 + \frac{1}{4} + \frac{1}{9} + \frac{1}{16} + \cdots$ converges. To demonstrate that this is true, you could draw a graph as shown in the figure below. The areas of the rectangles equal the terms of the tail after the fourth partial sum. The **remainder,** R_4, equals $t_5 + t_6 + t_7 + \cdots$.

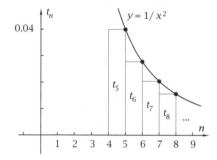

1. Explain why R_4 is a lower Riemann sum for the improper integral

$$\int_4^\infty 1/x^2 \, dx$$

2. By evaluating the improper integral in Problem 1, find an upper bound for R_4.

3. Calculate the first, second, and third partial sums of the tail of the series starting at t_5.

4. Explain why the sequence of partial sums in Problem 3 is increasing although the terms themselves are decreasing.

5. If a sequence is **increasing** and **bounded above,** then the sequence converges. How does this property allow you to conclude that the *series* for R_4 converges?

6. Based on the results of Problem 5, explain why the entire *p*-series converges.

7. The rectangles representing the terms of R_4 could have been drawn to form an *upper* sum.

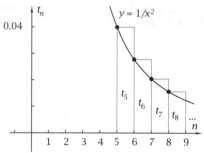

Explain why the improper integral from 5 to infinity would *not* be sufficient to prove that the tail of the series converges.

8. What did you learn as a result of doing this Exploration that you did not know before?

Exploration 12-7b: Convergence of a Series of Constants

Objective: Determine whether or not various series of constants converge.

1. The **geometric series** $100 + 80 + 64 + \cdots$ can be shown to converge using the *definition* of convergence of a series. Demonstrate that you understand the definition by using it to prove that the series converges.

2. The **harmonic series** $\sum_{n=1}^{\infty} \frac{1}{n}$ diverges, even though the terms get smaller and approach 0 as a limit. Use an appropriate method to explain *why* the series diverges. A graph might help you do the explaining.

3. The Maclaurin series for $\cosh x$ is

$$\cosh x = 1 + \frac{1}{2!}x^2 + \frac{1}{4!}x^4 + \frac{1}{6!}x^6 + \cdots$$

If you evaluate $\cosh 2$ using this series, you get

$$\cosh 2 = 1 + \frac{4}{2} + \frac{16}{24} + \frac{64}{720} + \cdots$$

Write the fifth term of the series.

4. Explain why the partial sums of the series in Problem 3 are *increasing* although the terms of the series (after the second term) are *decreasing*.

5. The ratio t_3/t_2 equals $(64/720)/(16/24)$, which equals $4/30$. Write the first few terms of a geometric series with first term $16/24$ and common ratio $4/30$. How do the terms of the geometric series compare with the terms of the cosh 2 series?

6. To what number does the geometric series in Problem 5 converge? How does the convergence of the geometric series imply convergence of the cosh 2 series?

7. What did you learn as a result of doing this Exploration that you did not know before?

Exploration 12-8a: Error Analysis
by Improper Integral

Objective: Use improper integrals to find upper and lower bounds for the remainder of a convergent p-series.

1. Find the fourth partial sum, S_4, of the p-series

$$\sum_{n=1}^{\infty} \frac{1}{n^2}$$

2. Write the first few terms of the tail of the series following S_4.

3. R_4 is the remainder of the series following S_4. Write R_4 using sigma notation.

4. The figure below shows the first few terms in the tail of the series along with the graph of $y = 1/x^2$. Draw appropriate rectangles, then shade the corresponding region under the graph so that the area of the region is an upper bound for R_4.

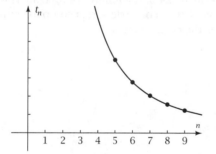

5. By evaluating an appropriate improper integral, find an upper bound for R_4.

6. On this copy of the figure from Problem 4, draw appropriate rectangles. Shade the corresponding region under the graph so that the area of the region is a lower bound for R_4.

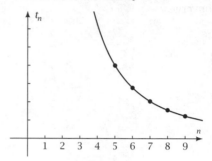

7. By evaluating an appropriate improper integral, find a lower bound for R_4.

8. Find S_{100} for this p-series. Find upper and lower bounds for R_{100}. What is your best estimate of the limit to which the series converges?

9. The actual limit of the series involves π. Just for fun, see if you can figure out what this limit is.

10. What did you learn as a result of doing this Exploration that you did not know before?

Exploration 12-8b: Derivation of the Lagrange Remainder

Objective: Show that the remainder of a Maclaurin series after *n* terms is a multiple of the (*n* + 1)st term.

1. Write the first five terms of the Maclaurin series for $f(x) = e^x$. Use the result to find an estimate of $e^{0.6}$ using $S_3(0.6)$, the fourth partial sum of the series evaluated at $x = 0.6$.

2. Calculate the **error** in using S_3 to approximate $e^{0.6}$ by subtracting $e^{0.6} - S_3$, where the value of $e^{0.6}$ is found on your calculator.

3. The error you calculated in Problem 2 is equal to the **remainder** of the series, $R_3(0.6)$. This remainder is the limit of the sum of all the terms in the **tail** of the series. Show that this remainder is greater than $t_4(0.6)$, the first term of the tail of the series, but not much greater.

4. $R_3(0.6)$ is a multiple of $t_4(0.6)$. That is,
   $$R_3(0.6) = kt_4(0.6)$$
   Find the value of k.

5. Later in this Exploration you will show that k in Problem 4 is the value of the **fourth derivative** of e^x, evaluated at some number $x = c$. Find the value of c. Show that it is between 0 and 0.6.

6. Write the conclusion of the mean value theorem as it applies to a differentiable function f on the interval $[0, x]$. Transform your answer so that $f(x)$ is on the left and everything else is on the right.

7. If f' is a differentiable function on $[0, x]$, the mean value theorem would conclude that there is a value $x = c$ in $(0, x)$ such that
   $$f''(c) = \frac{f'(x) - f'(0)}{x}$$
   Transform this equation so that $f'(x)$ is on the left and everything else is on the right. Then integrate both sides, using the initial condition that $(0, f(0))$ is on the graph. Show that the answer is the first two terms of the Maclaurin series for $f(x)$ and that the third term is a multiple of t_2, the third term of the series.

(Over)

Exploration 12-8b: Derivation of the Lagrange Remainder continued

8. If f'' is a differentiable function on $[0, x]$, then there is a point $x = c$ in $(0, x)$ involving $f'''(c)$ such that the conclusion of the mean value theorem is true for $f''(x)$.

   • Write $f''(x)$ as you wrote $f'(x)$ in Problem 7.

   • Integrate as you did in Problem 7, using the initial condition $(0, f'(0))$, to get an equation for $f'(x)$.

   • Integrate again, using the initial condition, $(0, f(0))$, to get an equation for $f(x)$.

   • From the answer, show that $f(x)$ is exactly equal to the first three terms of the Maclaurin series for $f(x)$ plus a remainder term involving $f'''(c)$.

9. Use the pattern you observe in Problem 8 to write $f(x)$ exactly as the first four terms (through x^3) of the Maclaurin series for $f(x)$ plus a remainder term involving $f^{(4)}(c)$.

10. Look up the Lagrange form of the remainder in Section 12-8. Tell how the result of Problems 5 and 9 relate to what you find.

11. Write the **Lagrange form of the remainder,** R_n, for the tail of the series after S_n. Also, write the **Lagrange error bound** for R_n.

12. What did you learn as a result of doing this Exploration that you did not know before?

Solutions for the Explorations

Chapter 1

Exploration 1-1a

1. Such a graph might look like this:

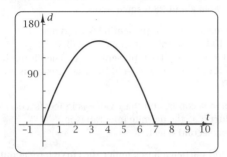

2. $d = 200t \cdot 2^{-t}$:

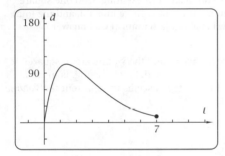

3.

t	d
0	0.0°
1	100.0°
2	100.0°
3	75.0°
4	50.0°
5	31.3°
6	18.8°
7	10.9°
8	6.3°
9	3.5°
10	2.0°

4. Door appears to be opening. The graph of d shows that d was less than 100° before $t = 1$ s and greater than 100° after $t = 1$ s.

5. Average Rate = (change in value)/(Time)
   = $(200(1.1) \cdot 2^{-1.1} - 200(1) \cdot 2^{-1})/(1.1 - 1)$
   ≈ $(102.6° - 100°)/0.1$ s
   = 26°/s
   This number is greater than zero, which shows that the door is still opening because d is increasing.

6. Average rate for time interval [1, 1.01] ≈ 30°/s.
   Average rate for time interval [1, 1.001] ≈ 31°/s.
   Average rate for time interval [1, 1.0000001] ≈ 31°/s.
   The average rate seems to be approaching 30.68°/s ≈ 31°/s!

7. Answers will vary.

8. The example in Section 1-1 is the same as this Exploration!

Exploration 1-2a

1. a. $f(x) = 3^{-x}$:

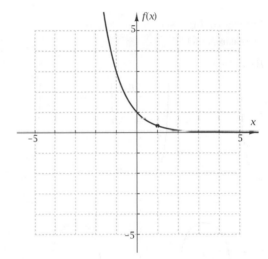

   b. Grapher confirms sketch.

   c. Decreasing slowly

2. a. $f(x) = \sin \frac{\pi}{2}x$:

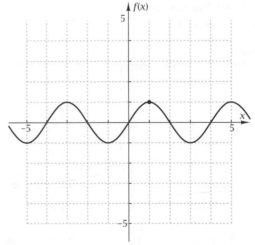

   b. Grapher confirms sketch.

   c. Not changing

3. a. $f(x) = x^2 + 2x - 2$:

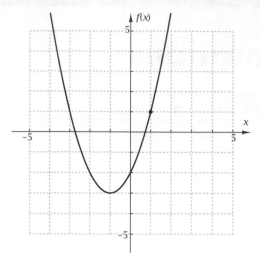

b. Grapher confirms sketch.

c. Increasing quickly

4. a. $f(x) = \sec x$:

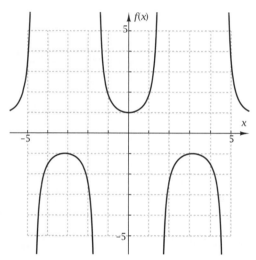

b. Grapher confirms sketch.

c. Increasing quickly

5. a. $f(x) = \dfrac{1}{x}$:

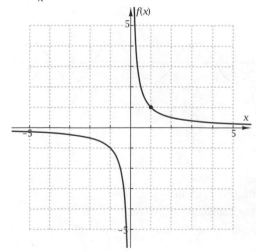

b. Grapher confirms sketch.

c. Decreasing slowly

Exploration 1-3a

1. From $t = 30$ and $t = 50$ s, the velocity seems to be about 60 ft/s. Distance = rate · time, so the distance traveled is about 60 ft/s · (50 s − 30 s) = 1200 ft.

2. The rectangle on the graph with height = 60 and base from $t = 30$ to $t = 50$ has area = base · height = 1200.

3. The sample partial square has about 0.6 square space under the curve. All the partial squares under the graph from $t = 0$ to $t = 20$ have area about 28.6 square spaces.

4. Each small space has base representing 5 s and height representing 10 ft/s. So the area of each small square = base · height = 5 s · 10 ft/s represents 50 ft. Therefore, the distance was about 28.6 · 50 = 1430 ft. (Exact answer is 1431.3207... ft.)

5. The x-value is in seconds, and the y-value is in feet/second, so their product (i.e., the definite integral) is in seconds · feet/second = feet.

6. The squares and partial squares under the curve have about 45.2 square spaces of area. Each square space has base representing 1 and height representing 5. So one square space represents 5 units of definite integral, and the total definite integral is about 226 units. (Exact answer is 226.1946....)

7. The x-units are in inches, and the y-units are in square inches. So their product, the definite integral, is in *cubic* inches. The definite integral seems to represent the *volume* of the football.

8. Answers will vary.

Exploration 1-4a

1. The graph shows time on the x-axis and velocity on the y-axis. A *definite integral* can be used to find time · velocity = distance.

2. There are about 60.8 square spaces under the graph. Each square represents about 25 miles, so the total distance is about 1520 miles.

3. $v(t) = t^3 - 21t^2 + 100t + 110$
   The graph confirms Ella's conclusion. Tracing to integer values of t shows the same $v(t)$ values as on the graph.

Calculus: Concepts and Applications Instructor's Resource Book
©2005 Key Curriculum Press

4. Divide the graph into "trapezoids" of width = 2.

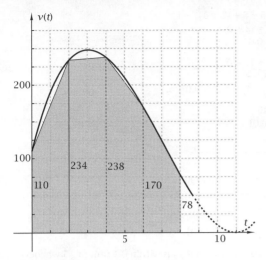

Areas of trapezoids are

$\frac{1}{2}(110 + 234) \cdot 2 = 344$

$\frac{1}{2}(234 + 238) \cdot 2 = 472$

$\frac{1}{2}(238 + 170) \cdot 2 = 408$

$\frac{1}{2}(170 + 78) \cdot 2 = 248$

Integral ≈ sum = 1472, which is reasonably close to the area found in Problem 2.

5. See program TRAPRULE in the Programs for Graphing Calculators section of the *Instructor's Resource Book*.

6. Using 20 trapezoids, the definite integral is about 1518.08 mi.

7. The approximate definite integral is
   1519.52 miles for 40 trapezoids
   1519.9232 miles for 100 trapezoids
   1519.999232 miles for 1000 trapezoids
   The exact definite integral appears to be 1520 mi!

8. According to the graph, Ella's greatest velocity was about 248 mi per minute at about $t = 3$ min. (Actual maximum was $124 + \frac{94}{3} \cdot \sqrt{\frac{47}{3}}$ mi, at $t = 7 - \sqrt{\frac{47}{3}}$ min.)

9. $v(4.9) = 213.439$, and $v(5.1) = 206.441$.
   Velocity changed −6.998 ft/s in 0.2 s.
   Rate of change ≈ −6.998/0.02 = −34.99.
   So, Ella was slowing down at about 35 miles/minute per minute.

10. Ella is first stopped at $t = 11$, because $v(11) = 0$. She stops gradually at $t = 11$ because the graph gently levels off to $v(t) = 0$ at that point.

11. Answers will vary.

Chapter 2

Exploration 2-1a

1.

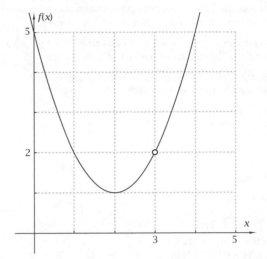

2. $f(3) = \frac{27 - 63 + 51 - 15}{3 - 3} = \frac{0}{0}$, an indeterminate form.

3. $f(x)$ is very close to 2 when x is close to 3. The limit is 2.

4.
x	$f(x)$
2.5	1.25
2.6	1.36
2.7	1.49
2.8	1.64
2.9	1.81
3.0	?.??
3.1	2.21
3.2	2.44
3.3	2.69
3.4	2.96
3.5	3.25

5. $f(x)$ stays between 1.25 and 3.25 if x is between 2.5 and 3.5 (and $x \neq 3$).

6. $f(x) = \frac{x^3 - 7x^2 + 17x - 15}{x - 3} = x^2 - 4x + 5, x \neq 3$.
   Set $x^2 - 4x + 5 = 1.99$ and solve algebraically or numerically. Repeat with $x^2 - 4x + 5 = 2.01$.
   If 2.99498743... $< x <$ 3.00498756..., then $f(x)$ will be between 1.99 and 2.01. (Also if x is between 0.9950... and 1.0050..., but this is not the interval of interest!)

7. On the left, keep x within 0.0050125... unit of 3.
   On the right, keep x within 0.0049875... unit of 3.

8. 0.0049875...

9. $L = 2$, $c = 3$, $\varepsilon = 0.01$, $\delta = 0.0049...$

10. Answers will vary.

Exploration 2-2a

1. For any number $\varepsilon > 0$, there is a number $\delta > 0$ such that if x is within δ units of 5 (but $x \neq 5$), then $f(x)$ is within ε units of 7.

2. $f(x)$ is less than $7 + 1 = 8$ if x is greater than about 2.6, so x must be kept within about 2.4 units of 5 on the left.

3. $f(x)$ is greater than $7 - 1 = 6$ if x is less than about 5.9, so x must be kept within about 0.9 unit of 5 on the right.

4. If δ is about 0.9, then $f(x)$ will be within 1 unit from 7 whenever x is within δ units of 5.

5. Set $f(x) = 6$.
$$5 - 2(x - 6)^{1/3} = 6$$
$$(x - 6)^{1/3} = -0.5$$
$$x - 6 = -0.125$$
$$|x - 5| = 0.875$$
Set $\delta = 0.875$.

6. If $f(x) = 7.01$,
$$5 - 2(x - 6)^{1/3} = 7.01$$
$$(x - 6)^{1/3} = -1.005$$
$$x - 6 = -1.015075125$$
$$|x - 5| = 0.015075125$$
If $f(x) = 6.99$,
$$5 - 2(x - 6)^{1/3} = 6.99$$
$$(x - 6)^{1/3} = -0.995$$
$$x - 6 = -0.985074875$$
$$|x - 5| = 0.014925125$$
Set $\delta = 0.014925125$.

7. If $f(x) = 7 + \varepsilon$,
$$5 - 2(x - 6)^{1/3} = 7 + \varepsilon$$
$$(x - 6)^{1/3} = -\left(1 + \frac{1}{2}\varepsilon\right)$$
$$x - 6 = -\left(1 + \frac{1}{2}\varepsilon\right)^3$$
$$|x - 5| = \left(1 + \frac{1}{2}\varepsilon\right)^3 - 1$$
$$= \frac{3}{2}\varepsilon + \frac{3}{4}\varepsilon^2 + \frac{1}{8}\varepsilon^3$$
If $f(x) = 7 - \varepsilon$,
$$5 - 2(x - 6)^{1/3} = 7 - \varepsilon$$
$$(x - 6)^{1/3} = -\left(1 - \frac{1}{2}\varepsilon\right)$$
$$x - 6 = -\left(1 - \frac{1}{2}\varepsilon\right)^3$$
$$|x - 5| = 1 - \left(1 - \frac{1}{2}\varepsilon\right)^3$$
$$= \frac{3}{2}\varepsilon - \frac{3}{4}\varepsilon^2 + \frac{1}{8}\varepsilon^3$$
This value is smaller, so set $\delta = 1 - (1 - \frac{1}{2}\varepsilon)^3$.
This is positive for all $\varepsilon > 0$, so there *is* a positive δ for any $\varepsilon > 0$.

8. Answers will vary.

Exploration 2-3a

1. $L = \lim_{x \to c} f(x)$ if and only if
for any positive number ε (no matter how small)
there is a positive number δ such that
if x is within δ units of c, but not equal to c,
then $f(x)$ is within ε units of L.

2. $L_1 = 11$, $L_2 = 4$

3. $11.05 = 5 + (2 + \delta_1) + 1$
$2.01 = (2 + \delta_1)$
$\delta_1 = 0.01$

4. $4.05 = (2 + \delta_2)^2$
$\sqrt{4.05} = 2 + \delta_2$
$\delta_2 = \sqrt{4.05} - 2 = 0.0124...$

5. $L = 15$
$\delta = 0.01$

x	y_3
2	15
2.001	15.009001
2.005	15.045025
2.009	15.081081
2.01	15.0901

The table shows that y_3 *is* within 0.1 unit of 15 whenever x is within 0.01 unit of 2.

6. $L_2 - \varepsilon/2 < h(x) < L_2 + \varepsilon/2$

7. $L_1 + L_2 - \varepsilon < g(x) + h(x) < L_1 + L_2 + \varepsilon$
$L_1 + L_2 - \varepsilon < f(x) < L_1 + L_2 + \varepsilon$
$\therefore L_1 + L_2$ is the limit of $f(x)$ as x approaches c.

8. The limit of a sum equals the sum of the limits. Or, limit distributes over addition.

9. Answers will vary.

Exploration 2-3b

1. For $n = 2$, $f_2(x) = g_1(x) + g_2(x)$.
By the limit of a sum (of two functions) property,
$\lim_{x \to c} f_2(x) = \lim_{x \to c} g_1(x) + \lim_{x \to c} g_2(x) = L_1 + L_2$.

2. Assume the property is false.
Then there is a number $n = j$ such that
$\lim_{x \to c} f_j(x) \neq L_1 + \cdots + L_j$.

3. 2 is in T and j is in F.

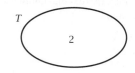 

4. $f_3(x) = g_1(x) + g_2(x) + g_3(x)$
$\quad = g_1(x) + [g_2(x) + g_3(x)]$
$\therefore \lim_{x \to c} f_3(x) = \lim_{x \to c} g_1(x) + \lim_{x \to c} [g_2(x) + g_3(x)]$
$\qquad\qquad$ By the limit of a sum of two functions
$\quad = \lim_{x \to c} g_1(x) + \lim_{x \to c} g_2(x) + \lim_{x \to c} g_3(x)$
$\qquad\qquad$ By the limit of a sum of two functions again
$\quad = L_1 + L_2 + L_3$.

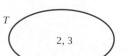 

5. Assume that $\lim\limits_{x \to c} f_6(x)$
    $= f_6(x) = g_1(x) + g_2(x) + g_3(x) + g_4(x) + g_5(x) + g_6(x)$.
    If the property is true for $n = 5$, then
    $\lim\limits_{x \to c} f_5(x) = L_1 + L_2 + L_3 + L_4 + L_5$.
    Then $\lim\limits_{x \to c} f_6(x)$
    $= \lim\limits_{x \to c} [g_1(x) + g_2(x) + g_3(x) + g_4(x) + g_5(x) + g_6(x)]$
    $= \lim\limits_{x \to c} [g_1(x) + g_2(x) + g_3(x) + g_4(x) + g_5(x)] + \lim\limits_{x \to c} g_6(x)$
              By the limit of a sum of two functions
    $= \lim\limits_{x \to c} f_5(x) + \lim\limits_{x \to c} g_6(x)$ By the definition of $f_5(x)$
    $= L_1 + L_2 + L_3 + L_4 + L_5 + L_6$
        By the assumption about $f_5(x)$ and the definition of L_6
    Thus the property is true for $n = 6$, Q.E.D.

6. The set is nonempty because $j \in F$ (by assumption in Problems 2 and 3 above).
    The elements of F are all positive because each element is greater than 2.

7. If $l \in F$, then $l > 2$, so $l - 1 > 1$ is positive. $l - 1$ cannot be in F, because l is the smallest element of F, and $l - 1$ is smaller than l.

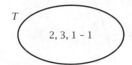 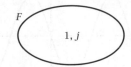

T 2, 3, $l - 1$ F 1, j

8. $\lim\limits_{x \to c} f_{l-1}(x) = L_1 + \cdots + L_{l-1}$ because $l - 1 \in T$.
    $\lim\limits_{x \to c} f_l(x) \neq L_1 + \cdots + L_{l-1} + L_l$ because $l \in F$.

9. $f_l(x) = g_1(x) + \cdots + g_{l-1}(x) + g_l(x)$
    $= f_{l-1}(x) + g_l(x)$

10. $\lim\limits_{x \to c} f_l(x) = \lim\limits_{x \to c} f_{l-1}(x) + \lim\limits_{x \to c} g_l(x)$
    $= \lim\limits_{x \to c} f_{l-1}(x) + L_l$

11. $\lim\limits_{x \to c} f_l(x) = (L_1 + \cdots + L_{l-1}) + L_l$
    $= L_1 + \cdots + L_{l-1} + L_l$

12. In Problem 8, $\lim_{x \to c} f_l(x) \neq L_1 + \cdots + L_{l-1} + L_l$, but in Problem 11, $\lim_{x \to c} f_l(x) = L_1 + \cdots + L_{l-1} + L_l$!

13. The assumption (property is false for some integers $n \geq 2$) must be false. Thus there are *no* positive integers, n, for which the property is false. Thus the property is true for all integers $n \geq 2$.

Proof:

Anchor:
    The property is true for $n = 2$ (Problem 1, above).

Induction hypothesis:
    Assume the property is true for $n = k > 2$, so $\lim_{x \to c} f_k(x) = L_1 + \cdots + L_k$.

Verification for $n = k + 1$:
    $f_{k+1}(x) = g_1(x) + \cdots + g_k(x) + g_{k+1}(x)$
         $= f_k(x) + g_{k+1}(x)$
    $\lim_{x \to c} f_{k+1}(x) = \lim_{x \to c} f_k(x) + \lim_{x \to c} g_{k+1}(x)$, because the property is true for $n = 2$.
    $\lim_{x \to c} f_{k+1}(x) = (L_1 + \cdots + L_k) + L_{k+1}$ using the induction hypothesis.
    The property is true for $n = k + 1$.

Conclusion:
    The property is true for *all* $n \geq 2$, Q.E.D.

14. Answers will vary.

Exploration 2-4a

1. $f(x) = \begin{cases} x + 1 & \text{if } x < 2 \\ (x - 5)^2 & \text{if } x \geq 2 \end{cases}$

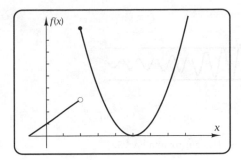

2. A function is discontinuous at a point if the function's value does not equal its limit, or if the limit does not exist, or if the function is undefined at that point.

3. $\lim\limits_{x \to 2^-} f(x) = \lim\limits_{x \to 2^-} (x + 1) = 3$
    $\lim\limits_{x \to 2^+} f(x) = \lim\limits_{x \to 2^+} k(x - 5)^2 = 9k$
    The two limits must be equal for f to be continuous.

4. $9k = 3 \Rightarrow k = \dfrac{1}{3}$
    $f(x) = \begin{cases} x + 1 & \text{if } x < 2 \\ \dfrac{1}{3}(x - 5)^2 & \text{if } x \geq 2 \end{cases}$

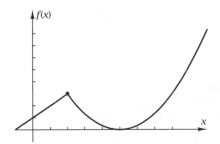

5. *Cusp* comes from the Latin *cuspis,* meaning a point or a pointed end. The word *bicuspid* for a tooth with two points comes from the same root. The word is appropriate for this graph because it comes to a point at $x = 2$.

6. At $x = 2$, f is neither increasing nor decreasing. The derivative is undefined because the backward difference quotients approach 1 as x approaches 2 from the left, and the forward difference quotients approach -2 as x approaches 2 from the right. There is no *one* number the derivative approaches.

7. Answers will vary.

Exploration 2-5a

1. Yes, the grapher confirms the figure.

2.

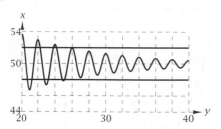

The smallest D is approximately 25.

3.

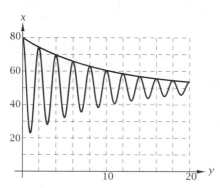

Yes, y_4 is an upper bound.

4. $30(0.9)^D = 2$
$(0.9)^D = 1/15$
$\ln (0.9)^D = \ln (1/15)$
$D \ln (0.9) = \ln (1/15)$
$D = \ln (1/15)/\ln (0.9) = 25.7027...$

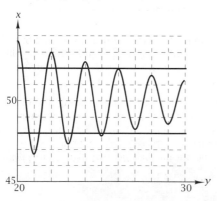

Yes, $d(x)$ stays within 2 units of 50 for $x > 25.7027...$.

5. $D = \ln (0.1/30)/\ln (0.9) = 54.1358...$
Replace $1/15$ with $0.1/30$, because that is the fraction that results if you replace 2 with 0.1 in the original equation in Problem 4.

6. $d(x)$ oscillates, so as x gets larger, $d(x)$ does not consistently get closer to 50. The words "stays within" avoid the misconception because they indicate that $d(x)$ *stays within* ε units of L, not that it *approaches L*.

7. In its rest position, the pendulum will be 50 cm from the wall.

8. Answers will vary.

Exploration 2-7a

1. $\lim\limits_{x \to 2} f(x) = \lim\limits_{x \to 2} x^3 = 8$
Make $f(x)$ within 0.1 unit of 8.
$7.9 < x^3 < 8.1$
$\sqrt[3]{7.9} < x < \sqrt[3]{8.1}$
$1.99163170... < x < 2.00829885...$
$-0.008368... < x - 2 < 0.008298...$
Keep x within $\delta = 0.008298...$ unit of 2.
Make $f(x)$ within ε unit of 8.
$\sqrt[3]{8 - \varepsilon} < x \sqrt[3]{8 + \varepsilon}$
Keep x within $\delta = \sqrt[3]{8 + \varepsilon} - 2$.
δ is positive for any $\varepsilon > 0$ because $\sqrt[3]{8 + \varepsilon} > 2$.
Because there is a positive number δ for any positive value of ε such that keeping x within δ unit of 2 keeps $f(x)$ within ε unit of 8, 8 really is the limit of $f(x)$ as x approaches 2.

2. $g(0.5) = \sin \dfrac{\pi}{2} = 1$

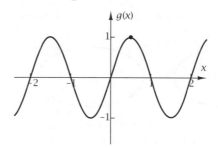

Make $g(x)$ within 0.01 of 1.
$0.99 < \sin \pi x < 1.01$
$\sin \pi x$ is bounded above by 1, so only the left inequality is meaningful.
$\dfrac{1}{\pi} \sin^{-1} 0.99 < x < \dfrac{1}{\pi} (\pi - \sin^{-1} 0.99)$
$0.4549... < x < 0.5450...$
Keep x within $\delta = 0.0450...$ unit of 0.5.
Make $g(x)$ within ε unit of 1.
Keep x within $\delta = 0.5 - \dfrac{1}{\pi} \sin^{-1}(1 - \varepsilon)$ of 0.5.
δ is positive when ε is small and positive.

3. $h(x) = 2^{x-3} + 5$
$h(3) = 2^0 + 5 = 6$
Make $h(x)$ within ε unit of 6.
$6 - \varepsilon < 2^{x-3} + 5 < 6 + \varepsilon$
$1 - \varepsilon < 2^{x-3} < 1 + \varepsilon$
$\log_2 (1 - \varepsilon) < x - 3 < \log_2 (1 + \varepsilon)$
$\left| \log_2 (1 - \varepsilon) \right| > \left| \log_2 (1 + \varepsilon) \right|$,
so make $\delta = \log_2 (1 + \varepsilon)$

4. $r(x) = \dfrac{\sin \pi x - 0.5}{x - 1/6}$
$r(1/6)$ takes on the *indeterminate form* 0/0.
The graph shows that the limit appears to be just below 3. (exact value: $\pi \cos (\pi/6) = 2.7206...$)

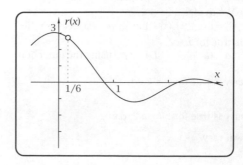

5. $p(x)$ oscillates as x increases, but with decreasing amplitude, and approaches 3. So there is some value D for which $p(x)$ is within 0.2 unit of 3 when $x > D$.
The amplitude of $p(x)$ is determined by $2(0.95)^x$. So
$$2(0.95)^D = 0.2$$
$$(0.95)^D = 0.1$$
$$\ln(0.95)^D = \ln(0.1)$$
$$D\ln(0.95) = \ln(0.1)$$
$$D = \ln(0.1)/\ln(0.95) = 44.8905...$$

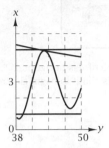

6. $2(0.95)^D = \varepsilon$
$(0.95)^D = \varepsilon/2$
$\ln(0.95)^D = \ln(\varepsilon/2)$
$D\ln(0.95) = \ln(\varepsilon/2)$
$D = \ln(\varepsilon/2)/\ln(0.95)$
$y = 3$ is a horizontal asymptote because it satisfies the definition of a limit as x approaches ∞.

7.

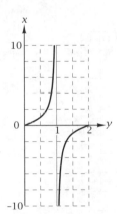

$\lim_{x \to 1^-} T(x) = -\infty$ and $\lim_{x \to 1^+} T(x) = \infty$
$\lim_{x \to 1} T(x) \neq \infty$ because $T(x)$ approaches ∞ from the positive side, but $-\infty$ from the negative side. $\lim_{x \to 1} T(x)$ is infinite because $T(x)$ values do increase or decrease without bound as x is approached from either side of 1.

8. $\tan\frac{\pi}{2}x > 1000$

$\frac{\pi}{2}x > \tan^{-1} 1000$

$x > (\tan^{-1} 1000)/(\pi/2)$

$x > 0.9993...$
For any positive number E, you can make $T(x) > E$ by keeping $x > (\tan^{-1}E)/(\pi/2)$.

9. Answers will vary.

Exploration 2-7b

1. There are about 9 square spaces under the curve from $x = 1$ to $x = 7$. Each square space represents 10 units of area, so the definite integral is about 90.

2. The graph shows the tangent line at $x = 1$ with slope that appears to be about 1.5. Each vertical space is 10 units and each horizontal space is 1 unit, so the derivative is about 15.

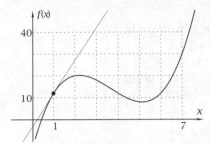

3. The graph is correct.

4. $f'(1) \approx \dfrac{f(1.01) - f(0.99)}{0.02} = 15.0001$
This is very close to the estimate in Problem 2.

5. Using the trapezoidal rule with $n = 6$, the definite integral is about 91, which is reasonably close to the guess in Problem 1.

6. Using the trapezoidal rule with
$n = 10$: integral ≈ 90.36
$n = 100$: integral ≈ 90.0036
$n = 1000$: integral ≈ 90.000036
The exact value appears to be 90.

7. In Problem 6, the exact value was found by taking the number of increments, n, to be very large. So, a definition of the definite integral might be the *limit* of the trapezoidal rule value as n approaches infinity.

8. $f(1) = 12$, so
$$m(x) = \frac{x^3 - 11x^2 + 34x - 12 - 12}{x - 1}$$
$$= \frac{x^3 - 11x^2 + 34x - 24}{x - 1}$$

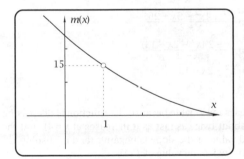

9. $m(x) = \dfrac{x^3 - 11x^2 + 34x - 24}{x - 1}$

$= \dfrac{(x - 1)(x^2 - 10x + 24)}{x - 1}$

$= x^2 - 10x + 24 \quad (x \neq 1)$

$\lim_{x \to 1} m(x) = \lim_{x \to 1} (x^2 - 10x + 24)$

$\hspace{4.5cm}$ Because $x \neq 1$ by definition of a limit

$= \lim_{x \to 1} (x - 6)(x - 4)$ $\hspace{2.5cm}$ Algebra

$= \lim_{x \to 1} (x - 6) \lim_{x \to 1} (x - 4)$ $\hspace{1.5cm}$ Limit of a product

$= (-5)(-3)$ $\hspace{2.5cm}$ Limit of a linear function, twice

$= 15$, Q.E.D.

10. Answers will vary.

Chapter 3

Exploration 3-2a

1. $f(4) = 10$, as shown on the graph.

2. $f'(4) = \lim_{x \to 4} \dfrac{f(x) - f(4)}{x - 4}$

3. $f'(4) = \lim_{x \to 4} \dfrac{x^3 - 4x^2 - 9x + 46 - 10}{x - 4}$

   $= \lim_{x \to 4} \dfrac{x^3 - 4x^2 - 9x + 36}{x - 4}$

   $= \lim_{x \to 4} \dfrac{(x - 4)(x^2 - 9)}{x - 4}$

   $= \lim_{x \to 4} (x^2 - 9)$

   $= 7$

4. Graph $y = 7x - 18$.

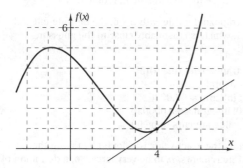

   The line with slope 7 going through the point (4, 10) is tangent to the graph.

5. $f(2) = 20$

   $f'(2) = \lim_{x \to 2} \dfrac{f(x) - f(2)}{x - 2}$

   $= \lim_{x \to 2} \dfrac{x^3 - 4x^2 - 9x + 46 - 20}{x - 2}$

   $= \lim_{x \to 2} \dfrac{x^3 - 4x^2 - 9x + 26}{x - 2}$

   $= \lim_{x \to 2} \dfrac{(x - 2)(x^2 - 2x - 13)}{x - 2}$

   $= \lim_{x \to 2} x^2 - 2x - 13$

   $= -13$

   This appears reasonable because the function is decreasing at $x = 2$ (about twice as fast as it increases at $x = 4$), and the calculated value of the slope is negative (and in absolute value about twice the value of $f'(4)$).

6. Answers will vary.

Exploration 3-3a

1. The graph is correct.

2. $d'(t) = \dfrac{d(1.001) - d(0.999)}{0.002} = 30.6853...$

3. Numerical derivative $= 30.6853...$
   Answer agrees with Problem 2.

4. $d'(2) \approx -19.3147...$
   $d'(1)$ is positive, which corresponds to the graph of d increasing at $t = 1$. $d'(2)$ is negative, which corresponds to the graph of d decreasing at $t = 2$.

5. (Instructor check.)

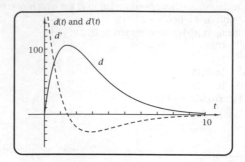

6. At the point where $d'(t) = 0$, the graph of d is horizontal. The door has just finished opening and is about to begin closing at this time.

7. $d'(t) = 0$ at $t \approx 1.4426...$

8. Minimum is at $x \approx 2.8853...$
   $f(2.8853...) = 78.0991...$

9. At the point in Problem 8, the graph changes from bending downward to bending upward.

10. Answers will vary.

Exploration 3-3b

1.

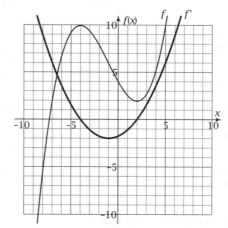

2.

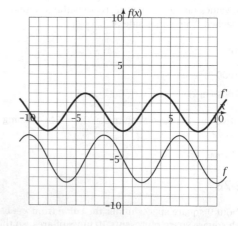

3.

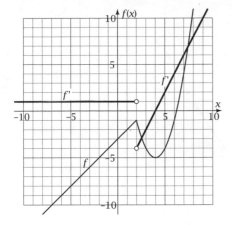

4.

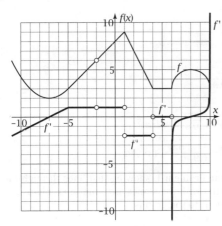

5. Answers will vary.

Exploration 3-4a

1. $f'(c) = \lim_{x \to c} \dfrac{f(x) - f(c)}{x - c}$

$= \lim_{x \to c} \dfrac{x^5 - c^5}{x - c}$

2. $f'(c) = \lim_{x \to c} \dfrac{x^5 - c^5}{x - c}$

$= \lim_{x \to c} \dfrac{(x - c)(x^4 + cx^3 + c^2x^2 + c^3x + c^4)}{x - c}$

$= \lim_{x \to c} (x^4 + cx^3 + c^2x^2 + c^3x + c^4)$

$= 5c^4$

3. $f'(3) = 5 \cdot 3^4 = 405$
   Numerical derivative ≈ 405.0001
   Formula seems to work.

4. Conjecture: For $f(x) = x^{10}$, $f'(x) = 10x^9$
   Test at $c = 2$:
   $10 \cdot 2^9 = 5120$
   Numerical derivative ≈ 5120.0154
   Formula seems to work.

5. The formula for the derivative of x^n seems to be $f'(x) = nx^{n-1}$, for any positive integer n!

6. Answers will vary.

Exploration 3-5a

1. Displacement tells how far an object is from a reference point, and in which direction. Distance tells how far an object is from the reference point, without regard to direction.

2. Velocity tells how fast an object moves, and in which direction. Speed tells only how fast an object moves, without regard to direction.

3. y', $f'(t)$, $\dfrac{dy}{dt}$, $\dfrac{d}{dt}(y)$

4. v', $g'(t)$, $\dfrac{dv}{dt}$, $\dfrac{d}{dt}(v)$

5. y'', $f''(t)$, $\dfrac{d^2y}{dt^2}$, $\dfrac{d^2}{dt^2}(y)$

6. False. If acceleration and velocity are *both* negative, then the object is speeding up (in the negative direction).

7. A small object

8. $v = 3t^2 - 18t + 23$

9. The particle starts at $x = -15$, moves to the right, stops, moves back to the left, stops, then moves to the right and goes off the screen.

10. $v(2) = 3(2)^2 - 18(2) + 23 = 12 - 36 + 23 = -1$
    $a(t) = 6t - 18$
    $a(2) = 12 - 18 = -6$
    The particle is speeding up at 1 ft/s because v and a are the same sign.

11. Answers will vary.

Exploration 3-5b

1. $x(t) = at^b$
   $a = 2820.5148...$
   $b = 0.8222...$
   The correlation coefficient is $r = 0.9974....$

2. Equation fits data reasonably well.

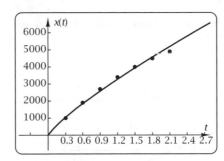

3. Using the regression equation for the displacement, $v(t) = x'(t) = b \cdot at^{b-1}$.

4. $v(0.9) \approx 0.8222... \cdot 2820.5128... (0.9)^{0.8222...-1}$
   $= 2363.1354...$ ft/s

5. Velocity $\approx \dfrac{3400 - 1900}{1.2 - 0.6} = 2500$ ft/s, which is reasonably close to the answer in Problem 4.

6. Using the regression equation for the displacement:
   $a(t) = v'(t) = (b - 1) \cdot b \cdot at^{b-2}$.

7. $x(1) = 2820.5148...$ ft
   $v(1) = 2319.3025...$ ft/s
   $a(1) = -412.1456...$ (ft/s)/s

8. At 1 min, $x(60) \approx 81752$ ft (≈ 15.5 mi!).
   This does not seem reasonable; the data show the bullet
   to be slowing down more than the regression equation
   suggests.

9. Answers will vary.

Exploration 3-6a

1. Yes

2.

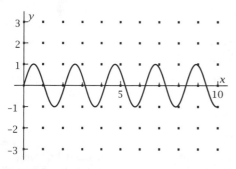

3. Conjectures will vary.

4. $g'(x) = 3 \cos 3x$

5.

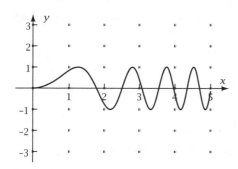

6. $h'(x) = 2x \cos x^2$

7. Take the derivative of $\sin x^2$ and get $\cos x^2$. Then multiply by
   $2x$, the derivative of x^2.

8.

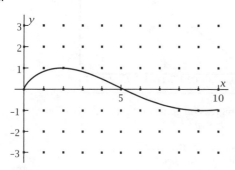

$t'(x) = 0.7 \cos x^{0.7}$

9. Answers will vary.

Exploration 3-7a

1.

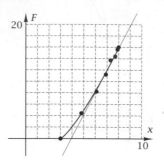

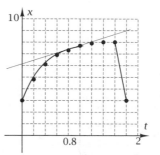

2. $\dfrac{dx}{dt}(0.8) \approx \dfrac{7.7 - 6.9 \text{ in.}}{1.0 - 0.6 \text{ s}} = 2$ in./s

3. $\dfrac{dF}{dx}(7.3) \approx \dfrac{14.4 - 11.2 \text{ oz}}{7.7 - 6.9 \text{ in.}} = 4$ oz/in.

4. See the graph in Problem 1, showing that lines through the
   respective points with the slopes as found in Problems 2
   and 3 are tangent to the graphs.

5.

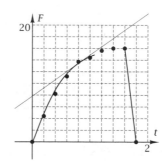

6. $\dfrac{dF}{dt} = \dfrac{dF}{dx} \cdot \dfrac{dx}{dt} = 4$ oz/in. $\cdot$ 2 in./s $= 8$ oz/s

7. $\dfrac{dF}{dt}(0.8) = \dfrac{14.4 - 11.2 \text{ oz}}{1.0 - 0.6 \text{ s}} = 8$ oz/s—same answer as in
   Problem 6!

8. See the graph in Problem 5. The line with slope 8 is tangent
   to the graph. (Observe the different scales for the two axes.)

9. Answers will vary.

Exploration 3-8a

1. $y(-0.1) = 0.9983\ldots$
   $y(0.1) = 0.9983\ldots$
   $y(-0.01) = 0.999983\ldots$
   $y(0.01) = 0.999983\ldots$
   $y(-0.001) = 0.99999983\ldots$
   $y(0.001) = 0.99999983\ldots$
   y appears to approach 1 near $x = 0$.

2. $\sin 0.1 = 0.0998\ldots < 0.1 < 0.1003\ldots = \tan 0.1$
   $\sin 0.01 = 0.0099\ldots < 0.01 < 0.0100\ldots = \tan 0.01$
   $\sin 0.001 = 0.0009\ldots < 0.001 < 0.0010\ldots = \tan 0.001$
   Statement appears to be true.

3. $\sin x < x < \tan x = \dfrac{\sin x}{\cos x}$

   Divide by $\sin x$.

   $1 < \dfrac{x}{\sin x} < \dfrac{1}{\cos x} = \sec x$

4. Problem 3 says $1 < \frac{x}{\sin x} < \frac{1}{\cos x}$ as x approaches 0 from the right; therefore,

   $1 > \dfrac{\sin x}{x} > \cos x$ as x approaches 0 from the right.

   Let $f(x) = \dfrac{\sin x}{x}$, $g(x) = 1$, and $h(x) = \cos x$.

   Then $f(x)$ is between $g(x)$ and $h(x)$ as x approaches 0 from the right;
   $\lim\limits_{x \to 0^+} g(x) = \lim\limits_{x \to 0^+} 1 = 1$; and
   $\lim\limits_{x \to 0^+} h(x) - \lim\limits_{x \to 0^+} \cos x = 1$.
   So, by the squeeze theorem, $\lim\limits_{x \to 0^+} f_2(x) = 1$ also.

5. Use h for Δx. Recall:

   $\sin A - \sin B = 2 \cos \frac{1}{2}(A + B) \sin \frac{1}{2}(A - B)$

   $= \dfrac{\sin(x + h) - \sin x}{h} = \dfrac{2 \cos \frac{1}{2}(2x + h) \sin \frac{1}{2}h}{h}$

   $= \cos\left(x + \frac{1}{2}h\right) \cdot \dfrac{\sin \frac{1}{2}h}{\frac{1}{2}h}$

   As h approaches zero, the first factor approaches $\cos x$ and the second factor approaches 1.
   Thus, $\frac{d}{dx}(\sin x) = \cos x$, Q.E.D.

6. A *lemma* is something you prove as an important step in proving something else. So, if you want to prove that all (live) cats are warm-blooded, you might first prove the lemma that all cats are mammals, and then use the well-known properties of mammals to reach your conclusion.

7. Answers will vary.

Exploration 3-9a

1. Each year the interest is paid on higher and higher principal amounts.

2. The ratio is constant, $0.086177\ldots$.
   Multiply $M(x)$ by $0.086177\ldots$ to find the derivative.

3. $M'(x) = \lim\limits_{h \to 0} \dfrac{1000(1.09^{x+h}) - 1000(1.09^x)}{h}$

   $= \lim\limits_{h \to 0} \dfrac{1000(1.09^x)(1.09^h - 1)}{h}$

   $= 1000(1.09^x) \cdot \lim\limits_{h \to 0} \dfrac{(1.09^h - 1)}{h}$

   $\dfrac{(1.09^h - 1)}{h} \to 0.086177\ldots$ as $h \to 0$, Q.E.D.

4. $f'(x) = \lim\limits_{h \to 0} \dfrac{e^{x+h} - e^x}{h}$

   $= \lim\limits_{h \to 0} \dfrac{e^x(e^h - 1)}{h} = e^x \cdot \lim\limits_{h \to 0} \dfrac{e^h - 1}{h}$

   The limit appears to be 1.
   $\therefore f'(x) = e^x \cdot 1$, the original function.

5. $e = 2.718281828\ldots$

6. $\ln 1.09 = 0.086177\ldots$, the same as the limit in Problem 3 and the ratio in Problem 2.
   Conjecture: $M'(x) = M(x) \cdot \ln 1.09$

7. Conjecture: $f'(x) = 2^x \cdot \ln 2$
   The conjecture agrees.

8. Answers will vary.

Chapter 4

Exploration 4-2a

1. $g(x) = x^7 \Rightarrow g'(x) = 7x^6$
   $h(x) = x^{11} \Rightarrow h'(x) = 11x^{10}$

2. $f(x) = g(x) \cdot h(x) = x^7 \cdot x^{11} = x^{18} \Rightarrow f'(x) = 18x^{17}$

3. $g'(x) \cdot h'(x) = (7x^6)(11x^{10}) = 77x^{16} \neq 18x^{17} = f'(x)$

4. $18x^{17} = 7x^6 \cdot x^{11} + x^7 \cdot 11x^{10}$

5. $f'(x) = g'(x) \cdot h(x) + g(x) \cdot h'(x)$

6. Use $g(x) = x^2$, $h(x) = \sin x$.
   Then $g'(x) = 2x$, $h'(x) = \cos x$, and
   $f'(x) = g'(x) \cdot h(x) + g(x) \cdot h'(x) = 2x \sin x + x^2 \cos x$

7. The graph of $f(x)$, its numerical derivative, and $f'(x)$ from Problem 6 shows that the numerical and algebraic derivatives are equivalent.

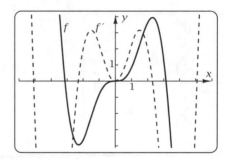

8. Answers will vary.

Exploration 4-3a

1. $f(x) = \dfrac{x^3}{\sin x}$

   $f'(1) = 2.8021\ldots$ (numerically)

2. $\dfrac{d}{dx}(x^3) = 3x^2$, $\dfrac{d}{dx}(\sin x) = \cos x$

   $\dfrac{3(1)^2}{\cos 1} = 5.5524 \neq f'(1)$

3. $y + \Delta y = \dfrac{\Delta u + u}{\Delta v + v}$

4. $\dfrac{dy}{dx} = \lim\limits_{\Delta x \to 0} \dfrac{\Delta y}{\Delta x} = \lim\limits_{\Delta x \to 0} \dfrac{\frac{\Delta u + u}{\Delta v + v} - \frac{u}{v}}{\Delta x}$

5. $\frac{\Delta y}{\Delta x} = \frac{1}{\Delta x}\left(\frac{\Delta u + u}{\Delta v + v} - \frac{u}{v}\right)$

$= \frac{1}{\Delta x}\left[\frac{(\Delta u + u)v}{(\Delta v + v)v} - \frac{u(\Delta v + v)}{v(\Delta v + v)}\right]$

$= \frac{1}{\Delta x}\left[\frac{\Delta u \cdot v - u\Delta v}{v(\Delta v + v)}\right]$

6. $\frac{\Delta y}{\Delta x} = \frac{\frac{\Delta u}{\Delta x} \cdot v - u\frac{\Delta v}{\Delta x}}{v(\Delta v + v)}$

7. $\lim_{\Delta x \to 0} \frac{\Delta y}{\Delta x} = \lim_{\Delta x \to 0} \frac{\frac{\Delta u}{\Delta x} \cdot v - u\frac{\Delta v}{\Delta x}}{v(\Delta v + v)}$

$= \lim_{\Delta x \to 0} \frac{\frac{\Delta u}{\Delta x} \cdot v - \lim_{\Delta x \to 0} u\frac{\Delta v}{\Delta x}}{\lim_{\Delta x \to 0} v(\Delta v + v)}$

$= \frac{\frac{du}{dx} \cdot v - u\frac{dv}{dx}}{v^2} = \frac{u'v - uv'}{v^2}$

8. $y = x^3 \sin x$

Use $u(x) = x^3$, $v(x) = \sin x$

$\frac{dy}{dx} = \frac{u'v - uv'}{v^2} = \frac{3x^2 \sin x - x^3 \cos x}{(\sin x)^2}$

$\frac{dy}{dx}(1) = \frac{3 \sin 1 - \cos 1}{(\sin 1)^2} = 2.8021...$

The numerical derivative is 2.8021..., which agrees with the algebraic derivative.

9. Take the derivative of the top function times the bottom function, minus the top function times the derivative of the bottom function, all divided by the bottom function squared.

10. Answers will vary.

Exploration 4-5a

1.

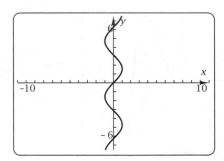

2. The graphs are reflections of each other across the line $x = y$.

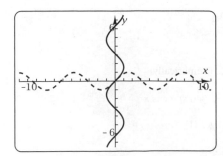

3. $x = \sin y$

$1 = \cos y \cdot y'$, using the chain rule.

$y' = \frac{1}{\cos y}$

4.

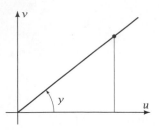

$y' = \frac{1}{\cos y}$

$\cos y = \frac{\text{adjacent}}{\text{hypotenuse}} = \frac{\sqrt{1 - x^2}}{1}$

$\therefore y' = \frac{1}{\sqrt{1 - x^2}}$

5. At $x = 0.5$, $y' = \frac{1}{\sqrt{1 - 0.25}} = 1.1547...$

The line through $(0.5, \sin^{-1} 0.5)$ with slope 1.15... is tangent to the graph.

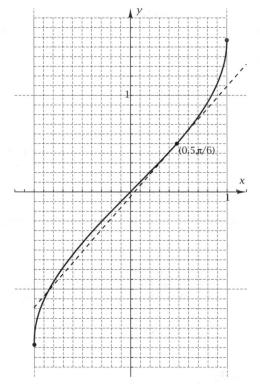

6. $y = \tan^{-1} x \Rightarrow x = \tan y \Rightarrow 1 = (\sec y)^2 \cdot y' \Rightarrow$

$y' = \frac{1}{(\sec y)^2} = \frac{1}{1 + (\tan y)^2} = \frac{1}{1 + x^2}$

$y = \sec^{-1} x \Rightarrow x = \sec y \Rightarrow 1 = \tan y \sec y \cdot y' \Rightarrow$

$y' = \frac{1}{\tan y \sec y} = \frac{1}{\sqrt{(\sec y)^2 - 1} \sec y}$

$= \frac{1}{|x|\sqrt{x^2 - 1}}$

(See text for justification of $|x|$.)

7. Answers will vary.

Exploration 4-6a

1. $f(x)$ is continuous at $x = c$ if
   $f(c)$ exists, $\lim_{x \to c} f(x)$ exists, and $\lim_{x \to c} f(x) = f(c)$.

2. $\lim_{x \to c}[f(x) - f(c)] = 0$ Given (note $f(c)$ exists)
   $\lim_{x \to c} f(c) = f(c)$ Limit of a constant
   $\lim_{x \to c}[f(x) - f(c)] + \lim_{x \to c} f(c) = f(c)$ Add equations
   $\lim_{x \to c}[f(x) - f(c) + f(c)] = f(c)$ Sum of limits
   $\lim_{x \to c} f(x) = f(c)$
   Therefore, $f(x)$ is continuous at $x = c$.
   (See text for a slightly different set of algebraic steps.)

3. $f'(c) = \lim_{x \to c} \dfrac{f(x) - f(c)}{x - c}$

4. The limit of the denominator is zero.

5. $\lim_{x \to c}[f(x) - f(c)] = \lim_{x \to c}\left[[f(x) - f(c)] \cdot \dfrac{x - c}{x - c}\right]$
   $= \lim_{x \to c} \dfrac{f(x) - f(c)}{x - c} \cdot \lim_{x \to c}(x - c)$
   $= f'(c) \cdot 0$

6. If f is differentiable at c, then $f'(c)$ is a real number
   $\Rightarrow f'(c) \cdot 0 = 0$ $f'(c)$ is a real number
   $\Rightarrow \lim_{x \to c}[f(x) - f(c)] = 0$ Problem 5
   $\Rightarrow f$ is continuous at $x = c$ Problem 2

7. The converse is "If f is continuous at $x = c$, then f is differentiable at $x = c$."
   Counterexample: $f(x) = |x|$ is continuous at $x = 0$, but not differentiable at $x = 0$.

8. A *lemma* for a theorem is something you prove as an important step in proving the main theorem. An easy consequence of a previously proved result is called a *corollary*.

9. Answers will vary.

Exploration 4-6b

1. $f'(x) = \begin{cases} 2ax, & \text{if } x < 3 \\ b, & \text{if } x > 3 \end{cases}$

   There is no derivative at an endpoint of a graph, so $x < 3$, not $x \le 3$.

2. $\lim_{x \to 3^-} f'(x) = 6a$, $\lim_{x \to 3^+} f'(x) = b$

3. $\lim_{x \to 3^-} f'(x) = 6a = 6 \cdot 1 = 6$
   $\lim_{x \to 3^+} f'(x) = b = 6$
   They are equal!

4.
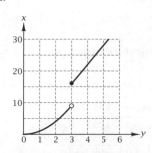

5. A function can be discontinuous, even if the derivatives approach the same value.

6. $\lim_{x \to 3^-} f(x) = 9a$, $\lim_{x \to 3^+} f(x) = 3b - 2$
   $9a = 3b - 2$
   Also: $6a = b$
   $\therefore 9a = 3(6a) - 2 \Rightarrow a = 2/9$
   $b = 6(2/9) = 4/3$

7.
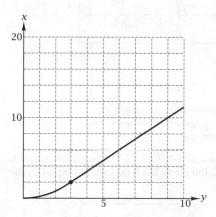

8. Answers will vary.

Exploration 4-7a

1.
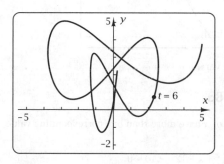

2. $\dfrac{dx}{dt} = 0.4 \cos t - 0.4t \sin t$

   $\dfrac{dy}{dt} = 0.3 + 4 \cos 2t$

   $x'(6) = 0.4 \cos 6 - 2.4 \sin 6 = 1.0546...$

   $y'(6) = 0.3 + 4 \cos 12 = 3.6754...$

3. $\dfrac{dy}{dx} = \dfrac{dy/dt}{dx/dt} = \dfrac{0.3 + 4 \cos 2t}{0.4 \cos t - 0.4t \sin t}$

   $\dfrac{dy}{dx}(6) = \dfrac{3.6754...}{1.0546...} = 3.4849...$

   At $t = 6$, Adam is at the point $(2.3044..., 0.7268...)$ on the graph. At this point the graph is sloping upward with slope considerably greater than 1. (Alternately: A line through this point with slope 3.4849... appears tangent to the graph.)

4. dy/dx (numerically) equals 3.4849..., which agrees with the algebraic answer in Problem 3.

5. Adam turns around between about $t = 0.82$ and $t = 0.86$.

6. $y = 0$ at about 1.87:

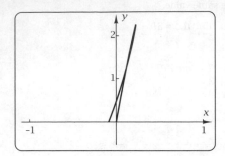

7. $y' = 0.3 + 4\cos 2t = 0$
   $\cos 2t = -0.075$
   $t = 0.5 \cos^{-1} -0.075 = 0.8229...$

8. At this time, Adam is not moving in the y-direction, but is still moving rightward in the x-direction because $x'(0.8229...) = 0.0306....$

9. The graph shows an x-dilation of 50 and a y-dilation of 10. At $t = 0.8229...$, the graph has a horizontal tangent so there is no cusp.

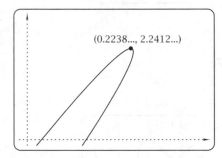

(0.2238..., 2.2412...)

10. Answers will vary.

Exploration 4-8a

1. Many values of x have more than one corresponding value of y.

2. $x^2 - 4xy + 4y^2 + x - 12y - 10 = 0$
   At $x = 6$, $36 - 24y + 4y^2 + 6 - 12y - 10 = 0$.
   $4y^2 - 36y + 32 = 4(y - 1)(y - 8) = 0 \Rightarrow y = 1$ or 8.
   The graph shows these points:

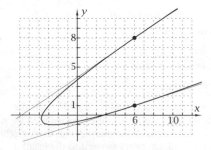

3. $2x - 4y - 4xy' + 8yy' + 1 - 12y' = 0$
   $2x - 4y + 1 = 4xy' - 8yy' + 12y'$
   $y' = \dfrac{2x - 4y + 1}{4x - 8y + 12} = \left(\dfrac{1}{2} - \dfrac{5}{4x - 8y + 12}\right)$

4. $y'(6, 1) = \dfrac{12 - 4 + 1}{24 - 8 + 12} = \dfrac{9}{28}$
   $y'(6, 8) = \dfrac{12 - 32 + 1}{24 - 64 + 12} = \dfrac{19}{28}$
   See the graph in Problem 2, showing that lines through (6, 1) and (6, 8) with slopes 9/28 and 19/28, respectively, are tangent to the graph.

5. The formula gives $y'(3, 1) = \dfrac{6 - 4 + 1}{12 - 8 + 12} = \dfrac{3}{16}$, but this has no meaning for the problem because (3, 1) does not even lie on the graph!

6. Rewrite the equation:
   $4y^2 - (4x + 12)y + (x^2 + x - 10) = 0$
   $$y = \frac{4x + 12 \pm \sqrt{(4x + 12)^2 - 16(x^2 + x - 10)}}{8}$$
   $$= \frac{1}{2}(x + 3 \pm \sqrt{5x - 19})$$
   $y' = \dfrac{1}{2} \pm \dfrac{5}{4}(5x - 19)^{-1/2}$

7. For $Ax^2 + Bxy + Cy^2 + Dx + Ey + F = 0$, the discriminant is $B^2 - 4AC$. If the discriminant is positive, the graph is a hyperbola; if negative, an ellipse; and if zero, a parabola. For the given figure, $B^2 - 4AC = (-4)^2 - 4(1)(4) = 0$. Thus, the graph is a parabola, Q.E.D.

8. Answers will vary.

Exploration 4-8b

1. $[(x - 6)^2 + y^2][(x + 6)^2 + y^2] = 1200$
   $(x - 6)^2(x + 6)^2 + (x - 6)^2y^2 + (x + 6)^2y^2 + y^4 = 1200$
   $(x^2 - 36)^2 + (x^2 - 12x + 36 + x^2 + 12x + 36)y^2 + y^4 = 1200$
   $x^4 - 72x^2 + 1296 + 2x^2y^2 + 72y^2 + y^4 = 1200$
   $x^4 - 72x^2 + 2x^2y^2 + 72y^2 + y^4 + 96 = 0$
   Differentiate implicitly:
   $4x^3 - 144x + 4xy^2 + 4x^2yy' + 144yy' + 4y^3y' = 0$
   $(4x^2y + 144y + 4y^3)y' = -4x^3 + 144x - 4xy^2$
   $y' = \dfrac{-x^3 + 36x - xy^2}{x^2y + 36y + y^3}$

2. Substitute $x = 8$.
   $y^4 + 200y^2 - 416 = 0$
   $y^2 = \dfrac{-200 \pm \sqrt{41664}}{2} = 2.0588...$ or $-202.0...$
   $y = \pm 1.4348...$ (-202.0 gives no real solutions.)
   At (8, 1.434...), $y' = -1.64211....$
   At (8, -1.434...), $y' = 1.64211....$
   Lines with these slopes are tangent to the graph.

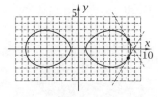

3. y' seems to be infinite at the four x-intercepts.
   At the x-intercepts, $y = 0$.
   $(x - 6)^2(x + 6)^2 = 1200$
   $(x^2 - 36)^2 = 1200$
   $x = \pm\sqrt{36 \pm \sqrt{1200}} = \pm 8.4048...$ or $\pm 1.1657...$
   The largest intercept is $x = \sqrt{36 \pm \sqrt{1200}} = 8.4048....$
   At $x = 8.4048...$, $y' = \dfrac{-(8.4...)^3 + 36(8.4...) - (8.4...)(0)}{(8.4...)^2(0) + 36(0) + 0^3}$
   $= \dfrac{896.29...}{0}$, which is infinite.

Calculus: Concepts and Applications Instructor's Resource Book
©2005 Key Curriculum Press

4. $x^4 - 72x^2 + 2x^2y^2 + 72y^2 + y^4 = -96$

$y^4 + (2x^2 + 72)y^2 + (x^4 - 72x^2 + 96) = 0$

$y^2 = \dfrac{-(2x^2 + 72) \pm \sqrt{(2x^2 + 72)^2 - 4(1)(x^4 - 72x^2 + 96)}}{2}$

$y^2 = -x^2 - 36 \pm \sqrt{144x^2 + 1200}$

Only the positive part of the ambiguous sign $\pm$ gives real solutions for y, so

$y = \pm\sqrt{-x^2 - 36 + \sqrt{14x^2 + 1200}}$

The graph agrees.

5. Replacing 1200 with 1400 gives

$y = \pm\sqrt{-x^2 - 36 + \sqrt{14x^2 + 1400}}$

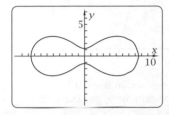

The graph shows that the two ovals in the original graph merge into a single closed figure resembling an (unshelled) peanut.

6. The two factors in the equation $[(x - 6)^2 + y^2][(x + 6)^2 + y^2] = 1200$ are the squares of the distances from (x, y) to the points $(6, 0)$ and $(-6, 0)$, respectively. So the original equation has the form $d_1^2 \cdot d_2^2 = 1200$, where d_1 and d_2 are the distances to the two foci. $\therefore d_1 \cdot d_2 = \sqrt{1200}$, a constant. This is analogous to $d_1^2 + d_2^2 = $ constant for ellipses. See the Internet.

7. Answers will vary.

Chapter 5

Exploration 5-2a

1. $f(1) = \sec 1 = 1.8508\ldots$
   $f'(1) = \sec 1 \tan 1 = 2.8824\ldots$
   $y = 1.8508\ldots + 2.8824\ldots(x - 1)$

2. The linear function is tangent to the curve at $x = 1$.

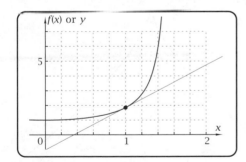

3. Local linearity

4. The graph shows $dx = 0.4$, dy being the corresponding rise to the linear function graph, and Δy being the corresponding rise to the function graph.

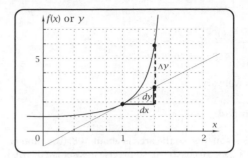

5. $dy \div dx = \dfrac{f'(1) \cdot (x - 1)}{(x - 1)} = f'(1)$.

   So, $dy \div dx$ is the same as the derivative, $\frac{dy}{dx}$.

6. $dx = \Delta x$ always. $dy = f'(x)\,dx$
   or: dy is the rise along the tangent line and Δy is the rise along the graph itself.
   or: dy is close to Δy if dx is small.

7.

x	y	$f(x)$	Error
0.97	1.7643...	1.7689...	0.0046...
0.98	1.7931...	1.7952...	0.0020...
0.99	1.8219...	1.8225...	0.0005...
1.00	1.8508...	1.8508...	0.0
1.01	1.8796...	1.8801...	0.0005...
1.02	1.9084...	1.9107...	0.0022...
1.03	1.9372...	1.9424...	0.0051...

As x approaches 1, the error approaches zero.

8. Solving $f(x) - y = 0.001$ numerically, the error will be less than 0.001 if $0.9862\ldots < x < 1.0134\ldots$, so if x is kept within $0.0134\ldots$ of 1, then the error will be less than 0.01.

9. Answers will vary.

Exploration 5-2b

1. $v(t) = 3t^{0.6}$

t	Velocity	$v(t)$
0	0	0.0
2	4.5	4.5471...
4	6.9	6.8921...
6	8.8	8.7904...
8	10.4	10.4466...
10	11.9	11.9432...

Thus the values of $v(t)$ fit the data closely.

2. $a(t) = v'(t) = 1.8t^{-0.4}$
   $a(t)$ is a decreasing function for all $t > 0$, because $a'(t) = -7.2t^{-1.4} < 0$ for all $t > 0$.

3. $x(t) = \dfrac{3}{1.6}t^{1.6} + C = 5t^{1.6} + C$
   $x(0) = -50 \Rightarrow -50 = 0 + C \Rightarrow C = -50$
   $x(t) = 5t^{1.6} - 50$

4. $x(10) = 24.6450\ldots \approx 24.6$ ft, or about three-fourths of the way through the intersection.

5. Trapezoidal rule:

$$x(10) = -50 + 2 \cdot \left(\frac{0}{2} + 4.5 + 6.9 + 8.8 + 10.4 + \frac{11.9}{2} \right)$$

$$= 23.1 \text{ ft}$$

6. Solve $100 = \frac{3}{1.6} t^{1.6} - 50$.

$$t = \sqrt[1.6]{\frac{1.6}{3} \cdot 150} = 15.4678\ldots \approx 15.5 \text{ s}$$

7. Answers will vary.

Exploration 5-4a

1. About 15.4 squares, so the area is about 308. (Equation is $f(x) = 10 + 2x + 10 \cos(0.5x)$, so precise answer is 308.3103....)

2.

c	$f(c)$
3	17
5	12
7	15
9	26
11	39
13	46

3.

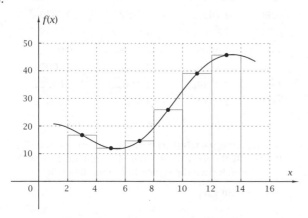

For each rectangle, the part of the graph above the rectangle is roughly the same as the part of the rectangle above the graph, so the area of each rectangle is about the same as the area under the corresponding portion of the graph. Thus the sum of the areas of the rectangles represents the definite integral.

4. Area of rectangles
$= 2 \cdot 17 + 2 \cdot 12 + 2 \cdot 15 + 2 \cdot 26 + 2 \cdot 39 + 2 \cdot 46$
$= 310$, which is close to the 308 in Problem 1.

5.

c	$f(c)$
2	19
4	14
6	12
8	19
10	33
12	44

6. Area of rectangles
$= 2 \cdot 19 + 2 \cdot 14 + 2 \cdot 12 + 2 \cdot 19 + 2 \cdot 33 + 2 \cdot 46$
$= 282$

7. Both methods approximate the height of the function within each subinterval, then multiply that height by the width of the subinterval.

8. Answers will vary.

Exploration 5-5a

1.

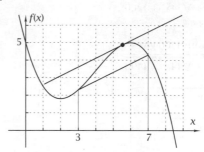

$f(3) = 2.3$, $f(7) = 4.3$, slope of secant line $= 0.5$
$c \approx 5.5$ (numerically, graphically, or by solving $-0.3c^2 + 2.4c - 3.6 = 0.5$)
$c \approx 5.5$ $\left(\text{exactly } 4 + \frac{1}{3}\sqrt{21} \right)$
f is differentiable on $(3, 7)$.
f is continuous on $[3, 7]$.

2.

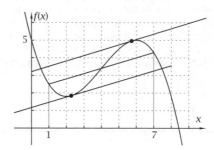

$c \approx 2.3$ or 5.7 $\left(\text{exactly } 4 \pm \sqrt{3} \right)$
f is differentiable on $(1, 7)$.
f is continuous on $[1, 7]$.

3.

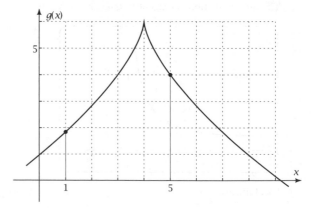

g is not differentiable on $(1, 5)$.
g is continuous on $[1, 5]$.
No such $x = c$ exists. The slope of the secant line is positive. The slope of the tangent line is greater than the slope of the secant when x is between 1 and 4, and it is negative when x is between 4 and 5.

4.

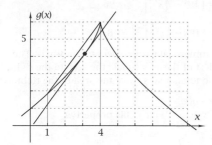

$c \approx 3.1$
g is differentiable on $(1, 4)$.
g is continuous on $[1, 4]$.

5.

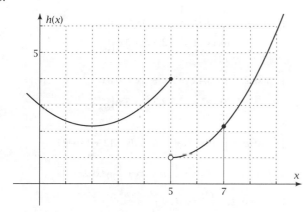

h is differentiable on $(5, 7)$.
h is not continuous on $[5, 7]$.
The slope of the secant line is $\frac{2.2 - 4}{7 - 5} = -0.9$. The slope of the curve on $(5, 7)$ is determined by $0.6(x - 5)$, which is positive for all $x > 5$. So the slope of the curve cannot equal the slope of the secant line.

6.

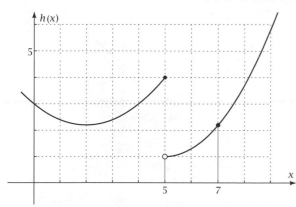

h is differentiable on $(5, 9)$.
h is not continuous on $[5, 9]$.
$c \approx 5.75$

7.

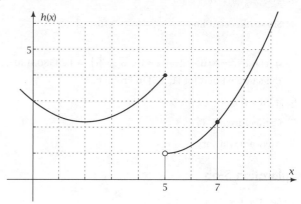

The slope of the secant line is $\frac{4 - 2.4}{5 - 1} = 0.4$. The slope of the curve on $(1, 4)$ is determined by $0.4(x - 2)$. So, $c = 3$ (by solving $0.4 = 0.4(x - 2)$).
h is differentiable on $(1, 5)$.
h is continuous on $[1, 5]$ even though there is a step continuity at $x = 5$ because $\lim_{x \to 5^-} h(x) = h(5)$.

8. The hypotheses and conclusion are true for Problems 1, 2, 4, and 7.
The hypotheses and conclusion are not true for Problems 3 and 5.
The conclusion is true but the hypotheses are not for Problem 6.

9. If $f(x)$ is (1) differentiable on (a, b), and (2) continuous at $x = a$ and $x = b$, then there is a number $x = c$ between a and b for which
$$f'(c) = \frac{f(b) - f(a)}{b - a}$$
If a function satisfies the hypotheses, then that is enough (sufficient) to make the function satisfy the conclusion. But for a function that satisfies the conclusion, it is not necessary for the hypotheses to be satisfied. For example, the function in Problem 5 between $x = 2$ and $x = 8$ does not meet the hypotheses of the mean value theorem, but these are not necessary for $c = 2.625$ and $c = 5.416...$ to satisfy the conclusion.

10. Answers will vary.

Exploration 5-6a

1. Trapezoidal rule:
$I \approx 0.5 + \sqrt{2} + \sqrt{3} + 1 = 4.6462...$
Underestimates I because parts of the region lie above the trapezoids.

2. Midpoint sum:
$I \approx \sqrt{1.5} + \sqrt{2.5} + \sqrt{3.5} = 4.6767...$
Overestimates I because the part of the region above the top of each rectangle is slightly less than the part of each rectangle above the region.

3. $I \approx \sqrt{1.4858425557} + \sqrt{2.4916102607} + \sqrt{3.4940277163}$
$= 4.6666...$
This estimate is between the trapezoidal and midpoint sums.

4. $I \approx \frac{1}{2}(\sqrt{1.2458051304} + \sqrt{1.7470136081} + \sqrt{2.2476804000}$
$+ \sqrt{2.7481034438} + \sqrt{3.2483958519} + \sqrt{3.7486100806}) =$
$4.6666...$, same as in Problem 3.

5. $g(1) = \frac{2}{3}$, $g(1.5) = \sqrt{1.5}$

Slope of secant line $= \dfrac{\sqrt{1.5} - \frac{2}{3}}{0.5} = \sqrt{6} - \frac{4}{3}$

$g'(c) = c^{1/2} = \sqrt{6} - \frac{4}{3} \Rightarrow c = \left(\sqrt{6} - \frac{4}{3}\right)^2 = 1.2458051303\ldots$,
the sample point for [1, 1.5] in Problem 4!

6. $g'(x) = f(x)$

7. Conjecture: $I = 4\frac{2}{3}$

8. Answers will vary.

Exploration 5-6b

1. See the text.

2. See the text.

3. g is differentiable on (a, b) because it has a derivative f, and g is continuous on (a, b) because differentiability implies continuity.

4. There is a point $c_1 \in (a, x_1)$, such that
$$g'(c_1) = \frac{g(x_1) - g(a)}{\Delta x}$$
The graph shows $x = c_1$ with tangent line parallel to secant line.

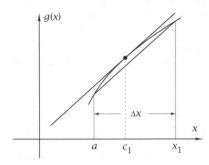

5. $R_n = f(c_1)(x_1 - a) + f(c_2)(x_2 - x_1) + f(c_3)(x_3 - x_2)$
$$+ \cdots + f(c_n)(b - x_{n-1})$$
$$= [f(c_1) + f(c_2) + f(c_3) + \cdots + f(c_n)]\Delta x$$

6. $R_n = [g'(c_1) + g'(c_2) + g'(c_3) + \cdots + g'(c_n)]\Delta x$
$$= \left[\frac{g(x_1) - g(a)}{\Delta x} + \frac{g(x_2) - g(x_1)}{\Delta x} + \cdots + \frac{g(b) - g(x_{n-1})}{\Delta x}\right]\Delta x$$
$$= g(x_1) - g(a) + g(x_2) - g(x_1) + g(x_3) - g(x_2)$$
$$+ \cdots + g(b) - g(x_{n-1})$$
$$= g(b) - g(a)$$

7. $L_n \le R_n \le U_n \Rightarrow L_n \le g(b) - g(a) \le U_n$ Problem 6
$\lim\limits_{n\to\infty} L_n \le g(b) - g(a) \le \lim\limits_{n\to\infty} U_n$ Properties of limits
                                 $(g(b) - g(a)$ is a constant.)
But the two limits equal the definite integral, by definition.
$$\therefore \int_a^b f(x)\, dx = g(b) - g(a), \text{ Q.E.D.}$$

8. $g(x) = \displaystyle\int x^{1/2}\, dx = \frac{2}{3}x^{3/2} + C$
$$\int_1^4 x^{1/2}\, dx = \frac{2}{3}4^{3/2} + C - \frac{2}{3}1^{3/2} - C = 4\frac{2}{3}$$
Note that the C's cancel out!

Exploration 5-7a

1. For all x, $f(-x) = f(x)$.
(Even powers of x (e.g., x^2) have this property.)

2. $\displaystyle\int_{-3}^3 (19 - x^2)\, dx = \left(19x - \frac{1}{3}x^3\right)\Big|_{x=-3}^{x=3} = 96$
$\displaystyle\int_0^3 (19 - x^2)\, dx = \left(19x - \frac{1}{3}x^3\right)\Big|_{x=0}^{x=3} = 48$

The region is symmetrical with respect to the y-axis. Thus the area to the left of the axis equals the area to the right, meaning that the total area is twice the area to the right.

3. For all x, $g(-x) = -g(x)$.
(Odd powers of x (e.g., x^1) have this property.)

4. $\displaystyle\int_{-4}^4 x^3\, dx = \frac{1}{4}x^4\Big|_{x=-4}^{x=4} = 0$

The two parts of the region are congruent and thus have the same area. Because the left part of the region is below the y-axis, the integral is negative and thus cancels the integral for the right part.

5. $\displaystyle\int_1^3 h(x)\, dx = \int_1^3 (0.4x^3 - 3x^2 + 5x + 5)\, dx$
$$= (0.1x^4 - x^3 + 2.5x^2 + 5x)\Big|_{x=1}^{x=3}$$
$$= 12$$
$\displaystyle\int_3^6 h(x)\, dx = \int_3^6 (0.4x^3 - 3x^2 + 5x + 5)\, dx$
$$= (0.1x^4 - x^3 + 2.5x^2 + 5x)\Big|_{x=3}^{x=6}$$
$$= 15$$

6. $\displaystyle\int_1^6 h(x)\, dx = \int_1^3 h(x)\, dx + \int_3^6 h(x)\, dx = 12 + 15 = 27$

7. a. $\displaystyle\int_2^7 [u(x) + v(x)]\, dx = \int_2^7 u(x)\, dx + \int_2^7 v(x)\, dx = 42$

   b. $\displaystyle\int_2^7 v(x)\, dx = \int_2^4 v(x)\, dx + \int_4^7 v(x)\, dx$
$$\Rightarrow 13 = 8 + \int_4^7 v(x)\, dx$$
$$\int_4^7 v(x)\, dx = 5$$

8. Answers will vary.

Exploration 5-8a

1.

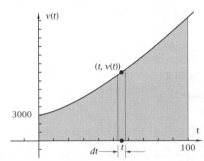

2. See the graph in Problem 1.

3. Distance = rate · time
If the rate throughout the time interval is essentially constant at $v(t)$, and the length of time is dt, then $D = v(t) \cdot dt$.

4. $R_n = \displaystyle\sum_{i=1}^n v(c_i)\, dt$

5. Each term in the upper sum is greater than or equal to the corresponding $v(c_i)\, dt$ in the Riemann sum, by definition of an upper sum, so that $U_n \ge R_n$.
Similarly, $L_n \le R_n$. Thus, $L_n \le R_n \le U_n$.
$$\therefore \lim_{n\to\infty} L_n \le \lim_{n\to\infty} R_n \le \lim_{n\to\infty} U_n.$$

If the function is integrable, the limits of the upper and lower sums equal the definite integral, by the definition of definite integral.

By the squeeze theorem, the limit of R_n is also equal to the definite integral. Thus,

$$\lim_{n \to \infty} R_n = \int_0^{100} v(t)\, dt, \text{ q.e.d.}$$

6. $\int_0^{100} (3000 + 18t^{1.4})\, dt = \left(3000t + \frac{18}{2.4} \cdot t^{2.4}\right)\Big|_{t=0}^{t=100}$

$= 300{,}000 + 7.5 \cdot 100^{2.4} = 773{,}218.0083...$
≈ 773 thousand ft

7. Solve $3000 + 18t^{1.4} = 26000$
$t = 165.5376... \approx 166$ s

8. Distance $\approx \int_0^{166} (3000 + 18t^{1.4})\, dt = \left(3000t + \frac{18}{2.4} \cdot t^{2.4}\right)\Big|_{t=0}^{t=166}$

$= 498{,}000 + 7.5 \cdot 166^{2.4} = 2{,}095{,}057.9488...$
≈ 2.095 million ft

9. Both the $f(x)$ and the dx have physical meanings. The dx is multiplied by $f(x)$ to get the part of the value of the integral corresponding to the vertical strip.

Exploration 5-9a

1. The volume of a disk is $\pi r^2 h$, where r = radius and h = thickness (think of a disk as a very short cylinder). The slice shown is not exactly a disk, because the radius changes ever so slightly from the top to the bottom. But the radius of this slice is always very close to x, and the height is dx, so the volume is approximately $dV = \pi x^2\, dy$. (In the limit, the difference between the cylinders and the actual disk volumes approaches zero.)

2. $y - 4 - x^2 \rightarrow x^2 = 4 - y$, so
$dV = \pi x^2\, dy = \pi(4 - y)\, dy$.

3. $V = \int_{y=0}^{y=4} \pi \cdot (4 - y)\, dy$

$= \left(4\pi y - \frac{1}{2}\pi y^2\right)\Big|_{y=0}^{y=4}$
$= 8\pi$

4. The circumscribed cylinder has $r = 2$, $h = 4$, and
$V_{\text{cyl}} = \pi r^2 h = 16\pi$.
The inscribed cone has $r = 2$, $h = 4$, and
$V_{\text{cone}} = \frac{1}{3}\pi r^2 h = 5\frac{1}{3} \cdot \pi$.
The calculated volume of the paraboloid falls between these numbers.

5. Conjecture: The volume of a paraboloid is half the volume of the circumscribed cylinder.

6. Answers will vary.

Exploration 5-9b

1. $A_{\text{washer}} = A_{\text{outer circle}} - A_{\text{inner circle}}$
$A = \pi y_1^2 - \pi y_2^2 = \pi(y_1^2 - y_2^2)$
$dV = A\, dx = \pi(y_1^2 - y_2^2)\, dx$

2. $y_1 = 6e^{-0.2x}$, $y_2 = \sqrt{x}$
$dV = \pi(36e^{-0.4x} - x)\, dx$

3. $V = \int_{x=1}^{x=4} \pi(36e^{-0.4x} - x)\, dx$

$= \left(-90\pi e^{-0.4x} - \frac{1}{2}\pi x^2\right)\Big|_{x=1}^{x=4}$
$= -90\pi e^{-1.6} + 90\pi e^{-0.4} - 7.5\pi$

4. $V = 108.8816...$

5. Numerical integration gives $108.8816...$, the same answer!

6. Same answer!
(Note that some students may already have looked in the text and found out that this problem is Example 3. They will no doubt think that they have "outfoxed" you by finding this problem in the book. But really *you* have outfoxed *them* by getting them to read the book!)

7. Answers will vary.

Exploration 5-10a

1. $\int_3^7 (-x^2 + 11x - 16)\, dx = \left(-\frac{1}{3}x^3 + \frac{11}{2}x^2 - 16x\right)\Big|_3^7$

$= \frac{-343}{3} + \frac{539}{2} - 112 + 9 - \frac{99}{2} + 48 = 50\frac{2}{3} = 50.6666...$

2.
x	y	Weighted y
3	8	8
5	14	56
7	12	12

Weighted average $= \dfrac{8 + 56 + 12}{6} = 12\frac{2}{3}$

3. $12\frac{2}{3} \cdot 4 = 50\frac{2}{3}$

The answer is the same as the integral from $x = 3$ to $x = 7$.

4.
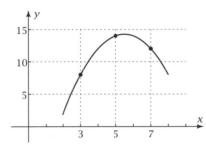

The area of the rectangle appears to be the same as the area under the curve.

5. $\int_6^{16} v\, dt \approx \dfrac{10 + 7 \cdot 4 + 12}{6} \cdot 10 = 83\frac{1}{3}$

$\int_{16}^{26} v\, dt = \dfrac{12 + 19 \cdot 4 + 22}{6} \cdot 10 = 183\frac{1}{3}$

$\therefore \int_6^{26} v\, dt = 83\frac{1}{3} + 183\frac{1}{3} = 266\frac{2}{3}$

6.
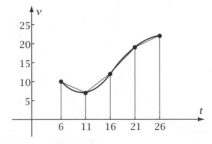

Simpson's rule is probably more accurate than the trapezoidal rule because velocity is likely to be approximated better by smooth curves than by straight line segments.

7. $\frac{1}{3}(\Delta x)(y_0 + 4y_1 + 2y_2 + 4y_3 + 2y_4 + \cdots + 2y_{n-2} + 4y_{n-1} + y_n)$

The formula is consistent because the value of y_2 is used twice and $\frac{1}{3}(\Delta x)$ is equivalent to $\frac{10}{6}$.

8. See the Programs for Graphing Calculators in this *Instructor's Resource Book*. The program should give the correct answer for Problem 5.

9. $S_{10} = 2.000109517$, $T_{10} = 1.983523538$
The Simpson's rule approximation is closer to the exact answer.

10. Answers will vary.

11. Answers will vary.

Exploration 5-10b

1.

x	f(x)	Factor	f(x) · Factor
1	2.2	1	2.2
3	1.2	4	4.8
5	1.0	2	2.0
7	2.6	4	10.4
9	5.8	1	5.8

$(1/3)(2)(2.2 + 4.8 + 2.0 + 10.4 + 5.8) = 16.8$

2. $h(x) = \begin{cases} 0.1x^2 - 0.9x + 3, & \text{if } 1 \le x \le 5 \\ 0.2x^2 - 1.6x + 4, & \text{if } 5 \le x \le 9 \end{cases}$

3.

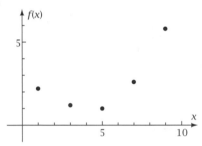

h is continuous at $x = 5$ because $0.1(5)^2 - 0.9(5) + 3 = 0.2(5)^2 - 1.6(5) + 4$.
h is not differentiable because
$h'(x) = \begin{cases} 0.2x - 0.9, & \text{if } 1 \le x \le 5 \\ 0.4x - 1.6, & \text{if } 5 \le x \le 9 \end{cases}$
and $0.2(5) - 0.9 \ne 0.4(5) - 1.6$.

4. $\int_1^9 h(x)\,dx = \int_1^5 (0.1x^2 - 0.9x + 3)\,dx + \int_5^9 (0.2x^2 - 1.6x + 4)\,dx$

$= 5\frac{1}{3} + 11\frac{7}{15} = 16.8$

This answer agrees with Problem 1.

5.

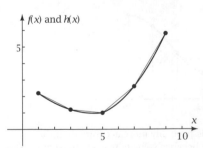

Simpson's rule connects the points more smoothly than the trapezoidal rule.

6. Answers will vary.

Chapter 6

Exploration 6-2a

1. $f(9) = \int_{t=1}^{t=9} t^{1/2}\,dt = \frac{2}{3}t^{3/2}\Big|_{t=1}^{t=9} = \frac{2}{3}(27 - 1) = \frac{52}{3}$

2. Graph, showing $f(x) = \int_{t=1}^{t=x} t^{1/2}\,dt$.

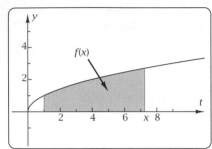

3. $f(x) = \int_{t=1}^{t=x} t^{1/2}\,dt = \frac{2}{3}t^{3/2}\Big|_{t=1}^{t=x} = \frac{2}{3}(x^{3/2} - 1)$

4. $f'(x) = \frac{d}{dx}\frac{2}{3}(x^{3/2} - 1) = x^{1/2}$

$f'(x)$ is the integrand of $f(x)$ evaluated at x!

5. $g(x) = \int_{t=3}^{t=x} t^3\,dt \Rightarrow g'(x) = x^3$

6. $h(x) = \int_{t=2}^{t=x^3} \cos t\,dt = \sin t\Big|_{t=2}^{t=x^3} = (\sin x^3 = \sin 2)$

7. $h'(x) = \frac{d}{dx}(\sin x^3 - \sin 2) = \cos x^3 \cdot 3x^2 = 3x^2 \sin x^3$

8. The pattern is: The integrand evaluated at the upper limit of integration, times derivative of the upper limit function (the "inside" function), which is an example of the chain rule.

$\frac{d}{dx}\left[\int_{t=0}^{t=\sin x} \tan^3 (t^5)\,dt\right] = \tan^3 (\sin^5 x) \cdot \cos x$

9. In the statement of the fundamental theorem of calculus in the problem, $g(x) = L(x)$, and $f(x) = 1/t$, so $L'(x) = 1/x$.

10. The power rule for antiderivatives works only with exponents not equal to -1.

Exploration 6-2b

1. The power rule gives $\frac{1}{0}x^0 + C$, which involves division by zero.

2. $g'(x) = 1/x$
The definition says $g(x) = \int f(x)\,dx$ if and only if $g'(x) = f(x)$ and $g'(x)$ *does* equal $f(x)$.

3. $\ln x = \int_1^x \frac{1}{t}\,dt$

4.

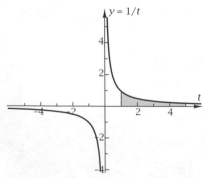

t is the variable of integration. x is the value of t at the end of the region.

5. $\int_3^7 \frac{1}{x}\,dx = 0.8472...$

   $\ln 7 - \ln 3 = 0.8472...$

6. The interval $[-5, 2]$ contains a vertical asymptote at which the value of $1/t$ becomes infinite.

7.

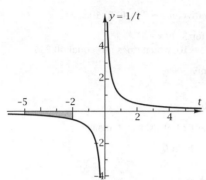

$\int_{-2}^{-5} \frac{1}{t}\,dt = 0.9162...$

The answer is a positive real number because the Riemann sums have negative y-values and negative dt-values.

8. $dx = -du$

   $x = -u$

   $\int \frac{1}{x}\,dx$

   $= \int \frac{1}{-u}(-du)$

   $= \int \frac{1}{u}\,du$

   $= \ln u + C$, Q.E.D.

   $\therefore \int \frac{1}{x}\,dx = \ln(-x) + C.$

9. You use x if x is positive, and the opposite of x if x is negative. This is the definition of absolute value.

10. Answers will vary.

Exploration 6-3a

1. $\ln x = \int_{t=1}^{t=x} 1/t\,dt$

2. $f(7) = \ln 21 = \int_{t=1}^{t=21} 1/t\,dt = 3.0445...$ (numerically)

   $g(7) = \ln 7 + \ln 3 = \int_{t=1}^{t=7} 1/t\,dt + \int_{t=1}^{t=3} 1/t\,dt$

   $= 1.9459... + 1.0986...$ (numerically)

   $= 3.0445... = f(7)!$

3. $f(1) = \ln 3$

   $g(1) = \ln 1 + \ln 3$

   but $\ln 1 = \int_{t=1}^{t=1} 1/t\,dt = 0$, so $f(1) = g(1)$.

4. $f'(x) = \frac{1}{3x} \cdot 3 = \frac{1}{x}$

   $g'(x) = 0 + \frac{1}{x} = \frac{1}{x}$

   $\therefore f$ and g are differentiable on $(1, b)$ for any $b > 0$.

5. f and g are differentiable for all $x > 0$.
   Thus they are differentiable at $x = 1$ and $x = b$.
   Because differentiability implies continuity, f and g are continuous at $x = a$ and $x = b$.

6. The sum or difference of continuous functions is continuous, and the sum or difference of differentiable functions is differentiable.

7. $h(1) = f(1) - g(1) = 0.$
   The mean value theorem says that for some c between 1 and b, $h'(c) = \frac{h(b) - h(1)}{b - 1} = \frac{h(b)}{b - 1}.$

8. $h(b) \ne 0$, so $h'(c) \ne 0.$

9. $h'(x) = f'(x) - g'(x) = \frac{1}{x} - \frac{1}{x} = 0$ for all $x > 0.$
   But then $h'(c) = 0$ because c is between 1 and b. Therefore the assumption made in Problem 8 must have been false, and there is no such number $b > 0$ for which $f(b) \ne g(b)$.
   Therefore, $f(x) = g(x)$ for all $x > 0.$

10. If $f'(x) = g'(x)$ for all values of x in the domain, and $f(a) = g(a)$ for one value, $x = a$, in the domain, then $f(x) = g(x)$ for all values of c in the domain.

11. Answers will vary.

Exploration 6-3b

1. $\ln 1 = 0$ because $\int_1^1 f(x)\,dx = 0$ for any function f.
   $\ln' x = 1/x$ by the fundamental theorem of calculus in its derivative of an integral form.

2. $f(x) = \ln 7x$, $g(x) = \ln 7 + \ln x$
   $f'(x) = \frac{1}{7x} \cdot 7 = \frac{1}{x}$ and $g'(x) = 0 + \frac{1}{x} = \frac{1}{x}$

   $\therefore f'(x) = g'(x)$ for all $x > 0.$
   $f(1) = \ln 7$ and $g(1) = \ln 7 + \ln 0 = \ln 7$
   $\therefore f(1) = g(1).$
   $\therefore f(x) = g(x)$ for all $x > 0$, Q.E.D.

3. $p(x) = \ln 7 - \ln x$ and $q(x) = \ln \frac{7}{x}$
   $p'(x) = 0 - \frac{1}{x} = -\frac{1}{x}$ and $q'(x) = \frac{x}{7} \cdot \frac{1}{7}(-x^{-2}) = -\frac{1}{x}$

   $\therefore p'(x) = q'(x)$ for all $x > 0.$
   $p(1) = \ln 7 - \ln 1 = \ln 7$ and $q(1) = \ln 7$
   $\therefore p(1) = q(1).$
   $\therefore p(x) = q(x)$ for all $x > 0$, Q.E.D.

4. $h(x) = \ln(x^5)$ and $j(x) = 5 \ln x$
   $h'(x) = \frac{1}{x^5} \cdot 5x^4 = \frac{5}{x}$ and $j'(x) = 5 \cdot \frac{1}{x} = \frac{5}{x}$

   $\therefore h'(x) = j'(x)$ for all $x > 0.$
   $h(1) = \ln 1 = 0$ and $j(1) = 5 \ln 1 = 5 \cdot 0 = 0$
   $\therefore h(1) = j(1).$
   $\therefore h(x) = j(x)$ for all $x > 0$, Q.E.D.

5. *Proof:*
   Let $f(x) = \log_e x$. Let $g(x) = \ln x.$
   $f'(x) = \frac{1}{x} \cdot \ln e = \frac{1}{x}$

   $g'(x) = \frac{1}{x}$

   $\therefore f'(x) = g'(x)$ for all $x > 0.$
   $f(1) = 0$ and $g(1) = 0$
   $\therefore f(1) = g(1).$
   $\therefore f(x) = g(x)$ for all $x > 0.$
   $\therefore \log_e x = \ln x$ for all $x > 0$, Q.E.D.

6. $\int_1^x \frac{1}{t}\,dt = 1$

   Solving numerically, $x \approx 2.718281828...$, which equals e to a large number of decimal places, Q.E.D.

7. Answers will vary.

Exploration 6-4a

1. $10{,}000 = M(0) = ae^{k0} = a \cdot 1$, so $a = 10{,}000$.
   $15{,}528.08 = M(4) = ae^{k4} = 10{,}000e^{k4}$
   $\Rightarrow 1.552808 = e^{4k} \Rightarrow 4k = \ln 1.552808$
   $\Rightarrow k = 0.11001622...$

2. $M'(0) = \$1100.1622... $ /year (numerically)
   $M'(4) = \$1708.3407... $ /year (numerically)

3. $\dfrac{M'(0)}{M(0)} = \dfrac{\$1100.1622...}{\$10{,}000.00} = 0.11001622...$

   $\dfrac{M'(4)}{M(4)} = \dfrac{\$1708.3407...}{\$15{,}528.08} = 0.11001622...$

   Both answers are equal to k!

4. $\dfrac{d}{dt}[M(t)] = ae^{kt} \cdot k$

   $\therefore \dfrac{\frac{d}{dt}[M(t)]}{M(t)} = \dfrac{ae^{kt} \cdot k}{ae^{kt}} = k.$

   This is the exponential constant, the coefficient of x in the exponent!

5. $M(8) = 10{,}000e^{8k} = \$24{,}112.13$

6. $M(50) = 10{,}000e^{50k} = \$2{,}448{,}905.34$

7. Solve $20{,}000 = 10{,}000e^{kt}$ for t:

   $2 = e^{kt} \Rightarrow kt = \ln 2 \Rightarrow t = \dfrac{\ln 2}{k} = 6.3004...$ yr.

8. Answers will vary.

Exploration 6-4b

1. $b^3 = b \cdot b \cdot b$
   $b^{1/3} = \sqrt[3]{b}$
   $b^{2/3} = \left(\sqrt[3]{b}\right)^2$
   $b^{-2/3} = \dfrac{1}{b^{2/3}}$

2. Each definition requires an integer numerator, and π cannot be expressed as a ratio of two integers.

3. $\ln y = \displaystyle\int_1^y \frac{1}{t}\, dt$

   Any real number can be an upper limit of integration.

4. *Proof:*
   Assume that $\ln y \le M$ for all $y > 0$.
   Let $y = e^{M+1}$.
   Then $\ln y = \ln e^{M+1} = M + 1$, which is greater than M, a contradiction.
   $\therefore \ln y$ is unbounded above, Q.E.D.

5. *Proof:*
   Assume that $\ln y \ge M$ for all $y > 0$.
   Let $y = e^{M-1}$.
   Then $\ln y = \ln e^{M-1} = M - 1$, which is less than M, a contradiction.
   $\therefore \ln y$ is unbounded below, Q.E.D.

6. $\ln y$ is continuous because it is differentiable.
   $\therefore \ln y$ takes on all values between its minimum and maximum. Because $\ln y$ is unbounded above and below, $\ln y$ is unbounded above and below, $\ln y$ can be *any* real number, and thus the range of $\ln y$ is all real numbers.

7. The domain of $y = e^x$ is the same as the range of $x = \ln y$, namely all real numbers.

8. $b^x = (e^{\ln b})^x = e^{x \cdot \ln b}$ by the power of a power property.

9. $5^\pi = 156.992545...$
   $e^{\pi \ln 5} = 156.992545...$

10. Answers will vary.

Exploration 6-4c

1. $y = 5x$
   Numerical derivative at $x = 2$ is $40.2359...$

2. The power rule for 5^x is $x \cdot 5^{x-1}$.
   At $x = 2$, $2 \cdot 5^{x-1} = 10$, which does not equal $40.2359...$

3. $\ln y = \ln 5^x = x \ln 5$
   $\dfrac{1}{y}y' = \ln 5$
   $y' = y \ln 5 = 5^x \ln 5$

4. $y'(2) = 5^2 \ln 5 = 40.2359...$ Correct answer!

5. $f(x) = b^x \Rightarrow f'(x) = b^x \ln b$

6. $f(x) = 5(0.6^x)$
   $f'(x) = 5(0.6^x) \ln 0.6$
   $f'(1) = 5(0.6) \ln 0.6 = -1.5324...$
   The graph shows that the line through $(1, f(1))$ with slope $-1.5324...$ is tangent to the graph.

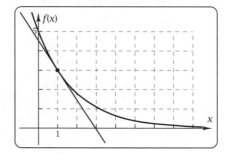

7. $\displaystyle\int 5^x\, dx = \dfrac{1}{\ln 5} \cdot 5^x + C$

8. Answers will vary.

Exploration 6-5a

1.

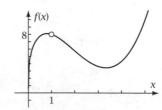

2. $f(1) \to \frac{0}{0}$, which is undefined.

   $\displaystyle\lim_{x \to 1} f(x)$ seems to be 8.

3. $\displaystyle\lim_{x \to 1} \dfrac{3x^2 - 16x + 21}{1/x} = 8$, the same as the limit in Problem 2.

4. If $\displaystyle\lim_{x \to c} f(x) = 0$ and $\displaystyle\lim_{x \to c} g(x) = 0$, then $\displaystyle\lim_{x \to c} \dfrac{f(x)}{g(x)} = \lim_{x \to c} \dfrac{f'(x)}{g'(x)}$, provided the latter limit exists.

5. The expression approaches $\infty \cdot 0$, which is indeterminate.

6. $\displaystyle\lim_{x \to \infty} x^2 e^{-x} = \lim_{x \to \infty} \dfrac{x^2}{e^x} \to \dfrac{\infty}{\infty}$

7. $\lim\limits_{x\to\infty}\dfrac{x^2}{e^x}\to\dfrac{\infty}{\infty}$

$=\lim\limits_{x\to\infty}\dfrac{2x}{e^x}\to\dfrac{\infty}{\infty}$

$=\lim\limits_{x\to\infty}\dfrac{2}{e^x}\to\dfrac{2}{\infty}$, which equals 0.

8. $\lim\limits_{x\to2}\dfrac{1-\cos 3(x-2)}{(x-2)^2}\to\dfrac{1-1}{0}=\dfrac{0}{0}$

$=\lim\limits_{x\to2}\dfrac{3\sin 3(x-2)}{2(x-2)}\to\dfrac{0}{0}$

$=\lim\limits_{x\to2}\dfrac{9\cos 3(x-2)}{2}=\dfrac{9}{2}$

9.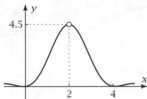

The function approaches (2, 4.5) as $x\to 2$.

10.

x	Fraction
1.98	4.49865...
1.99	4.49966...
2.00	undefined
2.01	4.49966...
2.02	4.49865...

The values are approaching 4.5 as $x\to 2$.

11. Answers will vary.

Exploration 6-6a

1. $\dfrac{d}{dx}(e^{2x})=2e^{2x}$

2. $\displaystyle\int e^{2x}\,dx=\dfrac{1}{2}e^{2x}+C$

3. $\dfrac{d}{dx}(3^{2x})=3^{3x}\cdot 2\ln 3$

4. $\displaystyle\int 3^{2x}\,dx=\dfrac{3^{2x}}{2\ln 3}+C$

5. $\dfrac{d}{dx}(x^3)=3x^2$

6. $\displaystyle\int x^3\,dx=\dfrac{1}{4}x^4+C$

7. $\dfrac{d}{dx}[(5x+1)^4]=4(5x+1)^3\cdot 5=20(5x+1)^3$

8. $\displaystyle\int (5x+1)^4\,dx=\dfrac{1}{5}\cdot\dfrac{1}{5}(5x+1)^5+C=\dfrac{1}{25}(5x+1)^5+C$

9. $\displaystyle\int (x^5+1)^2 x^4\,dx=\dfrac{1}{5}\int(x^5+1)^2(5x^4\,dx)=\dfrac{1}{15}(x^5+1)^3+C$

10. $\displaystyle\int (x^5+1)^2\,dx=\int(x^{10}+2x^5+1)\,dx=\dfrac{1}{11}x^{11}+\dfrac{1}{3}x^6+x+C$

11. $\dfrac{d}{dx}[(x-3)^{-1}]=-(x-3)^{-2}$

12. $\displaystyle\int (x-3)^{-1}\,dx=\ln|x-3|+C$

13. $\displaystyle\int (x-3)^{-2}\,dx=-(x-3)^{-1}+C$

14. $\displaystyle\int (3-x)^{-1}\,dx=-\ln|3-x|+C$

15. $\displaystyle\int \dfrac{3}{x-1}\,dx=3\ln|x-1|+C$

16. $\displaystyle\int \dfrac{3}{(x-1)^2}\,dx=-3(x-1)^{-1}+C$

17. $\displaystyle\int (x^2+6x+7)^5(x+3)\,dx=\dfrac{1}{2}\cdot\dfrac{1}{6}(x^2+6x+7)^6+C$

$=\dfrac{1}{12}(x^2+6x+7)^6+C$

18. $\displaystyle\int (x^2+6x+7)\,dx=\dfrac{1}{3}x^3+3x^2+7x+C$

19. $\lim\limits_{x\to4}\dfrac{\sin(5x-20)}{x-4}=\lim\limits_{x\to4}\dfrac{5\cos(5x-20)}{1}=5$

20. $\lim\limits_{x\to0}\dfrac{e^{3x}-1}{\sin 5x}\lim\limits_{x\to0}\dfrac{3e^{3x}}{5\cos 5x}=\dfrac{3}{5}$

21. Answers will vary.

Chapter 7

Exploration 7-2a

1. Let M be the amount of money at time t.

$\dfrac{dM}{dt}=kM$, where k is a constant.

2. $\dfrac{dM}{dt}=kM\Rightarrow M^{-1}\,dM=k\,dt$

$\displaystyle\int M^{-1}\,dM=\int k\,dt$

$\ln|M|=kt+C$

$|M|=e^{kt+C}$

$M=\pm e^{kt+C}$

3. $M=\pm e^{kt}\cdot e^C$

4. A positive number raised to any power is positive. Thus, e^C is positive.

5. If C_1 can be positive or negative, then when $M>0$ let $C_1=e^C$, and when $M<0$ (say, for debt outstanding on a credit card) let $C_1=-e^C$.

6. $M(0)=C_1 e^{k\cdot 0}=C_1\Rightarrow C_1=1000$

7. $k=0.05$

8. $M(5)=1000e^{0.25}\approx\$1284.03$
$M(10)=1000e^{0.5}\approx\$1648.72$
$M(50)=1000e^{2.5}\approx\$12,182.49$
$M(100)=1000e^{5}\approx\$148,413.16$

9. $2000=1000e^{0.05t}\Rightarrow t=\dfrac{\ln 2}{0.05}=13.8629...$ yr

10. Answers will vary.

Exploration 7-3a

1. $\dfrac{dy}{dt}=R-ky$

2. $(R-ky)^{-1}\,dy=dt$

3. $\displaystyle\int (R-ky)^{-1}\,dy=\int dt$

$-\dfrac{1}{k}\int(R-ky)^{-1}(-k\,dy)=\int dt$

$-\dfrac{1}{k}\cdot\ln|R-ky|=t+C$

4. $\ln|R-ky|=-kt+C_1$
$|R-ky|=e^{-kt+C_1}=e^{C_1}\cdot e^{-kt}$
$R-ky=\pm e^{C_1}\cdot e^{-kt}=C_2 e^{-kt}$
$ky=R-C_2 e^{-kt}$

5. $k\cdot 0=R-Ce^{-k\cdot 0}\Rightarrow C=R$
$\therefore ky=R-Re^{-kt}$
$y=\dfrac{R}{k}\cdot(1-e^{-kt})$

6. $R=100$; $ky=4$ when $y=10\Rightarrow k=0.4$
$y=250(1-e^{-0.4t})$

7. $y(3) = 250(1 - e^{-1.2}) = 174.7014... \approx 175$ names

8. Answers will vary.

Exploration 7-4a

1. $\dfrac{dy}{dx}\Big|_{(-5,\,-2)} = -0.9$ $\dfrac{dy}{dx}\Big|_{(-8,\,9)} = 0.32$

   The graph shows that the slopes at these points look reasonably close to -0.9 and 0.32.

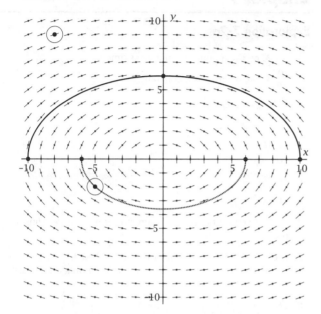

2. See the solid line in the graph in Problem 1. The graph looks like a half-ellipse. Below the x-axis, the graph would complete the ellipse, but would not satisfy the definition of a solution of a differential equation because it would not be a function.

3. See the dashed line in the graph in Problem 1. The graph looks like another half-ellipse of the same proportions, but smaller than the half-ellipse in Problem 2. This time only the bottom half of the ellipse is valid, because the initial y-value is negative.

4. $\dfrac{dy}{dx} = -\dfrac{0.36x}{y} \Rightarrow y\,dy = -0.36x\,dx$

   $\int y\,dy = \int -0.36x\,dx$

   $\dfrac{1}{2}y^2 = -\dfrac{1}{2} \cdot 0.36x^2 + C$

   $\left(\dfrac{x}{10}\right)^2 + \left(\dfrac{y}{6}\right)^2 = C_1$

   This is a standard form of the equation of an ellipse centered at the origin with x- and y-radii equal to $10\sqrt{C_1}$ and $6\sqrt{C_1}$, respectively.

5. Answers will vary.

Exploration 7-4b

1. See the graph with initial condition $(0, 5)$. The maximum height is at $x \approx 1.3$ s, and the ball hits the ground (height = 0) at $x \approx 2.7$ s. See the graph with initial condition $(0, -20)$. The ball hits the ground ($y = 0$) when $x \approx 0.6$ s or 2.0 s.

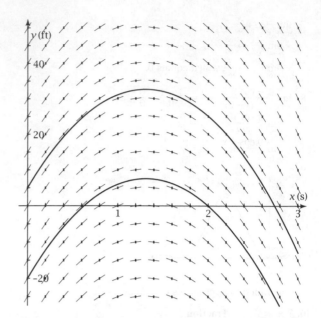

2. The first solution reaches a minimum at $x \approx -6$. The second solution rises at a decreasing rate, then at an increasing rate, approaching the first solution along a curved asymptote. The third solution reaches a maximum at $x \approx 5$.

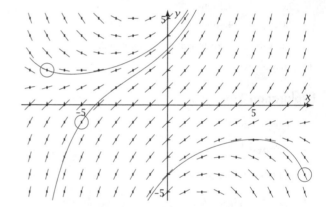

3. Without any treatments, the number of bacteria would decrease to an asymptote at $y = 11$, the maximum sustainable population. After the first treatment, the number of bacteria *rises* toward the same asymptote (because $y = 4$ is below the maximum sustainable population but above the minimum). After the second treatment, the bacteria decrease and become extinct (because 2 is below the minimum sustainable population).

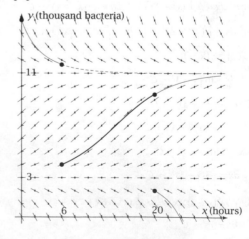

4.

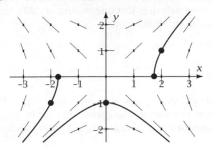

5. Answers will vary.

Exploration 7-5a

1. $dy = 0.3y\,dx$

2. $dy = 0.3(2)(0.50) = 0.3$

3. $y \approx 2 + dy = 2.3$; see the graph in Problem 6 showing dx and dy.

4. $dy = 0.3(2.3)(0.5) = 0.345$
$y \approx 2.3 + dy = 2.3 + 0.345 = 2.645$

5.

x	y	dy
1	2	0.3
1.5	2.3	0.69
2	2.645	0.39675
2.5	3.04175	0.4562...
3	3.4980...	0.5247...
3.5	4.0227...	0.6034...
4	4.6261...	0.6939...
4.5	5.3200...	0.7980...
5	6.1180...	0.9177...
5.5	7.0357...	1.0553...
6	8.0911...	1.2136...

6.

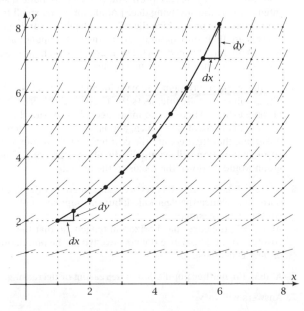

7. $\dfrac{dy}{y} = 0.3\,dx$
$\ln|y| = 0.3x + C$
$y = \pm e^{0.3x} \cdot e^C$
$y = C_1 e^{0.3x}$
$2 = C_1 e^{0.3(1)} \Rightarrow C_1 = 1.4186...$
$y = 1.4186...e^{0.3x}$
$y(5) = 1.4186...e^{0.3(5)} = 6.6402...$, which is about 0.5 above the 6.1180... found by Euler's method.

8. Answers will vary.

Exploration 7-6a

1. $P = 5$: $dP/dt = 0.35 > 0 \Rightarrow$ increasing
$P = 3$: $dP/dt = -0.45 < 0 \Rightarrow$ decreasing
$P = 15$: $dP/dt = -1.65 < 0 \Rightarrow$ decreasing
$P = 4$: $dP/dt = 0 \Rightarrow$ stable
$P = 12$: $dP/dt = 0 \Rightarrow$ stable
The slope-field lines agree with these values.

2. $t = 0$: $dP = 0.05(5 - 4)(12 - 5)(0.1) = 0.035$
New $P \approx 5 + 0.035 = 5.035$ at $t = 0.1$.
$t = 0.1$: $dP = 0.05(5.035 - 4)(12 - 5.035)(0.1) = 0.03604...$
New $P \approx 5.035 + 0.03604... = 5.07104...$ at $t = 0.2$.

3.

t	P
2	5.9
4	7.3
6	8.9
8	10.2
10	11.1
12	11.6
14	11.8
16	11.9

4. The curve does follow the slope lines.

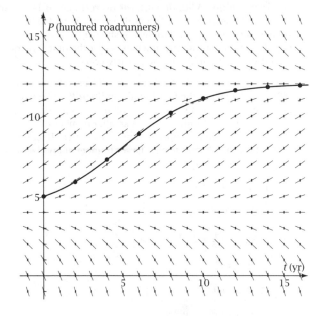

5. New $P \approx 10.2 + 6 = 16.2$ at $t = 8$.

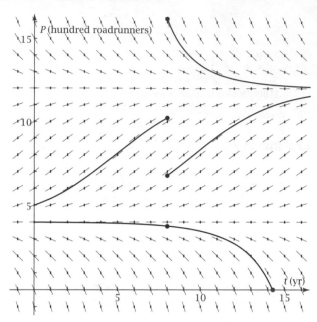

The population decreases from $P = 16.2$ toward $P = 12$. The effort to increase the population fails because the new population at $t = 8$ is above the maximum sustainable value, $P = 12$, and some roadrunners die or move away because of overcrowding.

6. Using $dt = 1$, $P(16) \approx 1.32$ and $P(17) \approx -0.11$. So the roadrunners appear to become extinct during the 17th year.

7. Using $dt = 0.1$, $P(14.2) \approx 0.19$ and $P(14.3) \approx -0.03$. So the roadrunners appear to become extinct during the 15th year. Because the convex side of the graph is upward for the given initial condition, all Euler's solutions will overestimate the algebraic solution. With $dt = 0.1$, the overestimate is less than with $dt = 1$, meaning that the graph will cross the t-axis sooner. See the graph in Problem 5, showing that the population remains almost unchanged for the first 5 years, then drops very rapidly in the last few years.

8. See the graph in Problem 5. Using $dt = 0.1$ as in Problem 7, $P(8) \approx 3.76$, making the new initial condition $P = 6.76$ when $t = 8$. The population rises by natural means, approaching $P = 12$ from below. (Introducing a smaller number of roadrunners at an appropriate time has a better effect on the population than introducing a larger number at an inappropriate time.)

9. $\ln \left| \dfrac{P - 4}{12 - P} \right| = 0.4t + C$

$\dfrac{P - 4}{12 - P} = C_2 e^{0.4t}$

Use $(0, 5)$: $\dfrac{5 - 4}{12 - 5} = C_2 e^0 \Rightarrow C_2 = \dfrac{1}{7}$

$\therefore \dfrac{P - 4}{12 - P} = \dfrac{1}{7} e^{0.4t}$

$\dfrac{7P - 28}{12 - P} = e^{0.4t}$

$7P - 28 = 12e^{0.4t} - Pe^{0.4t}$

$7P + Pe^{0.4t} = 12e^{0.4t} + 28$

$P = \dfrac{12e^{0.4t} + 28}{7 + e^{0.4t}}$

$P(8) = \dfrac{12e^{3.2} + 28}{7 + e^{3.2}} = 10.2240...$, or 1022 roadrunners

Euler's solution in Problem 3, before rounding, is 10.2111..., or 1021 roadrunners, which is just one roadrunner different from the precise, algebraic solution.

10. Answers will vary.

Exploration 7-6b

1. If there are relatively few coyotes, then one would expect the population of deer to increase. The graph will start by going to the right. Consequently, it also goes up, in order to follow the slope lines.
Note: The differential equation used is
$\dfrac{dy}{dx} = \dfrac{-0.64(x - 65)}{y - 35}$.

2. Initial condition $(80, 20)$. Both populations will increase until the population of coyotes gets too high. Then the deer population will begin to decrease, eventually causing the coyotes to starve off. The coyote population will then decrease to where the deer population can begin growing again, and the situation will return to where it started. The behavior is "cyclical."

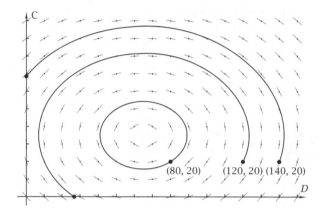

3. See the graph in Problem 2 with initial condition $(120, 20)$. The graph eventually intersects the D-axis, at which point the coyotes become extinct. There are so many deer to start with that too many coyotes are born, and the deer are hunted so intensely that the surviving deer population is too small to support any coyotes, which die off completely. Assuming the coyotes are their only natural enemy, the deer population will grow in an unrestrained way! (The graph, however, goes along the D-axis because there are no coyotes.)

4. See the graph in Problem 2 in with initial condition $(140, 20)$. The graph eventually intersects the C-axis and the deer become extinct. There are so many deer to start with that way too many coyotes are born, and all the deer are eaten. Assuming that the deer are the coyotes' only food source, the coyote population will eventually die off by starvation. (The graph would go down the C-axis to the origin.)

5. At $(100, 35)$, the curve has vertical tangent so that the deer born just balance the deer killed; but the population of coyotes is increasing.
At $(65, 80)$, the curve has horizontal tangent so that the coyotes born just balance the coyotes dying. The population of deer is decreasing.

6. At $(65, 35)$, neither population is increasing or decreasing.

7. Answers will vary.

Exploration 7-6c

1.

Year	t	Millions	$\Delta P/\Delta t$	$(\Delta P/\Delta t)/P$
1940	0	131.7	—	—
1950	10	151.4	2.38	0.01571...
1960	20	179.3	2.59	0.01444...
1970	30	203.2	2.36	0.01161...
1980	40	226.5	2.275	0.01004...
1990	50	248.7	—	—

2. $\dfrac{dP/dt}{P} \approx \dfrac{\Delta P/\Delta t}{P} \approx (-7.9274... \times 10^{-5})P + 0.02802...$
by linear regression, with correlation $r = -0.9853...$, graphed here.

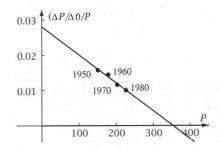

$\dfrac{dP}{dt} = P[(-7.9274... \times 10^{-5})P + 0.02802...]$
This is an example of a logistic differential equation.

3. Using the differential equation, the slopes for $P = 200$ are 2.4334... million people per year. Because the vertical scale is 1/5 of the horizontal scale, the geometric slopes should be $(1/5)(2.4332...) \approx 0.5$, which agrees with the slope field. The slope field plotted by grapher agrees with the one given here.

4.

t	P	t	P
−50	44.7	30	204.7
−40	57.0	40	228.3
−30	71.8	50	250.0
−20	89.3	60	269.4
−10	109.4	70	286.2
0	131.7*	80	300.3
10	155.5	90	311.8
20	180.1	100	321.2

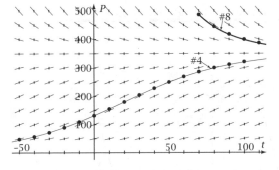

5. The calculated values match the given values within about 1%.

6. The population is stable if $dP/dt = 0$. This happens (trivially) at $P = 0$ and again if $(-7.9274... \times 10^{-5})P + 0.02802... = 0$.
$P = \dfrac{-0.02802...}{-7.9274... \times 10^{-5}} \approx 353.5$ million people
The slope-field graph confirms this number with the horizontal slope lines at $P \approx 350$.

7. Using the prediction $P \approx 286.2$ at $t = 70$ (year 2010), the new initial condition is $P = 286.2 + 200 = 486.2$.

70	486.2
80	444.6
90	417.8
100	399.8
110	387.2

The values of P decrease because of overcrowding.

8. See the graph in Problem 4, showing the decreasing population. The curve does follow the slope lines.

9.

1900	76,094,000
1910	92,407,000
1920	106,461,000
1930	123,076,741

www.census.gov
Answers will vary.

10. Answers will vary.

Chapter 8

Exploration 8-1a

1. $f'(x) - 12x^3 - 156x^2 + 600x - 672$
$= 12(x^3 - 13x^2 + 50x - 56)$
Factor by repeated synthetic substitution.

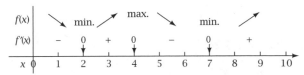

$f'(x) = 12(x - 2)(x - 4)(x - 7)$
$f'(x) = 0 \Leftrightarrow x = 2, 4, \text{ or } 7$

2.

$f(x)$ ↘ min. ↗ max. ↘ min. ↗
$f'(x)$ − 0 + 0 − 0 +
x 0 1 2 3 4 5 6 7 8 9 10

3. See the graph in Problem 2, showing intervals where $f'(x)$ is positive or negative, and thus where $f(x)$ is increasing or decreasing, respectively.

4. See the graph in Problem 2, showing max where $f(x)$ stops increasing and starts decreasing, and min where $f(x)$ stops decreasing and starts increasing. These extrema (maxima and minima) agree with the given figure.

5. $f''(x) = 36x^2 - 312x + 600$
   By quadratic formula, $f''(x) = 0 \Leftrightarrow x = 2.8803...$ or $5.7862....$
   The graph shows these zeros, and the intervals where $f''(x)$ is positive or negative, and thus the graph of $f(x)$ is concave up or down, respectively.

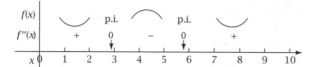

6. Yes, the arcs agree with the concavity of the given graph.

7. See the graph in Problem 5, showing points of inflection where the sign of $f''(x)$ changes. These points of inflection agree with the given figure.

8. Possible answer:

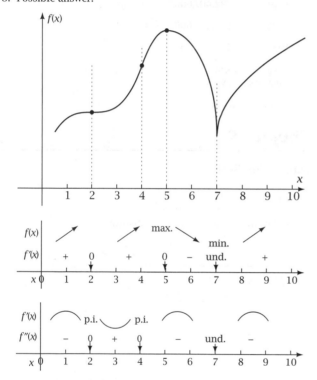

9. Answers will vary.

Exploration 8-2a

1. $y = 5x^{2/3} - x^{5/3}$
   $y' = \frac{10}{3}x^{-1/3} - \frac{5}{3}x^{2/3}$
   $= \frac{5}{3}x^{-1/3}(2 - x)$

2. y' is zero only when $x = 2$. At this x, the tangent line is horizontal, and the graph stops increasing and starts decreasing. As shown on the given figure, the graph has a maximum at $x = 2$.

3. y' is infinite at $x = 0$ because $0^{-1/3}$ is equivalent to $1/0^{1/3}$, which involves division by zero. The slope becomes infinite as x approaches zero from either direction. As shown on the given graph, there is a cusp at $x = 0$, where the value of y is a local minimum.

4. $y' = \frac{10}{3}x^{-1/3} - \frac{5}{3}x^{2/3}$
   $y'' = -\frac{10}{9}x^{-4/3} - \frac{10}{9}x^{-1/3}$
   $= -\frac{10}{9}x^{-4/3}(1 + x)$

5. At $x = 1$, $y'' = \frac{-20}{9} < 0$.

6. y'' is zero only when $x = -1$.

7. $y''(-2) = -\frac{10}{9} \cdot \sqrt[3]{16} \cdot -1 = \frac{20}{3}\sqrt[3]{2} > 0$
   Thus the graph is concave up at $x = -2$.

   $y''(-0.5) = -\frac{10}{9} \cdot \sqrt[3]{0.0625} \cdot 0.5 = -\frac{5}{18}\sqrt[3]{0.5} < 0$

   Thus the graph is concave down at $x = -0.5$.

8. Answers will vary.

Exploration 8-2b

1. The graph accounts for $h'(x)$ undefined at $x = 1$ with the open circles on the ends of the branches.

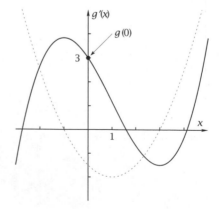

2. $h'(x)$ is not infinite at $x = 1$. The graph stays bounded on a neighborhood of 1.

3. h is continuous, but not differentiable, at $x = 1$.

4.

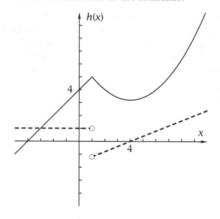

Calculus: Concepts and Applications Instructor's Resource Book
©2005 Key Curriculum Press

5.

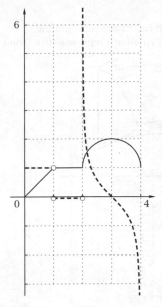

6. (Note that the graph is concave up for $2 < x < 3$ and concave down for $3 < x < 4$.)

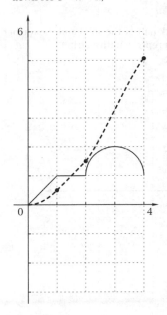

7. Answers will vary.

Exploration 8-3a

1. 20×20: 10 walls, 20 ft each $\Rightarrow$ $10 \cdot 20 = 200$ ft total
   10×40: 6 walls 10 ft each, 4 walls 40 ft each $\Rightarrow$
   $6 \cdot 10 + 4 \cdot 40 = 220$ ft total
   40×10: 6 walls 40 ft each, 4 walls 10 ft each $\Rightarrow$
   $6 \cdot 40 + 4 \cdot 10 = 280$ ft total

2.

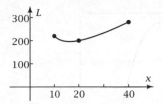

3. $L = 6x + 4y$
   $xy = 400 \Rightarrow y = \dfrac{400}{x}$
   $\therefore L = 6x + \dfrac{1600}{x}$

4.

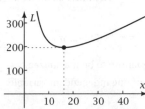

Minimum of $L = 195.9591...$ at $x = 16.3299...$

5. $L' = 6 - 1600x^{-2}$
   $L' = 0 \Leftrightarrow 6 = 1600x^{-2}$
   $6x^2 = 1600$
   $x = \pm16.3299...$ (But $-16.3299...$ is out of the domain.)
   For $x < 16.3299...$, L' is negative.
   For $x > 16.3299...$, L' is positive.
   $\therefore L$ is a minimum at $x = 16.3299...$, which agrees with Problem 4.

6. If $x = 16.3299...$, then $y = \dfrac{400}{16.3299...} = 24.4948....$

   (Note that for minimum wall length, $6x = 4y$, and there are 6 segments of length x and 4 segments of length y. This observation was pointed out by student James Guess [his real name!] in 2001.)
   Total breadth = $3(16.3299...) = 48.9897... \approx 49.0$ ft
   Total depth = $24.4948... \approx 24.5$ ft

7. Answers will vary.

Exploration 8-3b

1. $V = \pi r^2 h = \pi x^2 y$
   At $x = 0$, $y = 12$, $V = 0$ in.^{3}
   At $x = 1$, $y = 9$, $V = 9\pi$ in.^{3}
   At $x = 2$, $y = 6$, $V = 24\pi$ in.^{3}
   At $x = 3$, $y = 3$, $V = 27\pi$ in.^{3}
   At $x = 4$, $y = 0$, $V = 0$ in.^{3}

2. For the point (x, y) shown in the diagrams, $y = 12 - 3x$.
   So the radius of the inscribed cylinder is x, the altitude is $y = 12 - 3x$, and the volume is
   $V = \pi r^2 h = \pi x^2 (12 - 3x) = 12\pi x^2 - 3\pi x^3$.

3. $\dfrac{dV}{dx} = 24\pi x - 9\pi x^2$

4. $0 = 24\pi x - 9\pi x^2 = 9\pi x\left(\dfrac{24}{9} - x\right)$
   $\dfrac{dV}{dx} = 0$ at $x = 0$ and $x = \dfrac{24}{9} = \dfrac{8}{3}$.

5. $V = 12\pi x^2 - 3\pi x^3$:

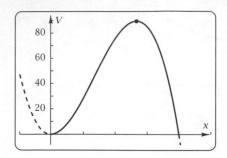

Maximum volume occurs at $x = \frac{8}{3}$. The other solution, $x = 0$, is a local minimum.

6. At $x = \frac{8}{3}$, $r = \frac{8}{3}$, $h = 4$, $V = \frac{256}{9}\pi = 28.4444\ldots \pi$ in.^{3}

7. • Find an equation for the quantity to be maximized.

• Get the equation in terms of one independent variable.

• Find the derivative.

• Find critical points where the derivative is zero (or undefined).

• Find out whether the critical points correspond to maximum or to minimum values.

• Answer the question that was asked.

8. Answers will vary.

Exploration 8-4a

1. The circumference is $2\pi x$, so
$dV - C \cdot h \cdot dx = 2\pi x \cdot y \cdot dx$.

2. $y = 4x - x^2$, so
$dV = 2\pi x \cdot (4x - x^2)\, dx = 8\pi x^2 - 2\pi x^3$.

3. $V = \int_{x=0}^{x=3} (8\pi x^2 - 2\pi x^3)\, dx$

$= \left(\frac{8}{3}\pi x^3 - \frac{1}{2}\pi x^4\right)\Big|_{x=0}^{x=3}$

$= 31.5\pi$

As x goes from 0 to 3, the shells generate the whole figure. The curve shown for negative values of x is just the *image* of the graph as it rotates, not the graph itself.

4. Slice the region parallel to the x-axis.
Pick a sample point (x, y) on the graph, within the slice. As the region rotates, the slice generates a cylindrical shell with radius y, altitude x, and thickness dy. Thus,
$dV = 2\pi y \cdot x \cdot dy$
Because $y = \ln x$, $x = e^y$. So,
$dV = 2\pi y e^y\, dy$

$V = \int_{y=1}^{y=2} 2\pi y e^y\, dy$

$= 46.4268\ldots$ (numerically)
(Exact answer is $2\pi e^2$, integrating by parts.)

5. Answers will vary.

Exploration 8-4b

1. Slicing horizontally makes the lengths of the strips a piecewise function of y, whereas slicing vertically makes the lengths a simple function of x.

2. $e^{0.4b} = 4 - b^2 \Rightarrow b \approx 1.48905\ldots$ (solving numerically close to $b = 1.5$)

3. (The graph shows the back half of the solid and the cylindrical shell formed by rotating a representative strip.)

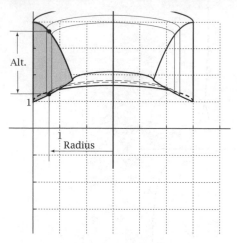

$dV = 2\pi(3 - x)((4 - x^2) - e^{0.4x})\, dx$

$V = 2\pi\int_0^b (3 - x)(4 - x^2 - e^{0.4x})\, dx$

$= 13.8409\ldots\pi = 43.4827\ldots$

4. (The graph shows the back half of the solid and the washer slice formed by rotating a representative strip.)

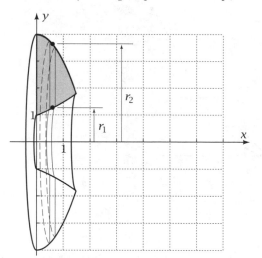

$dV = \pi\left(y_2^2 - y_1^2\right) dx$

$V = \pi\int [(4 - x^2)^2 - e^{0.8x}]\, dx$

$= 13.6211\ldots\pi = 42.7919\ldots$

5. The main difference is that with cylindrical shells you slice the rotated region *parallel* to the axis of rotation, rather than perpendicular as with washers.

6. Answers will vary.

Calculus: Concepts and Applications Instructor's Resource Book
©2005 Key Curriculum Press

Exploration 8-5a

1.

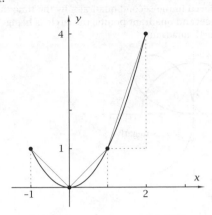

Distance $(-1, 1)$ to $(0, 0) = \sqrt{1^2 + 1^2} = \sqrt{2}$

Distance $(0, 0)$ to $(1, 1) = \sqrt{1^2 + 1^2} = \sqrt{2}$

Distance $(1, 1)$ to $(2, 4) = \sqrt{1^2 + 3^2} = \sqrt{10}$

Length of curve is about $2\sqrt{2} + \sqrt{10} = 5.9907....$

This method underestimates the length of the graph, because it fails to account for the curvature of the graph between the sample points.

2. Distance $(-1, 1)$ to $(-0.5, 0.25) = \sqrt{0.5^2 + 0.75^2} = \sqrt{0.8125}$

Distance $(-0.5, 0.25)$ to $(0, 0) = \sqrt{0.5^2 + 0.25^2} = \sqrt{0.3125}$

Distance $(0, 0)$ to $(0.5, 0.25) = \sqrt{0.5^2 + 0.25^2} = \sqrt{0.3125}$

Distance $(0.5, 0.25)$ to $(1, 1) = \sqrt{0.5^2 + 0.75^2} = \sqrt{0.8125}$

Distance $(1, 1)$ to $(1.5, 2.25) = \sqrt{0.5^2 + 1.25^2} = \sqrt{1.8125}$

Distance $(1.5, 2.25)$ to $(2, 4) = \sqrt{0.5^2 + 1.75^2} = \sqrt{3.3125}$

Length of curve is about $\sqrt{1.3125} + \sqrt{0.8125} + \sqrt{1.8125} + \sqrt{3.3125} = 6.0871....$

This estimate is better because the many shorter line segments better approximate the curve than the few long line segments.

3. The estimate gets better as Δx gets smaller, so to get the exact length, take the limit as $\Delta x \to 0$.

4. $\Delta L = \sqrt{\Delta x^2 + \Delta y^2} = \sqrt{1 + [\Delta y/\Delta x]^2}\ \Delta x$, but the mean value theorem states that for some c in the sample interval, $f'(c) = \Delta y/\Delta x$.

5. Because $\Delta x = dx$ and $\Delta y \approx dy = f'(x)\ dx$, dL can be written $dL = \sqrt{1 + [f'(x)]^2}\ dx = \sqrt{dx^2 + [f'(x)]^2\ dx^2} = \sqrt{dx^2 + dy^2}$, where dy is evaluated at the sample point $x = c$.

6. $y = x^2 \Rightarrow dy = 2x\ dx$

$dL = \sqrt{dx^2 + dy^2} = \sqrt{dx^2 + (2x\ dx)^2}$

$\quad = \sqrt{1 + 4x^2}\ dx$

$L = \int_{x=-1}^{x=2} dL = \int_{x=-1}^{x=2} \sqrt{1 + 4x^2}\ dx$

7. $L = 6.1257...$ (numerically)

$\left(\sqrt{17} + \frac{1}{4}\ln\left(\sqrt{17} + 4\right) + \frac{1}{2}\sqrt{5} - \frac{1}{4}\ln\left(\sqrt{5} - 2\right)\right.$ is exact.)

8. Answers will vary.

Exploration 8-6a

1. The graph shows a narrow slice whose surface resembles a frustum of a cone.

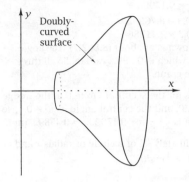

Rotate a curved graph,
get a doubly-curved surface.

2. The arc length of the base of the cone is $2\pi R$, so if you slit the cone down one side, and "unroll" it, the resulting section of a circle will have radius L and arc length $2\pi R$. A full circle of radius L would have arc length $2\pi L$ and area πL^2. But this section is only $\frac{2\pi R}{2\pi L}$ of a full circle, so it has area $\frac{2\pi R}{2\pi L} \cdot \pi L^2 = \pi RL$, Q.E.D.

3. First note that $\frac{r}{l} = \frac{R}{L}$ because of similar triangles, so $Rl - rL = 0$. Then, using Problem 2, the frustum has area

$A = \pi RL - \pi rl$

$\quad = \pi RL - \pi Rl + \pi Rl - \pi rL + \pi rL - \pi rl$

$\quad = \pi RL - \pi Rl + \pi(0) + \pi rL - \pi rl$

$\quad = \pi R(L - l) + \pi r(L - l)$

$\quad = \pi(R + r)(L - l)$

or: $A = \pi RL - \pi rl = \pi R\left(L - \frac{r}{R} \cdot l\right) = \pi R\left(L - \frac{l}{L} \cdot l\right)$

$\quad - \pi \frac{R}{L}(L^2 - l^2) = \pi\frac{R}{L}(L + l)(L - l)$

$\quad = \pi\left(R + R \cdot \frac{l}{L}\right)(L - l) = \pi\left(R + R \cdot \frac{r}{R}\right)(L - l)$

$\quad = \pi(R + r)(L - l)$

But the average radius is $\frac{1}{2}(R + r)$, the circumference at this radius is $\pi(R + r)$, and the slant height of the frustum is $(L - l)$, Q.E.D.

4. The slice is approximately a frustum of slant height dL and average radius y. So the surface area is about $2\pi y\ dL$.

5. $y = x^3 \Rightarrow dy = 3x^2\ dx$

$dL = \sqrt{dx^2 + dy^2} = \sqrt{1 + 9x^4}\ dx$

$dS = 2\pi y\ dL = 2\pi x^3\sqrt{1 + 9x^4}\ dx$

$S = \int_0^1 2\pi x^3\sqrt{1 + 9x^4}\ dx$

$\quad = \frac{1}{18}\pi \int_0^1 (1 + 9x^4)^{1/2}\ (36x^3\ dx)$

$\quad = \frac{1}{18}\pi \cdot \frac{2}{3}(1 + 9x^4)^{3/2}\Big|_0^1$

$\quad = \frac{\pi}{27}(10^{1.5} - 1)$

$\quad = 3.5631...$

6. Answers will vary.

Exploration 8-7a

1. The graph agrees with the given figure.

2. $r(0.3) = \dfrac{10}{3 - 2\cos 0.3} = 9.1799\ldots$

   $x(0.3) = r(0.3) \cdot \cos 0.3 = 8.7699\ldots$

   $y(0.3) = r(0.3) \cdot \sin 0.3 = 2.71286\ldots$

   The sample point shown is at about $(8.8, 2.7)$. The angle measures about $17°$, which is $0.296\ldots$ radian. So all three values agree with the graph.

3. At $\theta = 0.3$, the radius (of the sector of circle that the wedge approximates) is $r(0.3)$, and the central angle is $d\theta = 0.1$, so the approximate area is $\dfrac{0.1}{2\pi} \cdot \pi \cdot 9.1799\ldots^2 = 0.4589\ldots$ unit.

4. The sector is approximately $\dfrac{dq}{2\pi}$ of a circle of radius r and area πr^2, so $dA = \dfrac{dq}{2\pi} \cdot \pi r^2 = \dfrac{1}{2} r^2 \, d\theta$.

5. $A = \displaystyle\int_{\theta=0}^{\theta=2\pi} \dfrac{1}{2}\left(\dfrac{10}{3 - 2\cos\theta}\right)^2 d\theta$

   $= 84.2977\ldots$ (numerically)

6. The y-radius is approximately 4.5, so the area formula predicts that the area will be $\pi \cdot 6 \cdot 4.5 = 84.8230\ldots$. Close! ($y$-radius is exactly $6\sin(\cos^{-1}\frac{2}{3}) = 4.4721\ldots$, making the area $\pi \cdot 6 \cdot 4.4721\ldots = 84.2977\ldots$, which is precisely the numerical answer.)

7. Answers will vary.

Exploration 8-7b

1. The graph agrees with the given figure.

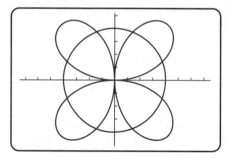

2. $6\sin 2\theta = 4$

   $\theta = 0.5\sin^{-1}(4/6)$

   $= 0.5(0.7297\ldots + 2\pi n)$ or $0.5(\pi - 0.7297\ldots + 2\pi n)$

   $= 0.3648\ldots$ or $1.2059\ldots$ in Quadrant I (Store as a and b.)

3. $dA = 0.5\left(r_2^2 - r_1^2\right) d\theta$

   $A = 0.5\displaystyle\int_a^b (36\sin^2 20 - 16)\, d\theta$

   $= 5.3132\ldots$ square units

4. Counting squares in the region gives about 5.3, thus confirming the answer.

5. $A = 0.5\displaystyle\int_0^{\pi/2} 36\sin^2\theta\, d\theta$

   $= 14.1371\ldots = 4.5\pi$, an interesting multiple of π.

6. $dL = \sqrt{(dr)^2 + (r\, d\theta)^2} = \sqrt{144\cos^2(2\theta) + 36\sin^2(2\theta)}\, d\theta$

   $L = \displaystyle\int_{\theta=0}^{\pi/2} dL = 14.5326\ldots$ units

   $14.5326\ldots/\pi = 4.6258\ldots$, so the answer is not an interesting multiple of π.

7. The graph shows that at an apparent intersection point in the second quadrant, r_1, is positive, but r_2 is negative, meaning that the rose is being traced in the fourth quadrant when the circle is being traced in the second quadrant. By the time the rose gets to the second quadrant points, the circle is being traced in the fourth quadrant.

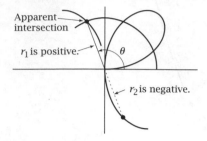

8. Answers will vary.

Exploration 8-7c

1. The graph agrees with the given figure.

2. $r(0.8) = 35.9554\ldots \approx 36.0$ thousand miles

3. $dA = \dfrac{1}{2}r^2\, d\theta = 3528(10 - 11\cos\theta)^{-2}\, d\theta$

   $A = \displaystyle\int_{0.8}^{5.5} 3528(10 - 11\cos\theta)^{-2}\, d\theta = 308.9953\ldots$

   ≈ 309 million square miles

4. $dL = \sqrt{(dr/d\theta)^2 + r^2}\, d\theta$

   $= \sqrt{[-84(10 - 11\cos\theta)^{-2}11\sin\theta]^2 + [84(10 - 11\cos\theta)^{-1}]^2}\, d\theta$

   $L = \displaystyle\int_{\theta=0.8}^{5.5} dL = 82.4852\ldots \approx 82.5$ thousand miles

5. Check: $r(0.8) \approx 36$ as the comet approaches Earth, and $r(5.5) = 38.1015\ldots \approx 38$ as the comet recedes from Earth. So the distance traveled on the curved path should be a bit greater than $36 + 38 = 72$ thousand miles. Thus the 82.5 thousand miles is reasonable.

6. Answers will vary.

Chapter 9

Exploration 9-3a

1. $\displaystyle\int x^2 \sin 3x\, dx$

u		dv
x^2	$+$	$\sin 3x$
$2x$	$-$	$-\frac{1}{3}\cos 3x$
2	$+$	$-\frac{1}{9}\sin 3x$
0	$-$	$\frac{1}{27}\cos 3x$

   $= -\dfrac{1}{3}x^2\cos 3x + \dfrac{2}{9}x\sin 3x + \dfrac{2}{27}\cos 3x + C$

Calculus: Concepts and Applications Instructor's Resource Book
©2005 Key Curriculum Press

2. $\int x^5 \ln 4x\, dx$

$$\begin{array}{cc} u & dv \\ \ln 4x \,\xrightarrow{\ +\ }\, & x^5 \\ x^{-1} \,\xrightarrow{\qquad}\, & \frac{1}{6}x^6 \\ \hline 1 & \frac{1}{6}x^5 \\ \xrightarrow{\ -\ } & \\ 0 \,\xleftarrow{\ +\ }\, & \frac{1}{36}x^6 \end{array}$$

$= \frac{1}{6}x^6 \ln 4x - \frac{1}{36}x^6 + C$

3. $\int e^{5x} \cos 6x\, dx$

$$\begin{array}{cc} u & dv \\ e^{5x} \,\xrightarrow{\ +\ }\, & \cos 6x \\ 5e^{5x} \,\xrightarrow{\ -\ }\, & \frac{1}{6}\sin 6x \\ 25e^{5x} \,\xrightarrow{\ +\ }\, & -\frac{1}{36}\cos 6x \end{array}$$

$= \frac{1}{6}e^{5x}\sin 6x + \frac{5}{36}e^{5x}\cos 6x - \frac{25}{36}\int e^{5x}\cos 6x\, dx$

$\frac{61}{36}\int e^{5x}\cos 6x\, dx = \frac{1}{6}e^{5x}\sin 6x + \frac{5}{36}e^{5x}\cos 6x + C$

$\int e^{5x}\cos 6x\, dx = \frac{6}{61}e^{5x}\sin 6x + \frac{5}{61}e^{5x}\cos 6x + C_1$

4. $\int x\,(\ln x)^3\, dx$

$$\begin{array}{cc} u & dv \\ (\ln x)^3 \,\xrightarrow{\ +\ }\, & x \\ 3(\ln x)^2 x^{-1} & \frac{1}{2}x^2 \\ \hline 3(\ln x)^2 \,\xrightarrow{\ -\ }\, & \frac{1}{2}x \\ 6(\ln x)\,x^{-1} & \frac{1}{4}x^2 \\ \hline 6\ln x \,\xrightarrow{\ +\ }\, & \frac{1}{4}x \\ 6x^{-1} & \frac{1}{8}x^2 \\ \hline 6 \,\xrightarrow{\ -\ }\, & \frac{1}{8}x \\ 0 \,\xleftarrow{\ +\ }\, & \frac{1}{16}x^2 \end{array}$$

$= \frac{1}{2}x^2\,(\ln x)^3 - \frac{3}{4}x^2\,(\ln x)^2 + \frac{3}{4}x^2 \ln x - \frac{3}{8}x^2 + C$

5. $\int \sin^{10} x\,(\cos x\, dx) = \frac{1}{11}\sin^{11} x + C$

6. $\int \sin^{10} x\, dx$

$$\begin{array}{cc} u & dv \\ \sin^9 x \,\xrightarrow{\ +\ }\, & \sin x \\ -9\sin^8 x\cos x \,\xrightarrow{\ -\ }\, & -\cos x \end{array}$$

$= -\sin^9 x\cos x + 9\int \sin^8 x\cos^2 x\, dx$

$= -\sin^9 x\cos x + 9\int \sin^8 x\,(1 - \sin^2 x)\, dx$

$= -\sin^9 x\cos x + 9\int \sin^8 x\, dx - 9\int \sin^{10} x\, dx$

$10\int \sin^{10} x\, dx = -\sin^9 x\cos x + 9\int \sin^8 x\, dx$

$\int \sin^{10} x\, dx = -\frac{1}{10}\sin^9 x\cos x + \frac{9}{10}\int \sin^8 x\, dx$

7. Answers will vary.

Exploration 9-4a

1. $\int \sin^{10} x\, dx$

$$\begin{array}{cc} u & dv \\ \sin^9 x \,\xrightarrow{\ +\ }\, & \sin x \\ -9\sin^8 x\cos x \,\xrightarrow{\ -\ }\, & -\cos x \end{array}$$

$= -\sin^9 x\cos x + 9\int \sin^8 x\cos^2 x\, dx$

$= -\sin^9 x\cos x + 9\int \sin^8 x\,(1 - \sin^2 x)\, dx$

$= -\sin^9 x\cos x + 9\int \sin^8 x\, dx - 9\int \sin^{10} x\, dx$

$10\int \sin^{10} x\, dx = -\sin^9 x\cos x + 9\int \sin^8 x\, dx$

$\int \sin^{10} x\, dx = -\frac{1}{10}\sin^9 x\cos x + \frac{9}{10}\int \sin^8 x\, dx$

2. $\int \sin^n x\, dx = -\frac{1}{n}\sin^{n-1} x\cos x + \frac{n-1}{n}\int \sin^{n-2} x\, dx$
   $(n \neq 0)$

3. $V = \int_0^\pi \pi(\sin^3 x)^2\, dx$

   $= \pi \int_0^\pi \sin^6 x\, dx$

   $= 3.0842\ldots$ (numerically)

4. $V = \int_0^\pi \pi\,(\sin^3 x)^2\, dx$

   $= \pi \int_0^\pi \sin^6 x\, dx$

$\int \sin^6 x\, dx = -\frac{1}{6}\sin^5 x\cos x + \frac{5}{6}\int \sin^4 x\, dx$

$= -\frac{1}{6}\sin^5 x\cos x + \frac{5}{6}\left(-\frac{1}{4}\sin^3 x\cos x + \frac{3}{4}\int \sin^2 x\, dx\right)$

$= -\frac{1}{6}\sin^5 x\cos x - \frac{5}{24}\sin^3 x\cos x$

$\quad + \frac{15}{24}\left(-\frac{1}{2}\sin x\cos x + \frac{1}{2}x\right) + C$

$= -\frac{1}{6}\sin^5 x\cos x - \frac{5}{24}\sin^3 x\cos x$

$\quad - \frac{5}{16}\sin x\cos x + \frac{5}{16}x + C$

$V = \pi\left(-\frac{1}{6}\sin^5 x\cos x - \frac{5}{24}\sin^3 x\cos x\right.$

$\quad \left.\left.- \frac{5}{16}\sin x\cos x + \frac{5}{16}x\right)\right|_0^\pi$

$= \pi\left(0 - 0 - 0 + \frac{5}{16}\pi + 0 + 0 + 0 + 0\right)$

$= \frac{5}{16}\pi^2 = 3.0842\ldots$, which agrees with Problem 3.

5. Answers will vary.

Exploration 9-5a

1. $\int \cos^7 x\,(\sin x\, dx) = \frac{1}{8}\cos^8 x + C$

2. The differential $\sin x\, dx$ of $\cos x$ does not appear in the integrand.

3. $\int \cos^7 x\, dx = \int (\cos^2 x)^3 \cos x\, dx$

   $= \int (1 - \sin^2 x)^3 \cos x\, dx$

   $= \int (1 - 3\sin^2 x + 3\sin^4 x - \sin^6 x)\cos x\, dx$

   $= \int \cos x\, dx - 3\int \sin^2 x\cos x\, dx$

   $\quad + 3\int \sin^4 x\cos x\, dx - \int \sin^6 x\cos x\, dx$

   $= \sin x - \sin^3 x + \frac{3}{5}\sin^5 x - \frac{1}{7}\sin^7 x + C$

4. The power of cos x is even, so converting to powers of $(1 - \sin^2 x)$ leaves no cos $x\,dx$ to be the differential of sin x.

5. $\int \tan^5 x (\sec^2 x \, dx) = \frac{1}{6} \tan^6 x + C$

6. The differential sec x tan $x\,dx$ of sec x does not appear in the integrand.

7. $\int \sec^8 x \, dx = \int (\sec^2 x)^3 \sec^2 x \, dx$

$= \int (\tan^2 x + 1)^3 \sec^2 x \, dx$

$= \int (\tan^6 x + 3 \tan^4 x + 3 \tan^2 x + 1) \sec^2 x \, dx$

$= \int \tan^6 x \sec^2 x \, dx + 3 \int \tan^4 x \sec^2 x \, dx$

$\quad + 3 \int \tan^2 x \sec^2 x \, dx + \int \sec^2 x \, dx$

$= \frac{1}{7} \tan^7 x + \frac{3}{5} \tan^5 x + \tan^3 x + \tan x + C$

8. The power of sec x is odd, so converting to powers of $(\tan^2 x + 1)$ does not leave sec^2 $x\,dx$ to be the differential of tan x.

9. Answers will vary.

Exploration 9-5b

1. cos $2x$ = cos $(x + x)$ = cos^2 x − sin^2 x

2. cos $2x$ = cos^2 x − sin^2 x
$= \cos^2 x - (1 - \cos^2 x)$
$= 2 \cos^2 x - 1$

3. cos $2x$ = cos^2 x − sin^2 x
$= (1 - \sin^2 x) - \sin^2 x$
$= 1 - 2 \sin^2 x$

4. $\cos 2x = 2 \cos^2 x - 1$
$\cos^2 x = \frac{1}{2}(1 + \cos 2x)$
$\cos 2x = 1 - 2 \sin^2 x$
$\sin^2 x = \frac{1}{2}(1 - \cos 2x)$

5. $\int \cos^2 x \, dx = \int \left(\frac{1}{2} + \frac{1}{2} \cos 2x \right) dx$
$= \frac{1}{2}x + \frac{1}{4} \sin 2x + C$
$\int \sin^2 x \, dx = \int \left(\frac{1}{2} - \frac{1}{2} \cos 2x \right) dx$
$= \frac{1}{2}x - \frac{1}{4} \sin 2x + C$

6. $\int \cos 7x \sin 5x \, dx$

u		dv
cos $7x$	$+$	sin $5x$
−7 sin $7x$	$-$	$-\frac{1}{5} \cos 5x$
−49 cos $7x$	$+$	$-\frac{1}{25} \sin 5x$

$= -\frac{1}{5} \cos 7x \cos 5x - \frac{7}{25} \sin 7x \sin 5x + \frac{49}{25} \int \cos 7x \sin 5x \, dx$

$-\frac{24}{25} \int \cos 7x \sin 5x \, dx$

$= -\frac{1}{5} \cos 7x \cos 5x - \frac{7}{25} \sin 7x \sin 5x + C \int \cos 7x \sin 5x \, dx$

$= \frac{5}{24} \cos 7x \cos 5x + \frac{7}{24} \sin 7x \sin 5x + C_1$

7. $\int \cos ax \sin bx \, dx$

$= \frac{a}{a^2 - b^2} \sin ax \sin bx + \frac{a}{a^2 - b^2} \cos ax \cos bx + C$

8. Answers will vary.

Exploration 9-6a

1. $A = 2 \int_{-2}^{7} \sqrt{64 - x^2} \, dx = 126.9622\ldots$ (numerically)

2. The differential $2x\,dx$ of the "inside function" $64 - x^2$ does not appear in the integrand, so the integral cannot be done as the antiderivative of a power.

3. $\frac{x}{8} = \sin \theta \Rightarrow x = 8 \sin \theta$
$dx = 8 \cos \theta \, d\theta$
By the Pythagorean theorem, the horizontal leg of the right triangle is $\sqrt{64 - x^2}$.
Thus, $8 \cos \theta = \sqrt{64 - x^2}$.
$\therefore \int \sqrt{64 - x^2} \, dx = \int (8 \cos \theta) \cdot 8 \cos \theta \, d\theta$
$= 64 \int \cos^2 \theta \, d\theta$

4. $64 \int \cos^2 \theta \, d\theta = 32 \int (1 + \cos 2\theta) \, d\theta$
$= 32\theta + 16 \sin 2\theta + C$

5. $64 \int \cos^2 \theta \, d\theta = 32\theta + 16(2 \sin \theta \cos \theta) + C$
$= 32 \sin^{-1} \frac{x}{8} + 32 \cdot \frac{x}{8} \cdot \frac{\sqrt{64 - x^2}}{8} + C$
$= 32 \sin^{-1} \frac{x}{8} + \frac{1}{2}x\sqrt{64 - x^2} + C$

6. $A = 2 \int_{-2}^{7} \sqrt{64 - x^2} \, dx = \left(64 \sin^{-1} \frac{x}{8} + x\sqrt{64 - x^2} \right) \Big|_{-2}^{7}$
$= 64 \sin^{-1} \frac{7}{8} + 7\sqrt{15} - 64 \sin^{-1} \frac{-1}{4} + 2\sqrt{60}$
$= 126.9622\ldots,$
which agrees with the answer found numerically in Problem 1.

7. Answers will vary.

Exploration 9-7a

1. $\frac{A}{x - 5} + \frac{B}{x + 1} = \frac{10x - 32}{(x - 5)(x + 1)}$
$\Rightarrow A(x + 1) + B(x - 5) = 10x - 32$
$\Rightarrow A + B = 10, A - 5B = -32$
$\Rightarrow A = 3, B = 7$

2. $\int \frac{10x - 32}{(x - 5)(x + 1)} \, dx = \int \frac{3}{x - 5} \, dx + \int \frac{7}{x + 1} \, dx$
$= 3 \ln |x - 5| + 7 \ln |x + 1| + C$

3. (Instructor input on Heaviside method.)

4. See Section 9-7 for reasons behind the Heaviside method.

5. $x^3 - 2x^2 - 5x + 6 = (x - 1)(x + 2)(x - 3)$
$\int \frac{11x^2 - 22x - 13}{(x - 1)(x + 2)(x - 3)} \, dx$
$= \int \frac{4}{x - 1} \, dx + \int \frac{5}{x + 2} \, dx + \int \frac{2}{x - 3} \, dx$
$= 4 \ln |x - 1| + 5 \ln |x + 2| + 2 \ln |x - 3| + C$

6. Answers will vary.

Exploration 9-8a

1. In the first form, dv would equal sin^{-1} $x\,dx$, and you don't know how to do this integration. In the second form, $dv = 1$ dx, which you can integrate.

2.

$$\begin{array}{ccc} u & & dv \\ \sin^{-1}x & \searrow\; + & dx \\ (1-x^2)^{-1/2} & \longleftarrow\; - & x \end{array}$$

$$I = x\sin^{-1}x - \int (1-x^2)^{-1/2}\, x\, dx$$

$$= x\sin^{-1}x + \frac{1}{2}\int (1-x^2)^{-1/2}\,(-2x\,dx)$$

$$= x\sin^{-1}x + \frac{1}{2}\cdot\frac{2}{1}(1-x^2)^{1/2} + C$$

$$= x\sin^{-1}x + \sqrt{1-x^2} = C$$

which agrees with the text.

3.

$$\begin{array}{ccc} u & & dv \\ \sin^{-1}x & \searrow\; + & dx \\ \dfrac{1}{|x|(x^2-1)^{1/2}} & \longleftarrow\; - & x \end{array}$$

$$I = x\sec^{-1}x - \int \frac{x}{|x|(x^2-1)^{1/2}}\, dx$$

For $x > 0$,

$$I = x\sec^{-1}x - \int \frac{1}{(x^2-1)^{1/2}}\, dx$$

Let $I_1 = \int \dfrac{1}{(x^2-1)^{1/2}}\, dx.$

Let $x = \sec\theta.$
$\therefore\; dx = \sec\theta\tan\theta\, d\theta$ and
$(x^2-1)^{1/2} = \tan\theta.$

$$I_1 = \int \frac{\sec q\tan q\, dq}{\tan q} = \int \sec\theta\, d\theta$$

$$= \ln|\sec\theta + \tan\theta| + C$$

$$= \ln|x + (x^2-1)^{1/2}| + C$$

$\therefore\; I = x\sec^{-1}x - \ln|x + (x^2-1)^{1/2}| + C,$
which agrees, for $x > 0$, with the text's
$x\sec^{-1}x - \operatorname{sgn}x\ln|x + \sqrt{x^2-1}| + C.$

4. Answers will vary.

Exploration 9-9a

1. u and v are asymptotic to y_3.

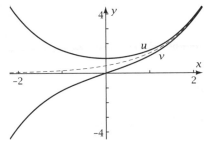

2. $u' = \dfrac{1}{2}(e^x - e^{-x}) = v \qquad \cos'x = -\sin x$

$u'' = \dfrac{1}{2}(e^x + e^{-x}) = u \qquad \cos''x = -\cos x$

$u''' = \dfrac{1}{2}(e^x - e^{-x}) = v \qquad \cos'''x = \sin x$

$u^{(4)} = \dfrac{1}{2}(e^x + e^{-x}) = u \qquad \cos^{(4)}x = \cos x$

The u and v derivatives follow the same pattern, but without any minus signs.

3. $u^2 = \dfrac{1}{4}(e^{2x} + 2 + e^{-2x})$

$v^2 = \dfrac{1}{4}(e^{2x} - 2 + e^{-2x})$

$u^2 - v^2 = \dfrac{1}{4}(4)$

$u^2 - v^2 = 1$

4. $u(1.3) = 1.9709..., \; v(1.3) = 1.6903...$

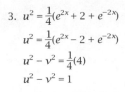

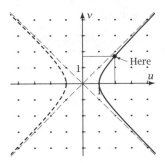

5. u is always positive. The extraneous negative branch arises from squaring in Problem 3.

6. $\cos 1.3 = 0.2674..., \; \sin 1.3 = 0.9635...$

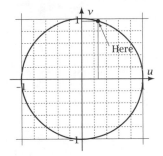

7. The coordinates u and v defined here have the same relationship to a unit hyperbola as $u = \cos x$ and $v = \sin x$ have to a unit circle, hence the names *circular functions* and *hyperbolic functions*.

8. Answers will vary.

Exploration 9-9b

1. (The following is simulated data, agreeing with the figure shown in the Exploration. Actual data will depend on the chain used.)
Vertex: $(0, 20)$
Left end: $(-90, 120)$, Right end: $(90, 120)$

2. $y = k\cosh\dfrac{1}{k}x + C$
$20 = k\cosh 0 + C \Rightarrow 20 = k + C$
$120 = k\cosh\dfrac{90}{k} + C$
Substitute $20 - k$ for C.
$120 = k\cosh\dfrac{90}{k} + 20 - k$
$0 = k\cosh\dfrac{90}{k} - 100 - k$
Solving numerically gives $k = 51.7801....$
$C = 20 - 51.7801... = -31.7801...$
Equation is
$y = 51.7801...\cosh\dfrac{1}{51.7801...}x - 31.7801...$

3. A typical medium-weight tow chain weighs about 0.015 lb/cm, which is the value of w.
$h = (51.7801...)(0.015) \approx 0.8$ lb

4.

x	y
0	20
20	23.9
40	36.2
60	58.8
80	95.1

5. The chain fits closely the data points.

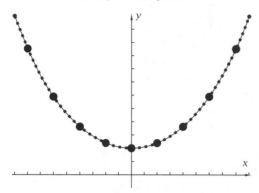

6. $dL = \sqrt{dx^2 + dy^2}$

$= \sqrt{1 + \sinh^2 \frac{1}{k}x}\; dx$

$L = \int_{-90}^{90} dL = 285.3490\ldots \approx 285$ cm

The measured length should be close to this.

7. See the text derivation.

8. Answers will vary.

Exploration 9-10a

1. For Calvin, $v(t) = 320(t+4)^{-1}$, so distance $d(t)$ is
$d(t) = \int 320(t+4)^{-1}\, dt = 320 \ln (t+4) + C$ for $t \geq 0$.
$d(0) = 0 \Rightarrow C = -320 \ln 4$
$d(t) = 320(\ln (t+4) - \ln 4)$
$d(10) = 320(\ln 14 - \ln 4) = 400.8841\ldots \approx 401$ ft
$d(20) = 320(\ln 24 - \ln 4) = 573.3630\ldots \approx 573$ ft
$d(50) = 320(\ln 54 - \ln 4) = 832.8606\ldots \approx 833$ ft

2. $d(b) = 320(\ln (b+4) - \ln 4)$ for $b \geq 0$
$1000 = 320(\ln (b+4) - \ln 4)$
$b = 87.0395\ldots \approx 87$ s
(Exactly $4(e^{3.125} - 1)$)

3. For Phoebe, $v(t) = 80e^{-0.1t}$, so distance $d(t)$ is
$d(t) = \int 80e^{-0.1t}\, dt = -800e^{-0.1t} + C$.
$d(0) = 0 \Rightarrow C = 800$
$d(t) = -800e^{-0.1t} + 800 = 800(1 - e^{-0.1t})$
$d(10) = 800(1 - e^{-1}) = 505.6964\ldots \approx 506$ ft
$d(20) = 800(1 - e^{-2}) = 691.7317\ldots \approx 692$ ft
$d(50) = 800(1 - e^{-3}) = 794.6096\ldots \approx 795$ ft

4. $d(b) = 800(1 - e^{-0.1b})$
$1000 = 800(1 - e^{-0.1b})$
$1.25 = 1 - e^{-0.1b}$
$e^{-0.1b} = -0.25$, which is impossible.
Phoebe never reaches 1000 ft!

5. $\lim_{b \to \infty} 800(1 - e^{-0.1b}) = 800 - 800 \lim_{b \to \infty} e^{-0.1b} = 800$
$\lim_{b \to \infty} 320(\ln (b+4) - \ln 4) = \infty$, since $\ln x$ is unbounded.

6. It is a seeming paradox that the velocity remains positive but the distance approaches a limit! The Greeks, including Zeno of Elea (ca. 490–430 B.C.E.), wrestled with such paradoxes. It was the invention of calculus that allowed people to find out what happens in such situations.

7. Answers will vary.

Exploration 9-11a

1. $\int \tan^5 4x\, dx = \int (\tan^3 4x)(\sec^2 4x - 1)\, dx$

$= \frac{1}{16} \tan^4 4x - \int (\tan^3 4x)\, dx$

$= \frac{1}{16} \tan^4 4x - \int (\tan 4x)(\sec^2 4x - 1)\, dx$

$= \frac{1}{16} \tan^4 4x - \frac{1}{8} \tan^2 4x + \int \tan 4x\, dx$

$= \frac{1}{16} \tan^4 4x - \frac{1}{8} \tan^2 4x + \frac{1}{4} \ln |\sec 4x| + C$

2. $\int \sqrt{1 + t^2}\, dt$
Let $t/1 = \tan \theta$.
Thus $dt = \sec \theta\, d\theta$ and $\sqrt{1 + t^2} = \sec \theta$.

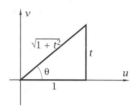

$\int \sqrt{1 + t^2}\, dt$

$= \int \sec \theta \sec^2 \theta\, d\theta = \int \sec^3 \theta\, d\theta$

$= \frac{1}{2} \sec \theta \tan \theta + \frac{1}{2} \ln |\sec \theta + \tan \theta| + C$

$= \frac{1}{2} t \sqrt{1 + t^2} + \frac{1}{2} \ln |\sqrt{1 + t^2} + t| + C$

3. $\int \tanh x\, dx = \ln (\cosh x) + C$

4. $\int x^3 e^{-x}\, dx$

u		dv
x^3	$+$	e^{-x}
$3x^2$	$-$	$-e^{-x}$
$6x$	$+$	e^{-x}
6	$-$	$-e^{-x}$
0	$+$	e^{-x}

$= -e^{-x}(x^3 + 3x^2 + 6x + 6) + C$

$\int_1^\infty x^3 e^{-x}\, dx = \lim_{b \to \infty} \int_1^b x^3 e^{-x}\, dx$

$= \lim_{b \to \infty} (-e^{-b}(b^3 + 3b^2 + 6b + 6) + 6)$

$\lim_{b \to \infty} e^{-b} b^3 = \lim_{b \to \infty} \frac{b^3}{e^b} \to \frac{\infty}{\infty}$

$= \lim_{b \to \infty} \frac{3b^2}{e^b} \to \frac{\infty}{\infty}$

$= \lim_{b \to \infty} \frac{6b}{e^b} \to \frac{\infty}{\infty}$

$= \lim_{b \to \infty} \frac{6}{e^b} \to \frac{6}{\infty}$

$= 0$

Similarly, each power of b multiplied by e^{-b} approaches zero as b approaches infinity.

$\therefore \int_1^\infty x^3 e^{-x}\, dx = 0 + 0 + 0 + 0 + 6 = 6$

5. $\int \dfrac{x}{(x-2)(x-3)(x-4)}\,dx$

$= \int \dfrac{1}{x-2}\,dx + \int \dfrac{-3}{x-3}\,dx + \int \dfrac{2}{x-4}\,dx$

$= \ln|x-2| - 3\ln|x-3| + 2\ln|x-4| + C$

6. $\int \sin^5 x\,dx = \int (1-\cos^2 x)^2 \sin x\,dx$

$\qquad = \int (1 - 2\cos^2 x + \cos^4 x)\sin x\,dx$

$\qquad = -\cos x + \dfrac{2}{3}\cos^3 x - \dfrac{1}{5}\cos^5 x + C$

7. $\int (x^4 + 2)^3\,dx = \int (x^{12} + 6x^8 + 12x^4 + 8)\,dx$

$\qquad = \dfrac{1}{13}x^{13} + \dfrac{2}{3}x^9 + \dfrac{12}{5}x^5 + 8x + C$

8. $\int x^2\,e^{x^3}\,dx = \dfrac{1}{3}\int e^{x^3}(3x^2\,dx) = \dfrac{1}{3}e^{x^3} + C$

9. $\int e^{ax} \cos bx\,dx$

$$
\begin{array}{ccc}
u & & dv \\
e^{ax} & \overset{+}{\searrow} & \cos bx \\
ae^{ax} & \overset{-}{\searrow} & \frac{1}{b}\sin bx \\
a^2 e^{ax} & \overset{+}{\longleftarrow} & -\frac{1}{b^2}\cos bx
\end{array}
$$

$= \dfrac{1}{b}e^{ax}\sin bx + \dfrac{a}{b^2}e^{ax}\cos bx - \dfrac{a^2}{b^2}\int e^{ax}\cos bx\,dx$

$\dfrac{a^2+b^2}{b^2}\int e^{ax}\cos bx\,dx$

$= \dfrac{1}{b}e^{ax}\sin bx + \dfrac{a}{b^2}e^{ax}\cos bx + C$

$\int e^{ax}\cos bx\,dx$

$= \dfrac{b}{a^2+b^2}e^{ax}\sin bx + \dfrac{a}{a^2+b^2}e^{ax}\cos bx + C_1$

10. $\int \sin^{-1} ax\,dx = x\sin^{-1} ax - \int \dfrac{ax}{\sqrt{1-(ax)^2}}\,dx$

$= x\sin^{-1} ax + \dfrac{1}{a}\sqrt{1-(ax)^2} + C$ $\hfill (a \neq 0)$

$\int \sin^{-1} ax\,dx = 0 + C$ $\hfill (a = 0)$

11. Answers will vary.

Chapter 10

Exploration 10-2a

1. Assume the average acceleration for the first time interval is
$a \approx \dfrac{1}{2}(5 + 12) = 8.5$.
If the initial velocity is $v = 3$, then the velocity at the end of the first time interval is
$v = 3 + 8.5(10) = 88$ m/s at $t = 10$.

2.
t	a	v
0	5	3
10	12	88
20	11	203
30	−4	238
40	−13	153
50	−20	−12
60	0	−112

3. Assume the average velocity for the first time interval is
$v = \dfrac{1}{2}(3 + 88) = 45.5$.
If the initial displacement is $d = 0$, then the displacement at the end of the first time interval is $d = 0 + 45.5(10) = 455$ m
at $t = 10$.

4.
t	a	v	d
0	5	3	0
10	12	88	455
20	11	203	1910
30	−4	238	4115
40	−13	153	6070
50	−20	−12	6775
60	0	−112	6155

5. The fact that v changes sign somewhere between $t = 0$ and $t = 60$ shows that the object stops and begins going backward.

6. The object did not go back beyond its starting point since the displacement at $t = 60$ is 6155 m, which is still positive.

7. Answers will vary.

Exploration 10-3a

1. $v(1) = 6 - 0.3 = 5.7$
$v(17) = 6 \cdot 17 - 0.3 \cdot 289 = 15.3$
Both (1, 5.7) and (17, 15.3) appear to lie on the graph.

2. Displacement $= \displaystyle\int_1^{17} (6t - 0.3t^2)\,dt = (3t^2 - 0.1x^3)\Big|_1^{17}$

$\qquad = 372.8$ ft

3. Average velocity $= \dfrac{372.8 \text{ ft}}{17 - 1 \text{ s}} = 23.3$ ft/s

4. No. $\dfrac{1}{2}[v(1) + v(17)] = 10.5$, not 23.3.

5.

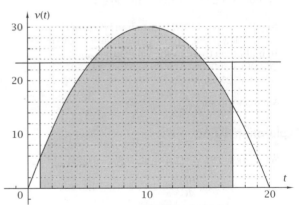

6. See the graph in Problem 5, showing that the area of the rectangle equals the area of the shaded region.

7. The shaded area above the rectangle equals the unshaded region within the rectangle.

8. There are about 26 squares under the curve for $0 \le t \le 10$, so the displacement is about 26 units, and the average velocity is $\dfrac{\text{total disp.}}{\text{time}} = \dfrac{26}{10} = 2.6$.
(The equation is $v(t) = 6e^{-0.2t}$, so the area is 25.9399..., and the average is 2.5939....)

9. Answers will vary.

Exploration 10-4a

1. Length of road through clearing = $3000 - x$
   Cost of road through clearing = $20 \cdot (3000 - x)$
   Length of road through woods = $\sqrt{1000^2 + x^2}$
   Cost of road through woods = $30 \cdot \sqrt{1000^2 + x^2}$
   Total cost = $C(x) = 60000 - 20x + 30\sqrt{1000^2 + x^2}$

2.

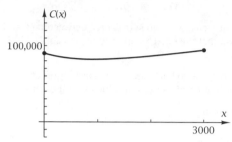

3. Cost appears to be a minimum around $x = 900$.

4. $C'(x) = -20 + 30x \cdot (1000^2 + x^2)^{-1/2}$
   $0 = C'(x) = -20 + 30x \cdot (1000^2 + x^2)^{-1/2}$
   $\Rightarrow 1.5x = \sqrt{1000^2 + x^2}$
   $\Rightarrow 2.25x^2 = 1000^2 + x^2$
   $\Rightarrow x = \dfrac{1000}{\sqrt{1.25}} = 894.4271... \approx 894$ ft
   At this point the derivative goes from negative to positive, so the graph stops decreasing and starts increasing.

5. Minimum cost of the road is
   $C(1000/\sqrt{1.25}) = 60,000 + 10,000\sqrt{5}$
   $= \$82,360.68$.
   To build to the closest point on the edge of the woods:
   $C(0) = \$90,000.00$, $\$7639.32$ more (about 9.3% more).
   To build directly from the gate to the cabin:
   $C(3000) = 30000\sqrt{10} = \$94,868.33$, $\$12,507.65$ more (about 15.2% more).

6. Answers will vary.

Exploration 10-6a

1. $\dfrac{dx}{dt} = -4 \sin 0.8t$, $\dfrac{dx}{dt}(1) = -4 \sin 0.8 = -2.8694...$

   $\dfrac{dy}{dt} = 2.4 \cos 0.8t$, $\dfrac{dy}{dt}(1) = 2.4 \cos 0.8 = 1.6720...$

2. The graph shows dx/dt and dy/dt as dotted vectors originating on the path of the pendulum.

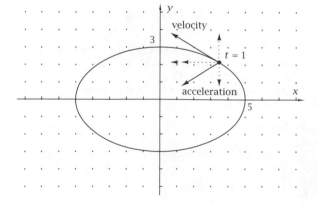

3. See the graph in Problem 2.
   The vector sum, $-2.8694... \, \vec{i} + 1.6720... \, \vec{j}$, is tangent to the graph at $t = 1$ and points in the direction of motion of the pendulum.

4. Speed = $|\vec{v}(1)| = \sqrt{2.8694...^2 + 1.6720...^2} = 3.3210...$
   Assuming that x and y are in feet, the velocity is about 3.32 ft/s.

5. $\dfrac{d^2x}{dt^2} = -3.2 \cos 0.8t$, $\dfrac{d^2x}{dt^2}(1) = -3.2 \cos 0.8 = -2.2294...$

   $\dfrac{d^2y}{dt^2} = -1.92 \sin 0.8t$, $\dfrac{d^2y}{dt^2}(1) = -1.92 \sin 0.8 = -1.3773...$

   See the graph in Problem 2, showing the second-derivative vectors in the x- and y-directions, and the resultant acceleration vector.

6. $\vec{a}(1) = -2.2294... \, \vec{i} - 1.3773... \, \vec{j}$
   The angle between $\vec{a}(1)$ and $\vec{v}(1)$ is smaller than 90°, so the acceleration has a component in the same direction of the velocity vector. Thus the speed is increasing.

7. Speed = $\sqrt{(dx/dt)^2 + (dy/dt)^2}$

   $\dfrac{d\text{Speed}}{dt} = \dfrac{\frac{d}{dt}[(dx/dt)^2 + (dy/dt)^2]}{2\sqrt{(dx/dt)^2 + (dy/dt)^2}}$

   $= \dfrac{\frac{dx}{dt} \cdot \frac{d^2x}{dt^2} + \frac{dy}{dt} \cdot \frac{d^2y}{dt^2}}{\sqrt{(dx/dt)^2 + (dy/dt)^2}}$

   $\dfrac{d\text{Speed}}{dt}(1)$

   $= \dfrac{(-2.8694...)(-2.2294...) + (1.6720...)(-1.3773...)}{3.3210...}$
   $= 1.2328...$ (ft/s)/s
   (See Example 2 in Section 10-6 for a way to do this problem using the vector projection of the acceleration vector onto the velocity vector.)

8. Answers will vary.

Exploration 10-6b

1. At $t = 0.5$: $5 \sin 0.5 = 2.3971...$, $5 \cos^2 0.5 = 3.8507...$
   At $t = 1$: $5 \sin 1 = 4.2073...$, $5 \cos^2 1 = 1.4596...$
   Both points $(2.3971..., 3.8507...)$ and $(4.2073..., 1.4596...)$ are on the graph.

2. The graph shows the position vectors at $t = 0.5$ and at $t = 1$.

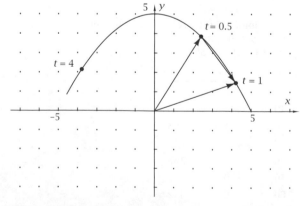

3. $\Delta \vec{r} = 1.8102... \, \vec{i} - 2.3911... \, \vec{j}$
   See the graph in Problem 2, showing that the head of $\Delta \vec{r}$ is at the head of $\vec{r}(1)$.

4. $\vec{v}_{av}[0.5, 1]$

$= \dfrac{5(\sin 1 - \sin 0.5)\vec{i} + 5(\cos^2 1 - \cos^2 0.5)\vec{j}}{0.5}$

$= 3.6204...\vec{i} - 4.8722...\vec{j}$

$\vec{v}_{av}[0.5, 0.6]$

$= \dfrac{5(\sin 0.6 - \sin 0.5)\vec{i} + 5(\cos^2 0.6 - \cos^2 0.5)\vec{j}}{0.1}$

$= 4.2608...\vec{i} - 4.4486...\vec{j}$

The graph shows the average velocity vectors from $t = 0.5$ to $t = 1$ and from $t = 0.5$ to $t = 0.6$.

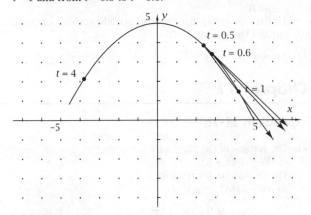

5. $\vec{v}(t) = 5\cos t\,\vec{i} - 10\cos t\sin t\,\vec{j}$

$\quad = 5\cos t\,\vec{i} - 5\sin 2t\,\vec{j}$

$\vec{v}(0.5) = 5\cos 0.5\,\vec{i} - 5\sin 1\,\vec{j}$

$\quad = 4.3879...\vec{i} - 4.2073...\vec{j}$

See the graph in Problem 4, showing $\vec{v}(0.5)$. The average velocity vectors seem to approach $\vec{v}(0.5)$ as a limit.

6. Speed $= |\vec{v}(0.5)| = 5\sqrt{\cos^2 0.5 + \sin^2 1}$

$\quad = 6.0791... \approx 6.1...$ ft/s

7. $\vec{v}(t) = 5\cos t\,\vec{i} - 5\sin 2t\,\vec{j}$

$\vec{a}(t) = -5\sin t\,\vec{i} - 10\cos 2t\,\vec{j}$

8. $\vec{r}(4) = -3.7840...\vec{i} + 2.1362...\vec{j}$

$\vec{v}(4) = -3.2682...\vec{i} - 4.9467...\vec{j}$

$\vec{a}(4) = 3.7840...\vec{i} + 1.4550...\vec{j}$

The graph shows the velocity and acceleration vectors.

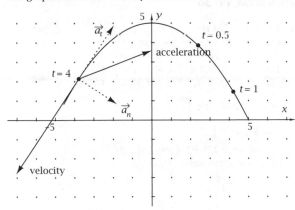

9. Speed $= |\vec{v}(4)| = 5\sqrt{\cos^2 4 + \sin^2 8} = 5.9289...$

$\quad \approx 5.9$ ft/s

10. $\vec{a}_t(4) = \dfrac{\vec{v}(4) \cdot \vec{a}(4)}{|\vec{v}(4)|} \dfrac{1}{|\vec{v}(4)|} \vec{v}(4)$

$= \dfrac{-25\sin 4\cos 4 + 50\sin 8\cos 8}{25(\cos^2 4 + \sin^2 8)} \cdot (5\cos 4\,\vec{i} - 5\sin 8\,\vec{j})$

$= 1.8189...\vec{i} + 2.7532...\vec{j}$

See the graph in Problem 8, showing the tangential component of the acceleration vector.

11. The object is slowing down.

Reasons: (1) The angle between $\vec{a}(4)$ and $\vec{v}(4)$ is larger than 90°.

(2) The dot product $\vec{v}(4) \cdot \vec{a}(4) = -19.5645...$, which is negative.

(3) $\vec{a}_t(4)$ points in the opposite direction of $\vec{v}(4)$.

The object is slowing down at $|\vec{a}_t(4)| = 3.2998...$

≈ 3.3 (ft/s)/s.

12. $\vec{a}_n(4) = \vec{a}(4) - \vec{a}_t(4) = 1.9650...\vec{i} - 1.2982...\vec{j}$

See the graph in Problem 8, showing the normal component of the acceleration vector.

13. $\vec{a}_n(4)$ points toward the concave side of the path. This component pulls the object out of a straight-line path into the curved path.

14. Answers will vary.

Exploration 10-6c

1. The grapher graph agrees with the figure.

2. $\vec{r}(t) = (6\cos 0.5t - \cos 3t)\vec{i} + (6\sin 0.5t + \sin 3t)\vec{j}$

$\vec{v}(t) = (-3\sin 0.5t + 3\sin 3t)\vec{i} + (3\cos 0.5t + 3\cos 3t)\vec{j}$

$\vec{a}(t) = (-1.5\cos 0.5t + 9\cos 3t)\vec{i} + (-1.5\sin 0.5t - 9\sin 3t)\vec{j}$

3. $\vec{v}(2) = (-3\sin 1 + 3\sin 6)\vec{i} + (3\cos 1 + 3\cos 6)\vec{j}$

$\approx -3.36\vec{i} + 4.50\vec{j}$

$\vec{a}(2) = (-1.5\cos 1 + 9\cos 6)\vec{i} + (-1.5\sin 1 - 9\sin 6)\vec{j}$

$\approx 7.83\vec{i} + 1.25\vec{j}$

4. The graph shows the position, velocity, and acceleration vectors at $t = 2$.

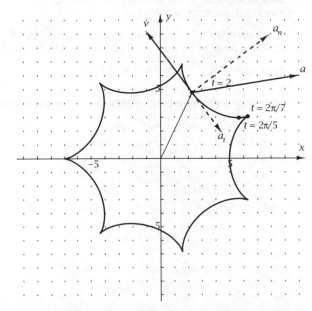

5. The object seems to be slowing down. The angle between $\vec{v}(2)$ and $\vec{a}(2)$ is larger than 90°.

6. $\dfrac{\vec{v}(2) \cdot \vec{a}(2)}{|\vec{v}(2)|} \approx \dfrac{-3.36 \cdot 7.83 + 4.50 \cdot 1.25}{\sqrt{3.36^2 + 4.50^2}} \approx -3.68$

7. The object is slowing down. The scalar projection of $\vec{a}(2)$ onto $\vec{v}(2)$ is negative.

8. $\vec{a}_t(2) = \dfrac{\vec{v}(2) \cdot \vec{a}(2)}{|\vec{v}(2)|^2}\, \vec{v}(2)$

   $\approx \dfrac{-3.36 \cdot 7.83 + 4.50 \cdot 1.25}{3.36^2 + 4.50^2}(-3.36\vec{i} + 4.50\vec{j})$

   $\approx 2.20\vec{i} - 2.95\vec{j}$

9. $\vec{a}_n(2) = \vec{a}(2) - \vec{a}_t(2) \approx 5.63\vec{i} + 4.20\vec{j}$

10. See the graph in Problem 4, showing the tangential and normal components of acceleration.

11. The tangential component is pulling the object in the direction opposite of motion, slowing it down. The normal component is pulling the object to the side, out of a straight path into a curve.

12. At a cusp, $\dfrac{dx}{dt} = \dfrac{dy}{dt} = 0$.

13. Technical way:
    Solve $-3\sin 0.5t + 3\sin 3t = 3\cos 0.5t + 3\cos 3t = 0$.
    Judging by the position of $t = 2$, the cusp near $(6, 3)$ will be close to $t = 1$.
    $\sin 0.5t - \sin 3t = 0$, $t \approx 1 \Rightarrow t = 0.8975...$
    $\cos 0.5t + \cos 3t = 0$, $t \approx 1 \Rightarrow t = 0.8975...$
    Check that $\frac{dx}{dt}(0.8975...) = \frac{dy}{dt}(0.8975...) = 0$ and that $(x(0.8975...), y(0.8975...))$ is near $(6, 3)$.
    (If the two numerical solutions had been different or the checks had failed, you would have had to solve again using another starting guess for t.)
    Intuitive way:
    Note the symmetry of the graph. The explanation of the shape (wheels turning within wheels) indicates that the seven cusps are evenly spaced; and the $\vec{j}$-component of $\vec{r}$ is an odd function—in particular $\vec{r}(0)$ is on the x-axis midway between two cusps. Therefore, the first of seven cusps should be at $t = \frac{4\pi}{14} = 0.8975...$
    Check that $\frac{dx}{dt}(0.8975...) = \frac{dy}{dt}(0.8975...) = 0$ and that $(x(0.8975...), y(0.8975...))$ is near $(6, 3)$.

14. Solve $3\cos 0.5t + 3\cos 3t = 0$ with an initial guess of about 1.2, with a range of $0.9 \le t \le 2$: $t = 1.2566...$ (Exactly $t = 0.4\pi$)

15. Speed $= |\vec{v}(2)| \approx \sqrt{3.36^2 + 4.50^2} \approx 5.62$ ft/s

16. $dL = \sqrt{x'(t)^2 + y'(t)^2}\, dt = |\vec{v}(t)|\, dt$

    $= [(-3\sin 0.5t + 3\sin 3t)^2 + (3\cos 0.5t + 3\cos 3t)^2]^{1/2}\, dt$

    $= 3\sqrt{2\cos 0.5t\cos 3t + \cos^2 3t}\, dt$

    $= 3\sqrt{2 + 2(\cos 0.5t\cos 3t - \sin 0.5t\sin 3t)}\, dt$

    $= 3\sqrt{2 + 2\cos 3.5t}\, dt$

    $= 3\sqrt{2 + 2(2\cos^2 1.75t - 1)}\, dt$

    $= 3\sqrt{4\cos^2 1.75t}\, dt$

    $= 6\,|\cos 1.75t|\, dt$

One complete cycle is $0 \le t \le 4\pi$, so

$L = \displaystyle\int_{t=0}^{t=4\pi} dL$

$= \displaystyle\int_0^{4\pi} 6\,|\cos 1.75t|\, dt$

$= 14\displaystyle\int_0^{2\pi/7} 6\cos 1.75t\, dt$ By symmetry

$= \dfrac{84}{1.75}\sin 1.75t\,\Big|_0^{2\pi/7}$

$= \dfrac{84}{1.75}\sin\dfrac{\pi}{2}$

$= 48$ ft

This is reasonably close to the circumference of a 7-ft-radius circle, $14\pi = 42.9822...$ ft.

17. Answers will vary.

Chapter 11

Exploration 11-2a

1. The volume of the slice is $dV = \pi x^2\, dy$, so the weight $= 63 \cdot \pi x^2\, dy$.
   The distance to lift the slice is $15 - y$, so $dW = 63\pi(15 - y)x^2\, dy$.

2. The radius x of the vat at height y is 6 ft at $y = 0$; also, x is 8 ft at $y = 10$ and varies linearly with y. Therefore,
   $x = 6 + 0.2y$
   $dW = 63\pi(15 - y)(6 + 0.2y)^2\, dy$
   $= 63\pi(540 - 1.8y^2 - 0.04y^3)\, dy$

3. $W = \displaystyle\int_{y=0}^{y=10} dW$

   $= 63\pi\displaystyle\int_0^{10} 540 - 1.8y^2 - 0.04y^3\, dy$

   $= 63\pi(540y - 0.6y^3 - 0.01y^4)\,\Big|_0^{10}$

   $= 63\pi(5400 - 600 - 100)$

   $= 296,100\pi = 930,225.58...$

   ≈ 930 thousand ft-lb

4. Answers will vary.

Exploration 11-3a

1. The volume of the slice is
   $dV = \pi x^2\, dy = \pi y\, dy$ (because $y = x^2$).
   $dm = \rho\, dV = 3y^{1/2} \cdot \pi y\, dy = 3\pi y^{3/2}\, dy$
   The mass, dm, of a slice at height y is
   $dm = 3y^{1/2}\, dV = 3y^{1/2}(2\pi x^2\, dy) = 3y^{1/2}(2\pi y\, dy)$.
   $m = \displaystyle\int_{y=0}^{y=4} dm = 3\pi\displaystyle\int_0^4 y^{3/2}\, dy$
   $= \dfrac{6}{5}\pi y^{5/2}\,\Big|_0^4$
   $= 38.4\pi = 120.6371... \approx 120.6$ g
   (Numerical integration is okay.)

2. The volume of a shell at radius x is
$dV = 2\pi x(4 - y)\,dx = 2\pi x(4 - x^2)\,dx$.
The mass, dm, of the shell is
$dm = (x + 5)\,dV = (x + 5) \cdot 2\pi x(4 - x^2)\,dx$
$= 2\pi(20x + 4x^2 - 5x^3 - x^4)\,dx$
$m = \int_{x=0}^{x=2} dm = 2\pi \int_0^2 (20x + 4x^2 - 5x^3 - x^4)\,dx$
$= 2\pi\left(10x^2 + \dfrac{4}{3}x^3 - \dfrac{5}{4}x^4 - \dfrac{1}{5}x^5\right)\Big|_0^2$
$= 48\dfrac{8}{15}\pi = 152.4719... \approx 152.5$ g

3. Answers will vary.

Exploration 11-4a

1. $dV = \pi x^2\,dy = \pi y\,dy$
$V = \pi \int_0^4 y\,dy = \dfrac{\pi}{2}y^2\Big|_0^4 = 8\pi$
(Or just recall $V =$ one-half the volume of the circumscribed cylinder.)

2. Within the disk, the displacement y from the xz-plane remains essentially constant.
So, $dM_{xz} = y\,dV$.

3. $dV = \pi y\,dy$
$dM_{xz} = \pi y^2\,dy$
$M_{xz} = \int_{y=0}^{y=4} dM_{xz} = \int_0^4 \pi y^2\,dy = \dfrac{\pi}{3}y^3\Big|_0^4 = \dfrac{64}{3}\pi$

4. $M_{xz} = \bar{y} \cdot V \Rightarrow \bar{y} = \dfrac{8}{3} = 2.6666...$
The graph shows the centroid. This point is more than halfway to the top because there is more volume at the top than at the bottom.

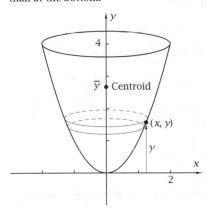

5. Answers will vary.

Exploration 11-4b

1. The volume of the slice is
$dV = \pi x^2\,dy = \pi y\,dy$ (because $y = x^2$).
$dm = \rho\,dV = 3y^{1/2} \cdot \pi y\,dy = 3\pi y^{3/2}\,dy$
The mass, dm, of a slice at height y is
$dm = 3y^{1/2}\,dV = 3y^{1/2}(2\pi x^2\,dy) = 3y^{1/2}(2\pi y\,dy)$.
$m = \int_{y=0}^{y=4} dm = 3\pi \int_0^4 y^{3/2}\,dy$
$= \dfrac{6}{5}\pi y^{5/2}\Big|_0^4$
$= 38.4\pi = 120.6371... \approx 120.6$ g
(Numerical integration is okay.)

2. Within the disk, the displacement, y, from the xz-plane remains essentially constant. So,
$dM_{xz} = y\,dm$.

3. $dm = 3y^{1/2}\,dV = 3\pi y^{3/2}\,dy$
$dM_{xz} = 3\pi y^{5/2}\,dy$
$M_{xz} = \int_{y=0}^{y=4} dM_{xz} = \int_0^4 3\pi y^{5/2}\,dy$
$= \dfrac{6\pi}{7}y^{7/2}\Big|_0^4 = \dfrac{768}{7}\pi$
$= 109\dfrac{5}{7}\pi = 344.6775... \approx 344.7$ g $\cdot$ cm

4. $M_{xz} = \bar{y} \cdot m$
$\bar{y} = \dfrac{768\pi}{7} \cdot \dfrac{1}{38.4} = \dfrac{20}{7} = 2.8751... \approx 2.88$ cm
The graph shows the center of mass.

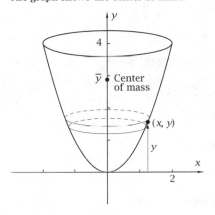

5. The centroid will coincide with the center of mass if the density of the solid is constant.

6. Answers will vary.

Exploration 11-4c

1. The volume of the paraboloid is half the volume of the circumscribed cylinder.
$V = \dfrac{1}{2}(\pi \cdot 2^2 \cdot 4) = 8\pi$ cm^3
The density is constant, so the mass is
$m = 2.7 \cdot V = 21.6\pi = 67.8584... \approx 67.9$ g.

2. Within each shell, the distance to the y-axis remains essentially constant. So, $dM_{2y} = x^2\,dm$.

3. $dM_{2y} = x^2\,dm = x^2 \cdot 2.7\,dV = 2.7x^2 \cdot 2\pi x(4 - y)\,dx$
$= 5.4\pi x^3(4 - x^2)\,dx$
$M_{2y} = \int_{x=0}^{x=2} dM_{2y} = \pi \int_0^2 21.6x^3 - 5.4x^5\,dx$
$= (5.4\pi x^4 - 0.9\pi x^6)\Big|_0^2$
$= 28.8\pi$ g $\cdot$ cm^2

4. $M_{2y} = \bar{r}^2 \cdot m \Rightarrow \bar{r}^2 = \dfrac{4}{3}$ cm$^2 \Rightarrow$
$\bar{r} = \dfrac{2\sqrt{3}}{3} = 1.1547... \approx 1.15$ cm

5. The second moment of mass is the mass times the *square* of the distance from the axis, so moving the weight three times as far from the axis will increase the second moment of mass by a factor of $3^2 = 9$.

6. Answers will vary.

Exploration 11-5a

1. $p = 62.4(12 - y)$

2. $dF = p \, dA = 62.4(12 - y) \cdot (2x \, dy)$

3. $dF = 62.4(12 - y) \dfrac{20}{\sqrt{3}} y^{1/2} \, dy$

$\quad = 416\sqrt{3}(12y^{1/2} - y^{3/2}) \, dy$

$\quad F = \displaystyle\int_{y=0}^{y=12} dF = 416\sqrt{3} \int_0^{12} (12y^{1/2} - y^{3/2}) \, dy$

$\quad = 416\sqrt{3}(8y^{3/2} - 0.4y^{5/2}) \Big|_0^{12}$

$\quad = 416\sqrt{3} \cdot \left(38.4\sqrt{12}\right) = 95{,}846.4 \text{ lb}$

4. $dM_x = y \, dF = 416\sqrt{3}(12y^{3/2} - y^{5/2}) \, dy$

$\quad M_x = 416\sqrt{3} \displaystyle\int_0^{12} (12y^{3/2} - y^{5/2}) \, dy$

$\quad = 416\sqrt{3}\left(4.8y^{5/2} - \dfrac{2}{7}y^{7/2}\right) \Big|_0^{12}$

$\quad = 416\sqrt{3}\left(4.8 \cdot 12^{5/2} - \dfrac{2}{7} \cdot 12^{7/2}\right)$

$\quad = \dfrac{3{,}450{,}470.4}{7} = 492{,}924\dfrac{24}{70} \text{ ft} \cdot \text{lb}$

5. $M_x = \bar{y} \cdot F \Rightarrow \bar{y} = \dfrac{36}{7} = 5\dfrac{1}{7} \text{ ft}$

6. Answers will vary.

Exploration 11-6a

1. $\dfrac{dB}{dt} = 100{,}000 \cdot 2^{-t/9}$

2. $B = \displaystyle\int_{t=0}^{t=9} dB = 100{,}000 \int_0^9 2^{-t/9} \, dt$

$\quad = 100{,}000 \cdot \dfrac{-9}{\ln 2} \cdot 2^{-t/9} \Big|_0^9$

$\quad = \dfrac{-900{,}000}{\ln 2}(2^{-1} - 1)$

$\quad = \dfrac{450{,}000}{\ln 2}$

$\quad = 649{,}212.7684\ldots$

$\quad \approx 649 \text{ thousand barrels}$

3. Assume that oil is worth $24 per barrel.
   Worth is $(649{,}212.7684\ldots)(24)$.
   $\approx \$15.6$ million!

4. $649{,}212.7684\ldots \cdot \dfrac{42.5}{44{,}000} = 627.08\ldots \approx 627$ or 628 tank cars
   Length $\approx 627(60) = 37{,}620$ ft
   or about 7.1 miles!

5. (See the referenced book.)

6. Answers will vary.

Chapter 12

Exploration 12-2a

1.

Hours	mg
0	30
1	27
2	24.3
3	21.87
4	19.683

2. $30 + 30(0.9) + 30(0.9)^2 + 30(0.9)^3 + 30(0.9)^4$

$\quad = 30[1 + (0.9) + (0.9)^2 + (0.9)^3 + (0.9)^4]$

$\quad = 30\dfrac{1 - 0.9^5}{1 - 0.9}$

$\quad = 30 \cdot 4.0951$

$\quad \approx 122.853 \text{ mg}$

3. Answer will depend on the particular grapher used. For a TI-83 the commands are
   sum(seq(30*0.9^N,N,0,4))
   and the result is 122.853 as in Problem 2.

4. At $t = 10$ h,
   $30 + 30(0.9) + \cdots + 30(0.9)^{10} = 205.8568\ldots$
   ≈ 206 mg.
   At $t = 20$ h,
   $30 + 30(0.9) + \cdots + 30(0.9)^{20} = 267.1743\ldots$
   ≈ 267 mg.

5. The partial sums converge to 300 mg. The patient will never have more than 300 mg of antibiotic in her body.

6. After 10 yr,
   $800 + 800(1.1) + 800(1.1)^2 + \cdots + 800(1.1)^{10}$
   $\approx \$14{,}824.93$.
   After 20 yr,
   $800 + 800(1.1) + 800(1.1)^2 + \cdots + 800(1.1)^{20}$
   $\approx \$51{,}202.00$.
   After 30 yr,
   $800 + 800(1.1) + 800(1.1)^2 + \cdots + 800(1.1)^{30}$
   $\approx \$145{,}554.74$.

7. The totals appear to be diverging to infinity.

8. Answers will vary.

Exploration 12-3a

1. $P_2(0.6) = 1 + 0.6 + \dfrac{1}{2}0.6^2 = 1.78$

$\quad P_3(0.6) = 1 + 0.6 + \dfrac{1}{2}0.6^2 + \dfrac{1}{6}0.6^3 = 1.816$

$\quad P_4(0.6) = 1 + 0.6 + \dfrac{1}{2}0.6^2 + \dfrac{1}{6}0.6^3 + \dfrac{1}{24}0.6^4 = 1.8214$

2.

n	$P_n(0.6)$
5	1.822048
6	1.8221128
7	1.822118354285…
8	1.822118770857…
9	1.822118798628…
10	1.822118800294…

The partial sums seem to be approaching 1.8221188….
(Exactly $e^{0.6}$)

3. $P_{10}(x) = 1 + x + \frac{1}{2!}x^2 + \cdots + \frac{1}{10!}x^{10}$

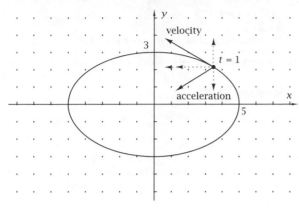

4. $P_{10}(1) = 1 + 1 + \frac{1}{2!} + \cdots + \frac{1}{10!} = 2.71828180\ldots$

   $P_{10}(1)$ is very close to $e = 2.7182\ldots$!

5. Conjecture: $P(x) \approx e^x$ when x is close to zero.
   Evidence: $P_{10}(1)$ is very close to e^1.
   $P_{10}(0.6)$ is very close to $e^{0.6} = 1.8221\ldots$
   $P_{10}(0) = 1$, which equals e^0.
   A table of $P_{10}(x)$ and e^x shows the values are almost indistinguishable as long as x is reasonably close to zero. The graph of $P_{10}(x)$ in Problem 3 resembles the graph of $y = e^x$.
   For most n, $P_n'(x)$ is similar to $P_n'(x) = P_{n-1}'(x)$.

6. $e^{10} = 22{,}026.4657\ldots$
   $P_{10}(10) = 12{,}842.3051\ldots$,
   which is *not* close to e^{10}.

7. Answers will vary.

Exploration 12-4a

1. $P'(x) = c_1 + 2c_2x + 3c_3x^2 + 4c_4x^3 + 5c_5x^4 + 6c_6x^5 + \cdots$
   $P''(x) = 2c_2 + 6c_3x + 12c_4x^2 + 20c_5x^3 + 30c_6x^4 + \cdots$
   $P'''(x) = 6c_3 + 24c_4x + 60c_5x^2 + 120c_6x^3 + \cdots$
   $P^{(4)}(x) = 24c_4 + 120c_5x + 360c_6x^2 + \cdots$
   $P^{(5)}(x) = 120c_5 + 720c_6x + \cdots$

2. $P(0) = c_0 = 0!c_0$
   $P'(0) = c_1 = 1!c_1$
   $P''(0) = 2c_2 = 2!c_2$
   $P'''(0) = 6c_3 = 3!c_3$
   $P^{(4)}(0) = 24c_4 = 4!c_4$
   $P^{(5)}(0) = 120c_5 = 5!c_5$
   $P^{(k)}(0)$ (using factorials) $= k!c_k$

3. $f(x) = \sin x \Rightarrow f(0) = 0$
   $f'(x) = \cos x \Rightarrow f'(0) = 1$
   $f''(x) = -\sin x \Rightarrow f''(0) = 0$
   $f'''(x) = -\cos x \Rightarrow f'''(0) = -1$
   $f^{(4)}(x) = \sin x \Rightarrow f^{(4)}(0) = 0$
   $f^{(5)}(x) = \cos x \Rightarrow f^{(5)}(0) = 1$

4. $c_0 = 0$, $c_1 = 1$, $c_2 = 0$, $c_3 = -1/3!$, $c_4 = 0$, $c_5 = 1/5!$

5. $\sin x = x - \frac{1}{3!}x^3 + \frac{1}{5!}x^5 - \frac{1}{7!}x^7 + \frac{1}{9!}x^9 - \frac{1}{11!}x^{11} + \cdots$

6. $f(x) = x - \frac{1}{3!}x^3 + \frac{1}{5!}x^5 - \cdots$, same as in Problem 5.

7. The graph shows $f(x)$ solid and $\sin x$ dashed. There is a reasonable fit for $-4 < x \le 4$.

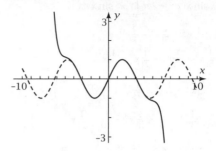

8. $y_2(4) - y_1(4) = 0.0100020\ldots$, which shows the partial sum is reasonably close.

9. $y_2(8) - y_1(8) = 66.6855\ldots$, which shows the partial sum is nowhere close.

10. The graph shows $f(x)$ solid and $\sin x$ dashed. There is a reasonable fit for the wider interval $-9 < x \le 9$.

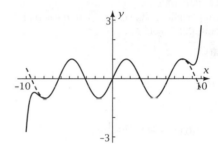

11. $y_2(4) - y_1(4) = -2.6506\ldots \times 10^{-9}$, which is much closer!

12. Answers will vary.

Exploration 12-5a

1. $f(3) = -2 = c_0$
   $f'(3) = 7 = c_1$
   $f''(3) = 0.8 = 2!c_2 \Rightarrow c_2 = 0.4$
   $f'''(3) = -3.6 = 3!c_3 \Rightarrow c_3 = -0.6$
   $\therefore f(x) \approx -2 + 7(x-3) + 0.4(x-3)^2 - 0.6(x-3)^3$
   $f(2.5) \approx -2 + 7(-0.5) + 0.4(-0.5)^2 - 0.6(-0.5)^3 = -5.325$

2. $P(x) = -2 + 7(x^2 + 3 - 3) + 0.4(x^2 + 3 - 3)$
   $\qquad = -2 + 7x^2 + 0.4x^4$
   $g(x) = -2 + 7x^2 + 0.4x^4 + \cdots$
   $g'(x) = 7x + 1.6x^3 + \cdots$
   $g'(0) = 0$ (horizontal tangent)
   $g''(x) = 7 + 4.8x^2 + \cdots$
   $g''(0) = 7$ (concave up)
   $\therefore g(0)$ is a minimum because the tangent line is horizontal there, and the graph is concave up.

3. $f(x) \approx 3 - 2x + \frac{1.2}{2!}x^2 + \frac{3}{3!}x^3$
   $f(x) \approx 3 - 2x + 0.6x^2 + 0.5x^3$
   $f(0.4) \approx 3 - 2(0.4) + 0.6(0.4^2) + 0.5(0.4^3) = 2.328$

4. $g(x) \approx 3 - 2x^2 + 0.6x^4$

5. $h(x) = \int_0^x (3 - 2t + 0.6t^2)\, dt = (3t - t^2 + 0.2t^3)\Big|_0^x = 3x - x^2 + 0.2x^3$

6. $h(0.7)$ cannot be determined exactly because it is not known whether or not the series converges if $x = 0.7$.

7. Answers will vary.

Exploration 12-5b

1. $V = \int_0^\pi 2\pi x \cdot (x \sin x)\, dx = 2\pi \int_0^\pi x^2 \sin x\, dx$

2. $x^2 \sin x = x^2 \left(x - \frac{1}{3!}x^3 + \frac{1}{5!}x^5 - \frac{1}{7!}x^7 + \frac{1}{9!}x^9 - \cdots \right)$

$= x^3 - \frac{1}{3!}x^5 + \frac{1}{5!}x^7 - \frac{1}{7!}x^9 + \frac{1}{9!}x^{11} - \cdots$

3. $V = 2\pi \int_0^\pi \left(x^3 - \frac{1}{3!}x^5 + \frac{1}{5!}x^7 - \frac{1}{7!}x^9 + \frac{1}{9!}x^{11} - \cdots \right) dx$

$= 2\pi \left(\frac{1}{4}x^4 - \frac{1}{6}\cdot\frac{1}{3!}x^6 + \frac{1}{8}\cdot\frac{1}{5!}x^8 - \frac{1}{10}\cdot\frac{1}{7!}x^{10} + \cdots \right)\Big|_0^\pi$

$= 2\pi \left(\frac{1}{4}\pi^4 - \frac{1}{6}\cdot\frac{1}{3!}\pi^6 + \frac{1}{8}\cdot\frac{1}{5!}\pi^8 - \frac{1}{10}\cdot\frac{1}{7!}\pi^{10} + \cdots \right)$

$= 2\pi \left(\frac{1}{4}\pi^4 - \frac{1}{6}\cdot\frac{1}{3!}\pi^6 + \frac{1}{8}\cdot\frac{1}{5!}\pi^8 - \frac{1}{10}\cdot\frac{1}{7!}\pi^{10} + \cdots \right)$

$V \approx 36.8743\cdots$

4. $2\pi \int_0^\pi x^2 \sin x\, dx$

$= 2\pi(-x^2 \cos x + 2x \sin x + 2\cos x)\Big|_0^\pi$

$= 2\pi(\pi^2 - 4) = 36.8798\ldots$

The estimate from Problem 3 is very close to the actual answer, only about 0.015% off.

5. Answers will vary.

Exploration 12-6a

1. $\ln x = (x-1) - \frac{1}{2}(x-1)^2 + \frac{1}{3}(x-1)^3 - \cdots$

$\ln 1.6 \approx S_5 = 0.6 - \frac{1}{2}(0.6)^2 + \frac{1}{3}(0.6)^3 - \frac{1}{4}(0.6)^4 + \frac{1}{5}(0.6)^5$

$= 0.475152$

$\ln 1.6 - S_5 = 1.40003629\ldots - 0.475152 = -0.005148\ldots$ (close!)

2. The table confirms the values.

3. $\lim_{n\to\infty}\left| \frac{t_{n+1}}{t_n} \right| = \lim_{n\to\infty} \frac{0.6^{n+1}/(n+1)}{0.6^n/n}$

$= 0.6 \lim_{n\to\infty}\frac{n}{n+1} = 0.6$

Because $n/(n+1) < 1$ for all n, the ratio approaches 0.6 from below.

4.

n	$|t_n|$	Geom. series
6	0.007776	0.007776
7	0.0039990...	0.0054432
8	0.0020995...	0.00381024
9	0.0011197...	0.002667168
10	0.0006046...	0.0018670176

5. The term values are bounded above by the geometric series values. The geometric series converges to $0.007776/(1 - 0.7) = 0.02592$. So the tail of the $|t_n|$ series converges to a number less than 0.02592.

6. $t_n = (-1)^{n+1}\frac{1}{n}(x-1)^n = \frac{(-1)^{n+1}(x-1)^n}{n}$

$L = \lim_{n\to\infty}\left| \frac{(-1)^{n+2}(x-1)^{n+1}}{n+1} \cdot \frac{n}{(-1)^{n+1}(x-1)^n} \right|$

$= \lim_{n\to\infty}\left| (-1)(x-1) \cdot \frac{n}{n+1} \right|$

$= |x-1| \lim_{n\to\infty}\frac{n}{n-1}$

$= |x-1|$

7. Make $L < 1$.

$\therefore |x-1| < 1$

$-1 < x - 1 < 1$

$0 < x < 2$

The open interval of convergence is (0, 2).

8. Answers will vary.

Exploration 12-6b

1. $f(x) = \tan^{-1} x$

$f'(x) = (1 + x^2)^{-1}$

$f''(x) = -(1 + x^2)^{-2} \cdot 2x$

$f'''(x) = 2(1 + x^2)^{-3} \cdot (2x)^2 - (1 + x^2)^{-2} \cdot 2$

The derivatives involve products and thus get more and more complicated, making the process very tedious.

2. $\frac{1}{1 + t^2} = 1 + (-t^2) + (-t^2)^2 + (-t^2)^3 + (-t^2)^4 + \cdots$

$= 1 - t^2 + t^4 - t^6 + t^8 - \cdots$

$\int_0^x \frac{1}{1 + t^2}\, dt = \int_0^x (1 - t^2 + t^4 - t^6 + t^8 - \cdots)\, dt$

$= \left(t - \frac{1}{3}t^3 + \frac{1}{5}t^3 - \frac{1}{7}t^7 + \frac{1}{9}t^9 - \cdots \right)\Big|_0^x$

$= x - \frac{1}{3}x^3 + \frac{1}{5}x^5 - \frac{1}{7}x^7 + \cdots + \frac{(-1)^n}{2n+1}x^{2n+1} + \cdots$

(where n starts at 0)

3. The graphs show S_3 and S_4 (solid) and $\tan^{-1} x$ (dashed).

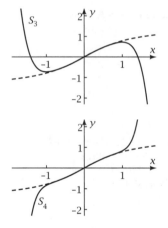

Conjecture: Interval of convergence is $-1 < x < 1$.

4. $L = \lim_{n\to\infty}\left| \frac{t_{n+1}}{t_n} \right|$

$= \lim_{n\to\infty}\left| \frac{x^{2n+3}}{2n+3} \cdot \frac{2n+1}{x^{2n+1}} \right|$

$= x^2 \cdot \lim_{n\to\infty}\frac{2n+1}{2n+3}$

$= x^2 \cdot 1 = x^2$

Make $L < 1$.

$x^2 < 1$

$-1 < x < 1$, which agrees with Problem 3.

5. Answers will vary.

Exploration 12-7a

1. R_4 is the remainder starting at t_5. As shown on the graph, if rectangles are drawn with their right sides touching the graph, they will be inscribed in the region under the graph. The left side of the rectangle for t_5 is at n or $x = 4$. Thus the integral from 4 to infinity is an upper bound for R_4, and hence R_4 is a lower sum for the integral.

Calculus: Concepts and Applications Instructor's Resource Book
©2005 Key Curriculum Press

2. $\int_4^\infty x^{-2}\,dx = -x^{-1}\Big|_4^\infty = \frac{1}{4}$

3. $t_5 = \frac{1}{25} = 0.04$

  $t_5 + t_6 = \frac{1}{25} + \frac{1}{36} = 0.0677...$

  $t_5 + t_6 + t_7 = \frac{1}{25} + \frac{1}{36} + \frac{1}{49} = 0.0881...$

4. Although the terms are decreasing, they are still positive. Adding positive terms produces increasing partial sums.

5. By definition, if the sequence of partial sums converges, the series converges. Since the sequence of partial sums for R_4 converges, so does the series.

6. By the closure axiom for addition of real numbers, any partial sum is a real number. If the remainder is also a real number, then the entire series converges.

7. The sequence of partial sums is increasing, but now the partial sums are not bounded above but rather bounded below by the value of the integral, so the property in Problem 5 cannot be used. Indeed, saying that a series is larger than some finite number does not prevent the series from being infinite!

8. Answers will vary.

Exploration 12-7b

1. For a geometric series, $S_n = t_1 \cdot \frac{1 - r^n}{1 - r}$.

  For this series, $S_n = 100 \cdot \frac{1 - 0.8^n}{1 - 0.8}$.

  Since the limit of 0.8^n is zero as n approaches infinity, S_n approaches $100(1/0.2) = 500$ as n approaches infinity. Since the sequence of partial sums converges, the series converges by definition.

2. The graph shows the terms of the series drawn as circumscribed rectangles for $f(x) = 1/x$, starting at $x = 1$.

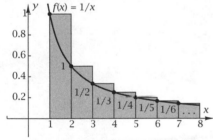

  Thus, $\displaystyle\sum_{n=1}^\infty 1/n > \int_1^\infty x^{-1}\,dx$

  $= \lim_{b\to\infty} \int_1^b x^{-1}\,dx = \lim_{b\to\infty} (\ln b - \ln 1) = \infty$.

  Since the sum is larger than an integral that becomes infinite, the series diverges.

3. $t_5 = \frac{256}{40320}$

4. Each term $\frac{1}{(2n)!}x^{2n}$ is positive. Adding positive terms increases the sum, regardless of whether the terms are large or small. If the terms being added are getting smaller, then the total sum is still increasing but increasing slowly.

5. $\frac{16}{24} + \frac{16}{24} \cdot \frac{4}{30} + \frac{16}{24} \cdot \frac{16}{900} + \frac{16}{24} \cdot \frac{64}{27000} + \cdots$

  $= \frac{16}{24} + \frac{64}{720} + \frac{256}{21600} + \frac{1024}{648000} + \cdots$

  Each term of the geometric series has numerator equal to the numerator of a corresponding term in the cosh series, but smaller denominator than that of its corresponding term. Therefore, each term of the geometric series is at least as large as the corresponding term in the cosh series.

6. The geometric series converges to

  $S = \frac{16}{24} \cdot \frac{1}{1 - 4/30} = \frac{10}{13}$.

  The sequence of partial sums for cosh 2 is increasing (see Problem 4), and bounded above by 10/13 (see Problem 5). Thus the series converges.

7. Answers will vary.

Exploration 12-8a

1. $S_4 = 1.4236111... = \frac{205}{144} = 1\frac{61}{144}$

2. $R_4 = \frac{1}{5^2} + \frac{1}{6^2} + \frac{1}{7^2} + \frac{1}{8^2} + \cdots$

3. $R_4 = \displaystyle\sum_{n=5}^\infty \frac{1}{n^2}$

4.

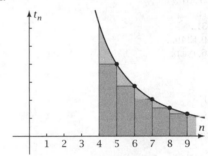

5. $R_4 < \int_4^\infty x^{-2}\,dx$

  $= \lim_{b\to\infty} \left(-x^{-1}\Big|_4^b\right)$

  $= \lim_{b\to\infty} (-b^{-1} + 4^{-1})$

  $= \frac{1}{4}$

6.

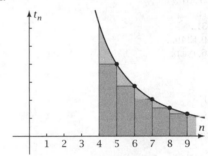

7. $R_4 < \int_5^\infty x^{-2}\,dx$

  $= \frac{1}{5}$

8. $R_{100} < \displaystyle\int_{100}^{\infty} x^{-2}\, dx = \dfrac{1}{100}$

   $R_{100} < \displaystyle\int_{101}^{\infty} x^{-2}\, dx = \dfrac{1}{101}$

   Use $R_{100} \approx \dfrac{1}{2}\left(\dfrac{1}{100} + \dfrac{1}{101}\right) = 0.00995024....$

   $S_{100} = 1.634983...$
   $\therefore\ S \approx 1.634983... + 0.00995024...$
   $\qquad = 1.64493439...$

9. $S = \pi^2/6 = 1.644934067...$ (quite close!)

10. Answers will vary.

Exploration 12-8b

1. $e^x = 1 + x + \dfrac{1}{2!}x^2 + \dfrac{1}{3!}x^3 + \dfrac{1}{4!}x^4 + \cdots$

   $e^{0.6} \approx S_3(0.6) = 1 + 0.6 + \dfrac{1}{2}(0.6^2) + \dfrac{1}{6}(0.6^3)$
   $\qquad\qquad = 1.816$

2. $e^{0.6} = 1.8221...$
   $e^{0.6} - S_3(0.6) = 0.006118... = R_3(0.6)$

3. $R_3(0.6) = 0.006118...$
   $t_4(0.6) = \dfrac{1}{4!}(0.6^4) = 0.0054$
   $\therefore\ R_3(0.6) > t_4(0.6)$, but not by much.

4. $k = \dfrac{0.006118}{0.054} - 1.1331...$

5. $f^{(4)}(c) = e^c = 1.1331...$
   $c = \ln 1.1331... = 0.1249...$
   $0 < 0.1249... < 0.6$, Q.E.D.

6. $f'(c) = \dfrac{f(x) - f(0)}{x - 0}$
   $f'(c)x = f(x) - f(0)$
   $f(x) = f(0) + f'(c)x$

7. $f'(x) = f'(0) + f''(c)x$

   $f(x) = \displaystyle\int [f'(0) + f''(c)x]\, dx$

   $f(x) = f'(0)x + \dfrac{1}{2}f''(c)x^2 + C_1$

   $f(0) = f'(0) \cdot 0 + \dfrac{1}{2}f''(c) \cdot 0 + C_1 \Rightarrow C_1 = f(0)$

   $\therefore\ f(x) = f(0) + f'(0)x + \dfrac{1}{2}f''(c)x^2$

   This is the first two terms of the Maclaurin series, plus a remainder term.

   $t_2 = \dfrac{1}{2}f''(0)x^2$

   $\therefore\ \dfrac{1}{2}f''(c)x^2 = \dfrac{f''(c)}{f''(0)} \cdot t^2$

8. • $f''(x) = f''(0) + f'''(c)x$
   • Integrating once gives

     $f'(x) = f''(0)x + \dfrac{1}{2}f'''(c)x^2 + C_2$

     $f'(0) = f''(0) \cdot 0 + \dfrac{1}{2}f'''(c) \cdot 0 + C_2 \Rightarrow C_1 = f'(0)$

     $\therefore\ f'(x) = f'(0) + f''(0)x + \dfrac{1}{2}f'''(c)x^2$
   • Integrating again gives

     $f(x) = f'(0)x + \dfrac{1}{2}f''(0)x^2 + \dfrac{1}{6}f'''(c)x^3 + C_3$

     $f(0) = 0 + 0 + 0 + C_3 \Rightarrow C_3 = f(0)$

     $\therefore\ f(x) = f(0) + f'(0)x + \dfrac{1}{2}f''(0)x^2 + \dfrac{1}{6}f'''(c)x^3$
   • $f(x)$ is exactly equal to the first three terms of the Maclaurin series for $f(x)$ plus a remainder term involving $f'''(c)$, Q.E.D.

9. $f(x) = f(0) + f'(0)x + \dfrac{1}{2}f''(0)x + \dfrac{1}{6}f'''(0)x^3 + \dfrac{1}{4!}f^{(4)}(c)x^4$
   The first four terms are S_3. The last term is R_3.

10. $e^{0.6} = S_3(0.6) + \dfrac{1}{4!}f^{(4)}(c)x^4$, where c is between 0 and x.

11. $R_n(x) = \dfrac{1}{(n+1)!}f^{(n+1)}(c)x^{n+1}$, where $c \in (0, x)$.

    $|R_n(x)| \le \dfrac{M}{(n+1)!}x^{n+1}$, where M is the maximum value of $f^{(n+1)}(x)$ on the interval $(0, x)$.

12. Answers will vary.

Assessment Suggestions

Assessment is an opportunity for you to learn more about your students. Through assessment you can discover what students know and understand, how they think, what they still need to learn, and how they feel about their learning. Assessment is also an opportunity for students to learn more about themselves.

Assessment does not always mean recording a grade. You assess students when you read their journals or when you observe them interacting with other members of a group.

You might be one of the many instructors who structure mathematics classrooms and lessons differently from traditional classrooms and lessons. For this reason you need assessment practices that match your changing classroom. For example, instructors argue that if students work cooperatively, we should assess the work they do in groups. If we ask students open-ended questions, we should use open-ended questions as assessment items. If students connect mathematics with the world outside their classroom, we should evaluate projects that make these connections.

Instructors want assessment methods that are genuinely helpful to themselves and their students. They are finding that this kind of constructive assessment requires more than grading the results of a paper-and-pencil test.

According to *Assessment Standards for School Mathematics* (NCTM 1995), there are four major purposes of assessment:

- Monitoring students' progress

- Making instructional decisions

- Evaluating students' achievement

- Evaluating programs

In this section I will share with you some of the assessment techniques I use in my classroom and will point out some of the ways you can address NCTM's assessment purposes using the text and supplementary materials for *Calculus: Concepts and Applications.*

For more general information on assessment, I recommend *Constructive Assessment in Mathematics: Practical Steps for Classroom Teachers* (Key Curriculum Press 1997) by David Clark. It offers a good overview of assessment as well as some guidance in specific assessment strategies.

Calculus: Concepts and Applications
Student Text and Ancillaries

The student text and support materials for *Calculus: Concepts and Applications* provide you with ample opportunities to assess student learning. These include a calculus journal, Concept Problems, projects, experiments, Section, Chapter, and Cumulative Tests, Explorations, and Quick Review problems. In addition, supplemental resources for projects, graphing calculator activities, calculus laboratories, problems, and research papers are listed in the Bibliography of Calculus Resources section of the *Instructor's Guide,* as well as within each section's Lesson Guide.

Monitoring Students' Progress

Progress is distinct from achievement. Achievement is a measure of how well a student can do on predetermined tasks. Progress is a measure of how far a student has come along the path toward achievement or broader goals from that individual's starting point.

One of the better sources of monitoring student progress for this calculus course is the journal each student is expected to keep. In this journal, students write what they have learned over the past few days and anything about which they are still unsure. By reading sequential journal entries, you and the student can see what progress is being made. Typically, students learning mathematics feel as though they will never master what they have been exposed to today. Tomorrow, when the "Aha!" has hit, they realize that what was difficult before is easy now. But the *next* task seems insurmountable. Students who go back and read their journals will find out a lot about their own learning styles and about how they are making progress through the course.

Another way to monitor progress is to have students keep portfolios into which they put samples of their work. The project problems and experiments throughout the text and the Concept Problems at the ends of chapters make excellent candidates for portfolio entries. With ready access to computer-graphing utilities (not just graphing calculators) and word processors, students can write their work on the computer, plot graphs and paste them electronically into their papers, and print near-professional-quality work. The word processor allows students to edit their papers based on your review and comments, turning first drafts into polished products in a time-efficient way. Thus, students gain experience with how they will submit papers when they get out into the workforce. The portfolio provides the instructor with a way of monitoring progress and provides potential employers with samples of what the student can do.

> **The main reason you *write* something is for someone else to *read*.**

This maxim appears on the bulletin board in my classroom. It focuses on the importance of the verbal component of mathematics education and gives credence to the reasons students write in their journals and keep portfolios.

> **The safest place to be is at the board!**

Having students work at the board will give you an insight into how they are progressing, both individually and as a class. I use a procedure in which a student volunteers or is picked to be at the board. This student then calls on other students, by name, to read the problem, tell what to do first, take the next step, and so forth. The student called on must supply an answer, whether or not she or he knew the answer when the question was asked. If Tom, for example, is asked a question he cannot answer, I say to the class, "You have a classmate in distress. Tom must answer the question, and you are obligated to help him." Then someone gives Tom hints about how to answer the question, and Tom supplies the answer to the student at the board. (The safest place to be, in this mode of presentation, is at the board!) You can tell how well your students are progressing in the course by how well they respond to the questions.

Note that monitoring progress does not necessarily mean assigning grades. Sometimes the most important result of the monitoring is the one-on-one discussions that you may initiate as a result of having read journal entries or portfolio papers or having seen boardwork presentations.

Making Instructional Decisions

This phase of assessment focuses on you rather than on the student. In its simplest form, this process can involve such things as deciding what to do next based on how well students have done on the previous test. The boardwork previously mentioned might call your attention to the need to try a different approach for a particular topic. On their papers or at the board, you will find students coming up with insightful ways to do things that you can add to your repertoire, such as the Carter Mayfield (my former student) way of differentiating a quotient,

$$y = \frac{u}{v} \Rightarrow y' = \frac{u'}{v} - u\frac{v'}{v^2}$$

The Quick Review problems in each section can provide a way of checking your instruction. We all omit a topic from time to time, occasionally unintentionally. Sooner or later that topic will arise as a quickie problem. When it does, just say, "Oh, here's how you do that." In five minutes you have filled a gap in their knowledge that might have taken a whole day of instruction if you had presented it as an independent topic.

One thing to remember as you assess your instruction is that there are four fundamental concepts of calculus: limits, derivatives, definite integrals, and indefinite integrals. For each of these concepts, there are four things to be accomplished: defining, understanding, doing, and applying. These four concepts and the four things to be accomplished can be arranged in a 4-by-4 grid, like this:

	Define it	Understand it	Do it	Apply it
Limits				
Derivatives				
Definite integral				
Indefinite integral				

For each topic you present, you should ask yourself where the topic fits in the grid. You must also decide which one or ones of the four methods—graphical, numerical, algebraic, or verbal—is most appropriate for the topic. If a particular topic enhances students' knowledge in a grid square where enhancement is needed, the topic is worthwhile. Otherwise, the topic is a candidate for skipping.

Evaluating Students' Achievement

As instructors we are all familiar with the classic written test used to evaluate achievement. This text and its supplementary materials have many such testing instruments and suggestions.

> **You don't get paid till the job's done *right*!**

I use this maxim as a guide to grading students' work. If a student's raw score on a regular test is below passing, he or she is assigned a zero until the corrections are completed (*correctly!*). When the corrections are satisfactory, the student is assigned a score halfway between the raw score and the passing grade. This scheme lets the students know that I will not accept unsatisfactory work, but it gives them a chance to turn a disastrously low score into something that will not ruin their average. Yet the student cannot get a passing score simply by doing corrections. I do not use this grading procedure for cumulative tests, such as semester exams. The regular tests are regarded as "rehearsals" for these exams, and the student is expected to do satisfactorily the *first* time on the actual performance. This correction/new score grading procedure can be time-consuming, but it is rewarding from the standpoint of getting your students to do superior work.

> ## You worry about the mathematics.
> ## *I* worry about your grade!

This maxim gets at the idea that a grade is a *dependent* variable. The way to control a dependent variable is through the independent variable, in this case mathematical knowledge. I mention the correction/new score grading scheme to students only when it comes up in context, not at the beginning of the course. I count tests as 100 points each and homework (when it is graded) or group work as 10 or 20 points each. A cumulative test counts twice if it is above a student's average and just once if it is below. I determine the average simply by adding the student's points and dividing by the total possible points.

> ## Keep your pencil moving!
> ## You can't afford the luxury of feeling sorry for yourself.

This maxim relates to maintaining concentration during a test. As long as a student is aggressively trying to work a problem, adrenaline will help with concentration. If a student stops and starts thinking, "I don't know how to do this," the momentum is lost and the student's performance suffers. You can illustrate this idea with analogies drawn from such diverse activities as winning at sports to the elephant Dumbo's ability to fly!

Sometimes during a test a student will ask a question like "How much is Problem 5 worth?" Worrying about grades while taking a test can cause students to score lower than they would if they just concentrated on the mathematics. I deliberately leave off the point values of the problems. Students must decide from the context whether a particular problem is hard or easy.

> ## You can't afford to use up your creative energy
> ## on tasks that should be routine.

Students should be able to do certain tasks by reflex, without a lot of thought. In this regard, the Quick Review problems give you a chance, almost daily, to assess students' ability to do so. Multiple-choice questions appear occasionally in these problem sets but are avoided elsewhere. As I found from writing problems for the College Board's Mathematics Achievement Tests (now called SAT-2), it is harder to write good, unambiguous multiple-choice questions than it is to grade free-response questions on a classroom set of papers! You will also find multiple-choice questions in past Advanced Placement Calculus Exams. In the lesson guides in the *Instructor's Guide,* you will find lists of which of these problems are relevant to each chapter.

> **If in doubt, try it out!**

Making and testing conjectures is a skill you can assess more effectively now that there are graphing calculators. This maxim gets at this fact. The explorations in this *Instructor's Resource Book* are a particularly rich source of opportunities for conjecture. Students use conjecture for such varied purposes as learning the chain rule and determining whether a critical point is a maximum or a minimum for a function.

The availability of graphing technology has a drawback for grading students' tests. Students can plot a graph quickly. But if they have to transcribe the graph onto their papers, they lose time and may draw it inaccurately. One remedy is to include an accurately-drawn graph on the test, as is done in the student text, in Explorations, and in Section, Chapter, and Cumulative Tests. Students draw on these graphs or use calculus to make conclusions about the graphs. If your objective is to see if students can produce the graph on their grapher, ask them to show you their grapher with the completed graph. Put a checkmark on their paper when the graph is correct. Be sure to put such problems on a later part of the test so that not all students are crowding around your desk at the same time!

Evaluating Programs

One way to evaluate your course is to solicit student input. I use a four-item questionnaire at the end of the first semester and at the end of the course. For midyear the questions are

- What is the *one* most important thing you have learned about calculus so far?

- What has been the most interesting part of the course?

- What has been the hardest part to understand?

- What changes would you suggest for the second half of the course?

I modify the questions slightly for the end of the course. Students fill out the questionnaires anonymously. You will receive interesting insights into how effective you have been! Sometimes students find that the hardest part of the course has also been the most important or most interesting part.

> **What you know, you might never use.**
> **What you don't know, you'll *definitely* never use!**

This maxim is useful for students who ask, "When will I ever *use* this stuff?" It is good to be able to show students applications for what they are learning. However, your assessment of the worth of a particular topic in your course must be based on your knowledge of where it fits into the big picture of mathematics, not on whether the students can see an immediate application.

A primary concern in evaluating your course involves the existence of externally-written comprehensive exams, such as departmental finals or Advanced Placement Exams. You must assess what you are doing and make decisions about whether or not your instruction will lead students to success on these exams.

Conclusions

Calculus should draw students in, not filter them out.

This maxim is at the heart of the reform calculus movement. When calculus was entirely dependent on algebraic methods, students had to "demonstrate their worthiness" for higher mathematics by mastering the algebra. Those found "unworthy" were filtered out. With ready access to graphing, numerical, and computer technology, students can be "pumped into" the pipeline of people who must have mathematical skills. As you do the "pumping," keep in mind these important attributes of assessment laid out in "The Assessment Principle" of NCTM's *Principles and Standards for School Mathematics.*

- *Assessment should enhance students' learning.* Assessment of activities such as observations, conversations, interviews, and interactive journals can help students learn through articulating their ideas and answering their instructor's questions. Also, when students understand what a correct response should entail, they will assume more responsibility for their own learning. This can be done through the use of a scoring guide, feedback on assessment tasks, and group discussions in which students present and evaluate different approaches to solving complex problems.

- *Assessment is a valuable tool for making instructional decisions.* Multiple approaches to assessment allow students to show in different ways what they know and can do. This gives them the opportunity to show their strengths. Also, instructors should make an effort to find out what students think about the tasks they are given, which will give insight into how to proceed with the course.

Section, Chapter, and Cumulative Tests

In this section are tests to accompany *Calculus: Concepts and Applications.* These are adaptations of tests used in the author's classes. For each chapter there is at least one chapter test. There are also tests covering various subsets of the chapters. At the end of Chapter 3, there is a cumulative test covering the first three chapters of the text. At the end of Chapters 6 and 12, there are several cumulative tests equivalent to semester or final exams. Unless otherwise noted, each test is designed for a 50-minute class period.

You can use the tests in this section as they are or as a basis for writing your own tests. The most effective tests are the ones you write yourself, based on the way you have taught the topics and tailored to your own students' mathematical maturity at the time your test is given. The real-world problems you write are most effective if you use topics of current or local interest to your students. For example, the Twister Problem in Test 14 was written shortly after the movie *Twister* was released. Students were quick to pick up the fact that Jo and Bill are the names of the lead characters in the movie.

Textbook examples also provide a good source of test problems. For instance, Problem 6 in Test 30 duplicates an example that appears in Chapter 8. When you go over the test in the next class session, you can direct the students to the example rather than using class time. Students will soon catch on and start studying the examples, thinking they are outsmarting you. But really you are outsmarting *them* by getting them to read the book!

Occasionally, questions in the tests instruct the students to check their graphs with their instructor. This procedure gives a simple way for you to see that students have actually plotted a graph without their having to use test time to sketch it. Sometimes the "Check with your instructor" prompt is given in sequential problems where you want to make sure an intermediate answer is correct before students use it in later problems. Don't put such questions at the beginning of the test; if you do, all students will be flocking around your desk at the same time!

The last question in most of the sample tests is "What did you learn as a result of taking this test that you did not know before?" Sometimes the student will realize that you have asked a question that she or he has not seen before, yet has figured out using known information. You will sometimes find out nonmathematical things about your students by reading their responses. The author reads, but usually does not grade, these problems. Occasionally, a few extra points will be assigned to a student who has shown an unusual insight or revelation.

The author feels strongly that all calculus students should take a comprehensive final exam at the end of the course covering the whole year. Because high school seniors are often exempted from final exams, the author gives a comprehensive "Sixth 6-Weeks Test" such as Tests 47 and 48 at the end of the course. Because students may have been studying for the Advanced Placement Exam in the sixth 6-week portion of the school year, the test can be comprehensive while including only material from that 6-week interval.

Tests on the Instructor's Resource CD

On the CD accompanying this book, you'll find PDF and Microsoft Word files of the Section, Chapter, and Cumulative Tests. You can use the tests in these ways:

- To make minor changes to text and numbers in the problems, or to reorder problems to create different versions of tests for different classes

- To add problems of your own

- To delete problems from tests that are too long or that cover content in the book that you have chosen to skip

- To compile and edit problems from various tests or explorations to make cumulative tests or extra practice worksheets

Consult the ReadMe file on the CD for explicit instructions, warnings, and tips for working with the test files.

Name: _____ Date: _____

Test 1, Chapter 1

Objective: Show what you have learned about limits, derivatives, and definite integrals so far.

Part 1: No calculators allowed (1–5)

1. One concept of calculus is **limit.** Write the verbal definition of limit.

2. Below are the graphs of three functions, f, g, and h. Explain why $f(x)$ and $g(x)$ have limits as x approaches 7, but $h(x)$ does not have a limit.

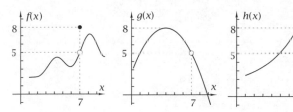

3. Another concept of calculus is **definite integral,** which is a means for finding the product of x and y in a function where y varies. Definite integrals can be calculated graphically. The following graph shows the velocity, $v(t)$, in feet per second, of a moving object. Find an estimate of the definite integral of $v(t)$ with respect to t from $t = 10$ to $t = 30$ s.

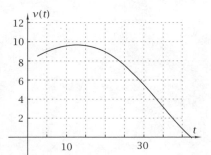

4. What is the physical meaning of the answer in Problem 3?

5. A third concept of calculus is **derivative,** which is an instantaneous rate of change. At $t = 20$ s, approximately what is the instantaneous rate of change of velocity? Is the velocity increasing or decreasing?

(Hand in this page to get the rest of the test.)

Test 1, Chapter 1 *continued*

Part 2: Graphing calculators allowed (6–15)

For Problems 6–8, derivatives and definite integrals can be estimated from tables of data. The following data show the heat capacity, $C(T)$, in British thermal units (Btu) per degree, of a pound of steam at various Fahrenheit temperatures, T.

T	$C(T)$
1000	9.2
1500	10.1
2000	10.8
2500	11.4
3000	12.0

6. Use the trapezoidal rule to estimate the definite integral of $C(T)$ with respect to T from $T = 1000°$ to $T = 3000°$.

7. What are the units of the integral in Problem 6? What does it represent in the real world?

8. Approximately what is the rate of change of heat capacity in Problem 6 at $T = 2000°$?

For Problems 9–14, Calvin and Phoebe start up a hill in their car. When they are 50 ft from the bottom of the hill, the car runs out of gas. They coast to a stop, then start rolling backward. Phoebe figures that their displacement, $D(t)$, in feet from the bottom of the hill, is given by

$$D(t) = -2t^2 + 20t + 50$$

9. How far are they from the bottom of the hill when $t = 3$ s?

10. Find Calvin and Phoebe's average velocity for the interval $t = 3$ to $t = 3.1$ s.

11. By using times closer and closer to $t = 3$, make a conjecture about the limit the average velocity approaches as t approaches 3.

12. The average velocity, $v_{av}(t)$, from 3 to t s can be written

$$v_{av}(t) = \frac{D(t) - D(3)}{t - 3}$$

Substitute appropriate expressions for $D(t)$ and $D(3)$. Then plot the graph of $v_{av}(t)$. Use a friendly window that includes $t = 3$. Sketch the graph, showing the behavior of the function at $t = 3$.

13. The instantaneous velocity at $t = 3$ would be the value of $v_{av}(t)$ at $t = 3$. Show what happens when you substitute $t = 3$, and thus tell why the instantaneous velocity cannot be found by direct substitution.

14. By appropriate algebra, simplify the rational expression in Problem 12. Show that the simplified expression gives you exactly the value of instantaneous velocity that you conjectured in Problem 11.

15. What did you learn as a result of taking this test that you did not know before?

Calculus: Concepts and Applications Instructor's Resource Book
©2005 Key Curriculum Press

Name: _____   Date: _____

Test 2, Chapter 1

Objective: Show what you have learned about limits, derivatives, and definite integrals so far.

Part 1: No calculators allowed (1–7)

1. Write the verbal definition of the **limit** of $f(x)$ as x approaches c.

2. Write the four concepts of calculus.

3. Sketch the graph of a function f for which $f(2) = 7$, but $\lim_{x \to 2} f(x) = 5$.

4. Sketch a graph showing the graphical meaning of definite integral.

For Problems 5–7, the figure shows the graph of the velocity, v, in feet per second, of a roller coaster as a function of the time, t, in seconds, since it started.

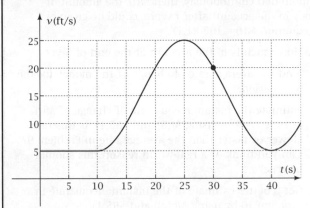

5. Which concept of calculus is used to find the distance the roller coaster travels from $t = 0$ to $t = 35$? Estimate this distance graphically.

6. Which concept of calculus is used to find the rate of change of speed at the instant when $t = 30$? Estimate this rate graphically. Tell the units of this rate of change and the physical name for this quantity.

7. Does the speed have a limit as time approaches 15? If so, write the limit. If not, tell why not.

(Hand in this page to get the rest of the test.)

Test 2, Chapter 1 *continued*

Part 2: Graphing calculators allowed (8–17)

Compound Interest Problem (8–14): Calculus involves finding *instantaneous* rates of change. For instance, if $1000 invested in a savings account has the interest compounded continuously, then $M(t)$, the amount of money in the account after t years, could be given by the equation $M(t) = 1000(1.1)^t$.

8. How much is in the account at the end of 5 yr?

9. Find the average rate of change of the money for the 5-yr period.

10. Estimate the instantaneous rate of change of $M(t)$ at time $t = 5$ by using $M(5)$ and $M(5.1)$. Is this rate slower or faster than the average rate in Problem 9? Can you think of a real-world reason this should be true?

11. Get a better estimate of the instantaneous rate in Problem 10 by using $M(4.9)$ and $M(5.1)$.

12. Get a better estimate of the instantaneous rate in Problem 10 by using $M(5)$ and $M(5.01)$, then by using $M(5)$ and $M(5.001)$.

13. Tell why the instantaneous rate in Problem 10 cannot be found exactly by direct substitution using the equation for $M(t)$.

14. Three hundred years ago, Newton and Leibniz found *algebraic* ways to calculate ("calculus") instantaneous rates. Using these methods, the instantaneous rate in Problem 10 is 153.497997.... Show that the average rate of change you have calculated in Problems 10 and 12 are approaching this number as t gets closer to 5.

15. **Definite integrals** are products of the x- and y-variables of a function. For instance, a definite integral is used to calculate distance (which equals rate times time) when the rate varies. Suppose that you record your speed in feet per second as you drive from a parking lot. Use trapezoids to estimate the distance you travel between $t = 0$ and $t = 20$ s. Show your method.

t	speed
0	6
5	13
10	17
15	22
20	14

16. As you later cruise down the highway, your speed in feet per second is given by

$$v(t) = 30 + 0.3\sqrt{t}$$

Use your trapezoidal rule program to estimate the distance you go between $t = 0$ and $t = 25$ s using $n = 10$ increments and using $n = 100$ increments. What integer value does your distance seem to be approaching as a limit as n gets larger?

17. What did you learn as a result of taking this test that you did not know before?

Calculus: Concepts and Applications Instructor's Resource Book
©2005 Key Curriculum Press

Test 3, Chapter 1

Objective: Show what you have learned about limits, derivatives, and definite integrals so far.

Part 1: No calculators allowed (1–9)

1. Write the verbal definition of limit.

For Problems 2–4, the figure shows the graph of function f for which 1 is the limit of $f(x)$ as x approaches 2, but $f(2) = 3$.

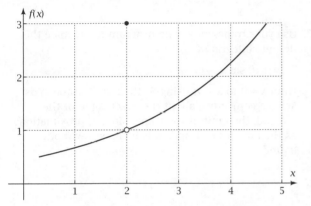

2. The function value will be within 0.3 unit of 1 if $f(x)$ is between 0.7 and 1.3. Draw horizontal lines at $y = 0.7$ and $y = 1.3$. Shade the part of the x-axis for which $f(x)$ will be within 0.3 unit of 1 if x is within this shaded interval.

3. Explain how the restriction ". . . but not equal to c" in the definition of limit applies to function f.

4. How could you keep $f(x)$ arbitrarily close to 1?

For Problems 5–9, the velocity of a car, $v(t)$, in feet per second, is given as a function of t by this graph.

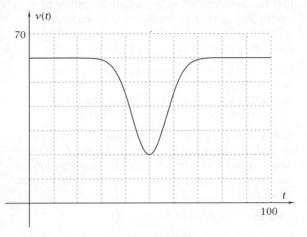

5. Draw a line tangent to the graph at the point on the graph where $t = 60$. Use it to estimate the instantaneous rate of change of $v(t)$ at that time. Which concept of calculus is this instantaneous rate?

6. How far did the car go between $t = 0$ and $t = 20$ s?

7. By counting squares on the graph, estimate the distance the car went between $t = 30$ and $t = 70$ s. Which of the four concepts of calculus do you use to find this distance?

8. Draw four trapezoids on the given figure that you could use to estimate the distance in Problem 7.

9. Tell what might have happened in the real world to make the car's velocity-time graph look this way.

(Hand in this page to get the rest of the test.)

Test 3, Chapter 1 *continued*

Part 2: Graphing calculators allowed (10–18)

Problems 10–12 refer to $f(x) = x + \frac{3\sin(x-3)}{x-3}$.

10. Plot the graph of f. Use a friendly x-window of about [0, 10] and a suitable y-window. (Use radian mode.) Sketch the result on your paper. Show particularly what the graph looks like in a neighborhood of $x = 3$.

11. Function f has a discontinuity at $x = 3$. What kind of discontinuity? What is the limit of $f(x)$ as x approaches 3? Explain why $f(x)$ can be said to have this number as its limit as x approaches 3.

12. About how far away from 3 on the right side can x go and still have $f(x)$ be within 0.5 unit of the limit? About how far on the left side? What *one* number could you use for δ in the definition of limit if ε is equal to 0.5?

Problems 13–15 refer to $h(x) = \frac{1}{(x-2)^2}$.

13. Function h has a discontinuity at $x = 2$. Sketch the graph of h showing what happens at $x = 2$. What kind of discontinuity is it?

14. The derivative of a function is the instantaneous rate of change of the y-value with respect to x. Estimate the derivative of function h at $x = 2.3$. Show your method.

15. Is $h(x)$ increasing or decreasing at $x = 2.3$? How does the answer to Problem 14 tell this?

16. The table shows the force (in pounds) needed to stretch a bungee cord to a certain length (in feet). The amount of work done in stretching a bungee cord equals the force exerted on the cord times the distance it stretches.

Feet	Pounds
10	17
12	20
14	24
16	30
18	37
20	48

Perform an appropriate computation to find the amount of work done in stretching the cord from 10 ft to 20 ft. Name the method used. Tell the units of work in this instance.

17. Use your trapezoidal rule program to estimate the definite integral of

$$y = 10\sin x$$

from $x = 0$ to $x = \pi$ using 5, 10, and 50 trapezoids. Make a conjecture about the exact value of the integral, the limit of the trapezoidal approximations as the number of trapezoids increases without bound.

18. What did you learn as a result of taking this test that you did not know before?

Calculus: Concepts and Applications Instructor's Resource Book
©2005 Key Curriculum Press

Test 4, Sections 2-1 to 2-3

Objective: Show that you understand the definition and properties of limit.

Part 1: No calculators allowed (1–9)

1. Write the formal epsilon-and-delta definition of limit.

Problems 2–6 relate to function f graphed below.

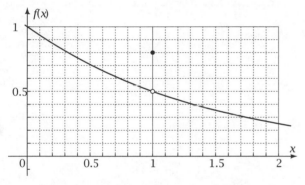

2. Estimate L, where $L = \lim_{x \to 1} f(x) \approx$ _____.

3. Suppose that ε in the definition of limit is chosen to be 0.2. On the graph, draw lines to show what this means.

4. Estimate to one decimal place the interval of values of x around $x = 1$ (but not equal to 1) for which $f(x)$ is within $\varepsilon = 0.2$ unit of L if x is in that interval.

   _____ $< x <$ _____

5. Approximately what is the largest value of δ for which $f(x)$ is within $\varepsilon = 0.2$ unit of L if x is within δ unit of 1 (but not equal to 1)?

   Maximum $\delta \approx$ _____

6. What is the reason for the restriction ". . . but not equal to 1" that comes from the definition of limit?

7. State the limit of a sum property.

8. Explain why the limit of a quotient property can be used to write

   $$\lim_{x \to 3} \frac{3x^2 - 10x - 8}{x - 4}$$

   as the quotient of two limits, but cannot be used for

   $$\lim_{x \to 4} \frac{3x^2 - 10x - 8}{x - 4}$$

9. Factor the numerator of the second limit in Problem 8, and simplify the fraction. Then use the limit theorems to evaluate the limit. At each step, state the name of the limit theorem you used.

(Hand in this page to get the rest of the test.)

Test 4, Sections 2-1 to 2-3 *continued*

Part 2: Graphing calculators allowed (10–20)

Problems 10–12 relate to function f graphed below. This is the same graph as on Part 1 of this test.

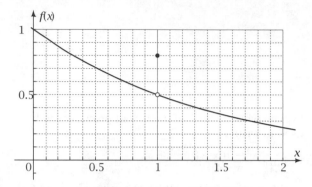

10. The equation of function f is

$$f(x) = \begin{cases} 2^{-x}, & \text{if } x \neq 1 \\ 0.8, & \text{if } x = 1 \end{cases}$$

Calculate precisely the range of x-values (excluding $x = 1$) for which $f(x)$ is within $\varepsilon = 0.2$ unit of the limit $L = 0.5$ when x is within that interval.

11. What is the maximum δ could be in order to reach the conclusion in the definition of limit, which says, "... then $f(x)$ is within 0.2 unit of L"?

12. What is the maximum δ could be in order to ensure that "... then $f(x)$ is within ε units of L?"

13. Let $g(x) = (2x + 7)(3x + 1)$. Find $g(1)$. Then, using the appropriate limit properties, prove that $g(1)$ is the limit of $g(x)$ as x approaches 1.

Problems 14–19 relate to the function $c(x) = x^3$.

14. Estimate the derivative of $c(x)$ at $x = 5$ using the values of $c(5)$ and $c(5.01)$. Estimate the derivative again using the values of $c(5)$ and $c(5.001)$.

15. The exact derivative is the limit of the estimate of the derivative as the second value of x approaches 5. Based on your answers to Problem 14, make a conjecture about what the limit equals.

16. Let $m(x)$ be the difference quotient

$$m(x) = \frac{c(x) - c(5)}{x - 5}$$

Plot the graph of $m(x)$ on your grapher. Sketch the result on your paper. Show, especially, what happens at $x = 5$.

17. By appropriate algebra, simplify the equation for $m(x)$ in Problem 16 to remove the discontinuity at $x = 5$.

18. Use the appropriate limit properties to find the limit of $m(x)$ as x approaches 5. How does the answer compare with the numerical answers in Problem 14 and the conjecture in Problem 15?

19. Figure out a way to calculate the derivative in Problem 18 algebraically, just using the equation for $c(x)$ and the value $x = 5$.

20. What did you learn as a result of taking this test that you did not know before?

Test 5, Chapter 2

Objective: Demonstrate that you understand the definitions and properties of limit and continuity.

Part 1: No calculators allowed (1–7)

1. Write the formal epsilon-and-delta definitions of limit.

2. Sketch the graph of a function f for which $f(3) = 2$ but $\lim_{x \to 3} f(x) = 5$. What kind of discontinuity does f have at $x = 2$?

3. Sketch the graph of a function g for which $\lim_{x \to 2^-} g(x) = 7$ but $\lim_{x \to 2^+} g(x) = 4$. What kind of discontinuity does g have at $x = 2$?

4. Sketch the graph of a function h for which $\lim_{x \to 1^-} h(x) = \infty$ but $\lim_{x \to 1^+} h(x) = -\infty$. What feature does the graph have at $x = 1$?

5. Sketch a graph showing a function that satisfies the hypothesis of the intermediate value theorem on the interval $[1, 5]$ and illustrates the conclusion of that theorem.

6. State the property of the limit of a product of two functions.

7. Mae thinks that if the right and left limits of function f are equal at $x = c$, and if $f(c)$ exists, then f is continuous at $x = c$. Show Mae that she has made an error.

(Hand in this page to get the rest of the test.)

Part 2: Graphing calculators allowed (8–19)

For Problems 8 and 9, let $f(x) = 2 + \sin x - \frac{|x-1|}{x-1}$.

8. Plot the graph of f using a friendly x-window of about $[-10, 10]$ and an appropriate y-window. Sketch the graph on your paper.

9. Find $\lim_{x \to 1^-} f(x)$ and $\lim_{x \to 1^+} f(x)$. Does $f(x)$ have a limit as x approaches 1? Justify your answer.

For Problems 10 and 11, let $g(x) = \begin{cases} 3x, & \text{if } x \le 2 \\ k/x, & \text{if } x > 2 \end{cases}$

10. Use limits to find the value(s) of k that make g continuous at $x = 2$.

11. Plot the graph of g using the value of k found in Problem 10. Use a friendly window for which $x = 2$ is a grid point. Have your instructor check here when you have completed your graph. _____

Problems 12 and 13 apply to function h, defined and graphed below.

$$h(x) = \begin{cases} -x^2 + 4x + 1, & \text{if } x < 3 \\ 4(0.6^{x-3}), & \text{if } x \ge 3 \end{cases}$$

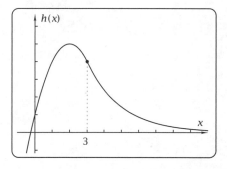

12. h appears to be continuous at $x = 3$ where the rule changes. Show that it *is* continuous there by finding the right and left limits of $h(x)$ and showing that the definition of continuity is met.

13. The graph of h appears to be "smooth" (i.e., no cusp) at $x = 3$. By exploring the quotient

$$\frac{h(x) - h(3)}{x - 3}$$

for $x < 3$ on the left branch and for $x > 3$ on the right branch, decide whether or not the graph really *is* smooth at $x = 3$. Show how you reached your decision.

For Problems 14–16, let $r(x) = 3 + \frac{1}{(x-4)^2}$.

14. The limit of $r(x)$ as x approaches 4 is infinite. Sketch a graph showing clearly that you understand how the graph behaves in a neighborhood of $x = 4$.

15. How close to 4 (on the positive side) must you keep x in order for $r(x)$ to be greater than one million?

16. The limit of $r(x)$ as x approaches infinity is 3. How large would you have to keep x in order for $r(x)$ to be within 0.01 unit of 3? How large would you have to keep x in order for $r(x)$ to be within ε units of 3, where ε is a small positive number?

17. The limit of $p(x) = 7x + 13$ is 48 as x approaches 5. Use the limit properties to prove that this is true.

18. Let $q(x) = x^4$. Evaluate $q(2)$ and $q(3)$. Use the intermediate value theorem to conclude that there is a number between 2 and 3 that is *exactly* equal to the fourth root of 51.

19. What did you learn as a result of taking this test that you did not know before?

Calculus: Concepts and Applications Instructor's Resource Book
©2005 Key Curriculum Press

Test 6, Chapter 2

Objective: Demonstrate that you understand the definitions and properties of limit and continuity.

Part 1: No calculators allowed (1–9)

1. Write the definition of continuity at a point.

2. Write the definition of continuity on an interval.

3. What special modification to the definition of continuity on an interval is made for closed intervals?

4. Sketch the graph of a function g for which $\lim_{x\to 1^-} g(x) = 5$ and $\lim_{x\to 1^+} g(x) = 3$.

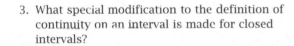

5. What kind of discontinuity does function g in Problem 4 have at $x = 1$?

6. Sketch the graph of a function f that has 8 for its limit as x approaches 6 from *both* sides and that has a value of $f(6)$ but is *not* continuous at $x = 6$.

Problems 7–9 relate to function h graphed below. Function h has a removable discontinuity at $x = 3$ and has 1 as the limit of $h(x)$ as x approaches 3.

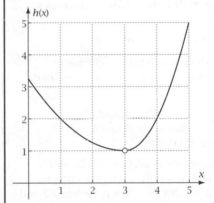

7. Let $\varepsilon = 0.4$ in the definition of limit. Show an interval around $x = 3$ (but not equal to 3) for which $h(x)$ is within 0.4 unit of 1 whenever x is in that interval.

8. What is the largest value of δ such that $h(x)$ is within 0.4 unit of 1 whenever x is within δ units of 3 (but not equal to 3)?

9. How does function h illustrate the reason the restriction ". . . but not equal to c" is necessary in the definition of limit?

(Hand in this page to get the rest of the test.)

Test 6, Chapter 2 *continued*

Part 2: Graphing calculators allowed (10–18)

10. Plot the graph of $c(x) = 5 - (x - 2)^{2/3}$. Use a friendly window that has $x = 2$ as a grid point. Sketch the result. What feature does function c have at $x = 2$? Does $c(x)$ have a limit as x approaches 2?

11. Let $f(x) = \begin{cases} x^2, & \text{if } x \le 2 \\ kx + 10, & \text{if } x > 2 \end{cases}$

    Use limits to find the value(s) of k that make f continuous at $x = 2$. Sketch the graph.

12. Let $r(x) = 5 + \frac{1}{(x-4)^2}$. Plot the graph of r on your grapher and sketch the result. Show, especially, the behavior of $r(x)$ near $x = 4$ and for large values of x.

For Problems 13–17, let $q(x) = x^4$.

13. Find the average rate of change of $q(x)$ with respect to x from $x = 3$ to $x = 3.2$.

14. Write an expression for the average rate of change of $q(x)$ from 3 to x. Simplify the resulting fraction as much as possible. Recall that

    $$a^4 - b^4 = (a - b)(a^3 + a^2 b + ab^2 + b^3)$$

15. Find the limit of the average rate of change in Problem 14 as x approaches 3. For each step, name the limit properties you use.

16. The limit in Problem 15 is the *instantaneous* rate of change at $x = 3$. What name is given to this instantaneous rate of change?

17. Function q is continuous at *all* values of x and has values $q(2) = 16$ and $q(3) = 81$. Give reasoning to show that there is a value of x, $x = c$, between 2 and 3 for which $q(x)$ is *exactly* equal to 37. Find a decimal approximation for c.

18. What did you learn as a result of taking this test that you did not know before?

Calculus: Concepts and Applications Instructor's Resource Book
©2005 Key Curriculum Press

Test 7, Sections 3-1 to 3-4

Objective: Find derivatives of power functions *algebraically*, and show that the answers correspond to numerical derivatives.

Part 1: No calculators allowed (1–11)

1. Write the definition of derivative at a point ($f'(c)$ form).

2. Write the definition of derivative as a function ($f'(x)$ form).

3. Find $f'(x)$: $f(x) = 6x^{100} - 17x^{-3}$

4. Find $\dfrac{dy}{dx}$: $y = (2x + 5)^3$

5. Find $\dfrac{d}{dx}(4x^{0.7} + 13^5)$.

6. Use the definition of derivative (either form) to show that the derivative of $f(x) = x^4$ is $4x^3$.

For Problems 7–11, the figure shows the graph of a function f.

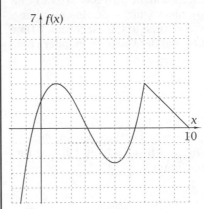

7. On the figure, sketch a reasonable graph of $f'(x)$.

8. Estimate $\lim_{x \to 7^+} f'(x)$ and $\lim_{x \to 7^-} f'(x)$. Based on your answers, tell why there is *no* value of $f'(7)$.

9. Is f continuous at $x = 7$? Explain.

10. Name the feature that appears in the graph of f at $x = 7$.

11. What does the word "differentiable" mean? Is f differentiable at $x = 7$?

(Hand in this page to get the rest of the test.)

Part 2: Graphing calculators allowed
(12–17)

12. Let $g(x) = x^7$. Evaluate $g'(2)$ algebraically. Then use a symmetric difference quotient with $\Delta x = 0.01$ to find $g'(2)$ approximately. Show your work. How close does the approximate value come to the exact value? How close does the numerical derivative by grapher come to the exact value?

13. The graph shows the function $h(x) = x^2 - 5x + 7$. Calculate $h'(2)$ algebraically. On the diagram, draw a line through $(2, h(2))$ with slope $h'(2)$. Tell how the line is related to the graph.

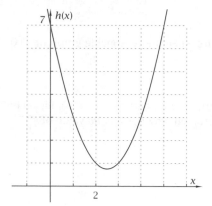

14. Write an equation for the line in Problem 13. Tell how you can use your grapher to verify that the graph of h has the property of local linearity at the point where $x = 2$.

15. What kind of discontinuity does $g(x) = \frac{1}{x-3} + 2$ have at $x = 3$? How close to 3 must x be kept on the right in order to make $g(x) > 1,000,000$?

16. For g in Problem 15, what does $\lim_{x \to \infty} g(x)$ equal? How large must x be kept in order for $g(x)$ to be within 0.0001 of this limit?

17. What did you learn as a result of taking this test that you did not know before?

Test 8, Sections 3-1 to 3-8

Objective: Find derivatives of polynomial and sinusoidal functions *algebraically*.

Part 1: No calculators allowed (1–12)

For Problems 1–5, find an equation for the derivative.

1. $y = \sin^7 x$

2. $f(x) = \cos 18x$

3. $g(x) = \sin(\cos x^4)$

4. $\dfrac{d}{dx}(x^2 + 5x - 7)^8$

5. $\dfrac{d}{dx}(5 - x)^{100}$

For Problems 6–7, find the second derivative.

6. $f(x) = 7x^{10}$

7. $\dfrac{d^2}{dx^2}(\sin 4x)$

8. The figure shows the velocity and acceleration of a moving object as functions of time, *t*. For the times shown, tell whether the object is speeding up or slowing down.

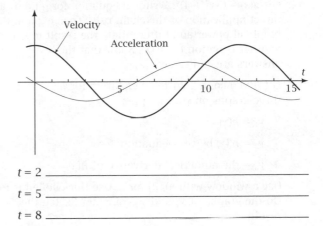

t = 2 _____

t = 5 _____

t = 8 _____

t = 11 _____

9. For the object in Problem 8, write a time when the object is stopped, but the acceleration is not zero.

10. If the velocity of a moving object is given by

$$v(t) = 6t^2$$

where $v(t)$ is in cm/s, write an equation for the acceleration function, $a(t)$.

11. If $v(t) = 6t^2$ as in Problem 10, write an equation for the displacement, $x(t)$, if $x(0) = 11$ cm.

12. The graph shows a function with a removable discontinuity at the point (4, 7). On the graph, show why the conclusion of the intermediate theorem might *not* be true on the interval [1, 5].

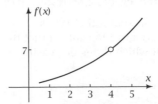

(Hand in this page to get the rest of the test.)

Part 2: Graphing calculators allowed (13–25)

13. Let $f(x) = \sin 4x$. Write an equation for $f'(x)$. Use the equation for $f'(x)$ to tell whether $f(x)$ is increasing or decreasing when $x = 3$, and at what rate.

14. Let $g(x) = (5x^3 + 4)^2$. Write an equation for $g'(x)$ by a direct application of the chain rule. Then expand the binomial power and differentiate the result to get another equation for $g'(x)$. Show that the two answers are equivalent.

15. Let $h(x) = \cos x^3$. Write an equation for $h'(x)$. Plot three graphs on your grapher,

    $y_1 = h(x)$

    $y_2 = h'(x)$ by your equation

    $y_3 =$ the numerical derivative of $h(x)$

    Use a window with [0, 2] for x. Use thick style for y_3. Do the graphs of y_2 and y_3 coincide? Sketch the result.

16. Let $f(x) = 5x^2 - 13x + 4$. Find $f(2)$. Find $\lim_{x \to 2} f(x)$, justifying your answer by showing how the limit theorems are applied. What does the equality of the two answers imply about function f at $x = 2$?

For Problems 17–19, the figure shows the graph of the distance between the tip of the second hand on a clock and the floor varying sinusoidally with time.

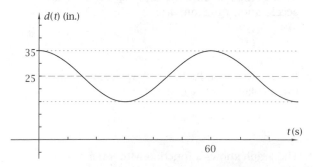

17. Write the particular equation for $d(t)$, where t is time in seconds and $d(t)$ is distance in inches.

18. Find an equation for the algebraic derivative, $d'(t)$.

19. At time $t = 70$, the graph shows that $d(t)$ is decreasing. Use the derivative to confirm that this is true. Tell the rate at which $d(t)$ is decreasing.

Problems 20–24 pertain to the proofs of the algebraic derivatives of sine and cosine.

20. $\lim_{x \to 0} \frac{\sin x}{x}$ is equal to 1. Give numerical evidence to show that this is true.

21. The figure shows a sector of a unit circle with positive central angle x radians and two right triangles also with acute angle x. By comparing areas of these three figures, show that this inequality is true:

    $$\cos x \le \frac{\sin x}{x} \le \frac{1}{\cos x}$$

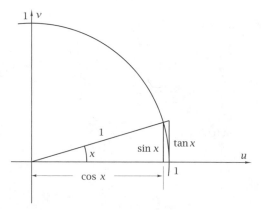

22. Name the theorem that allows you to conclude from the inequality in Problem 21 that the limit of $(\sin x)/x$ really is 1.

23. By the definition of derivative, if $f(x) = \sin x$, then

    $$f'(x) = \lim_{h \to 0} \frac{\sin(x + h) - \sin x}{h}$$

    By trigonometry, this equation is equivalent to

    $$f'(x) = \lim_{h \to 0} \frac{\cos(x + 0.5h) \cdot \sin 0.5h}{0.5h}$$

    Show that the limit really does approach $\cos x$ as h approaches zero.

24. Let $g(x) = \sin(\pi/2 - x)$. Find $g'(x)$. How does the result allow you to conclude that the derivative of $\cos x$ is $-\sin x$?

25. What did you learn as a result of taking this test that you did not know before?

Test 9, Section 3-9

Objective: Find derivatives of exponential and logarithmic functions *algebraically*.

Part 1: No calculators allowed (1–14)

For Problems 1–10, find the derivative.

1. $f(x) = 7e^{2x}$

2. $g(x) = 10e^{\sin x}$

3. $h(x) = 5\cos(e^{-0.3x})$

4. $f(x) = 8\ln 13x$

5. $y = 6\ln x^{11}$

6. $u = 9\ln(\cos 2x)$

7. $y = 5\ln e^x$

8. $f(x) = 4^x$

9. $g(x) = 0.3^{\sin x}$

10. $\dfrac{d}{dx}(\ln 5^x)$

For Problems 11 and 12, find the second derivative.

11. $y = \ln x^7$

12. $f(x) = 4e^{-3x}$

For Problems 13 and 14, find the antiderivative function.

13. $f'(x) = 8^x \ln 8$

14. $y' = 15e^{3x}$

(Hand in this page to get the rest of the test.)

Test 9, Section 3-9 *continued*

Part 2: Graphing calculators allowed (15–27)

15. The figure shows the graph of $y = 2^x$. Plot this function as y_1 and the numerical derivative as y_2 on your grapher. Sketch the derivative graph here.

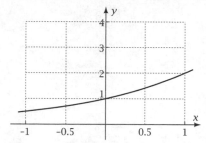

16. The derivative of $y = 2^x$ is a constant times 2^x. What does this constant equal? Plot the graph of $y_3 = $ (this constant)(2^x) using thick style. Does this graph coincide with the numerical derivative graph?

17. The figure shows the graph of $y = 4^x$. Plot this function as y_1 and the numerical derivative as y_2 on your grapher. Sketch the derivative graph here.

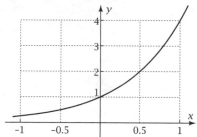

18. The derivative of $y = 4^x$ is a constant times 4^x. What does this constant equal? Plot the graph of $y_3 = $ (this constant)(4^x) using thick style. Does this graph coincide with the numerical derivative graph?

19. The figure shows the graph of $y = e^x$. Plot this function as y_1 and the numerical derivative as y_2 on your grapher. Sketch the derivative graph here.

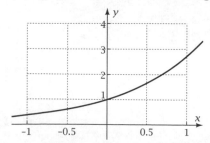

20. In calculus, what is the advantage of using exponential functions with the irrational number e as the base instead of some integer such as 2, 4, or 10?

21. Use the definition of derivative to show that

$$\frac{d}{dx}(5^x) = 5^x \lim_{h \to 0} \frac{5^h - 1}{h}$$

22. Give numerical evidence to support the conjecture that the limit given in Problem 21 equals ln 5.

23. Let $y = \ln x$. Write this equation in exponential form, then differentiate both sides implicitly with respect to x to show that the derivative of the natural logarithm function is the reciprocal function.

24. The figure shows the graph of $y = \ln x$. Plot this function as y_1 and the numerical derivative as y_2 on your grapher. Sketch the derivative graph here.

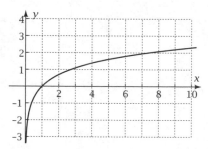

25. Plot as y_3 the algebraic derivative of $y = \ln x$ that you derived in Problem 23. Use thick style. What graphical evidence do you have that the algebraic derivative is correct?

26. The figure shows the graph of $y = \ln 0.5x$. Find the algebraic derivative, y'. Plot

$y_1 = \ln 0.5x$

$y_2 = $ numerical derivative of y_1

$y_3 = $ algebraic derivative of $\ln 0.5x$

Sketch your results on the graph below. Do the two derivative graphs coincide? How is the derivative of $\ln 0.5x$ related to the derivative of $\ln x$ in Problems 24 and 25?

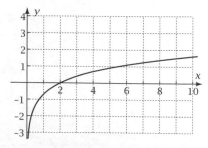

27. What did you learn as a result of taking this test that you did not know before?

Calculus: Concepts and Applications Instructor's Resource Book
©2005 Key Curriculum Press

Test 10, Chapter 3

Objective: Find derivatives of polynomial and sinusoidal functions *algebraically*.

Part 1: No calculators allowed (1–15)

1. Write the definition of derivative (either form).

2. Write the physical meaning of derivative.

3. Write the graphical meaning of derivative.

4. What does the word "differentiate" mean in the context of calculus?

5. Write the chain rule as a *verbal procedure*.

6. Find $f'(x)$: $f(x) = (x^3 + 11)^6$

7. Find $g'(x)$: $g(x) = \cos^4(x^7)$

8. Find $h(x)$: $h'(x) = x^{2001}$

9. Find y': $y = 2^{\sin x}$

10. Find $\dfrac{d}{dx}\left(e^{x^3}\right)$.

11. Find y'': $y = \ln x^5$

12. Find $\dfrac{d^2y}{dx^2}$: $y = 6^x$

13. Find the antiderivative, $f(x)$, if $f'(x) = 10e^{5x}$.

14. Find $m(x)$: $m'(x) = 35 \sin 5x$

15. Find the particular solution for the antiderivative in Problem 14 if $m(0) = 3$.

(Hand in this page to get the rest of the test.)

Test 10, Chapter 3 *continued*

Part 2: Graphing calculators allowed (16–27)

16. Let $f(x) = 5x^3$. Use the definition of derivative to prove that $f'(x) = 15x^2$.

17. Find an estimate of $f'(4)$ for the function in Problem 16 using a symmetric difference quotient with $\Delta x = 0.01$. Compare this approximate answer with the exact answer you get algebraically from the derivative formula in Problem 16.

18. Plot the graph of $y = (\sin x)/x$ in a friendly window that includes $x = 0$ as a grid point. Sketch the result on your paper. What graphical evidence do you have that $\lim_{x \to 0} [(\sin x)/x] = 1$?

19. In the proof that $\frac{d}{dx}(\sin x) = \cos x$, you found that

$$\frac{d}{dx}(\sin x) = \lim_{\Delta x \to 0} \frac{\cos(x + 0.5\Delta x) \cdot \sin 0.5\Delta x}{0.5\Delta x}$$

Show that the limit really does approach $\cos x$ as Δx approaches zero.

20. Mae thinks that because $\sin' x = \cos x$, then $\sin' 3x$ should equal $\cos 3x$. Give Mae graphical evidence that her answer is an error. Tell her what rule she forgot to apply.

21. Use the definition of derivative to show that if $f(x) = 6^x$, then

$$f'(x) = 6^x \cdot \lim_{h \to 0} \frac{6^h - 1}{h}$$

Give numerical evidence that the limit approaches ln 6.

22. Transform the equation $y = \ln x$ to exponential form. Then differentiate implicitly to show that $y' = 1/x$.

Earth's Rotation Problem (Problems 23–26): As Earth rotates on its axis, a point on the equator gets closer to and farther from the Sun. Assume that the center of Earth is 93 million miles from the Sun and that the radius of Earth is 4 thousand miles. The period of Earth's rotation is, of course, 24 hours.

23. Assuming that the distance varies sinusoidally with time, write an equation for the distance as a function of time of day, letting $t = 0$ hours represent midnight.

24. Use the answer to Problem 23 to find an equation for the velocity of a point on the equator as it moves away from or toward the Sun. Find the velocity at dawn, $t = 6$ hr. Interpret the sign and magnitude of this velocity.

25. Use the velocity equation in Problem 24 to calculate the velocity at noon, $t = 12$ hr. How do you interpret this answer physically?

26. Find an equation for the acceleration of the point on the equator as a function of time. At what time of day is the acceleration a maximum? What is this maximum acceleration?

27. What did you learn as a result of taking this test that you did not know before?

Test 11, Chapters 1, 2, and 3

Objective: Show that you understand limits, derivatives, antiderivatives, and definite integrals.

Graphing calculators allowed

1. Show that $f(x) = \frac{3x^2 - 2x - 1}{x - 1}$ takes on an **indeterminate form** at $x = 1$.

2. The graph shows function f as it would appear on your grapher. Name the feature that appears at $x = 1$.

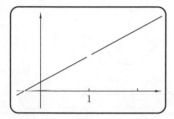

3. The concept of **limit** was invented to handle functions that cannot be evaluated directly by substitution. Make a table of values of $f(x)$ from Problem 1 for these values of x. From the table, figure out what $\lim_{x \to 1} f(x)$ equals.

x	$f(x)$
0.995	
0.996	
0.997	
0.998	
0.999	
1.000	
1.001	
1.002	
1.003	
1.004	
1.005	

4. Using only the data from the table in Problem 3, tell what range of values x must be kept within in order for $f(x)$ to be within 0.01 unit of the limit.

5. Limits can sometimes be found algebraically. Simplify the fraction for $f(x)$ in Problem 1, then take the limit of the resulting expression as x approaches 1. Name the limit properties you use.

6. Limits are defined using ε and δ. If $\varepsilon = 0.007$, what is the largest value of δ which ensures that $f(x)$ in Problem 1 is within ε units of the limit whenever x is within δ units of 1 (but not equal to 1)?

7. Limits are used to find **derivatives,** the second major concept of calculus. These instantaneous rates of change always take the indeterminate form 0/0. Suppose that the **velocity** of a model rocket is given by

$$v(t) = 2^t$$

where $v(t)$ is in feet/second and t is in seconds. The **acceleration** is the derivative of the velocity. Estimate the acceleration of the rocket when $t = 3$ s using a symmetric difference quotient with $\Delta t = 0.1$.

8. Use the numerical derivative command on your grapher to estimate the acceleration in Problem 7.

9. Use the algebraic derivative to find the acceleration in Problem 7 precisely.

10. The third major concept of calculus is the **definite integral,** which gives a way to find the product of x and y for a function if y varies. Because distance equals rate times time, the distance traveled by the rocket in Problem 7 is given by a definite integral. The graph shows function v from Problem 7. Draw three trapezoids and use the areas of these trapezoids to estimate the distance traveled by the rocket from $t = 0$ to $t = 3$ s.

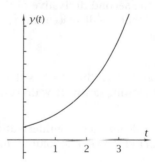

11. The exact value of the distance in Problem 10 is the limit of T_n, the areas of n trapezoids, as n approaches infinity. Use your **trapezoidal rule** program to find T_{50}, T_{100}, and T_{500}.

12. Use your grapher's **numerical integration** command to find the distance in Problem 10. Do the values of T_n in Problem 11 seem to be approaching this number as n increases?

(Over)

Test 11, Chapters 1, 2, and 3 *continued*

13. You have learned how to find some derivatives **algebraically.** Use the **chain rule** to find $f'(x)$ if $f(x) = (\sin 2x)^3$.

14. The figure shows the graph of f from Problem 13. Evaluate $f'(1)$. Show that a line through $(1, f(1))$ with slope $f'(1)$ calculated by your answer to Problem 13 really is **tangent** to the graph.

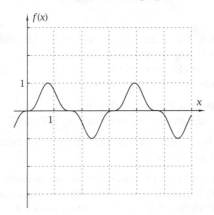

15. If you were to zoom in on the point $(1, f(1))$ in Problem 14, you would see a property called **local linearity.** Tell what this property means. (It is not necessary to *do* the zooming.)

16. The acceleration of a moving object is the rate of change of velocity, or the **second derivative** of the displacement. Suppose that the displacement, y, of an object is given by

$$y = t^3 - 5t^2$$

Find equations for y' and y''. At time $t = 1$, is the object speeding up or slowing down? How do you decide?

17. The fourth concept of calculus is the **antiderivative, or indefinite integral.** Find the general solution for y if $y' = 20e^{4x}$.

18. A function is **continuous** at a point if the limit of the function equals the function value at that point. A function is **differentiable** at a point if there is a value for the derivative at that point. The graph shows the piecewise function

$$f(x) = \begin{cases} -x^2 - 2x + 3, & \text{if } x < 0 \\ 3 + \sin x, & \text{if } x \geq 0 \end{cases}$$

Explain why f is continuous, but not differentiable at $x = 0$.

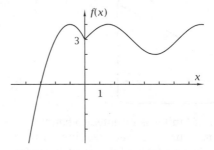

19. Let $g(x) = \begin{cases} -x^2 - 2x + 3, & \text{if } x < 0 \\ 3 + k \sin x, & \text{if } x \geq 0 \end{cases}$

where k stands for a constant. Find the value of k that makes g differentiable at $x = 0$.

20. Plot the graph of function g on your grapher. Check your graph with your instructor. _____

21. What did you learn as a result of taking this test that you did not know before?

Calculus: Concepts and Applications Instructor's Resource Book
©2005 Key Curriculum Press

Test 12, Sections 4-1 to 4-5

Objective: Find derivatives of combinations of elementary transcendental functions.

Part 1: No calculators allowed (1–13)

For Problems 1–8, write the algebraic derivative for the given function.

1. $y = \cos^{-1} x$

2. $y = \tan x$

3. $y = \tan^{-1} x$

4. $y = \sec^{-1} x$

5. $y = \sec x$

6. $y = 3^x$

7. $y = e^x$

8. $y = \ln x$

For Problems 9–13, use the chain rule, power rule, product rule, and quotient rule to find the algebraic derivative of the given function.

9. $y = e^{2x} \cos 3x$

10. $y = \cot^3 (5x)$

11. $y = \ln (x^{1.7})$

12. $y = \dfrac{2^x}{x^2}$

13. Find $\dfrac{d^2 y}{dx^2}$ if $y = e^{3x}$.

(Hand in this page to get the rest of the test.)

Test 12, Sections 4-1 to 4-5 *continued*

Part 2: Graphing calculators allowed (14–22)

14. Wanda Wye wonders why the derivative of a product of two functions does not equal the product of the two derivatives. Show her that if $f(x) = g(x) \cdot h(x)$, where $g(x) = x^5$ and $h(x) = x^8$, then $f'(x)$ does *not* equal $g'(x) \cdot h'(x)$.

15. Use the product rule to find $f'(x)$ if $f(x) = x^4 \sin^3 x$. Show that $f'(2)$ found this way equals $f'(2)$ found numerically by your grapher.

16. If $y = \frac{u}{v}$, where u and v are differentiable functions of x, write the formula for $\frac{dy}{dx}$.

17. Use the quotient properties from trigonometry in conjunction with the quotient rule to show how to derive the formula

$$\frac{d}{dx}(\tan x) = \sec^2 x$$

18. Given $y = \sec^{-1} x \Rightarrow y' = \frac{1}{|x|\sqrt{x^2 - 1}}$, find $f'(x)$ if $f(x) = \sec^{-1} x^3$. Simplify.

19. You have previously conjectured that the derivative of a power with a *negative* exponent could be found using the power rule, which was derived for positive integer exponents. Now that you know how to algebraically find the derivative of a quotient, you have been able to *prove* that this is true. Demonstrate this proof by finding y' for $y = x^{-3}$, first transforming x^{-3} to a quotient.

20. Let $y = \sin^{-1} x$. Take the sine of both sides and simplify. Then differentiate implicitly to derive the formula for the derivative of $\sin^{-1} x$. Show how the formula can be written as an algebraic function of x by drawing y as an angle in standard position in a *uv*-coordinate system and marking the reference triangle with x, 1, and a radical.

21. The figure shows the graph of $f(x) = \tan^{-1} x$. Use the algebraic derivative formula to calculate $f'(2)$. Plot a line through the point $(2, f(2))$ with slope equal to $f'(2)$. How does the result confirm that the algebraic formula is correct?

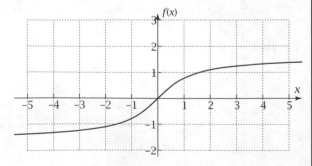

22. What did you learn as a result of taking this test that you did not know before?

Test 13, Sections 4-6 to 4-8

Objective: Find algebraic derivatives of parametric functions and implicit relations, and relate differentiability and continuity.

Part 1: No calculators allowed (1–7)

1. State, in three words, the relationship between differentiability and continuity.

2. Let $f(x) = x^3$. Prove, quickly, that f is continuous at $x = 4$.

3. The statement

$$\lim_{x \to c} [f(x) - f(c)] = f'(c) \cdot 0$$

occurs in the proof that differentiability implies continuity. Explain why the hypothesis "f is differentiable at $x = c$" allows you to conclude that the limit is zero. Then use the properties of limits to conclude that f really *is* continuous at $x = c$.

4. For the parametric function

$$x = \sec t$$
$$y = t \ln t$$

find $\dfrac{dx}{dt}$, $\dfrac{dy}{dt}$, and $\dfrac{dy}{dx}$.

5. Differentiate implicitly to find dy/dx.

$$x\sqrt{y} + x^3 \sec^3 y = 3^2$$

6. Let $y = x^{11/3}$. Transform this equation to an implicit relation involving only integer exponents. Then differentiate implicitly to find y'. Show that your answer agrees with the answer found directly by using the power rule for derivatives on the original equation.

7. Let $y = \ln x$. Write this equation in exponential form, then differentiate both sides implicitly with respect to x to show that the derivative of the natural logarithm function is the reciprocal function.

(Hand in this page to get the rest of the test.)

Test 13, Sections 4-6 to 4-8 *continued*

Part 2: Graphing calculators allowed (8–20)

Problems 8-11 refer to the deltoid graphed here, with parametric equations

$$x = 2 \sin t + \sin 2t$$

$$y = 2 \cos t - \cos 2t$$

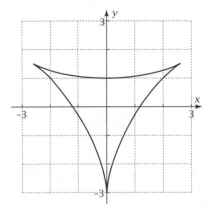

8. The cusp in Quadrant I occurs where $t = \pi/3$. Find the values of x and y at this cusp.

9. Find equations for dx/dt and dy/dt. Evaluate these derivatives at the cusp in Quadrant I.

10. If an object is moving along the deltoid and t is the number of seconds since it started moving, what can you conclude about the motion of the object at the cusp in Quadrant I? How do you reach this conclusion?

11. Find an equation for dy/dx as a function of t. What form does dy/dx take at the cusp in Quadrant I? What number does dy/dx seem to be approaching as t approaches $\pi/3$?

For Problems 12 and 13, piecewise function f is defined by

$$f(x) = \begin{cases} x^3 + 1, & \text{if } x \leq 1 \\ a(x - 2)^2 + b, & \text{if } x > 1 \end{cases}$$

12. Use one-sided limits in an appropriate way to find the values of the constants a and b that make f differentiable at $x = 1$.

13. Show that the limit of $f'(x)$ as x approaches 1 from the right and from the left can be equal, but f still is not differentiable at $x = 1$.

Problems 14-18 refer to the hyperbola graphed here, specified by the implicit relation

$$x^2 + 4xy - y^2 = 29$$

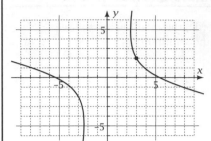

14. Find an equation for y'.

15. The point (3, 2) is on the graph. Use the equation in Problem 14 to find the slope of the tangent line at (3, 2).

16. Construct a line at (3, 2) with slope as in Problem 15. Is the line really tangent to the graph?

17. Amos substitutes $(x, y) = (5, 7)$ into the equation for y' in Problem 14 and finds, correctly, that y' equals $-19/3$. Explain to Amos that although he gets an answer, the answer has no meaning in this problem.

18. Just for fun, see if you can find the *other* point on the graph (not shown in the figure) at which $x = 3$.

19. *Second Derivative Problem:* By the parametric chain rule, you know that

$$\frac{dy}{dx} = \frac{y'(t)}{x'(t)}$$

where the ′ derivatives are taken with respect to t. Use the quotient formula, the chain rule (assuming that t is a function of x), and the fact that dt/dx is the reciprocal of dx/dt to prove that

$$\frac{d^2y}{dx^2} = \frac{y''(t) \cdot x'(t) - y'(t) \cdot x''(t)}{[x'(t)]^3}$$

20. What did you learn as a result of taking this test that you did not know before?

Calculus: Concepts and Applications Instructor's Resource Book
©2005 Key Curriculum Press

Name: _____   Date: _____

Test 14, Sections 4-7 and 4-8

Objective: Find derivatives of parametric functions and implicit relations.

Graphing calculators allowed

Twister Problem: Jo and Bill track a tornado. At 2-min intervals they record the following data, where x and y are in miles east and north, respectively, of their tracking station, and t is time in minutes.

t	x	y
0	3.0	1.0
2	5.0	1.8
4	6.1	3.4
6	5.5	5.6
8	3.8	5.0
10	4.2	3.6
12	6.1	3.4
14	7.6	4.6
16	8.2	6.5
18	7.0	9.3

1. Plot the x- and y-coordinates on this graph. Connect the points with a smooth curve.

2. How do you explain the fact that two different points have the same x- and y-coordinates?

3. Use symmetric difference quotients to estimate dx/dt and dy/dt when $t = 14$.

4. Use the parametric chain rule and your answers to Problem 3 to estimate dy/dx when $t = 14$.

5. Find an estimate of dy/dx at $t = 14$ again, directly from the x- and y-data in the table.

6. On your graph in Problem 1, plot a line at the twister's position when $t - 14$ with slope equal to dy/dx. What does this line tell about the tornado?

7. Just for fun, see if you can find an estimate of how fast the tornado is moving at $t = 14$ min.

For Problems 8–13, the figure shows part of the epicycloid with parametric equations

$x = 4 \cos t + \cos 4t$

$y = 4 \sin t + \sin 4t$

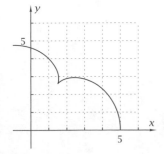

8. Confirm that the cusp shown is at the point where $t = \pi/3$.

9. Find algebraic derivatives dx/dt and dy/dt. Evaluate these derivatives at $t = \pi/3$.

10. A line from the origin through the cusp is tangent to the graph at the cusp, as you can see by drawing the line. What is the slope of this tangent line?

11. Explain why the parametric chain rule fails to give an answer for dy/dx at $t = \pi/3$.

12. Plot the parametric equations of the epicycloid on your grapher. Windows of [−9.4, 9.4] for x and [−6.2, 6.2] for y will be reasonable for a TI-82, TI-83, or TI-84. Use a t-step of $\pi/48$ and a t-range of 0 to 2π.

13. Trace your graph in Problem 12 to the cusp (that is, $t = \pi/3 = 1.0471...$). Then find numerically the value of dy/dx at that point. Explain why the grapher gives an answer, but the answer is *wrong*!

14. The derivative of a power formula was derived for *integer* exponents, but works for any rational constant exponent. Demonstrate that this is true for $y = x^{13/7}$ by first transforming the equation so that it involves only integer exponents, then differentiating implicitly with respect to x.

15. In order to get correct answers for implicit differentiation problems you must observe the power rule and the chain rule. Find an equation for dy/dx for this implicit relation:

$$x^5 y^3 + \tan^4 y = 10^5$$

Problems 16–19 involve the ellipse shown below. It is specified by the implicit relation $9x^2 + 25y^2 = 900$.

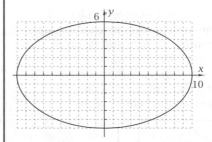

16. Calculate the values of y when $x = 8$.

17. By implicit differentiation, find an equation for dy/dx in terms of x and y.

18. Show that your equation in Problem 17 gives reasonable answers for dy/dx at the two points where $x = 8$.

19. What did you learn as a result of taking this test that you did not know before?

Test 15, Section 4-9

Objective: Work problems involving related rates.

Graphing calculators allowed

Ellipse Animation Problem: For Problems 1–5, Annie plots an ellipse on a computer screen. It has horizontal radius *a* and vertical radius *b*. She investigates the rate of change of the area of the ellipse as *a* increases at 7 mm/s and *b* decreases at 11 mm/s.

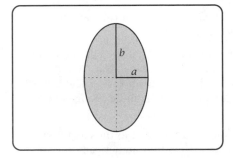

1. Assuming that *a* and *b* change smoothly, write the known rate and the wanted rate as derivatives.

2. Annie recalls that the area of an ellipse is $A = \pi ab$. Use this relationship among the variables to get an equation for the wanted rate.

3. Annie sets the animation in motion. When $a = 30$ and $b = 50$, will the area be increasing or decreasing? At what rate?

4. Annie resets the animation and starts it in motion again. When $a = 40$ and $b = 20$, will the area be increasing or decreasing? At what rate?

5. Annie resets the animation and starts the motion a third time. When the rate of change of area is zero, will *b* be larger than *a* or smaller than *a*? By what factor?

Cylinder-in-Cone Animation Problem: For Problems 6–9, Peggy plots a cylinder inscribed in a cone on a computer screen. The cone has altitude 120 mm and radius 50 mm. The sample point (x, y) is at the place where the top base of the cylinder touches an element of the cone. She sets a slider to increase *x* at a uniform rate of 4 mm/s and investigates the rate of change of volume of the cone.

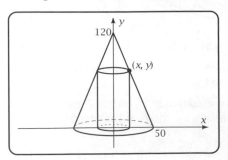

6. Assuming that *x* changes uniformly, write the known rate and the wanted rate as derivatives.

7. Find the volume of the cylinder as a function of *x* alone. Then differentiate to find the rate of change of volume as a function of *x*.

8. Show that the volume is increasing at the instant when $x = 10$ and decreasing at the instant when $x = 50$.

9. The volume of the cylinder will be a maximum when its rate of change is zero. Find the value of *x* when this happens, and calculate the maximum volume.

10. *Baseball Problem:* A baseball "diamond" is a square 90 ft on a side. Chris is running from second base to third base at 20 ft/s. Sam is running from third base to home plate at 15 ft/s. When Chris is 30 ft from third base and Sam is 40 ft from third base, is the distance between them increasing or decreasing? At what rate?

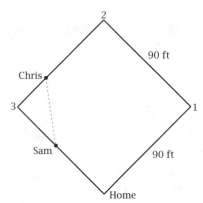

11. What did you learn as a result of taking this test that you did not know before?

Test 16, Chapter 4

Objective: Find algebraic derivatives, including products, quotients, parametrics, and implicit relations.

Part 1: No calculators allowed (1–6)

1. Write the quotient rule for derivatives. That is, write y' if $y = u/v$, where u and v are differentiable functions of x.

2. Use the quotient rule to find

$$\frac{d}{dx}\left(\frac{\sin 3x}{x^6}\right)$$

Simplify the answer.

3. Rewrite the quotient in Problem 2 as a product with x to an appropriate power. Show that the product rule gives a derivative equivalent to the answer in Problem 2.

4. Use the definition of inverse trig functions and appropriate trig and calculus to show that

$$y = \tan^{-1} x \Rightarrow y' = \frac{1}{1 + x^2}$$

5. For the following parametric function, find $\frac{dy}{dx}$ and $\frac{d^2y}{dx^2}$.

$$x = t^2$$

$$y = t^5$$

6. In deriving the product rule from the definition of derivative, you encountered this limit:

$$y' = \lim_{\Delta x \to 0} \frac{\Delta u \cdot v + u \cdot \Delta v + \Delta u \Delta v}{\Delta x}$$

Show how the product rule follows by taking this limit.

(Hand in this page to get the rest of the test.)

Test 16, Chapter 4 *continued*

Part 2: Graphing calculators allowed (7–19)

Implicit Relation Problem (7–9): The graph shows the implicit relation $x^3 y^2 = 256$.

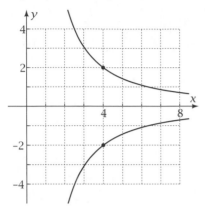

7. Confirm algebraically that the points (4, 2) and (4, −2) are on the graph, as indicated in the figure.

8. Differentiate $x^3 y^2 = 256$ implicitly with respect to x. Solve for y', and simplify the resulting fraction. Use the answer to find y' at the point (4, −2).

9. Show on the graph that the derivative in Problem 8 is correct.

Parametric Function Problem (10–12): The figure shows the circle with parametric equations

$x = 5 \cos t$

$y = 5 \sin t$

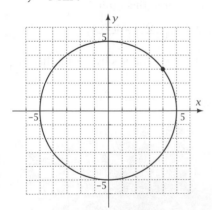

10. Find equations for $\frac{dy}{dt}$, $\frac{dx}{dt}$, and $\frac{dy}{dx}$.

11. The point (4, 3) seems to be on the graph. Find t when $x = 4$, and substitute this value, without round-off, into the y-equation. Is (4, 3) really on the graph?

12. Find $\frac{dy}{dx}$ at the point in Quadrant I where $x = 4$. Show graphically that your answer is correct.

Continuity and Differentiability Problem (13–15): The graph shows the piecewise function

$$f(x) = \begin{cases} x^3, & \text{if } x < 1 \\ 3x - 2, & \text{if } x \geq 1 \end{cases}$$

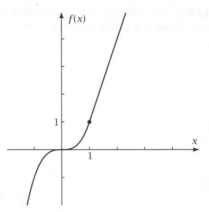

13. By taking one-sided limits, prove that f is continuous at $x = 1$.

14. Function f appears to be differentiable at $x = 1$. Is the fact that f is continuous at $x = 1$ sufficient to imply that it is differentiable there? Explain.

15. Find the derivative, $f'(x)$. By taking one-sided limits, prove that f is differentiable at $x = 1$.

16. For $f(x) = (3x + 7)^8 (4x - 5)^3$, find $f'(x)$. Simplify the answer by appropriate factoring. Use the answer to find the *three* values of x at which the graph of f will have a horizontal tangent line.

17. Use the quotient rule to show that the derivative of $y = \tan x$ is $y' = \sec^2 x$.

18. Find $\frac{d}{dx}(\sin^{-1} 5x^3)$.

19. What did you learn as a result of taking this test that you did not know before?

Test 17, Sections 5-1 to 5-4

Objective: Find antiderivatives, and estimate definite integrals using Riemann sums.

Part 1: No calculators allowed (1–11)

1. Write the definition of **indefinite integral.**

2. Write another name for indefinite integral.

3. The figure shows the graph of $y = f(x)$. Show on the graph that you understand the meaning of **upper Riemann sum,** U_4, with $n = 4$ increments for this definite integral. Show the sample points.

$$\int_1^9 f(x)\,dx$$

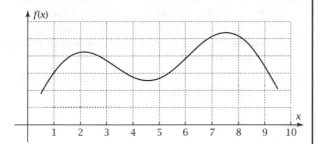

4. On this copy of the figure in Problem 3, show the corresponding **lower Riemann sum,** L_4. Show the sample points.

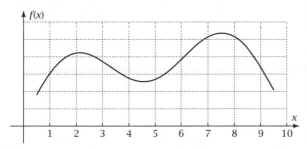

5. Write the definition of **definite integral.**

6. Find dy if $y = 5x \tan x$.

7. Find y if $dy = 72x^3\,dx$.

8. On this figure, sketch the difference in meaning between Δy and the differential dy.

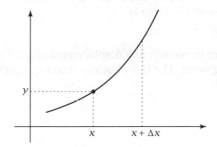

9. Evaluate: $\int \cos u\,du$

10. In Problem 9, the du is the **differential** of the inside function, where the outside function is the cosine function. Show how the following integral can be transformed to this form by clever multiplication and division by a constant. Then evaluate the integral.

$$\int \cos x^3 (x^2\,dx)$$

11. What is the difference in meaning between a *left* Riemann sum and a *lower* Riemann sum?

(Hand in this page to get the rest of the test.)

Test 17, Sections 5-1 to 5-4 *continued*

Part 2: Graphing calculators allowed (12–22)

12. Find the particular equation for

$$f(x) = \int (\cos x)^7 \sin x \, dx$$

if $f(0) = 3$.

Work Problem (13–16): The amount of work done in dragging a box across the floor equals the force you exert on the box times the displacement through which you drag it. Suppose that the force is

$$F(x) = 80x \cdot 2^{-x}$$

where $F(x)$ is force in pounds at a displacement of x ft from the starting point. The figure below shows the graph of F.

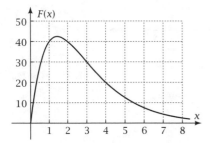

13. Explain why a definite integral must be used to find the work done in dragging the box from $x = 0$ to $x = 8$ ft.

14. Show the calculations in finding M_4, a **midpoint Riemann sum** with 4 increments, to approximate this integral.

15. Find the equation of the linear function that best fits F at $x = 1$.

16. What words describe the appearance of the graph of F if you were to zoom in on the point $(1, 40)$?

Problems 17–21 concern the integral $\int_1^3 x^3 \, dx$.

17. Explain why a trapezoidal rule sum would be an overestimate for this integral.

18. Explain why a midpoint Riemann sum would be an underestimate for this integral.

19. Find lower sums L_{50} and L_{200} and upper sums U_{200} and U_{50}. What number do the lower and upper sums seem to be approaching as n increases? How does the existence of such a number illustrate the definition of definite integral?

    $L_{50} =$ _____

    $L_{200} =$ _____

    $U_{200} =$ _____

    $U_{50} =$ _____

20. Find the trapezoidal rule sum, T_{200}, and the midpoint Riemann sum, M_{200}. How do these sums confirm your answers to Problems 17–19?

21. Let $g(x) = \int x^3 \, dx$. Find $g(3)$, $g(1)$, and the quantity $g(3) - g(1)$. What happens to the constant of integration? What does the result of your calculations suggest as an algebraic way to evaluate definite integrals?

22. What did you learn as a result of taking this test that you did not know before?

Calculus: Concepts and Applications Instructor's Resource Book
©2005 Key Curriculum Press

Test 18, Sections 5-5 to 5-7

Objective: Show that you understand the fundamental theorem of calculus and its derivation, and properties of definite integrals.

Part 1: No calculators (1–10)

1. Write the definition of **indefinite integral.**

2. The fundamental theorem of calculus and the definition of definite integral both conclude something about the integral of $f(x)\, dx$ from a to b. Show that you understand the difference between the two by writing this conclusion.

   Definition: $\displaystyle\int_a^b f(x)\, dx =$

   Theorem: $\displaystyle\int_a^b f(x)\, dx =$

3. The proof of the fundamental theorem uses the mean value theorem as a lemma. State the mean value theorem.

4. Rolle's theorem may be considered to be a special case of the mean value theorem. Sketch the graph of a function that illustrates both the hypotheses and the conclusion of Rolle's theorem.

The fundamental theorem gives a way to find the exact value of a definite integral algebraically. For Problems 5–7, use the theorem to evaluate the integral.

5. $\displaystyle\int_1^4 x^{3/2}\, dx$

6. $\displaystyle\int_{-\pi}^{\pi} (5\cos x + 4\sin x)\, dx$

7. $\displaystyle\int_{20}^{50} dx$

For Problems 8–10, suppose that

$$\int_3^7 f(x)\, dx = 17, \int_3^{11} f(x)\, dx = 40, \text{ and } \int_3^{11} g(x)\, dx = 10$$

8. Find $\displaystyle\int_7^3 f(x)\, dx.$

9. Find $\displaystyle\int_7^{11} f(x)\, dx.$

10. Find $\displaystyle\int_3^{11} [f(x) - g(x)]\, dx.$

(Hand in this sheet to get the rest of the test.)

Test 18, Sections 5-5 to 5-7 *continued*

Part 2: Graphing calculators allowed (11–23)

For Problems 11–15, let $I = \int_0^{\pi/2} \cos x \, dx$.

11. Sketch a graph that shows why any *left* Riemann sum is also an *upper* Riemann sum for this integral.

12. Sketch a graph that shows why a midpoint Riemann sum is an *overestimate* for I.

13. Find an upper Riemann sum, U_{50}, for I.

14. Find a midpoint Riemann sum, M_{50}, for I.

15. Evaluate I exactly, using the fundamental theorem. Show that the answers to Problems 13 and 14 are consistent with this exact value.

16. Evaluate this integral. Explain why it is negative.

$$\int_1^4 (x^2 - 6x + 2) \, dx$$

17. Evaluate this integral. Explain why it is negative, even though the integrand is positive for all values of x within the limits of integration.

$$\int_2^1 e^{2x} \, dx$$

18. Evaluate this integral. Explain why it is positive, even though the integrand is negative for all values of x within the limits of integration.

$$\int_{2\pi}^{\pi} \sin x \, dx$$

19. Evaluate this integral using the fundamental theorem. Explain why it is zero.

$$\int_3^3 x \, dx$$

Fundamental Theorem Proof Problem (20–22): The fundamental theorem of calculus was proved by showing that by a clever choice of the sample points for a Riemann sum, you can get a value for R_n that is independent of n, no matter how large n is. The same reasoning can be used to find a Riemann sum with $n = 1$ increment. The figures show $f(x) = 3x^2$, and $g(x) = \int f(x) \, dx$ (with $C = 0$).

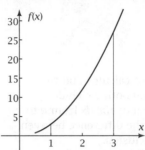
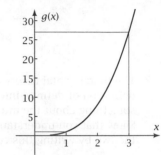

20. On the g graph, illustrate the point $x = c$ in (1, 3) where the conclusion of the mean value theorem is true for g on the interval [1, 3]. Then calculate the value of c and store it in your grapher.

21. On the f graph, show a Riemann "sum" with one rectangle, using the $x = c$ from Problem 20 as the sample point. Then calculate the value of this Riemann "sum."

22. Show that the Riemann sum in Problem 21 is exactly equal to the value of the integral of $f(x) \, dx$ from 1 to 3, as found by the fundamental theorem.

23. What did you learn as a result of taking this test that you did not know before?

Test 19, Sections 5-8 to 5-10

Objective: Evaluate and apply definite integrals to volume and other problems.

Part 1: No calculators allowed (1–4)

Work Problem (1–2): Manuel Dexterity drags a heavy piece of furniture π feet (unusual in the real world!) across the floor, exerting a varying force F, in pounds, given by

$F = 100 \cos 0.5x$

where x is the number of feet he has dragged it.

1. Sketch the graph of F. Draw a narrow vertical strip of width dx in the region under the graph. Show a sample point (x, F) on the graph, within the strip.

2. Work is defined to be force times displacement. Write dW, the amount of work done dragging the furniture by the displacement dx, and evaluate the integral to find W, the total amount of work done dragging the furniture from 0 to π ft.

Dead-Reckoning Problem (3–4): Submarines measure the distance they have gone using "dead-reckoning" (short for "deduced reckoning"), using the velocity measured at various times. Suppose that the following velocities in knots (nautical miles per hour) have been measured.

x hours	v knots
0.0	4
0.1	7
0.2	6
0.3	8
0.4	11

3. Use Simpson's rule with $n = 4$ increments to calculate the approximate number of nautical miles the submarine goes in the 0.4 h shown.

4. On this graph of the data, sketch something to show why Simpson's rule might be expected to give less error than the trapezoidal rule.

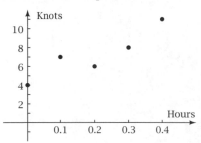

(Hand in this page to get the rest of the test.)

Test 19, Sections 5-8 to 5-10 *continued*

Part 2: Graphing calculators allowed (5–11)

Exponential Horn Problem (5–8): The figure shows the graph of $y = 10e^{-0.1x}$.

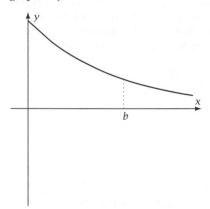

5. On a copy of the figure, draw a thin vertical strip of width dx. Write the differential of area, dA. By appropriate integration, find the area of the region under the graph from $x = 0$ to $x = b$.

6. A solid "horn" is formed by rotating about the x-axis the region under the graph from $x = 0$ to $x = b$. Sketch the horn formed by the rotating region and the disk formed by the rotating slice in Problem 5.

7. Find dV, the volume of the disk. By appropriate integration, find V, the volume of the horn between $x = 0$ and $x = b$.

8. Find the limit of the volume of the horn as b approaches infinity. Surprising?

Volcano Problem (9–10): A volcano-like solid is formed by rotating the region under the graph of $y = x^2$ from $x = 0$ to $x = 2$ about the line $x = 3$, as shown in the figure.

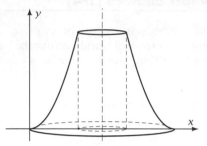

9. Find the volume of the solid by writing an appropriate integral and evaluating it using numerical integration.

10. Evaluate the integral again using Simpson's rule with $n = 100$ increments. Is the answer close to the value in Problem 9?

11. What did you learn as a result of taking this test that you did not know before?

Calculus: Concepts and Applications Instructor's Resource Book
©2005 Key Curriculum Press

Test 20, Chapter 5

Objective: Find definite and indefinite integrals.

Part 1: No calculators allowed (1–12)

1. Write an equation for dy if $y = (3 - 4x)^7$.

2. Find a general equation for y if $dy = \sec^2 x\, dx$.

3. Evaluate the integral: $\displaystyle\int 24e^{3x}\, dx$

4. Evaluate the integral: $\displaystyle\int 48\tan^5 x \sec^2 x\, dx$

5. Differentiate: $h(x) = x^3 \ln 2x$

6. Evaluate: $\displaystyle\int_2^5 6x^2\, dx$

7. Find the area of the region under one arch of the graph of $f(x) = \cos x$.

8. State the definition of indefinite integral.

9. State the definition of definite integral.

10. State the fundamental theorem of calculus.

11. State the mean value theorem.

12. On what interval does Rolle's theorem apply for function h, graphed here? Sketch something to show that you understand the conclusion of Rolle's theorem.

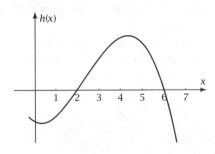

(Hand in this page to get the rest of the test.)

Part 2: Graphing calculators allowed (13–24)

13. Evaluate the integral, showing clearly that you understand the properties of odd and even functions integrated between symmetrical limits:

$$\int_{-1}^{1} (20x^4 + 60x^5)\, dx$$

Problems 14–19: The graph shows $f(x) = 0.3x^2$ and function g, which is an indefinite integral of f.

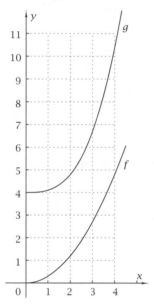

14. Find the *exact* value of $\int_{1}^{4} f(x)\, dx$ using the fundamental theorem.

15. Find an approximation for the integral in Problem 14 using the Simpson's rule with $n = 100$ increments.

16. Find another approximation for the integral in Problem 14 using a midpoint Riemann sum with $n = 100$ increments. Which approximation is closer to the actual value in Problem 14, the Riemann sum or the Simpson's rule sum?

17. Write the particular equation for $g(x)$, observing that $g(0) = 4$.

18. Find the value of $x = c$ in the open interval $(1, 4)$ at which the conclusion of the mean value theorem is true for function g.

19. Draw lines on the graph of g showing clearly that you understand what the conclusion of the mean value theorem says.

X-Ray Problem (20–22): A radiologist treats a patient with X-rays. Over the 1-second period that the X-ray source is on, the intensity, $R(t)$, in roentgens per second, is given by the equation

$$R(t) = 20t(0.1)^t$$

where t is time in seconds.

20. On the graph of R, below, draw a narrow vertical strip of width dt. Pick a sample point $(t, R(t))$ on the graph within the strip. What is true about the values of $R(t)$ for any value of t within the strip?

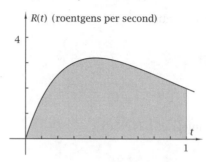

21. The radiation dosage, D, equals the intensity multiplied by time. Write the differential of dosage, dD, as a function t and dt.

22. Write an integral for the dosage the patient receives in the 1-second time interval. Evaluate the integral using the numerical integration feature of your grapher.

23. The region under the graph of $y = -4 \cos x$ from $x = \pi/2$ to $x = \pi$ is rotated about the y-axis to form a solid. Sketch the solid. Find its volume. Use your grapher's built-in numerical integration feature to evaluate the integral.

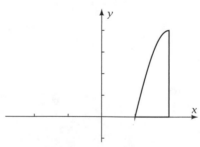

24. What did you learn as a result of taking this test that you did not know before?

Calculus: Concepts and Applications Instructor's Resource Book
©2005 Key Curriculum Press

Test 21, Sections 6-1 to 6-4

Objective: Differentiate natural logs and exponential functions, and integrate exponential and reciprocal functions.

Part 1: No calculators allowed (1–11)

1. State the definition of ln x as a definite integral.

2. State the fundamental theorem of calculus in its "derivative of a definite integral" form.

3. Show how the fundamental theorem in its derivative of an integral form allows you to write in one step the derivative ln' x.

4. State the uniqueness theorem for derivatives.

5. Write in "plain English" what the uniqueness theorem means.

6. Find y' if $y = (\cos x)^{\tan x}$.

7. Find $f'(x)$: $f(x) = \int_{2}^{\sin x} \tan t\, dt$.

8. Integrate: $\int \dfrac{1}{\cos x} \sin x\, dx$

9. Integrate: $\int \tan x\, dx$

10. Find: $\dfrac{d}{dx}(\log_5 x)$

11. Integrate: $\int 5^x\, dx$

(Hand in this page to get the rest of the test.)

Test 21, Sections 6-1 to 6-5 *continued*

Part 2: Graphing calculators allowed (12–21)

12. The uniqueness theorem states:

    If $f'(x) = g'(x)$ for *all* x in the domain, and
    if $f(a) = g(a)$ for *one* $x = a$ in the domain,
    then $f(x) = g(x)$ for *all* x in the domain.

    Use the uniqueness theorem to prove that

    $$\ln(ax) = \ln a + \ln x$$

    for all positive values of x (where a is a positive constant).

13. Let $y = \ln 7x$. Find y' two ways: (a) by differentiating directly, with the aid of the chain rule, and (b) by first transforming $\ln 7x$ using the property in Problem 12. Show that both answers are equivalent.

14. Explain why $\int x^{-1}\,dx$ cannot be done using the power rule for integrals.

15. Evaluate

    $$\int_{12}^{4} \frac{1}{x}\,dx$$

    using the fundamental theorem. Get a decimal approximation, too, by evaluating the terms in the exact answer.

16. Explain why the answer to Problem 14 is negative. A graph may help.

17. Use the properties of ln to write the exact answer to Problem 16 as a *single* ln of *one* number.

18. Logarithmic differentiation can be used to find derivatives of exponential functions. Use this method to derive the formula

    $$\frac{d}{dx}(b^x) = b^x \ln b$$

    where b is a positive constant.

19. *Compound Interest Problem 1:* You recall from algebra that if money is left in a savings account earning interest compounded continuously at an annual percentage rate (APR) of 6%, then the amount of money, M, after t years is given by

    $$M = M_0(1.06^t)$$

    Suppose that an investment of $M_0 = \$1000$ is made at time $t = 0$ yr.

    Find the instantaneous rate of change of the amount of money at $t = 0$, at $t = 10$, and at $t = 100$ yr.

20. *Compound Interest Problem 2:* The amount of money, M, in an account at any time t can be calculated starting with the basic property that dM/dt is directly proportional to M. Suppose that

    $$\frac{dM}{dt} = 0.04M$$

    By algebra the variables can be separated.

    $$M^{-1}\,dM = 0.04\,dt$$

    If there is $500 in the account at $t = 0$ and x dollars at $t = 20$, then

    $$\int_{500}^{x} M^{-1}\,dM = \int_{0}^{20} 0.04\,dt$$

    Evaluate the integral. Then solve numerically for x to find the amount of money after 20 yr.

21. What did you learn as a result of taking this test that you did not know before?

Calculus: Concepts and Applications Instructor's Resource Book
©2005 Key Curriculum Press

Test 22, Sections 6-5 and 6-6

Objective: Find limits and derivatives of exponentials and logs, and integrals of exponentials and reciprocals.

Part 1: No calculators allowed (1–11)

1. On this graph, illustrate the definition of $\ln x$ as a definite integral.

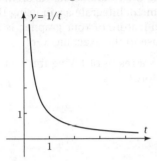

2. State the fundamental theorem of calculus in its "derivative of a definite integral" form.

3. Differentiate: $y = e^{5x}$

4. Integrate: $\int e^{7x}\, dx$

5. Differentiate: $y = \log_6 8x$

6. Integrate: $\int e^{\tan x} (\sec^2 x\, dx)$

7. Differentiate: $y = \int_1^{e^{2x}} x^5\, dx$

8. Integrate: $\int_1^7 \frac{1}{p}\, dp$

9. Evaluate: $\displaystyle \lim_{x \to 4} \frac{3x^2 - 14x + 8}{x - 4}$

10. Evaluate: $\displaystyle \lim_{x \to 0} \frac{x^2 + \cos 5x - 1}{x^2}$

11. Evaluate: $\displaystyle \lim_{x \to \infty} x^{1/x}$

(Hand in this page to get the rest of the test.)

Test 22, Sections 6-5 and 6-6 *continued*

Part 2: Graphing calculators allowed (12–20)

Problems 12–15 apply to the function $f(x) = 10x^2 e^{-x}$ graphed below.

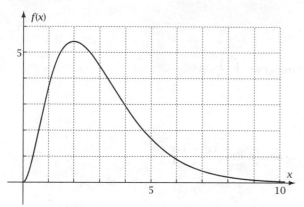

12. Find an equation for $f'(x)$.

13. Find $f'(3)$. Plot a line on the graph above at the point $(3, f(3))$ having slope $f'(3)$. How is the line related to the graph at that point?

14. The graph appears to have a high point at $x = 2$. By appropriate use of the derivative, tell whether or not it *actually* does.

15. The function in Problem 12 appears to approach zero as x approaches infinity. By appropriate use of l'Hospital's rule, find out whether or not this is true.

16. The definition of e is $\lim_{x \to \infty} (1 + x^{-1})^x$. By appropriate use of l'Hospital's rule, show that this is actually true.

17. On your grapher, plot the graph of $y = e^{\ln x}$. Sketch the result. What do you notice about the graph?

18. Recall that if $y = 2^x$, then $dy = 2^x \ln 2\, dx$. Using this information, it is possible to write the antiderivative,

$$\int 2^x\, dx$$

What does this integral equal?

19. Evaluate $\int_0^2 2^x\, dx$ using the fundamental theorem and the results of Problem 18. Integrate again using the numerical integration feature of your grapher. Is the numerical answer close to the exact answer?

20. What did you learn as a result of taking this test that you did not know before?

Calculus: Concepts and Applications Instructor's Resource Book
©2005 Key Curriculum Press

Test 23, Section 6-6

Objective: Find limits, derivatives, and integrals involving logs and exponentials.

Graphing calculators allowed

Find the derivative, differential, integral, or limit.

1. y', if $y = \ln(5x - 7)^3$

2. $f'(x)$, if $f(x) = \ln(\cos x)$

3. $\dfrac{d}{dx}(e^{4x})$

4. $\dfrac{dy}{dx}$, if $y = \log_9 x$

5. $\dfrac{d(6^x)}{dx}$

6. $\displaystyle\int e^{7x}\, dx$

7. $\displaystyle\int 8^x\, dx$

8. $\displaystyle\int e^{x\ln 8}\, dx$

9. $\displaystyle\int x^3\, e^{x^4}\, dx$

10. $\displaystyle\int e^3\, dx$

11. $f'(x)$ if $f(x) = \displaystyle\int_1^x \dfrac{1}{1 + t^2}\, dt$

12. $g'(x)$ if $g(x) = \tan^{-1} x$

13. $f'(x)$ and $g'(x)$ in Problems 11 and 12 are identical, yet f and g are not the same function. Explain why not.

14. $\displaystyle\int (\ln x)^4\, (dx/x)$

15. y' if $y = \tan x$

16. $\displaystyle\int \tan x\, dx$

17. $\displaystyle\int \dfrac{1}{f(x)}\, f'(x)\, dx$

18. $\displaystyle\int \dfrac{du}{u}$

19. $\displaystyle\int \dfrac{\sec^2 x + \sec x \tan x}{\sec x + \tan x}\, dx$

20. $\displaystyle\int \sec x\, dx$

21. $\displaystyle\int \sec^2 x\, dx$

22. $\displaystyle\lim_{x \to \infty} \dfrac{7x^2 - 4}{3 - 4x^2}$

23. $\displaystyle\lim_{x \to 0} \dfrac{x^2 - \cos 5x + 1}{e^x - x - 1}$

24. $\displaystyle\lim_{x \to 0} (1 + 0.2x)^{1/x}$

25. Show numerically that $(1 + 0.2x)^{1/x}$ is close to the limit you found in Problem 24 by substituting 0.001 for x.

Population Problem: The town of Scorpion Gulch is home to 800 people. Last year the population increased by 60, so the City Council figures that the population is growing at a rate of 60/800 = 0.075, or 7.5% a year. They wish to make projections of the future population based on this information.

26. Let P be the population at time t years after the present. They assume that the rate of change of population is directly proportional to the population

$$\dfrac{dP}{dt} = 0.075P$$

Separate the variables and integrate both sides of this differential equation.

27. By appropriate use of the properties of natural logs, transform the answer to Problem 26 so that P is expressed explicitly in terms of t.

28. The Scorpion Gulch City Council believes that the town should incorporate when the population reaches 2000. According to the mathematical model in Problem 26, when is this likely to be?

29. What did you learn as a result of taking this test that you did not know before?

Test 24, Chapter 6

Objective: Find derivatives of exponential functions and integrals of reciprocal functions using logs.

Graphing calculators allowed

1. The fundamental theorem of calculus in the derivative of an integral form provides a way to define a function whose derivative is any function you like. Show that the theorem works for

$$f(x) = \int_2^x \cos t \, dt$$

   by evaluating the integral, then finding $f'(x)$.

2. By finding $g'(x)$ for

$$g(x) = \int_3^{\tan x} \sec t \, dt$$

   show that the theorem can be used to find the derivative of a function defined as an integral even if you don't know how to do the integrating.

3. Explain why the power rule for integrals does not work for

$$\int x^{-1} \, dx$$

4. Write the definition of natural log, ln x, as a definite integral. Show that the integral, evaluated numerically with 5 as its upper limit of integration, gives the same answer as ln 5.

5. As a result of the fundamental theorem and the definition of ln, what does ln$'$ x equal?

6. Explain why ln, defined as a definite integral, is **continuous** for all $x > 0$.

7. Use the definition of indefinite integral to write $g'(x)$ if

$$g(x) = \int \frac{1}{x} \, dx$$

8. The integral of the reciprocal function can be used for other functions you could not integrate algebraically before. Use the quotient property from trig to write

$$\int \tan x \, dx$$

   as the integral of the reciprocal function. Then evaluate the integral.

9. Show numerically that ln 2 + ln 7 = ln 14.

10. The definition of e is

$$e = \lim_{n \to 0} (1 + n)^{1/n}$$

   Find an approximate numerical value for e by letting $n = 0.0001$. How close is the answer to the precise value of e from your calculator?

11. You have found that

$$\frac{d}{dx}(\log_b x) = \frac{1}{x} \log_b e$$

   Tell what the advantage is in calculus for using base-e logs.

12. Without doing a formal proof, tell how the uniqueness theorem for derivatives lets you conclude that $\log_e x = \ln x$ for all $x > 0$.

13. The change-of-base property can be used to differentiate logs without having to memorize the formula in Problem 12. Find $f'(x)$:

$$f(x) = \log_{10} (\tan x)$$

14. Use logarithmic differentiation to find y' if $y = 5^x$.

15. Quick! Find $\frac{d}{dx}(10^{\sin x})$.

16. Integrate: $\int 5^x \, dx$

17. The calculus of exponential functions is easier if you use the natural exponential function, $y = e^x$. Why is y' so easy to find in this case?

18. Evaluate: $\int e^{3x} \, dx$

19. Use the algebraic definition of logarithm along with the property $\log_e x = \ln x$ to explain why $e^{\ln x} = x$.

20. Use l'Hospital's rule to find

$$\lim_{x \to \infty} \frac{5x^2 - 11x + 7}{4 + 3x - 2x^2}$$

21. Use l'Hospital's rule in an appropriate way to find this limit:

$$\lim_{x \to 0} (1 + 5x)^{1/x}$$

22. Integrate: $\int x \, e^{x^2} \, dx$

23. Find $f'(x)$: $f(x) = x^3 \ln x$

24. Integrate by the fundamental theorem: $\int_{-20}^{-5} \frac{1}{x} \, dx$

25. Differentiate: $y = 5e^{\ln x^3}$

26. Integrate: $\int \frac{(\ln x)^5}{x} \, dx$

27. What did you learn as a result of taking this test that you did not know before?

Test 25, Chapters 1 to 6 [120 minutes]

Objective: Show that you understand the definitions and techniques of calculus (Chapters 1 to 6).

Graphing calculators allowed

At the beginning of the course, you learned that the **derivative** of a function is its instantaneous rate of change. With just this knowledge you were able to differentiate any function **numerically.**

1. For $f(x) = 2^x$, find an approximation for $f'(1)$ using a **symmetric difference quotient** with $\Delta x = 0.01$. Show your work.

A derivative has a **graphical** meaning.

2. Show the graphical meaning of the derivative in Problem 1 by constructing a line at $(1, f(1))$ with slope equal to $f'(1)$.

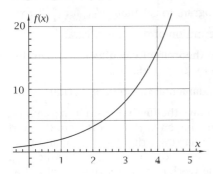

Derivatives can be **applied** to real-world problems.

3. Suppose that $f(x) = 2^x$ in Problems 1 and 2 represents the velocity of a moving object in feet per second as a function of time in seconds. What physical quantity does $f'(x)$ represent?

At the beginning of the course, you learned that a **definite integral** gives you a way to multiply x by y for a function, where y varies with x.

4. If x and $f(x)$ are time and velocity as in Problem 3, what physical quantity does $\int_1^4 2^x \, dx$ represent?

5. After a brief time when you estimated definite integrals by **counting squares,** you learned to estimate them numerically by dividing the region under the graph of a function into **trapezoids.** Draw three trapezoids for $\int_1^4 2^x$.

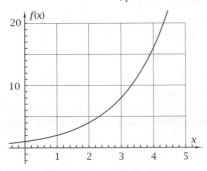

6. Estimate $\int_1^4 2^x$ by finding the areas of each of the three trapezoids in Problem 5 and adding them.

7. Explain why your answer to Problem 6 *overestimates* the definite integral.

8. To get better numerical estimates, you wrote a program to use the **trapezoidal rule,** which you used manually in Problems 5 and 6. Find T_{100} for the integral in Problem 5.

Numerical and graphical methods are good for illustrating a concept, but they are tedious to use. So **Newton** and **Leibniz** found **algebraic** ways. These algebraic ways are based on the concept of **limit.**

9. Write the definition of limit.

10. Write the definition of derivative, which is based on the concept of limit.

The first algebraic technique you learned was the derivative of the **power function.**

11. Show the steps in using the definition of derivative to get $f'(x) = 3x^2$ from $f(x) = x^3$.

12. Which step in your solution to Problem 11 is justified by the **limit of a sum** property?

13. Does the power rule for derivatives work for **exponential functions** such as $f(x) = 2^x$?

Next, you differentiated **trigonometric** (or **circular**) functions algebraically.

14. In the derivation of the formula $\sin' x = \cos x$, you encountered this limit:

$$\lim_{h \to 0} \frac{\sin h}{h}$$

Give numerical evidence that this limit equals 1.

15. The **chain rule** lets you find derivatives of **composite functions.** Find

$$\frac{d}{dx} [\cos(x^3 + 5)]$$

16. The **product rule** for derivatives lets you differentiate products (obviously!). Find y' if $y = x^5 \sin 2x$.

17. The **quotient rule** for derivatives lets you differentiate the other trigonometric functions. Use the quotient rule to show that $\tan' x = \sec^2 x$.

18. **Implicit differentiation** can be used to find derivatives of inverse trig functions. If $y = \tan^{-1} x$, derive the formula

$$y' = \frac{1}{1 + x^2}$$

(Continued on the next page.)

Test 25, Chapters 1 to 6 [120 minutes] *continued*

One-sided limits are useful in describing a function that is **discontinuous** at a given point.

19. For $f(x) = \begin{cases} ax^2, & \text{if } x < 3 \\ 10x, & \text{if } x \geq 3 \end{cases}$

    write $\lim_{x \to 3^-} f(x)$ and $\lim_{x \to 3^+} f(x)$.

20. What value of the constant a makes **piecewise** function f be **continuous** at $x = 3$?

21. Show that f in Problem 20 is *not* differentiable at $x = 3$. Explain why this fact does *not* contradict the **relationship between differentiability and continuity.**

Motion in two dimensions can be modeled with **parametric functions.**

22. A pendulum swings in an elliptical path given by

    $x = 5 \cos t$

    $y = 3 \sin t$

    where x and y are in feet and t is in seconds. What is the velocity in the x-direction when $t = 2$? Is x increasing or decreasing?

23. In Problem 22, what is the acceleration in the x-direction when $t = 2$? Is the pendulum speeding up or slowing down in the x-direction at that time? How do you tell?

24. The **parametric chain rule** lets you find the slope of the path in Problem 22. Find an algebraic expression for dy/dx.

25. Find dy/dx in Problem 24 when $t = 2$. Show graphically that your answer is correct.

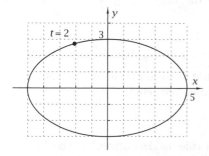

Once you learned algebraic methods for differentiating, you could understand the fourth concept of calculus, the **indefinite integral.**

26. Write the definition of indefinite integral.

27. Write the other name for indefinite integral.

28. Find: $\int x^3 (10 - x^4)^7 \, dx$

The definition of definite integral uses the concept of **Riemann sum.**

29. Show graphically the meaning of Riemann sum by illustrating a midpoint sum, M_3, with $n = 3$ increments, for $\int_1^4 2^x \, dx$ from Problem 5.

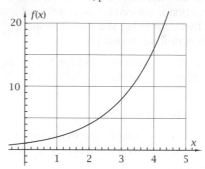

30. Use your program to calculate M_{100} for $\int_1^4 2^x \, dx$.

31. Write the definition of definite integral.

The **fundamental theorem of calculus** lets you evaluate definite integrals *exactly*, by algebra.

32. State the fundamental theorem of calculus.

33. The graph shows the **force**, $F = \sin 0.2x$ (pounds), exerted in moving an object at x ft from the starting point. Draw a narrow strip of width dx, and pick a sample point (x, F) on the graph, within the strip. Write dW, the **work** done in moving the object a distance dx.

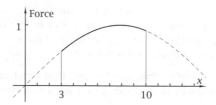

34. The integral $\int_3^{10} \sin 0.2 \, dx$ equals the work done in moving the object in Problem 33 from $x = 3$ to $x = 10$ ft. Find this amount of work by using the fundamental theorem to evaluate the integral.

35. The proof of the fundamental theorem is based on the **mean value theorem.** Sketch a graph which shows clearly that you understand the conclusion of the mean value theorem.

The fundamental theorem has another form, the **derivative of an integral** form.

36. Let $f(x) = \int_1^{\sin x} t^3 \, dt$. Find $f'(x)$.

37. The fundamental theorem in its second form lets you find a function whose derivative is $1/x$. This function is called $\ln x$. Write the definition of $\ln x$, the **natural logarithm** function, as a definite integral.

(Continued on the next page.)

38. You found that $\frac{d}{dx}\log_b x = \frac{1}{x}\log_b e$. Show that $f(x) = \ln x$ and $g(x) = \log_e x$ have identical derivatives, and also a point in common.

39. Name the theorem which allows you to conclude that $\ln x$ and $\log_e x$ are the same function.

40. Show why $\int \tan x\, dx = \ln|\sec x| + C$.

Natural logs and exponentials let you differentiate and integrate **exponential functions** algebraically, a problem you did numerically and graphically at the beginning of this test.

41. By **logarithmic differentiation,** find $f'(x)$ if $f(x) = 2^x$.

42. By observing the pattern in the answer to Problem 41, find the antiderivative, $\int 2^x\, dx$.

43. Use the fundamental theorem to evaluate $\int_1^4 2^x\, dx$.

44. Which comes closer to the exact value of $\int_1^4 2^x\, dx$, T_{100} from Problem 8 or M_{100} from Problem 30?

Limits involving $0/0$ or ∞/∞ can be evaluated by **l'Hospital's rule.** This technique is particularly useful for limits involving both exponential functions and trig functions, for which simplification of the fraction cannot be done.

45. Evaluate: $\lim\limits_{x\to 0} \dfrac{1-e^x}{\sin 7x}$

Definite integrals can be estimated from **data** even if you don't know an algebraic formula for the integrand.

46. Time-clock records show the following numbers of employees working at the construction site for Scorpion Gulch Dam at various times starting at midnight ($t = 0$) on one day.

t	People
0	27
6	38
12	120
18	110
24	31

The total number of hours put in by these employees that day equals the number of workers times the number of hours. Because the number of workers varies, the total number of hours can be found by a definite integral. Use **Simpson's rule** to estimate this number of hours. Your work should reveal that you know how Simpson's rule works.

47. What is the *one* most important thing you have learned so far as a result of taking calculus?

Test 26, Chapters 1 to 6 [120 minutes]

Objective: Show that you understand the definitions and techniques of calculus (Chapters 1 to 6).

Graphing calculators allowed

There are four concepts of calculus, and there are four major phases in the study of each concept. The first phase is formal definition.

1. Write the definition of limit.

2. Write the definition of derivative.

3. Write the definition of definite integral.

4. Write the definition of indefinite integral.

Being able to write a definition is not enough. You must also *understand* what it means. Understanding of a concept usually comes slowly over a period of time.

5. The function $f(x) = \frac{(5x + 3)(x - 2)}{(x - 2)}$ takes on the indeterminate form 0/0 for $f(2)$. But $\lim_{x \to 2} f(x) = 13$. Show that you understand the definition of limit by finding out how close x must be kept to 2 in order for $f(x)$ to be within 0.01 unit of 13.

6. Economists make statements such as "The inflation rate right now is 4% per year." Explain why the inflation rate is a derivative.

7. As you leave the parking lot after this exam, the distance you've gone equals velocity times time. Explain why a definite integral must be used to find the distance rather than simple multiplication.

8. Tell why the concept of indefinite integral had to await your learning to find derivatives *algebraically* rather than simply numerically or graphically.

Defining and understanding concepts is good. But you must also be able to *do* them. Evaluations can be done numerically, graphically, or algebraically.

9. If $f(x) = 2 + x^{-1} \sin x$, give numerical evidence to show that $\lim_{x \to \infty} f(x) = 2$.

10. The figure below shows graphically that the limit of $f(x)$ in Problem 9 is 2. Plot this graph on your grapher. Use a friendly window of about [0, 100] for x and [0, 3] for y.

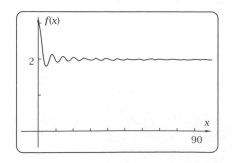

11. On your grapher the graph of f in Problem 10 looks like a straight line beyond $x = 50$. Zoom in on the point (90, 2), thus showing that the graph really is not a straight line. Check with your instructor when you have done this. _____

12. Sometimes you get a better insight about a concept as you work with it. Based on your work in Problems 9–11, why do you suppose the words "$f(x)$ stays arbitrarily close to 2" are more descriptive of the concept of limit than the words "$f(x)$ gets closer and closer to 2"?

13. The second term of $f(x)$ in Problem 9 takes on the indeterminate form $\infty \cdot 0$ as x approaches 0. Use l'Hospital's rule to find the limit of the second term as x approaches 0.

14. If $g(x) = 5^x$, estimate $g'(2)$ numerically, using a symmetric difference quotient with $\Delta x = 0.01$.

15. Find $g'(x)$ algebraically, and use the result to show that the estimate of $g'(2)$ in Problem 14 is close to the actual value.

16. Estimate $h'(3)$ graphically.

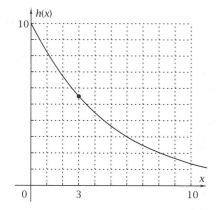

17. Use the graph in Problem 16 to estimate $\int_0^3 h(x)\, dx$ numerically.

18. The fundamental theorem of calculus gives you a way to calculate definite integrals algebraically. If $f(x) = 10e^{-0.2x}$, evaluate $\int_0^3 f(x)\, dx$ using the fundamental theorem. Get a decimal approximation for the answer.

19. The fundamental theorem in its derivative of the integral form can be used to define a function that has a given derivative. Show how this is done by writing the definition of $\ln x$.

20. The derivative of $\ln x$ is $1/x$. Confirm this by finding the numerical derivative of $\ln x$ at $x = 3$ using the built-in derivative feature of your grapher. Write all the digits your grapher gives.

(Continued on the next page.)

21. By direct application of the definition of derivative, you found that if $g(x) = \log_b x$, then

$$g'(x) = \frac{1}{x} \log_b e$$

Use the uniqueness theorem for derivatives to show that $\ln x$ is the same function as $\log_e x$.

22. If $f(x) = x^3 \sin^{-1} x$, find $f'(x)$.

23. If $y = 2^x$, find y' by logarithmic differentiation.

24. If $y^5 = x^7$, find y' using implicit differentiation. Show that the result is the same as you would get from using the power rule on $y = x^{7/5}$.

25. The hyperbola below has the parametric equations

$$x = \tan t$$

$$y = \sec t$$

Use the parametric chain rule to find dy/dx. Show graphically that the resulting equation gives you a reasonable value for dy/dx where $t = 1$.

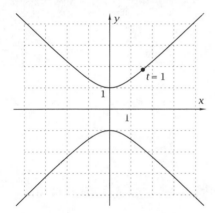

26. Find: $\int (10x - 7)^5 \, dx$

27. Find: $\int \frac{1}{\sin x} \cos x \, dx$

28. Find: $\int e^{\tan x} \sec^2 x \, dx$

29. Find: $\int 3^x \, dx$

Calculus can be applied to real-world problems.

30. The velocity of a moving object is given by $v(t) = 200t \cdot e^{-t}$, where $v(t)$ is in ft/min and t is in min. Find the acceleration at time $t = 3$ min. At that time, is the object speeding up or slowing down?

31. By a suitable numerical method, find the distance traveled by the object in Problem 30 between times $t = 1$ and $t = 5$. Indicate which method you used.

32. Suppose that $f(x) = \begin{cases} x^3, & \text{if } x \leq 1 \\ a(x - 2)^2, & \text{if } x > 1 \end{cases}$

What value of a makes the derivatives of the two branches of the graph approach the same value as x approaches 1 from the left and from the right?

33. Differentiability implies continuity. How do you explain why function f in Problem 32 is *not* continuous at $x = 1$?

34. The work done in moving an object from one place to another equals the force exerted on the object times the displacement it moves. Calvin Butterball pulls Phoebe Small's chair across the floor from $x = 1$ ft to $x = 10$ ft with force in pounds $F = (10 - x)^{0.5}$, as shown on the graph. Draw a narrow vertical strip of width dx. Show a sample point (x, F) on the graph within the strip.

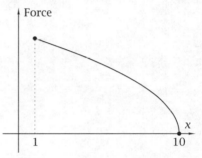

35. Let dW be the work done moving Phoebe by the small amount dx. Write dW in terms of x and dx.

36. By suitable integrating, add all the dW's and take the limit, thus finding the amount of work Calvin does to move Phoebe from $x - 1$ to $x = 10$.

37. The following table shows the force Phoebe exerts on Calvin's chair as she drags him back again. Show that you understand Simpson's rule by using it to calculate the work Phoebe does.

x feet	F pounds
0	35
5	41
10	50
15	44
20	23

38. For $F = (10 - x)^{0.5}$ in Problem 34, find the value $x = c$ in the interval $(1, 10)$ at which the conclusion of the mean value theorem is true.

39. If the inflation rate is 4% per year, then the price P of a pair of shoes that costs \$100 now changes at a rate given by the differential equation

$$\frac{dP}{dt} = 0.04P$$

Separate the variables and integrate the equation. Get P explicitly in terms of t. Then use the result to predict the cost of the shoes 10 years from now.

40. What did you learn as a result of taking this test that you did not know before?

Test 27, Sections 7-1 to 7-3

Objective: Write a differential equation, solve it, and use the solution as a mathematical model.

Part 1: No calculators allowed (1–2)

1. Solve $\frac{dy}{dx} = 10xy^2$ subject to the initial condition that $y = 0.2$ when $x = 3$.

2. Write a differential equation which says that dy/dx is directly proportional to y. Then show that y varies exponentially with x by solving the differential equation.

(Hand in this page to get the rest of the text.)

Test 27, Sections 7-1 to 7-3 *continued*

Part 2: Graphing calculators allowed (3–12)

Oak Tree Problem (3–7): Ann Aggie plants some acorns. She figures that as the tree grows, the cells will divide in such a way that the rate of change of the tree's mass will be directly proportional to the mass. (The more cells there are, the greater the rate of increase in cells.) She digs up one seedling after 3 mo and finds that the mass of roots, trunk, leaves, and so on, is 200 g. The original acorns were each 70 g.

3. Write an equation expressing mass of an oak tree as a function of number of months since the acorn was planted.

4. How long after the acorn was planted will the oak be Ann's mass, 50 kg?

5. Predict the mass of an oak 1, 2, and 3 years after the acorn was planted.

6. Use the results of Problem 5 to show that the oak grows by a *constant* factor each year.

7. Explain to Ann why her mathematical model would probably not give reasonable answers for the tree's mass after *many* years.

Dam Problem (8–11): Lee King Construction Co. builds a dam across Scorpion Gulch. The engineers realize that the water flowing in will go two places:

• To fill up the lake behind the dam.

• To leakage and evaporation at a rate proportional to the amount, W, of water in the lake.

The water will flow in at a constant rate of F ft^3/day.

8. Write a differential equation which says that the rate at which the lake fills, dW/dt, equals the rate at which water flows in, F, minus the rate of leakage and evaporation.

9. Solve the differential equation in Problem 8 subject to the initial condition that $W = 0$ when $t = 0$. Express W in terms of t.

10. If water is lost at 20 ft^3/day when $W = 10{,}000$ ft^3, then the leakage rate constant in the differential equation is 20/10,000, or 0.002. Suppose that water flows in at $F = 300{,}000$ ft^3/day. How much water would you predict in the lake after 100 days?

11. How much water could the lake ultimately hold?

12. What did you learn as a result of taking this test that you did not know before?

Test 28, Sections 7-4 to 7-6

Objective: Solve differential equations graphically, numerically, and algebraically.

Part 1: No calculators allowed (1–7)

For Problems 1–3, consider the differential equation

$$\frac{dy}{dx} = x(y - 1)^2$$

1. On these axes, sketch a slope field for the given differential equation at the 11 points indicated.

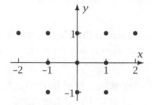

2. Use the slope field for the given differential equation to explain why a solution could not have this graph.

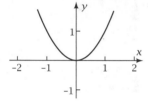

3. Find the particular solution to the given differential equation with the initial condition $y = -1$ if $x = 0$.

Logistic Differential Equation Problem (4–7): The logistic differential equation states that a population y grows in such a way that its instantaneous rate of change with respect to time is proportional to the product of the value of y and the fraction of the maximum sustainable value of y.

4. If m is the maximum sustainable value of y and t is time, write the logistic differential equation.

5. On these axes, sketch two particular solutions of the logistic differential equation, one with initial condition $y_1 < m$ at $t = 0$, the other with initial condition $y_2 > m$ at $t = 0$.

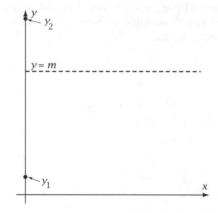

6. On your graph in Problem 5, show the point of inflection for the solution containing y_1 and the relationship of this point to the line $y = m$.

7. What special name is given to the constant m in the logistic differential equation?

(Hand in this page to get the rest of the test.)

Calculus: Concepts and Applications Instructor's Resource Book
©2005 Key Curriculum Press

Name: _____   Date: _____

Test 28, Sections 7-4 to 7-6 *continued*

Part 2: Graphing calculators allowed (8–17)

On Part 1 of this test, you plotted the slope field for

$$\frac{dy}{dx} = x(y-1)^2$$

The figure shows the slope field for this differential equation, enlarged, with slope lines each 0.5 unit.

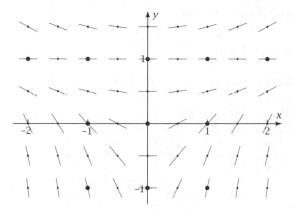

8. If the initial condition is $y = -1$ when $x = 0$, show how to use Euler's method with $dx = 0.5$ to find estimates for y when $x = 0.5$, 1, 1.5, and 2. You may use your Euler's program to check your answers, but you must show how you calculate each value of y in order to receive credit for this problem.

9. Plot each point you calculated in Problem 8 on the given figure. Connect the points in a way which reveals that you understand how Euler's method works.

10. On Part 1 of this test, you found that the solution of the differential equation in Problem 8 is

$$y - 1 - \frac{2}{x^2 + 1}$$

How does the exact answer for y at $x = 2$ compare with the approximate answer by Euler's method in Problem 8?

Skydiver's Acceleration Problem (11–16): Let $v(t)$ be the velocity, in feet per second, of a skydiver at time t, in seconds, since her parachute opened ($t \geq 0$). Her velocity satisfies the differential equation

$$\frac{dv}{dt} = -2v - 32$$

The slope field for this equation is shown in the next column.

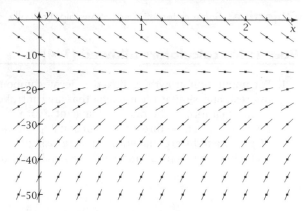

11. The figure above shows the slope field for this differential equation. Calculate the slope at the point $(1, -20)$. Explain how the slope field agrees with this value.

12. If the skydiver opens her parachute as she leaves the plane, her initial velocity is zero. Sketch the particular solution subject to this initial condition.

13. The skydiver actually free-falls until her velocity is $v = -50$ ft/s, then opens her parachute at time $t = 0$. Separate the variables and solve the differential equation algebraically, subject to this initial condition.

14. Use your answer to Problem 13 to make a table of values of v for each 0.4 second from 0 to 2 seconds. Round to the nearest 0.1 ft/s.

t	v
0.0	
0.4	
0.8	
1.2	
1.6	
2.0	

15. Plot the points in Problem 14 on the slope field. Connect them with a smooth curve. Does the curve seem to follow the slope lines?

16. Use your program for Euler's method with $dt = 0.1$ s to calculate an estimate of $v(2.0)$. How does this estimate compare with the exact value you calculated in Problem 14? Based on the theory behind Euler's method, explain why the discrepancy between the actual value and the estimate is reasonable.

17. What did you learn as a result of taking this test that you did not know before?

Test 29, Chapter 7

Objective: Solve differential equations algebraically, graphically, and numerically.

Part 1: No calculators allowed (1–4)

1. For population growth, radioactive decay, compound interest, and similar phenomena that are controlled by internal forces, the rate of change of y with respect to x can be directly proportional to the value of y. Write a differential equation expressing this fact. Show the steps in finding the general solution.

Coyote Problem (2–4): Suppose that coyotes are brought into a region inhabited by roadrunners. Let C be the number of coyotes and P be the number of roadrunners as functions of time. Suppose that the differential equations are

$$\frac{dP}{dt} = 0.1P - 0.01\ PC \text{ and}$$

$$\frac{dC}{dt} = -0.1C + 0.02PC$$

The following slope field shows the relative populations.

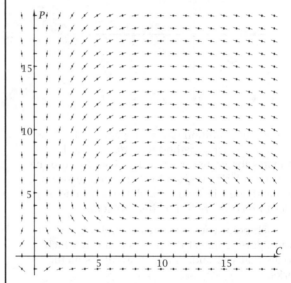

2. Starting at $(C, P) = (12, 9)$, show by graph what happens to the populations.

3. Show that there are times at which the roadrunner population is changing but the coyote population is not changing.

4. Show that there is a fixed point at which neither population is changing.

(Hand in this page to get the rest of the test.)

Calculus: Concepts and Applications Instructor's Resource Book
©2005 Key Curriculum Press

Test 29, Chapter 7 *continued*

Part 2: Graphing calculators allowed (5–14)

Coffee Cup Problem (5 and 6): Suppose you pour a cup of coffee. When it is poured, it is at $D = 130°$ F above room temperature. Three minutes later it has cooled to $D = 117°$ F above room temperature. As the coffee cools, the instantaneous rate of change of D with respect to time t, in minutes, is directly proportional to D.

5. You recall from Problem 1 on the first part of this test that if dD/dt is directly proportional to D, then D varies exponentially with t. Use this fact to write the general solution for D. Use the given information to find the two constants in the particular solution.

6. The coffee in Problem 5 is "drinkable" if it is at least 50° F above room temperature. Will it still be drinkable if you let it sit for 15 min after you pour it? Justify your answer.

Restrained Population Growth Problem (7 and 8): For restrained population growth, the rate of change of y can be a linear function of x. Suppose that

$$\frac{dy}{dx} = 1 - 0.2y$$

7. Solve this differential equation subject to the initial condition that $y = 0$ when $x = 0$. Sketch the graph of this particular solution.

8. Based on this differential equation, what would be happening to the population if y were ever greater than 5?

Logistic Population Growth Problem (9–13): For logistic population growth, the rate of change of population is low when the population is small, reaches a maximum for moderate population, then gets lower again as the population becomes very large. In this case, dy/dx can be a quadratic function of y. Suppose that

$$\frac{dy}{dx} = 0.35y - 0.05y^2$$

9. Between what two values of y will the population be increasing?

10. The slope field below is for this differential equation. Show that you understand what the slope field means by circling the point (5, 9) on the graph and by showing that the differential equation gives the slope at this point.

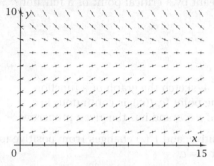

11. On the slope field in Problem 10, sketch the graphs of two particular solutions, one for $y = 1$ when $x = 0$ and the other for $y = 10$ when $x = 0$. Tell the major difference in behavior between the two solutions.

12. Euler's method can be used to find numerical solutions to differential equations. Show that you know how Euler's method works by calculating the next value of y for this differential equation, starting at (0, 1) and using $dx = 0.5$.

13. Use your program for Euler's method with $dx = 0.5$ to calculate estimated values of y for $x = 5$, 10, and 15. Plot these points on your graph for Problem 10. How closely do your graphical solution in Problem 10 and your numerical solution in this problem agree with each other?

14. What did you learn as a result of taking this test that you did not know before?

Test 30, Sections 8-1 to 8-3

Objective: Find critical points of functions.

Part 1: No calculators allowed (1–6)

1. What is meant by a critical point of a function?

For Problems 2–4, sketch the graph of a function that contains the point $(c, f(c))$, is continuous in a neighborhood of $x = c$, and has the given properties.

2. $f'(c)$ is positive, and $f''(x)$ changes from positive to negative at $x = c$.

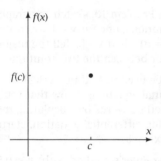

3. $f(x)$ is decreasing on a neighborhood of c, and $f''(c) = 0$.

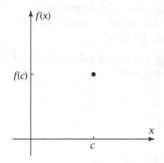

4. $f(c)$ is a maximum, but $f'(c)$ is infinite.

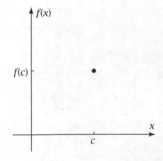

5. Draw number-line graphs for $f'(x)$ and $f''(x)$ showing what happens to $f(x)$ in a neighborhood of the critical point at $x = 2$.

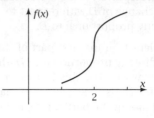

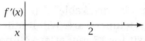

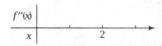

6. The number lines show critical features of $f'(x)$ and $f''(x)$. Mark the number lines with arrows and arcs to show increasing and decreasing behavior and directions of concavity of $f(x)$. Sketch a continuous function containing the point $(4, 0)$ that has these features.

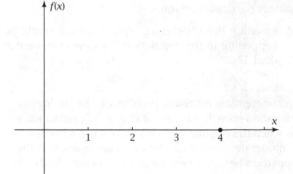

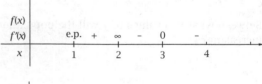

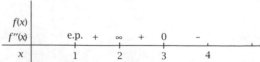

(Hand in this page to get the rest of the test.)

Test 30, Sections 8-1 to 8-3 *continued*

Part 2: Graphing calculators allowed (7–14)

For Problems 7–9, the figure shows the graph of

$$f(x) = 5x^{2/3} - x^{5/3}$$

7. Use derivatives to find algebraically the *x*-coordinates of all critical points of *f* and *f'*.

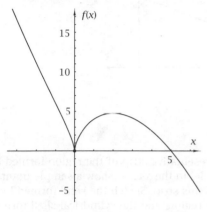

8. Explain why there is a tangent line at the cusp, even though $f'(x)$ is undefined there.

9. Is there a point of inflection at the cusp? Is there a point of inflection anywhere else?

10. The graph shows a cubic function with general equation $f(x) = ax^3 + bx^2 + cx + d$. The function has a local maximum at (6, 30) and a point of inflection at (4, 14). Find the particular equation consistent with this information.

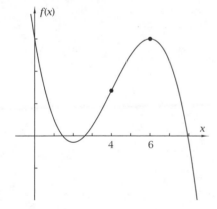

11. The graph of $y = 1 - x^4$ from $x = 0$ to $x = 1$ is rotated about the *y*-axis to form a surface. A cylinder is inscribed inside this surface, coaxial with it. Find algebraically the maximum volume the cylinder can have. Justify that the value you find really is a maximum.

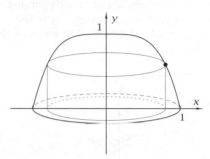

12. Motel Three is building a new three-room motel on a small tract of land. The rooms are to be laid out rectangularly as shown in the diagram. Each one is to contain 360 ft² of floor space. The total length of the three-room building must be no more than 30 ft. Find the minimum total length of wall that could be used in building the motel. Justify your answer.

13. Describe the steps one goes through in solving a max-min problem such as Problems 11 and 12 on this test.

14. What did you learn as a result of taking this test that you did not know before?

Test 31, Section 8-4

Objective: Find the volume of a solid by slicing into cylindrical shells.

Part 1: No calculators allowed (1–5)

1. The figure shows a cylindrical shell formed by rotating a strip of a region about an axis parallel to the *w*-axis in a *uw*-coordinate system. Write the differential volume, *dV*, of this shell in terms of the dimensions shown.

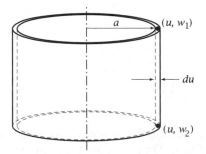

2. The figure below shows the solid formed by rotating about the *y*-axis the region in Quadrant I bounded by the graphs of y_1 and y_2. Write an integral for the volume of the solid if the region is sliced parallel to the axis of rotation.

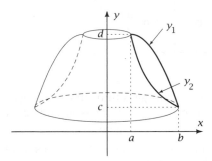

3. Write another integral for the volume of the solid in Problem 2 if the region is sliced perpendicular to the axis of rotation, as you did earlier in the course.

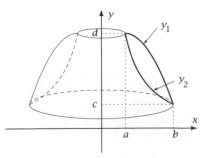

For Problems 4 and 5, a solid is formed by rotating about the *x*-axis the region under the graph of $y = x^{2/3}$ from $x = 0$ to $x = 8$.

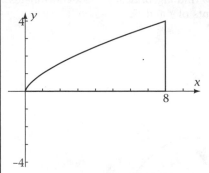

4. Draw a representative strip of the region formed by slicing parallel to the *x*-axis. Show a sample point at each end of this strip. Sketch the solid formed by rotating the region, and the cylindrical shell formed as the strip rotates.

5. Write an integral for the volume of the solid. Evaluate the integral using the fundamental theorem, simplifying as much as possible.

(Hand in this page to get the rest of the test.)

Test 31, Section 8-4 *continued*

Part 2: Graphing calculators allowed (6–16)

For Problems 6 and 7, the solid shown is formed by rotating about the line $x = 5$ the triangular region under the graph of $y = 2x$ from $x = 0$ to $x = 3$.

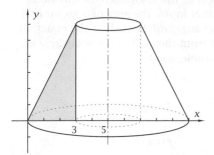

6. Find the volume of the solid by slicing into cylindrical shells.

7. Find the volume of the solid without calculus by appropriate use of the cone and cylinder volume formulas from geometry. (You recall that the volume of a cone is one-third the volume of the circumscribed cylinder.)

Problems 8–11 concern the region shown, bounded by the graphs of $y = x + 4$, $y = x^{3/2}$, and $x = 1$.

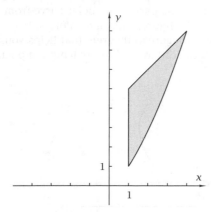

8. In doing calculus using this region, explain why it is better to slice parallel to the y-axis than it would be to slice parallel to the x-axis.

9. Find the area of the region.

10. On the given figure, sketch the solid formed by rotating the region about the y-axis. Then find the volume of the solid.

11. The "average radius" of the solid in Problem 10 is the distance $\bar{x}$ (pronounced "x bar") for which

$$2\pi\bar{x} \cdot \text{area} = \text{volume}$$

where "area" is the area of the cross section. Find the average radius of the solid. Mark the distance $\bar{x}$ on the given figure.

Fuel Tank Problem, Review of Plane Slicing (12–15): A fuel tank for a new design of airplane is to be built in the shape shown. At the left end, the cross section is a rectangle 1-ft-by-2-ft perpendicular to the x-axis. At the right end, the cross section is a rectangle 3-ft-by-6-ft perpendicular to the x-axis, at $x = 8$ ft.

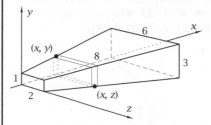

12. Write an equation for dV, the volume of the rectangular slice shown, in terms of the sample points (x, y) in the xy-plane and (x, z) in the xz-plane.

13. By suitable algebra, transform the equation in Problem 12 so that dV is in terms of x alone.

14. Find the volume of the tank.

15. A cubic foot is equivalent to about 7.5 gal. How many gallons of fuel will the tank hold?

16. What did you learn as a result of taking this test that you did not know before?

Test 32, Sections 8-5 to 8-7

Objective: Find the length of a plane curve and the area of a surface of revolution in rectangular or polar coordinates.

Part 1: No calculators allowed (1–4)

1. The figure shows the graph of y as a function of x. On the figure, sketch something that you can use as a memory aid to write dL, the differential of arc length between the two marked points.

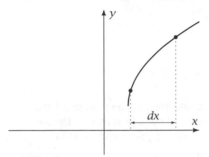

2. The figure shows the arc of the graph in Problem 1 rotated about the y-axis to form a surface of area dS. You recall that dS is approximated by the area of a frustum of a cone, and that the area of the frustum is the distance traveled by the average of the upper and lower radii, multiplied by the arc length dL. Show the frustum on the figure. Show where the sample point would have to be taken on the graph so that the radius to the sample point is exactly equal to the average of the two radii. Write an equation for dS.

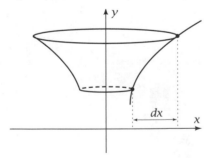

3. The figure shows part of a polar curve $r = f(\theta)$ and a sample point (r, θ). The area swept out by the ray from the origin as the angle increases by $d\theta$ is approximately equal to dA, the area of a sector of a circle with central angle $d\theta$. Show how the equation for dA is derived from the area of a whole circle of radius r at the sample point.

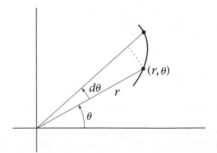

4. The figure shows the part of the polar curve from Problem 3. On the figure, show a memory aid based on the Pythagorean theorem that helps you remember dL, the differential of arc length in polar coordinates.

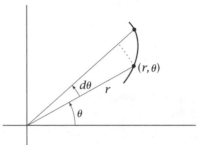

(Hand in this page to get the rest of the test.)

Calculus: Concepts and Applications Instructor's Resource Book
©2005 Key Curriculum Press

Test 32, Sections 8-5 to 8-7 *continued*

Part 2: Graphing calculators allowed (5–14)

5. The figure shows the part of the parabola $y = x^2$ from $x = 1$ to $x = 2$. Sketch the surface formed by rotating this curve about the y-axis.

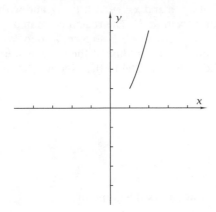

6. The figure shows the same graph as in Problem 5. Sketch the surface formed by rotating this curve about the x-axis.

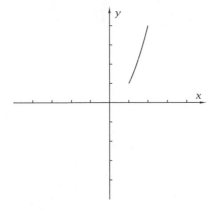

7. Make a conjecture about which of the surfaces in Problems 5 and 6 has the larger area. Give reasons to support your conjecture.

8. Find the areas of the surfaces in Problems 5 and 6 by suitable calculus. Do the answers confirm or refute your conjecture in Problem 7?

9. In Problem 8, you used $dL = \sqrt{dx^2 + dy^2}$. You probably got dy in terms of x and dx, then factored out dx^2 and took its square root. It is possible to get dx in terms of y and dy, then factor out dy^2. Show that you get the same answer this way for the area of the surface in Problem 5. (If you already did it this way, do it the other way and show that the answers are equal.)

10. Find the length of the curve in Problems 5 and 6.

11. The "average radius" of a curved surface is the distance $\bar{x}$ for which the surface area, S, is

$$S = 2\pi\bar{x} \cdot L$$

where L is the length of the curve being rotated. Find the average radius of the surface in Problem 5.

12. The figure shows the spiral with polar equation

$$r = 0.2\theta$$

What range of θ is needed to generate the part of the spiral shown? Find the length of this part of the spiral. Show that your answer is reasonable.

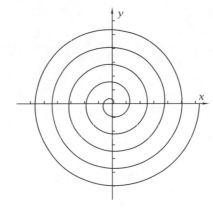

13. Find the area of the "band shaped" region in the outermost revolution shown.

14. What have you learned as a result of taking this test that you did not know before?

Test 33, Chapter 8

Objective: Find volume, area, length, max-min, and points of inflection for geometric figures.

Part 1: No calculators allowed (1–8)

1. Sketch the graph of a continuous function whose derivatives are consistent with the information on these number lines, containing the point shown.

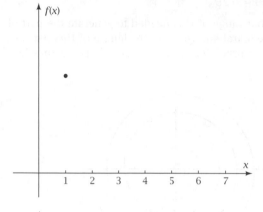

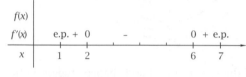

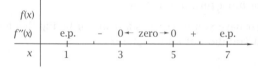

2. Write the formula for dL, the differential of arc length, in Cartesian coordinates.

3. Write the formula for dL, the differential of arc length, in polar coordinates.

4. Write the formula for dA, the differential of area, in polar coordinates.

5. Write the formula for dS, the differential of surface area of a surface of revolution, in Cartesian coordinates.

6. A region is bounded by two graphs,

$$y_1 = f(x) \quad \text{and} \quad y_2 = g(x)$$

intersecting at $x = a$ and $x = b$, with $b > a$, and with $g(x) > f(x)$ for all x in (a, b). The region is rotated about the line $x = c$ (with $c > b$) to form a solid. Write an integral equal to the volume of the solid as found by slicing the region parallel to the axis of rotation.

7. The figure below shows the graph of

$$f(x) = (x - 2)^5 + x + 20$$

Show that there are no local maximum or minimum values of $f(x)$ if the domain of x is {real numbers}.

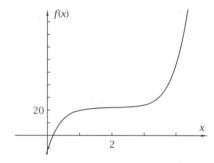

8. Show that the graph in Problem 7 is "straight" but not horizontal at $x = 2$.

(Hand in this page to get the rest of the test.)

Test 33, Chapter 8 *continued*

Part 2: Graphing calculators allowed (9–18)

For Problems 9–13, the figure shows the region in Quadrant I bounded by the *y*-axis and the graphs of

$$y = e^{0.5x} \quad \text{and} \quad y = x^2$$

intersecting at $x = b$.

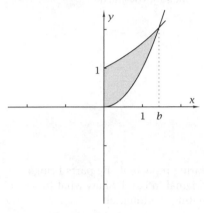

9. Find numerically the value of $x = b$ close to 1.4 at which the two curves intersect. Store the answer, without round-off, as *b*.

10. On the figure, sketch the solid formed by rotating the region about the *y*-axis.

11. Find the volume of the solid in Problem 10.

12. Find the length of the exponential curve $y = e^{0.5x}$ from the *y*-axis to the point $x = b$ where the curves intersect.

13. Find the area of the outer surface of the solid in Problem 10, formed by rotating the parabola.

14. The figure shows the region under the graph of

$$y = x^{2/3}$$

A rectangle is inscribed in the region. Use derivatives to find algebraically all critical points of the area of the rectangle as a function of x at the sample point. Use the results to find the maximum area of the rectangle if x is restricted to the domain $4 \le x \le 8$.

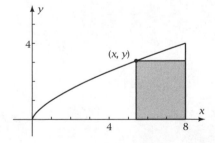

For Problems 15–17, the figure shows the limaçon with polar equation

$$r = 5 + 15 \cos \theta$$

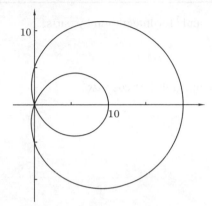

15. What range of θ-values generates the inner loop?

16. Find the area of the region enclosed by the inner loop.

17. Find the length of the outer loop.

18. What did you learn as a result of taking this test that you did not know before?

Test 34, Sections 9-1 to 9-4

Objective: Integrate by parts.

Part 1: No calculators allowed (1–6)

1. Write the formula for integration by parts.

2. Evaluate the integral: $\int x^2 \cos x \, dx$

3. Evaluate the integral: $\int x^2 \ln x \, dx$

4. To integrate by parts for $\int x^2 \ln x \, dx$, you let $dv = x^2 \, dx$. To integrate by parts for $\int x^2 \cos x \, dx$, you let $dv = \cos x \, dx$. Explain why the procedure is different for the two integrals.

5. What is the primary consideration for selecting the parts in an integration-by-parts problem? If this consideration can be met for both possible ways of choosing the parts, what is the secondary consideration for choosing the parts?

6. Sometimes integrating repeatedly by parts brings you back to the original integral. Show what to do in this case by evaluating the integral:

$$\int e^{2x} \cos 3x \, dx$$

(Hand in this page to get the rest of the test.)

Calculus: Concepts and Applications Instructor's Resource Book
©2005 Key Curriculum Press

Test 34, Sections 9-1 to 9-4 *continued*

Part 2: Graphing calculators allowed (7–12)

7. Evaluate the integral: $\int \cos 5x \sin 3x \, dx$

8. Integration by parts can be used to find reduction formulas for integrals of powers of trig functions. For the integral

$$\int \sin^8 x \, dx$$

integrate once by parts. Then transform the answer to get the original integral in terms of $\int \sin^6 x \, dx$. From the result, make a conjecture about the reduction formula for $\int \sin^n x \, dx$, where n stands for a positive integer.

9. Use the reduction formula

$$\int \sec^n x \, dx = \frac{1}{n-1} \sec^{n-2} x \tan x + \frac{n-2}{n-1} \int \sec^{n-2} x \, dx$$

to evaluate this integral:

$$\int \sec^5 x \, dx$$

10. Integration by parts lets you find indefinite integrals of functions you couldn't antidifferentiate before. Use integration by parts to show that

$$\int \ln x \, dx = x \ln x - x + C$$

11. *Bundt Cake Problem:* A kitchenware manufacturer plans to make bundt cake pans in the shape of the surface formed by rotating around the y-axis the graph of

$$y = 7 \cos \frac{\pi}{6} x$$

from $x = 3$ to $x = 9$, where x and y are in centimeters (see figure below). What will be the volume of cake the pan can hold when it is filled up to the brim? Show that the answer you get using the fundamental theorem and integrating by parts agrees with the answer you get numerically on your grapher.

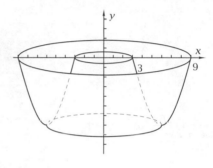

12. What did you learn as a result of taking this test that you did not know before?

Test 35, Section 9-7

Objective: Integrate rational functions by partial fractions, and use the result to find the solution of a logistic differential equation.

Part 1: No calculators allowed (1–5)

1. Resolve into partial fractions using the Heaviside shortcut:

$$\frac{4x - 26}{x^2 + 2x - 8}$$

2. Integrate: $\int \frac{4x - 26}{x^2 + 2x - 8}\, dx$

3. Integrate by first dividing to make the integrand a sum of a polynomial and a proper algebraic fraction.

$$\int \frac{x^2 + 3x - 37}{x - 5}\, dx$$

4. Integrate without using partial fractions:

$$\int \frac{2x + 10}{x^2 + 10x + 13}\, dx$$

5. Integrate: $\int \frac{8}{(x - 1)(x - 3)(x - 5)}\, dx$

(Hand in this page to get the rest of the test.)

Test 35, Section 9-7 *continued*

Part 2: Graphing calculators allowed (6–10)

6. On Part 1 of this test, you found that

$$\frac{4x - 26}{x^2 + 2x - 8} = \frac{7}{x + 4} - \frac{3}{x - 2}$$

Let $\dfrac{4x - 26}{x^2 + 2x - 8} = \dfrac{A}{x + 4} + \dfrac{B}{x - 2}$

where A and B stand for constants. Find a common denominator on the right of the second equation, and find values of A and B by equating numerators and solving the resulting equations simultaneously to find values of A and B.

Logistic Equation Problem (7–9): In Chapter 7, you solved graphically the logistic differential equation

$$\frac{dP}{dt} = 0.038(P)(10.5 - P)$$

Now that you can integrate by partial fractions, you can understand the technique for integrating this equation *algebraically.*

7. Separate the variables and integrate both sides. Evaluate the integral using the appropriate techniques. (Be careful that you really have the differential of the "inside" function when you evaluate the integral!)

8. Use the answer to Problem 7 to find the particular solution of the differential equation for the initial condition that $P = 1$ when $t = 0$. Do the necessary transformations to get

$$P = \frac{10.5}{1 + 9.5e^{-0.399t}}$$

9. The figure shows the slope field for the differential equation. Using the TRACE or TABLE feature of your grapher, plot P for each integer value of t that shows on the graph. Show that the resulting graph really *does* follow the slope field.

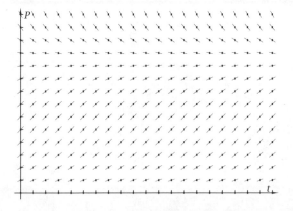

10. What did you learn as a result of taking this test that you did not know before?

Test 36, Sections 9-5 to 9-8

Objective: Show that you can use various algebraic integration techniques.

Graphing calculators allowed

1. Show how the double-argument properties from trigonometry can be used to integrate

$$\int \cos^2 5x \, dx$$

2. Integrate without the help of a reduction formula:

$$\int \sin^5 x \, dx$$

3. Integrate without the help of a reduction formula:

$$\int \sec^6 x \, dx$$

4. Integrate $\int \sin^6 x \, dx$ using the reduction formula.

5. Integrate by trig substitution:

$$\int \frac{1}{\sqrt{81 + x^2}} \, dx$$

6. Without actually evaluating the integral, tell what trigonometric substitution you would use for

$$\int \sqrt{x^2 - 100} \, dx$$

7. Integrate by partial fractions:

$$\int \frac{2x - 22}{x^2 + 2x - 8} \, dx$$

8. Use appropriate integration techniques to derive the formula for

$$\int \sin^{-1} x \, dx$$

9. The figure below shows the zone of the circle

$$x^2 + y^2 = 25$$

from $x = -2$ to $x = 1$. Find the area of the zone *exactly*, using the fundamental theorem and the appropriate integration techniques. Compare the answer with what you get by numerical integration.

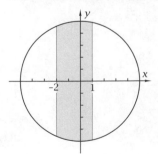

10. The figure shows the spiral with polar equation

$$r = 0.2\theta$$

from $\theta = 0$ to $\theta = 10\pi$. Find the length of the spiral exactly, using the fundamental theorem and the appropriate integration techniques. Compare the answer with what you get by numerical integation.

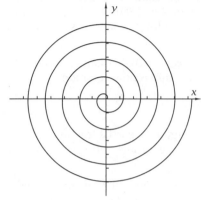

11. What did you learn as a result of taking this test that you did not know before?

Test 37, Sections 9-9 and 9-10

Objective: Do calculus of hyperbolic functions and improper integrals.

Part 1: No calculators allowed (1–10)

1. Write the definitions of cosh x and sinh x in terms of the natural exponential function.

2. Write the definitions of tanh x and sech x in terms of cosh x and sinh x.

3. What special name is given to the graph of $y = \cosh x$?

For Problems 4–7, differentiate or integrate.

4. $y = \cosh 5x$

5. $\int \sinh 3x \, dx$

6. $y = \tanh^3 x$

7. $\int \cosh^5 x \sinh x \, dx$

8. Write the Pythagorean property for cosh x and sinh x. How does this property compare with the Pythagorean property for cos x and sin x?

9. Derive the formula for y' if $y = \cosh^{-1} x$.

10. Integrate by parts to find $\int \sinh^{-1} x \, dx$.

(Hand in this page to get the rest of the test.)

Test 37, Sections 9-9 and 9-10 *continued*

Part 2: Graphing calculators allowed (11–21)

For Problems 11–17, the figure shows the graph of $y = \cosh x$.

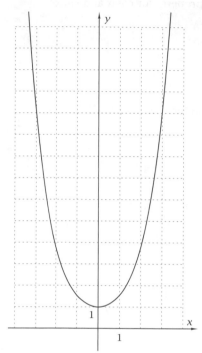

11. You recall that $\cosh x = 0.5(e^x + e^{-x})$. Use this formula to find $\cosh 3$. Show that the answer agrees with the graph.

12. For $y = \cosh x$, evaluate dy/dx when $x = 2$. Show that a line with this slope, drawn through the point where $x = 2$, is really tangent to the graph.

13. By counting squares, find approximately the area of the region under the graph of $y = \cosh x$ from $x = -2$ to $x = 3$.

14. Evaluate exactly, using the fundamental theorem, the area of the region under the graph of $y = \cosh x$ from $x = -2$ to $x = 3$. Confirm that your answer to Problem 13 is close to the exact answer.

15. A chain hangs between two tall poles 30 ft apart. Each end of the chain is 50 ft above the ground. At its lowest, the chain comes down to 3 ft above the ground. As you recall, the catenary formed by this chain has the general equation

$$y = k \cosh \frac{1}{k} x + C$$

where the vertex is on the y-axis and k and C stand for constants. Find the particular equation for this catenary.

16. By suitable calculus, find the length of the chain in Problem 15.

17. The constant k in Problem 15 equals h/w, where h is the horizontal tension in the chain and w is the weight of the chain per unit length. If the chain in Problem 15 weighs 6 lb/ft, find the weight of the entire chain and the horizontal tension exerted by the chain.

18. The figure below shows the region under the graph of $y = 1/x^{0.99}$ from $x = 0$ to $x = 5$. By appropriate use of improper integrals, show that the area of the region approaches a finite number as the lower limit of integration approaches zero.

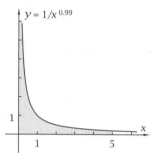

19. The figure below shows the region under the graph of $y = 1/x$ from $x = 0$ to $x = 5$. By appropriate use of improper integrals, show that the area of the region is infinite.

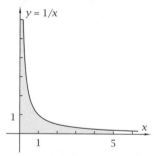

20. The region in Problem 19 is rotated about the y-axis to form a solid. By appropriate use of improper integrals, show that the volume of the solid approaches a finite number as the lower limit of integration approaches zero.

21. What did you learn as a result of taking this test that you did not know before?

Test 38, Chapter 9

Objective: Integrate the elementary transcendental functions using various algebraic techniques.

Graphing calculators allowed

1. Integrate: $\displaystyle\int x^5 e^{-x}\,dx$

2. Integrate: $\displaystyle\int e^x \cos 0.5x\,dx$

3. Use the result of Problem 2 to evaluate by the fundamental theorem the definite integral

   $$\int_1^3 e^x \cos 0.5x\,dx$$

4. Evaluate the integral in Problem 3 numerically, thus showing that you get (essentially) the same answer.

5. The reduction formula for powers of sine is

   $$\int \sin^n x\,dx = -\frac{1}{n}\sin^{n-1} x \cos x + \frac{n-1}{n}\int \sin^{n-2} x\,dx$$

   Show how this formula is *derived* by taking the first step in the integration by parts of

   $$\int \sin^6 x\,dx$$

6. Show how the reduction formula in Problem 5 is *used* by finishing the integration of

   $$\int \sin^6 x\,dx$$

7. Show that $\int \sin^7 x\,dx$ can be done *without* using the reduction formula.

8. Integrate $\int \sin^2 x\,dx$ using the double-argument properties for cosine in a clever way.

9. Integrate by trig substitution:

   $$\int \frac{1}{\sqrt{1+x^2}}\,dx$$

10. Integrate:

    $$\int \frac{1}{1+x^2}\,dx$$

11. Which trig substitution would you use?

    $$\sqrt{x^2 - 51}\,dx$$

12. Which trig substitution would you use?

    $$\sqrt{1 - x^2}\,dx$$

13. Integrate by partial fractions:

    $$\int \frac{40x - 72}{(x-1)(x-5)(x+3)}\,dx$$

14. Use integration by parts, and the differentiation formula for $\sin^{-1} x$, to derive the formula

    $$\int \sin^{-1} x\,dx = x\sin^{-1} x + \sqrt{1 - x^2} + C$$

15. Find the area under the graph of $y = \cosh 3x$ from $x = -2$ to $x = 2$.

16. Evaluate the improper integral: $\displaystyle\int_1^\infty x^{-1.001}\,dx$

17. In your journal you recorded methods of integrating the elementary functions. The integral below can be evaluated by any one of three different techniques. Tell what these techniques are.

    $$\int \frac{x\,dx}{x^2 - 1}$$

18. What did you learn as a result of taking this test that you did not know before?

Test 39, Sections 10-1 to 10-5

Objective: Find displacement and distance from acceleration, average values, and maxima or minima.

Part 1: No calculators allowed (1–6)

For Problems 1–4, the figure shows the velocity of a moving object in furlongs/min as a function of t min. The equation is

$$v(t) = (t - 1)(t - 4)$$

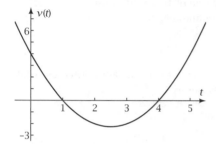

1. Find the velocity and the acceleration at $t = 2$. Is the object speeding up or slowing down at that time? How do you decide?

2. Find the net displacement of the object from $t = 2$ to $t = 5$. What does the sign of the displacement tell you?

3. Find the average velocity from $t = 2$ to $t = 5$.

4. Find the total distance traveled by the object from $t = 2$ to $t = 5$.

5. Find the non-negative number x that most exceeds its cube. Justify your answer.

6. *Bridge Problem:* The figure shows a roadway to be constructed to connect an offshore oil well 4 mi from the shoreline and the oil company's field office 10 mi along the shore from the point closest to the well. Cars can drive 70 mi/h on the road along the shore, but only 55 mi/h on the bridge connecting the well to the shore.

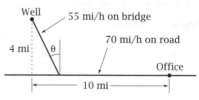

If the bridge is constructed so that cars take a minimum time getting from well to office, what do you know about angle θ shown on the figure?

(Hand in this page to get the rest of the test.)

Test 39, Sections 10-1 to 10-5 *continued*

Part 2: Graphing calculators allowed (7–16)

Bridge Problem, Continued (7–9): The figure shows the roadway from Problem 6, with a bridge to be built connecting an offshore oil well and the oil company's field office. Cars can drive 70 mi/h on the road along the shore, but only 55 mi/h on the bridge.

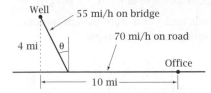

7. Let x be the distance along the road from the end of the shortest possible bridge to the end of the actual bridge. Find the total driving time, t, as a function of x. Use dt/dx to find out where the bridge should be constructed to minimize the driving time.

8. How much time will be saved per round-trip by building the bridge along the minimal path rather than by building the shortest possible bridge?

9. The oil company personnel will make about 30 round-trips a day between the field office and the well every day of the year. Their time is worth an average of $20 per hour. How much money will the oil company save in travel time each year by building the bridge along the minimal path instead of building the shortest possible bridge?

10. At time $t = 0$ s, a moving object has a velocity of 6 ft/s. The table below shows the acceleration of the object at 5-s time intervals. Calculate the approximate net displacement of the object for the 20 s.

t (s)	a (ft/s^2)
0	3
5	12
10	4
15	−7
20	−15

11. The figure shows the graph of

$$y = x + 2 \sin x$$

Find the average value of y for x in the interval [2, 7]. Show that this average value is *not* the average of the values of y at $x = 2$ and $x = 7$. Show on the graph at least one graphical meaning of this average value.

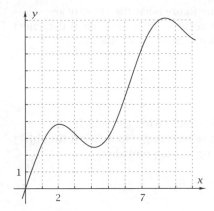

Calvin and Phoebe's Velocity Problem (12–15): Calvin and Phoebe are stopped at a traffic light. When the light turns green, each starts accelerating. The two cars have different acceleration characteristics. The distance gone by each car is given by

Calvin: $s_c(t) = t^3$

Phoebe: $s_p(t) = e^t - 1$

where s is in feet and t is in seconds.

12. Which car has the greater acceleration at first? How do you tell?

13. At what time does the other car catch up with the car that got ahead at first? In the interval between $t = 0$ and this time, what was the maximum distance by which the other car was ahead?

14. What is the maximum difference in velocities of the two cars in the time interval in Problem 13? Does the maximum difference in velocities occur at the same time as the maximum distance the two cars are apart?

15. Does the car that was ahead at first ever regain the lead? If so, at what time t? If not, tell how you know.

16. What did you learn as a result of taking this test that you did not know before?

Test 40, Section 10-6

Objective: Analyze motion in two dimensions with vector functions.

Part 1: No calculators allowed (1–4)

For Problems 1–3, the figure shows part of the path of an object moving in the coordinate plane.

1. Sketch on the figure what the velocity and acceleration vectors might look like if the object is slowing down at the point shown.

2. Sketch on the figure what the velocity and acceleration vectors might look like if the object is speeding up at the point shown.

3. Sketch on the figure what the velocity and acceleration vectors might look like if the object is moving, but neither speeding up nor slowing down at the point shown.

Epicycloid Problem: The figure shows the path of a point on the rim of a 2-cm-radius wheel that rotates along the outside of a fixed circle of radius 6 cm. The position vector is

$$\vec{r}(t) = (8 \cos 0.5t - 2 \cos 2t)\vec{i} + (8 \sin 0.5t - 2 \sin 2t)\vec{j}$$

where t is time in seconds and x and y are in centimeters. The graph is called an **epicycloid of 3 cusps.**

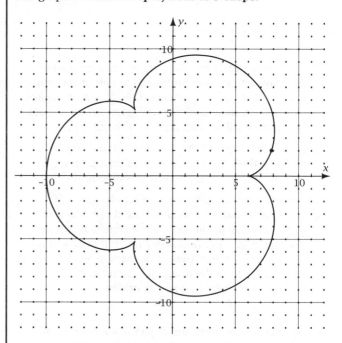

4. Find the velocity and acceleration vectors, $\vec{v}(t)$ and $\vec{a}(t)$.

(Hand in this page to get the rest of the test.)

Test 40, Section 10-6 *continued*

Part 2: Graphing calculators allowed (5–13)

Epicycloid Problem, continued (5-12): The figure shows the epicycloid from Part 1 of the test, traced by a point on a wheel rotating around a circle. The position, velocity, and acceleration are given by

$$\vec{r}(t) = (8 \cos 0.5t - 2 \cos 2t)\vec{i} + (8 \sin 0.5t - 2 \sin 2t)\vec{j}$$

$$\vec{v}(t) = (-4 \sin 0.5t + 4 \sin 2t)\vec{i} + (4 \cos 0.5t - 4 \cos 2t)\vec{j}$$

$$\vec{a}(t) = (-2 \cos 0.5t + 8 \cos 2t)\vec{i} + (-2 \sin 0.5t + 8 \sin 2t)\vec{j}$$

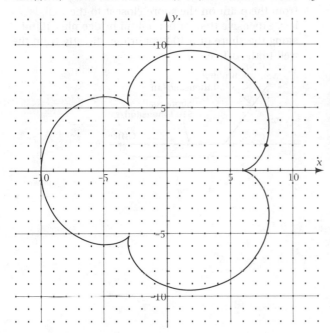

5. Find the position, velocity, and acceleration vectors at time $t = 1$ s. Round the components to three decimal places. Plot $\vec{r}(1)$ to the point shown on the given figure. Plot $\vec{v}(1)$ and $\vec{a}(1)$ with tails at the head of the position vector.

6. Based on your graph in Problem 5, does the point on the wheel seem to be speeding up or slowing down at $t = 1$? Justify your answer.

At $t = 3$ s, the position, velocity, and acceleration are

$$\vec{r}(3) \approx -1.354\vec{i} + 8.539\vec{j}$$

$$\vec{v}(3) \approx -5.108\vec{i} - 3.558\vec{j}$$

$$\vec{a}(3) \approx 7.540\vec{i} - 4.230\vec{j}$$

The velocity and acceleration vectors are shown on the figure.

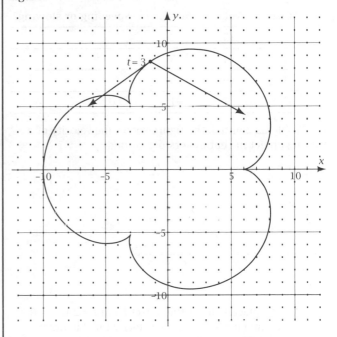

7. Is the point speeding up or slowing down at $t = 3$? How can you tell this graphically?

8. Find the dot product of the velocity and acceleration at $t = 3$. How does the answer confirm (or refute!) your answer to Problem 7?

9. Find the tangential component of the acceleration vector. Plot it on the figure, with its tail at the point on the graph. Tell the physical effect of the tangential component on the motion of the point.

10. Find the component of the acceleration vector at $t = 3$ that is normal to the path. Plot this vector with its tail at the point on the graph. Tell the physical effect of the normal component on the motion of the point.

11. The cusp in Quadrant II is at $t = 8\pi/3$. At this time the point on the wheel just touches the circle. Use the equations to show that the point is stopped at this time.

12. Find the acceleration vector at $t = 8\pi/3$. Plot it on the figure with its tail at this point.

13. What did you learn as a result of taking this test that you did not know before?

Test 41, Chapter 10

Objective: Analyze one- and two-dimensional motion, including average and extreme values.

Part 1: No calculators allowed (1–6)

1. The table shows the velocity and acceleration of a moving object at various times. For each time, tell whether the object is speeding up or slowing down.

Time	Vel.	Accel.	Speeding or slowing?
−3	−15	−2	
2	−4	5	
8	6	9	
13	7	−1	

For Problems 2 and 3, the figure shows the velocity of a moving object in centimeters per second.

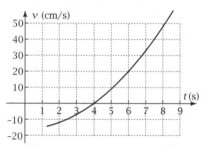

2. The displacement of the object from $t = 2$ to $t = 8$ s is 72 cm. Find the average velocity for this time interval. Show on the figure a graphical meaning of this average velocity.

3. Between $t = 4$ and $t = 8$, the object goes $85\frac{1}{3}$ cm. What is the total distance the object travels from $t = 2$ s to $t = 8$ s? What is its average speed for this time interval?

4. *Roadway Problem:* A roadway is to be constructed to connect an offshore oil well 4 mi from the shoreline and the oil company's field office 10 mi along the shore from the point closest to the well (see figure). The roadway along the shore costs $100 thousand per mile to build. The roadway across the bridge costs $250 thousand per mile to build. Show that the bridge built as shown, to a point 3 mi from the point on the shore closest to the well, is less expensive than either a 4-mi bridge plus 10 mi along the shore or a 10.8-mi bridge directly from the well to the office.

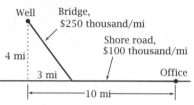

5. Draw a possible acceleration vector if the object is slowing down.

6. Draw a possible velocity vector if the object is speeding up.

(Hand in this page to get the rest of the test.)

Part 2: Graphing calculators allowed (7–18)

One-Dimensional Motion Problem (7–10): An object moves in the *x*-direction with velocity *v*, in ft/s, given by

$$v = e^t \cos t$$

7. Find the distance it travels between $t = 0$ s and $t = 5$ s.

8. Find the displacement from the starting point at time $t = 5$ s.

9. Find the average velocity of the object for the time interval [0, 5].

10. Find the acceleration of the object at time $t = 3$ s. At that time, is the object speeding up or slowing down? Justify your answer.

11. *Roadway Problem, continued:* A roadway is to be constructed to connect an offshore oil well 4 mi from the shoreline and the oil company's field office 10 mi along the shore from the point closest to the well (see figure). The roadway along the shore costs $100 thousand per mile to build. The roadway across the bridge costs $250 thousand per mile to build. Where should the bridge be constructed so that the cost is a minimum?

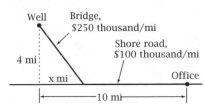

12. An object moves along the *x*-axis with a velocity $v(t) = 3(t - 1)(t - 3)$ m/s. Find the minimum acceleration of the object in the time interval [0, 5].

Two-Dimensional Motion Problem (13–17): An object moves back and forth along a parabolic path (see figure). The position vector is

$$\vec{r}(t) = (7 \sin 0.5t)\vec{i} + 3(1 + \cos t)\vec{j}$$

where *x* and *y* are in centimeters and *t* is in seconds.

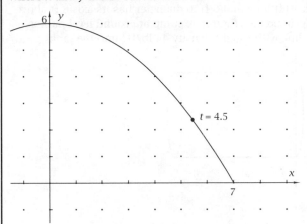

13. Find the velocity and acceleration vectors when $t = 4.5$ s. Plot these vectors on the figure with their tails at the point shown.

14. Tell why the velocity and acceleration vectors have the correct orientation with respect to the path.

15. Give graphical and algebraic evidence to show that the object is speeding up at $t = 4.5$ s.

16. Find the tangential and normal components of the acceleration vector. Plot these components at the appropriate place on the figure.

17. How fast is the object going at $t = 4.5$ s?

18. What did you learn as a result of taking this test that you did not know before?

Test 42, Chapter 11

Objective: Apply definite integrals to real-world problems.

Graphing calculators allowed

Gasoline Tank Problem: An above-ground gasoline storage tank 10 ft long and 6 ft in diameter has its axis 8 ft above the ground (see figure). A pump at ground level pumps gasoline with weight density 44 lb/ft³ into the tank.

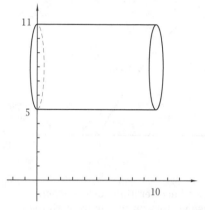

1. How much work does the pump do in filling the tank half full?

2. The tank is filled to the top with more gasoline. Find the force exerted by this gasoline on the circular end of the tank.

3. Find the first moment of force of the gasoline in Problem 2 with respect to a horizontal axis through the center of the circular end of the tank.

4. Find the center of pressure for the force in Problem 2. Explain why the center of pressure is *not* at the center of the circular end of the tank.

5. *Compost Heap Problem:* Ima Gardner digs a hole in her garden 40 cm deep. Over a period of time she fills it to the top with leftover organic material. As time passes the lower layers of compost pack down more tightly, and thus have a higher density than the upper layers. One day Ima measures the density of the compost at various depths. She also estimates the cross-sectional areas of the compost heap at the corresponding depths.

Depth (cm)	Density (g/cm³)	Area (cm²)
0	0.7	10,000
10	0.9	9,000
20	1.2	8,000
30	1.6	4,000
40	2.2	1,000

By appropriate numerical techniques, calculate the number of kilograms of compost Ima has in the heap. What is the average density of the compost in the heap?

6. *Coal Mine Problem:* A coal mine shaft that is 1000 ft long is to be extended to a length of 4000 ft. The mining contractor estimates that the price in dollars per foot, $p(x)$, for doing the digging is

$$p(x) = 200 \cdot 1.0003^x$$

where x is the number of feet from the entrance at which the miners are digging. Calculate the cost of extending the mine from 1000 ft to 4000 ft.

7. What did you learn as a result of taking this test that you did not know before?

Test 43, Sections 12-1 to 12-5

Objective: Write functions as Taylor or Maclaurin power series.

Part 1: No calculators allowed (1–6)

1. For $f(x) = 1 + \frac{1}{2!}x^2 + \frac{1}{4!}x^4 + \frac{1}{6!}x^6 + \cdots$

   • Write the series in sigma notation. Start at $n = 0$.
   • Tell which function the series represents.

2. For $f(x) = \displaystyle\sum_{n=0}^{\infty} (-1)^n \frac{1}{(2n+1)!} x^{2n+1}$

   • Write the first few terms of the series.
   • Tell which function the series represents.

3. Write the first few terms of the Maclaurin series for $f(x) = e^x$. Use the result to write the first few terms of the Maclaurin series for $g(x) = e^{-x}$.

4. You recall that the inverse tangent series is
   $\tan^{-1} x = x - \frac{1}{3}x^3 + \frac{1}{5}x^5 - \frac{1}{7}x^7 + \cdots$

   Show that the Maclaurin series for $\frac{d}{dx}(\tan^{-1} x)$ is a geometric series. What is the common ratio?

5. You recall from algebra that the partial sum of a geometric series is

   $$S_n = t_1 \cdot \frac{1 - r^n}{1 - r}$$

   where r is the common ratio. If $|r| < 1$, explain why the series converges, and write a formula for the value to which it converges.

6. Suppose that $f(x)$ is to be expanded as a Taylor series about $x = 5$ and that you know

   $f(5) = 3$, $f'(5) = -4$, $f''(5) = 0.4$
   $f'''(5) = -0.12$, and $f^{(4)}(5) = 0.0024$

   • By equating derivatives, find the first five terms of the Taylor series for $f(x)$ expanded about $x = 5$.
   • You realize that $f(x) = S_3(x) + R_3(x)$. Explain why $S_3(x)$ is the fourth partial sum, not the third partial sum.

(Hand in this page to get the rest of the test.)

Test 43, Sections 12-1 to 12-5 *continued*

Part 2: Graphing calculators allowed (7–18)

For Problems 7-10, let

$$f(x) = \frac{10}{1-x}$$

7. Plot the graph of f using a window with $[-4, 6]$ for x and $[-50, 50]$ for y. Sketch the result.

8. Let $P_n(x) = 10 + 10x + 10x^2 + 10x^3 + \cdots + 10x^n$. Plot P_5 on the same screen as in Problem 7. Sketch the result.

9. For what range of x-values does the polynomial function P_5 seem to fit the rational function f reasonably well?

10. The polynomial in Problems 8 and 9 is a subset of a geometric series, in which subsequent terms are found by multiplying the preceding term by the same number (x, in this case). It is a mathematical model for the amount of medicine remaining in a patient's system after n hours if she takes 10-mg doses every hour and if a fraction x of the amount at the beginning of an hour remains at the end of that hour. If $x = 0.95$, how many milligrams remain after the sixth dose ($n = 5$)? What limit would the number of milligrams remaining approach after many doses?

For Problems 11 and 12, the Maclaurin series for $\cos x$ is

$$\cos x = \sum_{n=0}^{\infty} (-1)^n \frac{1}{(2n)!} x^{2n}$$

11. Write the first five terms of this series ($n = 4$).

12. On the same screen, plot the graph of the fifth partial sums of the series in Problem 11 and the graph of $y = \cos x$. Use a window with $[-6, 6]$ for x and $[-3, 3]$ for y. Sketch the result. For what range of values of x do the fifth partial sums fit the cosine graph reasonably well?

For Problems 13 and 14, the Taylor series for $\ln x$ expanded about $x = 1$ is

$$\ln x = (x - 1) - \frac{1}{2}(x - 1)^2 + \frac{1}{3}(x - 1)^3 - \cdots$$

13. Write the series in sigma notation.

14. Show that the fifth partial sum of the series gives a reasonable estimate for $\ln 1.3$ but does not give a reasonable estimate for $\ln 4$.

For Problems 15-17, the Maclaurin series for $\sinh x$ is

$$\sinh x = x + \frac{1}{3!}x^3 + \frac{1}{5!}x^5 + \frac{1}{7!}x^7 + \cdots$$

15. By differentiation, derive the Maclaurin series for $\cosh x$.

16. Show that the Maclaurin series for $\cosh x$ can also be derived by integrating the series for $\sinh x$, if the proper constant of integration is used.

17. Write the first four terms of the Maclaurin series for $x^2 \sinh 3x$.

18. What did you learn as a result of taking this test that you did not know before?

Calculus: Concepts and Applications Instructor's Resource Book
©2005 Key Curriculum Press

Test 44, Chapter 12

Objective: Find the interval of convergence for a power series, and estimate the error in using a partial sum for a series.

Part 1: No calculators allowed (1–9)

1. Write the definition of convergence of a sequence.

2. Write the definition of convergence of a series.

3. The formula for the nth partial sum of a geometric series is

$$S_n = t_1 \cdot \frac{1 - r^n}{1 - r}$$

Based on the definition of convergence of a series, tell why a geometric series converges if $|r| \le 1$.

4. Explain why this sequence converges

$$1, 1.9, 1.99, 1.999, 1.9999, \ldots$$

but this series does not converge

$$1 + 1.9 + 1.99 + 1.999 + 1.9999 + \cdots$$

5. Explain why this alternating series diverges, even though the terms are strictly alternating and the absolute values of the terms are strictly decreasing.

$$1.7 - 1.07 + 1.007 - 1.0007 + \cdots$$

6. Based on your answers to Problems 4 and 5, tell one quick check you can make on a series to tell whether or not it might converge.

7. Show that the harmonic series

$$1 + \frac{1}{2} + \frac{1}{3} + \frac{1}{4} + \cdots$$

diverges, even though the terms are decreasing in value and approach zero as a limit.

8. Explain why the alternating harmonic series

$$1 - \frac{1}{2} + \frac{1}{3} - \frac{1}{4} + \cdots$$

converges, but not absolutely.

9. Write the general p-series in sigma notation. For what values of p does the p-series converge?

(Hand in this page to get the rest of the test.)

Part 2: Graphing calculators allowed (10–18)

10. Use the ratio technique to find the open interval of convergence for this series:

$$\sum_{n=1}^{\infty} \frac{1}{n^2}(5x - 7)^n$$

11. The series in Problem 10 converges on a bounded interval. Find out whether or not the series converges at the endpoints of that interval.

12. The Taylor series about $x = 1$ for $\ln x$ is

$$\ln x = (x - 1) - \frac{1}{2}(x - 1)^2 + \frac{1}{3}(x - 1)^3 - \cdots$$

The series converges on the interval $(0, 2]$. Give graphical evidence that this is true by plotting $\ln x$ and the fourth and fifth partial sums on the same screen. Check your graph with your instructor. _____

13. The p-series $\sum_{n=1}^{\infty} n^{-1.01}$ converges. By comparing the series with an appropriate improper integral, find an upper bound for the tail of the series after the 50th partial sum. What other hypothesis does the sequence of partial sums of the series meet that, together with boundedness, allows you to conclude that the series does converge?

14. Find an estimate for the remainder of the p-series in Problem 13 by finding a *lower* bound for the tail using a different improper integral. Use the results and the value of S_{50}, the 50th partial sum, to find a reasonable estimate for the number to which the series converges.

15. State the three hypotheses of the alternating series test for convergence.

16. Find an upper bound on the remainder, $|R_{20}|$, for the alternating harmonic series

$$1 - \frac{1}{2} + \frac{1}{3} - \cdots$$

17. The Maclaurin series for e^x is

$$e^x = \sum_{n=0}^{\infty} \frac{1}{n!}x^n$$

Write the Lagrange form of the remainder, $R_5(2)$, for the series for e^2. Use the Lagrange form of the remainder to find an upper bound for $R_5(2)$. Then find the partial sum $S_5(2)$. Calculate the remainder by finding the difference between e^2 on your calculator and $S_5(2)$. Is this difference within the upper bound found by Lagrange?

18. What did you learn as a result of taking this test that you did not know before?

Calculus: Concepts and Applications Instructor's Resource Book
©2005 Key Curriculum Press

Test 45, Chapter 12

Objective: Express functions as power series.

Graphing calculators allowed

1. By equating derivatives, show that the Taylor series for $\ln x$ expanded about $x = 1$ is

$$\ln x = (x - 1) - \frac{1}{2}(x - 1)^2 + \frac{1}{3}(x - 1)^3 - \cdots$$

2. Write the $\ln x$ series using Σ notation.

3. Use the ratio technique to show that the open interval of convergence of the series for $\ln x$ is $0 < x < 2$.

4. Plot on the same screen the graphs of $y_1 = \ln x$ and $y_2 = S_{10}(x)$, the tenth partial sum of the $\ln x$ series in Problem 1. Use an x-window of about $[-1, 3]$ and a y-window of $[-5, 5]$. Sketch the result. How does the graph confirm that the open interval of convergence is $0 < x < 2$?

5. Show that the series for $\ln x$ converges at $x = 2$, but diverges at $x = 0$.

6. Estimate $\ln 1.8$ by calculating $S_9(1.8)$.

7. The **tail** of a series after a particular partial sum is the remaining (infinite number of) terms following that partial sum. Demonstrate that you understand the meaning of the tail of a series by writing the first three terms of the tail of the $\ln 1.8$ series following $S_{10}(1.8)$.

8. The **remainder**, R_n, of a series following a particular partial sum S_n is the number to which the tail of the series converges. It is equal to the **error** involved in using S_n to estimate the entire series. Find R_{10} for the $\ln 1.8$ series in Problem 6 by subtracting S_{10} from the value of $\ln 1.8$ you get from your calculator.

9. Evaluate the first term of the tail in Problem 7. Show that the remainder of the series after S_{10} is less in absolute value than the absolute value of the first term of the tail.

10. Estimate $\ln 0.3$ by using S_{10} for the Taylor series for $\ln x$. Approximately what does the remainder of the series equal for this value of x? Is the absolute value of this remainder an upper bound for the absolute value of the error in approximating $\ln 0.3$ by $S_{10}(0.3)$?

11. By appropriate substitution into the Taylor series for $\ln x$ in Problem 1, write the first four terms of the Maclaurin series for $\ln (x + 1)$.

12. Which elementary function has the following power series?

$$\sum_{n=0}^{\infty} (-1)^n \frac{1}{(2n + 1)!} x^{2n+1}$$

13. Show that the interval of convergence for the series in Problem 12 is all real numbers.

14. In the most time-efficient way possible, derive a Maclaurin series for $f(x) = x^3 \cos 2x$. Write the first three nonzero terms.

15. Write $f(x) = \frac{1}{1 - x}$ as a Maclaurin series. What special name is given to this particular series?

16. By appropriate substitution, write the first four nonzero terms of the Maclaurin series for

$$g(x) = \frac{1}{1 + x^2}$$

17. You recall that $\frac{d}{dx}(\tan^{-1} x) = \frac{1}{1 + x^2}$. Thus,

$$\tan^{-1} x = \int \frac{1}{1 + x^2}\, dx$$

By appropriate operations, show how the familiar Maclaurin series for $\tan^{-1} x$ is derived.

18. Write the first few terms of the familiar Maclaurin series for $\sinh x$ and for $\cosh x$. What series do you get by adding $\sinh x$ and $\cosh x$? How is the answer consistent with the definitions of $\sinh x$ and $\cosh x$?

19. The series $1 + \frac{1}{4} + \frac{1}{9} + \frac{1}{16} + \cdots$ is a **p-series.** Explain why this name is appropriate.

20. The p-series in Problem 19 converges. To demonstrate that this is true, you could draw a graph as shown below. The rectangles represent the terms of the tail after the fourth partial sum. By comparing the tail with an appropriate improper integral, find an upper bound for the tail.

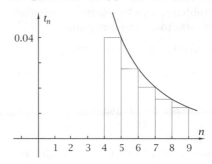

21. What did you learn as a result of taking this test that you did not know before?

Test 46, Chapters 7 to 12 [50 minutes]

Objective: Show that you know the algebraic techniques of calculus.

Graphing calculators allowed

In the second part of this course you have applied algebraic techniques to the geometrical and numerical concepts of limit, derivative, and definite integral. These techniques, invented more than 300 years ago by Newton and Leibniz, allowed the concepts to be used for real-world problems before there were computers that could apply the concepts more directly. On this test you are to show that you understand the algebraic techniques of calculus.

1. The figure below shows the region under the graph of $y = xe^{-x}$ from $x = 0$ to $x = b$. Find the volume of the solid formed by rotating the region about the y-axis.

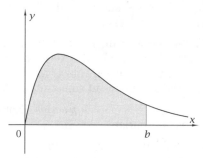

2. Confirm your answer to Problem 1 by evaluating it for $b = 3$ and showing that it agrees with the answer you get by numerical integration.

3. Name the theorem that allows you to calculate the integral in Problem 1 exactly. Name the integration technique you use to do the integrating.

4. $\int_0^\infty xe^{-x}\, dx$ is called a(n) —?— integral.

Geometric properties of figures can be discovered by algebraic calculus.

5. The figure below shows the parabola $y = a^2 - x^2$ between the two x-intercepts $x = -a$ and $x = a$. Find the average value of y in this interval. Show that the average is always 2/3 of the maximum value of y.

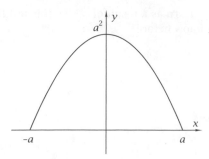

Integrals involving square roots of quadratic functions can be found by trigonometric substitution.

6. Integrate by trig substitution: $\int (49 - x^2)^{-1/2}\, dx$

Techniques for indefinite integration allow you to solve differential equations algebraically.

7. If interest for money in a savings account is compounded continuously, the instantaneous rate of change of money is directly proportional to the amount of money. Suppose that

    $$\frac{dM}{dt} = 0.06M$$

    where M is in dollars and t is in years. Show how algebraic integration methods are used to prove that M increases exponentially with t.

8. The figure below shows the slope field for the differential equation in Problem 7. Starting with the initial condition that $M = 80$ when $t = 0$, plot the values of M you calculate for $t = 5$, 10, and 15 years using your answer to Problem 7. Plot these points on the slope field, and thus show that the graph of M follows the slope field.

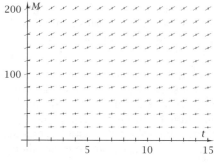

Derivatives can be used to find related rates of change and velocity vectors.

9. Prove that the instantaneous rate of change of the area of a circle of radius r is equal to the circumference of the circle times the instantaneous rate of change of the radius at that instant.

10. The position vector of a moving object is

    $$\vec{r}(t) = (\cosh 2t)\vec{i} + (\sin^{-1} t)\vec{j}$$

    Find an equation for the velocity vector.

Limits can be used to find intervals of convergence of power series.

11. Use the ratio technique to show that the open interval of convergence of the Taylor series for $\ln x$ expanded about $x = 1$ is $0 < x < 2$.

12. What is the one most important thing you have learned in the second half of this calculus course?

Test 47, Chapters 1 to 12 [50 minutes]

Objective: Do calculus numerically, graphically, algebraically, and verbally.

Graphing calculators allowed

You have learned the four concepts of calculus: limits, derivatives, and two kinds of integrals. There are four things you have learned about each concept: definition, meaning, technique, and application. In calculus as in other mathematical subjects, there are four ways of learning the concepts: numerically, graphically, algebraically, and verbally. On this test you will show that you understand these four approaches.

Numerical Methods

1. The function $f(x) = \frac{4 \ln x}{x - 1}$ is undefined at $x = 1$. Yet it does approach a **limit** as x approaches 1. Make a table of values of $f(x)$ for values of x close to 1 and make a conjecture about what this limit equals.

2. A **definite integral** can be used to find a product such as distance = (velocity)(time), where one factor, velocity, varies with the other, time. Suppose that as you leave the school zone after this test, your velocity is as shown in this table:

t (s)	v (ft/s)
0	25
4	30
8	37
12	43
16	47
20	50
24	52

   Use Simpson's rule to approximate the integral that equals the distance you have gone between 0 s and 24 s.

3. The **derivative** is the instantaneous rate of change of a variable with respect to another variable. Use a symmetric difference quotient to estimate the rate of change of v with respect to t in Problem 2 at time $t = 12$ s.

4. What name is given to the instantaneous rate of change of velocity with respect to time?

5. Numerical integration on your grapher can be used to evaluate integrals too complicated to evaluate by other methods. Suppose the graph of $y = e^x$ from $x = 1$ to $x = 2$ is rotated about the y-axis to form a surface. Write an integral for the area of this surface and evaluate it numerically.

Graphical Methods

6. The mean value theorem (mvt) is a property of **derivatives.** State its two hypotheses.

7. On the graph below, draw a sketch showing that you understand the mvt's conclusion.

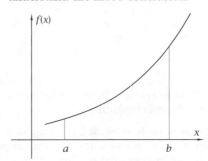

8. You can tell things about the graph of a function by looking at a graph of its derivative function. The graph of $f'(x)$ is shown below. For what value(s) of x does the graph of f have

   a. a local maximum?

   b. a local minimum?

   c. a point of inflection?

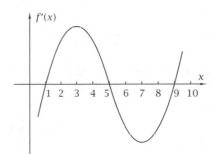

9. **Indefinite integrals** are used to solve differential equations. The solution can be found graphically with the aid of a slope field. The slope field at the top of the next page is for the differential equation

$$\frac{dy}{dx} = 0.5y(1 - 0.15y)$$

(Over)

Show that you understand the meaning of slope field by showing that the graph has the correct slope at the point (2, 3).

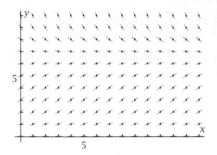

10. On the slope field in Problem 9, sketch the graph of the particular solution containing (2, 3).

11. The definition of definite integral has a graphical meaning in terms of Riemann sums. Draw an upper sum with $n = 4$ subintervals for the integral of f, graphed below, from $x = a$ to $x = b$.

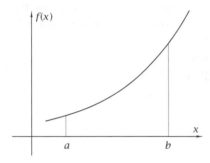

12. What graphical technique was the first you used in this course for estimating definite integrals?

Algebraic Methods

13. Algebraic methods allow you to find *exact* values of **derivatives.** Given $f(x)$ as shown below, find $f'(x)$ algebraically. Use the answer to find $f'(6)$ exactly.

$$f(x) = \sqrt{100 - x^2}$$

14. Algebraic methods let you find exactly the values of **definite integrals.** Suppose that the region under the graph of $y = e^x$ from $x = 1$ to $x = 2$ is rotated about the y-axis to form a solid. Write an integral for the volume of the solid. Integrate algebraically and use the result to find the volume exactly (in terms of e, π, etc.).

15. **Limits** can be found algebraically with the help of l'Hospital's rule. Find exactly the limit

$$\lim_{x \to 1} \frac{4 \ln x}{x - 1}$$

thus showing your conjecture in Problem 1 was correct.

16. Algebraic methods can be used to get *power series*, which can then be used to find values of functions numerically. Suppose that

$$f(x) = \int_0^x \frac{\sin t}{t}\, dt$$

By using the familiar Maclaurin series for sin t, then doing appropriate algebra, write the first few terms of the power series for $f(x)$.

17. Name the technique you have used to find the interval of convergence of a power series.

18. Algebraic methods can be used to analyze motion in two dimensions with the help of vectors and parametric functions. Suppose that the position, $\vec{r}(t)$, of a moving object is given by

$$\vec{r}(t) = (e^{0.5t})\vec{i} + (\sin t)\vec{j}$$

The diagram shows the velocity vector, $\vec{v}(1)$. On the diagram, draw the acceleration vector, $\vec{a}(1)$. Does the object appear to be speeding up or slowing down at $t = 1$? How do you tell?

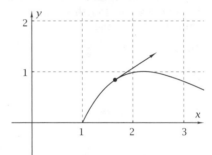

Verbal Methods

19. Write a paragraph telling what you feel is the most important thing you have learned as a result of taking calculus.

Calculus: Concepts and Applications Instructor's Resource Book
©2005 Key Curriculum Press

Test 48, Chapters 1 to 12 [120 minutes]

Objective: Show that you understand the four concepts of calculus and techniques for applying them.

Graphing calculators allowed

The first semester you spent learning the four concepts of calculus. The second semester you consolidated your knowledge of these concepts by applying them to various real-world phenomena. You also learned techniques that allowed you to integrate and differentiate a wider variety of functions algebraically, thus getting exact answers to problems you had done only graphically and numerically before.

Problems 1 through 7 refer to the region R under the graph of $y = 3 \sin x$ from $x = 0$ to $x = \pi$.

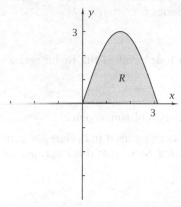

1. By an appropriate algebraic calculus technique, show that the area of R is exactly 6.

2. The first moment of R with respect to the y-axis, M_y, is defined to be the area of R times the displacement from the y-axis to R. Unfortunately the displacement is different for different points in R. Find M_y. You may use numerical calculus methods.

3. Find $\bar{x}$, the x-coordinate of the centroid, for which $\bar{x} \cdot A = M_y$.

4. Find the volume of the solid formed by rotating R about the y-axis.

5. Show that the theorem of Pappus could be used to find the volume of the solid in Problem 4. That is, show that the volume equals the area of R times the distance the centroid of R travels in one revolution.

6. Find the volume of the solid formed by rotating R about the x-axis.

7. The theorem of Pappus can be used backward to find the centroid of a region if the volume and area are known. Find the y-coordinate of the centroid of the solid formed by rotating R about the x-axis.

8. The graph (next column) shows the semicubical parabola

$$x = t^2$$
$$y = t^3$$

from $t = 0$ to $t = 2$. Find the area of the surface generated by rotating the following graph about the y-axis.

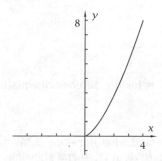

9. Sketch a graph that shows why the differential of arc length in polar coordinates is

$$dL = \sqrt{(dr)^2 + (r\,d\theta)^2}$$

10. Below is the graph of the polar equation $r = \theta$. Find the length of the three revolutions shown.

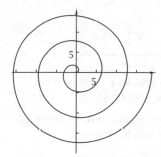

11. Ann Aggie has a stock tank 100 ft, perpendicularly, from the fence and 400 ft horizontally along the fence from the well that will supply the tank. She must pay \$3/ft to install pipe along the fence and \$5/ft to install it across the field. How should she run the pipe to have the minimum installation cost?

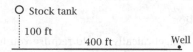

(Over)

12. The graph shows the catenary $y = \cosh x$. Find the area of the region under the graph from $x = 0$ to $x = 2$. Use the result to find the average value of y over the interval $[0, 2]$. On the graph, show the geometric significance of this average value.

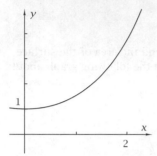

13. The slope field below is for the differential equation

$$\frac{dy}{dx} = 0.2(y - 5)(y - 1)$$

Show that you understand what the slope field means by calculating dy/dx at $(1, 4)$ and showing that the answer agrees with the diagram.

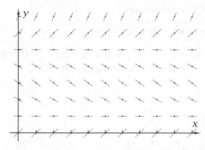

14. For the slope field in Problem 13, sketch the particular solution containing $(1, 4)$.

15. Solving the differential equation in Problem 13 algebraically requires you to integrate

$$\int \frac{1}{(y - 5)(y - 1)}\, dy$$

Do this integration.

16. Doing Problem 10 algebraically would require you to evaluate an integral of the form

$$\int \sqrt{1 + x^2}\, dx$$

Do this integration.

17. Doing Problem 4 algebraically would require you to evaluate an integral of the form

$$\int x \sin x\, dx$$

Do this integration.

18. Maxima, minima, and points of inflection can be found exactly with the help of algebraic differentiation. Find the exact x-coordinates of

the two points of inflection of the graph of

$$y = x^2 e^{-x}$$

Use radicals, π, e, and so on, if necessary.

19. Derivatives can be used to find related rates of change. Suppose that the length of a rectangle is increasing at 5 cm/h and its width is decreasing at 3 cm/h. When the length is 100 cm and the width is 50 cm, is the area of the rectangle increasing or decreasing? At what rate?

20. Approximate values of transcendental functions can be found by expanding them as Taylor or Maclaurin series. Write the first few terms of the Maclaurin series for $\cos x$. By appropriate operations on this series, write the first few terms of the Maclaurin series for

$$\int x \cos x\, dx$$

21. Write out the first four terms of the Taylor series

$$\sum_{n=1}^{\infty} \frac{(-1)^n}{2^n}(x - 1)^n$$

Find the (open) interval of convergence.

22. Improper integrals can be used to find upper bounds of series of constants. Show that this improper integral converges:

$$\int_{1}^{\infty} x^{-1.02}\, dx$$

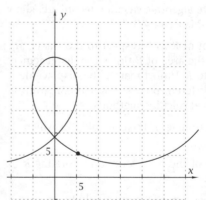

A roller coaster with a loop is to go on a track the shape of the prolate cycloid, above. Its position (meters) at time t seconds is given by the vector equation

$$\vec{r}(t) = (5t - 12 \sin t)\vec{i} + (15 + 12 \cos t)\vec{j}$$

23. Find the velocity and acceleration vectors at the point shown, where $t = 2.5$ s. Draw these vectors on the diagram, starting at the point on the graph.

24. At $t = 2.5$, how fast is the roller coaster going? Is it speeding up or slowing down?

25. What is the one most important thing you have learned as a result of taking this calculus course?

Calculus: Concepts and Applications Instructor's Resource Book
©2005 Key Curriculum Press

Solutions for the Section, Chapter, and Cumulative Tests

Test 1

1. L is the limit of $f(x)$ as x approaches c if and only if for any positive number ε, no matter how small, there is a positive number δ such that if x is within δ units of c, but not equal to c, then $f(x)$ is within ε units of L.

2. $f(x)$ and $g(x)$ are both close to 5 when x is close to (but not equal to) 7. $h(x)$ is close to 5 when x is close to 7 on the right side. But it is close to 8 when x is close to 7 on the left. Thus, there is no one number $h(x)$ is close to when x is close to 7 but not equal to 7.

3. Approximately 16.9 squares at 10 units per square. Integral ≈ 169. (Exact: 169.1941...) (Function is $v(t) = 0.2t \cos(t/15) + 8$.)

4. Units are (ft/s)(s), or ft. So the object goes a distance of about 169 ft.

5. Before taking into account the scales of the axes, the graph appears to slope down at about −0.5. So the actual rate is more nearly
$$\frac{(-0.5)(2)}{5} = -0.2$$
Velocity is decreasing at about 0.2 (ft/s)/s. (Exact: −0.21213...)

6. $500[0.5(9.2) + 10.1 + 10.8 + 11.4 + 0.5(12.0)] = 21{,}450$

7. Units are (Btu/degree)(degrees) = Btu. It means that about 21,450 Btu must be added to warm a pound of steam from 1000°F to 3000°F.

8. Rate $\approx \dfrac{11.4 - 10.1}{1000} = 0.0013$ (Btu/degree)/degree

9. $D(3) = -2(3^2) + 20(3) + 50 = 92$ ft

10. $v_{av}(3.1) = \dfrac{92.78 - 92}{0.1} = 7.8$ ft/s

11. $v_{av}(3.001) = 7.998$
    Conjecture: $v(3) = 8$ ft/s

12. $v_{av}(t) = \dfrac{D(t) - D(3)}{t - 3} = \dfrac{-2t^2 + 20t - 42}{t - 3}$

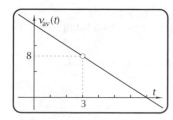

Discontinuity at $t = 3$.

13. $v_{av}(3)$ becomes 0/0, which is an indeterminate form. So, $v_{av}(3)$ cannot be found by direct substitution.

14. $v_{av}(t) = \dfrac{-2(t - 3)(t - 7)}{t - 3} = -2t + 14$, provided $x \ne 3$.
    Substituting $t = 3$ gives $-2(3) + 14 = 8$, which is the value conjectured in Problem 11.

15. Answers will vary.

Test 2

1. L is the limit of $f(x)$ as x approaches c if and only if for any positive number ε (no matter how small) there is a positive number δ such that if x is kept within δ units of c, but not equal to c, then $f(x)$ is within ε units of L.

2. Limit, derivative, definite integral, indefinite integral

3. Possible solution:

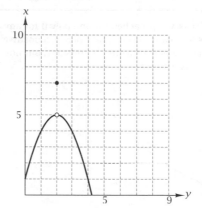

4.

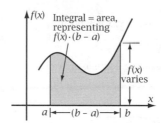

Integral = area, representing $f(x) \cdot (b - a)$

$f(x)$ varies

5. Definite integral; approximately 21.4 ft

6. Derivative; approximately −1.6 (ft/s)/s; acceleration

7. Yes; 10 ft/s

8. $M(t) = 1000(1.1)^t$
    $M(5) = 1610.51$
    $\$1610.51$ is in the account.

9. Average rate $= \dfrac{1610.51 - 1000}{5} = 122.102$ \$/yr

10. $\dfrac{M(5.1) - M(5)}{0.1} = 154.231...$ \$/yr
    This is greater than the average rate. That's because there is more money earning interest at the end of the 5 yr than there had been earlier.

11. $\dfrac{M(5.1) - M(4.9)}{0.2} = 153.5003...$ \$/yr

12. $\dfrac{M(5.01) - M(5)}{0.01} = 153.5711...$ \$/yr

$\dfrac{M(5.001) - M(5)}{0.001} = 153.5053...$ \$/yr

13. Substituting directly would give 0/0 for the rate, which is undefined because it is an indeterminate form.

14.

t	Average rate
0.1	154.231...
0.01	153.5711...
0.001	153.5053...
exact:	153.497997...

The average rates are approaching the exact rate.

15. Integral $\approx 5[0.5(6) + 13 + 17 + 22 + 0.5(14)] = 5(62) = 310$ ft

16. $T_{10} = 774.7691...$
$T_{100} = 774.99236...$
Conjecture: Limit is 775 ft.

17. Answers will vary.

Test 3

1. L is the limit of $f(x)$ as x approaches c if and only if for any positive number ε (no matter how small) there is a positive number δ such that if x is kept within δ units of c, but not equal to c, then $f(x)$ is within ε units of L.

2.

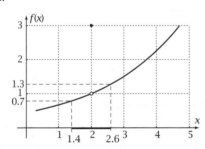

3. x cannot be equal to c because at c, $x = 3$, not 1.

4. Keep x sufficiently close to 2.

5. Approximately 3 (ft/s)/s (exact: 2.9429...); derivative

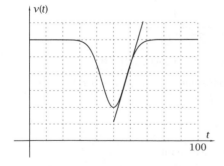

6. Approximately $(60)(20) = 1200$ ft

7. Approximately 17.0 squares, which represents about 1700 ft. (Exact: 1696.03...)
(Equation is $v(t) = 60 - 40[0.99^{(x-50)^2}]$.)

8.

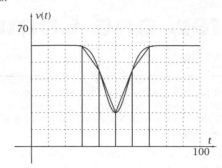

9. The car may have slowed down for traffic.

10.

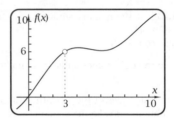

11. Removable discontinuity at $x = 3$.
The limit as x approaches 3 is 6 because $f(x)$ stays close to 6 when x is kept close to 3 ($x \neq 3$).

12. Right: $f(x) = 6.5 \Rightarrow x = 3.8425...$ (numerically)
Left: $f(x) = 5.5 \Rightarrow x = 2.5852...$
$\delta = 0.4147...$ (Left side is more restrictive.)

13. Vertical asymptote at $x = 2$.

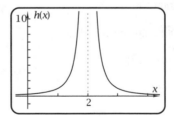

14. Derivative $\approx \dfrac{h(2.31) - h(2.29)}{0.02} = -74.2389...$

15. $h(x)$ is decreasing because the derivative is negative.

16. Definite integral by trapezoidal rule:
work $\approx 2[0.5(17) + 20 + 24 + 30 + 37 + 0.5(48)]$
$= 287$ ft-lb

17. $T_5 = 19.3376...$, $T_{10} = 19.8352...$, $T_{50} = 19.9934....$
Conjecture: Integral = 20

18. Answers will vary.

Test 4

1. L is the limit of $f(x)$ as x approaches c if and only if for any positive number ε (no matter how small) there is a positive number δ such that if x is kept within δ units of c, but not equal to c, then $f(x)$ is within ε units of L.

2. Limit = 0.5

3.

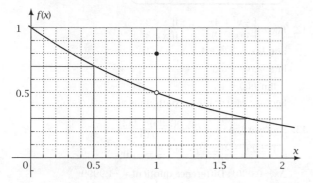

4. Keep x in the range $0.5 < x < 1.7$.

5. Maximum $\delta \approx 0.5$

6. x cannot be equal to 1 because at 1, $x = 0.7$, not 0.5.

7. $\lim\limits_{x \to c} [f(x) + g(x)] = \lim\limits_{x \to c} f(x) + \lim\limits_{x \to c} g(x)$

8. The limit of a quotient property cannot be used in the second case because $\lim_{x \to 4} (x - 4) = 0$ and division by zero is undefined.

9. $\dfrac{3x^2 - 10x - 8}{x - 4} = \dfrac{(3x + 2)(x - 4)}{x - 4} = 3x + 2, \ x \neq 4$

$\lim\limits_{x \to 4} \dfrac{3x^2 - 10x - 8}{x - 4} = \lim\limits_{x \to 4} (3x + 2)$ Because $x \neq 4$

$= \lim\limits_{x \to 4} 3x + \lim\limits_{x \to 4} 2$ Limit of a sum

$= 3 \lim\limits_{x \to 4} x + 2$ Limit of a constant times x, limit of a constant

$= 3 \cdot 4 + 2 = 14$ Limit of x

10. $2^{-x} = 0.7 \Rightarrow x = 0.5145...$
$2^{-x} = 0.3 \Rightarrow x = 1.7369...$
Range is $0.5145... < x < 1.7369....$

11. Maximum $\delta = 1 - 0.5145... = 0.4854...$

12. $2^{-x} = 0.5 + \varepsilon$

$x = -\dfrac{\log (0.5 + \varepsilon)}{\log 2}$

$\delta = 1 + \dfrac{\log (0.5 + \varepsilon)}{\log 2}$

13. $g(x) = (2x + 7)(3x + 1)$
$g(1) = 36$
$\lim\limits_{x \to 1} g(x) = \lim\limits_{x \to 1} (2x + 7)(3x + 1)$

$= \lim\limits_{x \to 1} (2x + 7) \lim\limits_{x \to 1} (3x + 1)$ Limit of a product

$= \left(\lim\limits_{x \to 1} 2x + \lim\limits_{x \to 1} 7\right)\left(\lim\limits_{x \to 1} 3x + \lim\limits_{x \to 1} 1\right)$ Limit of a sum

$= \left(2 \lim\limits_{x \to 1} x + 7\right)\left(3 \lim\limits_{x \to 1} x + 1\right)$ Limit of a constant function and limit of a constant

$= (2 \cdot 1 + 7)(3 \cdot 1 + 1)$ Limit of x (identity function)

$= 36$, Q.E.D.   Arithmetic

14. $c(x) = x^3$

Derivative $= \dfrac{5.01^3 - 5^3}{5.01 - 5} = 75.1501.$

Derivative $= \dfrac{5.001^3 - 5^3}{5.001 - 5} = 75.015001.$

15. Conjecture: Derivative = 75

16. $m(x) = \dfrac{x^3 - 5^3}{x - 5} = \dfrac{x^3 - 125}{x - 5}$

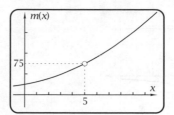

17. $m(x) = \dfrac{(x - 5)(x^2 + 5x + 25)}{x - 5}$
$m(x) = x^2 + 5x + 25, \ x \neq 5$

18. $\lim\limits_{x \to 5} m(x) = \lim\limits_{x \to 5} x^2 + \lim\limits_{x \to 5} 5x + \lim\limits_{x \to 5} 25$
$= \lim\limits_{x \to 5} x \cdot \lim\limits_{x \to 5} x + 5 \cdot \lim\limits_{x \to 5} x + 25$
$= 5 \cdot 5 + 5 \cdot 5 + 25 = 75$, Q.E.D.

19. Derivative $= 3 \cdot 5^2 = 75$. Raise 5 to one less power and multiply the answer by the original exponent.

20. Answers will vary.

Test 5

1. L is the limit of $f(x)$ as x approaches c if and only if for any positive number ε (no matter how small) there is a positive number δ such that if x is kept within δ units of c, but not equal to c, then $f(x)$ is within ε units of L.

2. Possible solution:

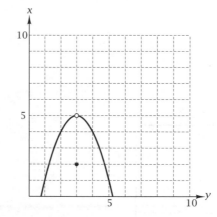

Removable discontinuity

3. Possible solution:

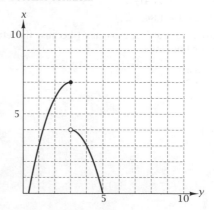

Step discontinuity

4. Possible solution:

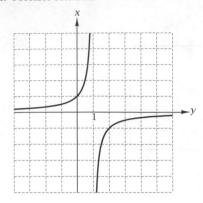

Vertical asymptote

5. Possible solution:

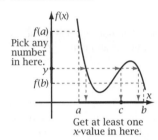

Get at least one
x-value in here.

6. $\lim\limits_{x \to c} [f(x) \cdot g(x)] = \lim\limits_{x \to c} f(x) \cdot \lim\limits_{x \to c} g(x)$

7. "Look, Mae, $f(c)$ has to equal the limit as x approaches c. The graph could look like this:"

8.

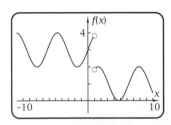

9. $\lim\limits_{x \to 1^-} f(x) = 2 + \sin 1 + 1 = 3.8414...$
   $\lim\limits_{x \to 1^+} f(x) = 2 + \sin 1 - 1 = 1.8414...$
   $f(x)$ does not have a limit as x approaches 1 because the left and right limits are not equal.

10. $g(x) = \begin{cases} 3x, & \text{if } x \le 2 \\ k/x, & \text{if } x > 2 \end{cases}$
    $\lim\limits_{x \to 2^-} g(x) = 3 \cdot 2 = 6$
    $\lim\limits_{x \to 2^+} g(x) = k/2$
    $\therefore k/2 = 6 \Rightarrow k = 12$

11. (Instructor check)

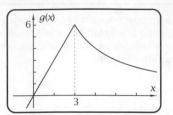

12. $h(x) = \begin{cases} -x^2 + 4x + 1, & \text{if } x < 3 \\ 4(0.6^{x-3}), & \text{if } x \ge 3 \end{cases}$
    $\lim\limits_{x \to 3^-} h(x) = -3^2 + 4 \cdot 3 + 1 = 4$
    $\lim\limits_{x \to 3^+} h(x) = 4(0.6^0) = 4$
    $\therefore \lim\limits_{x \to 3} h(x) = 4.$
    Because $h(3) = 4$, h is continuous at $x = 3$, Q.E.D.

13. Backward, $\Delta x = 0.01$: $\dfrac{h(2.99) - h(3)}{-0.01}$
    $= \dfrac{[-2.99^2 + 4(2.99) + 1] - 4}{-0.01} = -1.99$
    $\Delta x = 0.0001$: Difference quotient $= -1.9999$
    Limit appears to equal -2.
    Forward, $\Delta x = 0.01$: $\dfrac{h(3.01) - h(3)}{0.01}$
    $= \dfrac{4(0.6^{0.01}) - 4}{0.01} = -2.0380...$
    $\Delta x = 0.0001$: Difference quotient $= -2.0432...$
    Limit is clearly different from -2 because the forward difference quotients are going away from -2.
    Although the graph appears to be smooth at $x = 3$, it really is not quite smooth.
    (Exact limit of the forward difference quotient is $4(0.6^0) \ln 0.6$, which equals $-2.043302...$)

14. $r(x) = 3 + \dfrac{1}{(x - 4)^2}$ shows a vertical asymptote at $x = 4$.

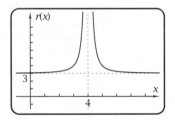

15. Keep x within 0.0010000015 on the positive side.

16. Let $r(x) = 3.01$.
    $3.01 = 3 + \dfrac{1}{(x - 4)^2}$
    $0.01 = \dfrac{1}{(x - 4)^2}$
    $(x - 4)^2 = 100 \Rightarrow x = 14$ or -6
    Keep $x > 14$.
    In general, keep $x > D = 4 + \sqrt{1/\varepsilon}$.

17. $\lim\limits_{x \to 5} p(x) = \lim\limits_{x \to 5} (7x + 13) = \lim\limits_{x \to 5} 7x + \lim\limits_{x \to 5} 13$
    $= 7 \lim\limits_{x \to 5} x + 13 = 7 \cdot 5 + 13 = 48$, Q.E.D.

18. $q(x) = x^4$
    $q(2) = 16$ and $q(3) = 81$
    Because q is continuous, the intermediate value theorem applies. Thus, there is a number $x = c$ between 2 and 3 for which $q(c) = 51$. This is the fourth root of 51, Q.E.D.

19. Answers will vary.

Test 6

1. $f(c)$ exists, $\lim_{x \to c}$ exists, and $\lim_{x \to c} = f(c)$.

2. Function f is continuous on an interval of x-values if and only if it is continuous at each value of x in that interval.

3. At each endpoint, c, only the one-sided limit must exist and equal $f(c)$.

4. Possible solution:

5. Step discontinuity

6. Possible solution:

7.

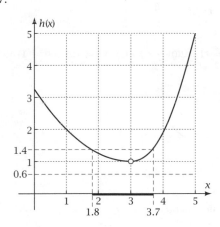

8. Maximum $\delta \approx 0.7$

9. x cannot be equal to 3 because at that value $h(x)$ does not exist.

10. There is a cusp at $x = 2$. The limit of $c(x)$ is 5.

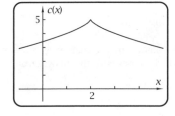

11. $f(x) = \begin{cases} x^2, & \text{if } x \le 2 \\ kx + 10, & \text{if } x > 2 \end{cases}$

$\lim_{x \to 2^-} f(x) = 2^2 = 4$

$\lim_{x \to 2^+} f(x) = 2k + 10$

$2k + 10 = 4 \Rightarrow k = -3$

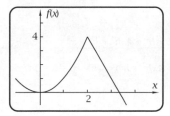

12.

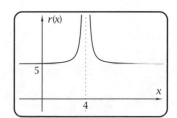

13. $q(x) = x^4$

Average rate $= \dfrac{3 \cdot 2^4 - 3^4}{0.2} = 119.288$

14. Average rate $= \dfrac{x^4 - 81}{x - 3}$

$= \dfrac{(x - 3)(x^3 + 3x^2 + 9x + 27)}{x - 3}$

$= x^3 + 3x^2 + 9x + 27$, if $x \ne 3$

15. $\lim_{x \to 3} (\text{Average rate}) = \lim_{x \to 3} (x^3 + 3x^2 + 9x + 27)$

$= \lim_{x \to 3} x^3 + \lim_{x \to 3} 3x^2 + \lim_{x \to 3} 9x + \lim_{x \to 3} 27$ Limit of a sum

$= \lim_{x \to 3} x^3 + 3 \lim_{x \to 3} x^2 + 9 \lim_{x \to 3} x + \lim_{x \to 3} 27$ Limit of a constant times a function

$= 3^3 + 3 \cdot 3^2 + 9 \cdot 3 + 27$ Limit of a power, limit of x, limit of a constant

$= 108$

16. Derivative

17. q satisfies the hypotheses of the intermediate value theorem. Therefore, there is a value of c between 2 and 3 such that $q(c)$ is exactly 37.

$c = 37^{1/4} = 2.46632571\ldots$

18. Answers will vary.

Test 7

1. $f'(c) = \lim_{x \to 0} \dfrac{f(x) - f(c)}{x - c}$

2. $f'(x) = \lim_{\Delta x \to 0} \dfrac{f(x + \Delta x) - f(x)}{\Delta x} = \lim_{h \to 0} \dfrac{f(x + h) - f(x)}{h}$

3. $f(x) = 6x^{100} - 17x^{-3}$

$f'(x) = 600x^{99} + 51x^{-4}$

4. $y = (2x + 5)^3 = 8x^3 + 60x^2 + 150x + 125$

$\dfrac{dy}{dx} = 24x^2 + 120x + 150$

5. $\dfrac{d}{dx}(4x^{0.7} + 13^5) = 2.8x^{-0.3}$

6. $f(x) = x^4$

$f'(x) = \lim_{h \to 0} \dfrac{(x + h)^4 - x^4}{h}$

$= \lim_{h \to 0} \dfrac{x^4 + 4x^3h + 6x^2h^2 + 4xh^3 + h^4 - x^4}{h}$

$= \lim_{h \to 0} (4x^3 + 6x^2h + 4xh^2 + h^3) = 4x^3 + 0 + 0 + 0$

$= 4x^3$, Q.E.D.

7. $f'(x)$ is shown dashed.

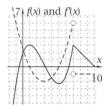

8. $\lim_{x \to 7^-} f'(x) \approx 6$, $\lim_{x \to 7^+} f'(x) \approx -1$

The two limits are unequal, so there is no single limit of $f'(x)$ as x approaches 7. Thus there is no value of $f'(7)$.

9. f is continuous at $x = 7$ because $\lim_{x \to 7} f(x) = 3 = f(3)$.

10. Cusp

11. "Differentiable" means "has a value for the derivative."
f is not differentiable at $x = 7$.

12. $g(x) = x^7$

$g'(x) = 7x^6 \Rightarrow g'(2) = 7 \cdot 2^6 = 448$

$g'(2) \approx \dfrac{2.01^7 - 1.99^7}{0.01} = 448.056...$, which is close.

By grapher, $g'(2) \approx 448.00056...$ (depending on the tolerance), which is also close.

13. $h(x) = x^2 - 5x + 7$
$h'(x) = 2x - 5 \Rightarrow h'(2) = -1$
The line is tangent to the graph.

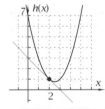

14. The equation is $y = -x + 3$.
Zoom in on (2, 1) and show that the graph becomes indistinguishable from the tangent line. Thus the graph is locally linear at $x = 2$.

15. $g(x) = \dfrac{1}{x - 3} + 2$

There is a vertical asymptote at $x = 3$.

$\dfrac{1}{x - 3} + 2 > 1{,}000{,}000$

$x - 3 < \frac{1}{999998}$ on the right of $x = 3$

Keep x within 1/999998 of 3 on the right.

16. $\lim_{x \to \infty} g(x) = 2$

$\dfrac{1}{x - 3} + 2 - 2 < 0.0001$

$x - 3 > 10{,}000$

Keep $x > 10{,}003$.

17. Answers will vary.

Test 8

1. $y = \sin^7 x \Rightarrow y' = 7 \sin^6 x \cos x$

2. $f(x) = \cos 18x \Rightarrow f'(x) = -18 \sin 18x$

3. $g(x) = \sin(\cos x^4)$
$g'(x) = \cos(\cos x^4)(-\sin x^4) \cdot 4x^3$
$= -4x^3 \cos(\cos x^4) \sin x^4$

4. $\dfrac{d}{dx}(x^2 + 5x - 7)^8 = 8(x^2 + 5x - 7)^7(2x + 5)$

5. $\dfrac{d}{dx}(5 - x)^{100} = 100(5 - x)^{99}(-1) = -100(5 - x)^{99}$

6. $f(x) = 7x^{10} \Rightarrow f'(x) = 70x^9 \Rightarrow f''(x) = 630x^8$

7. $\dfrac{d^2}{dx^2}(\sin 4x) \Rightarrow \dfrac{d}{dx}(4 \cos 4x) \Rightarrow (-16 \sin 4x)$

8. $t = 2$: slowing down; $t = 5$: speeding up; $t = 8$: slowing down; $t = 11$: speeding up

9. $t = 3$ or $t = 9$ or $t = 15$

10. $a(t) = 12t$

11. $x(t) = 2t^3 + C \Rightarrow 11 = 2(0)^3 + C \Rightarrow C = 11 \Rightarrow x(t) = 2t^3 + 11$

12. 7.

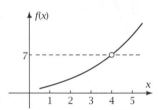

There is no x-value that makes $y = 7$.

13. $f(x) = \sin 4x$
$f'(x) = 4 \cos 4x$
$f'(3) = 4 \cos 12 = 3.3754158...$
$f(x)$ is increasing at 3.3754... y-units/x-unit.

14. $g(x) = (5x^3 + 4)^2$
By the chain rule, $g'(x) = 2(5x^3 + 4) \cdot 15x^2$
$= 30x^2(5x^3 + 4)$
Expanding: $g(x) = 25x^6 + 40x^3 + 16$
$g'(x) = 150x^5 + 120x^2$
Distribute the $30x^2$ in the answer by the chain rule:
$g'(x) = 150x^5 + 120x^2$, which agrees with the answer from expanding the binomial.

15. $h(x) = \cos x^3$
$h'(x) = -3x^2 \sin x^3$
Graphs of h (thick line), algebraic derivative (thin line), and numerical derivative (dotted line). y_2 and y_3 coincide.

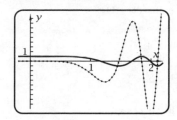

16. $f(x) = 5x^2 - 13x + 4$
$f(2) = 5(4) - 13(2) + 4 = -2$
$\lim\limits_{x \to 2} f(x) = \lim\limits_{x \to 2} (5x^2 - 13x + 4)$
$\quad\quad = \lim\limits_{x \to 2} 5x^2 + \lim\limits_{x \to 2} (-13x) + \lim\limits_{x \to 2} 4$
$\quad\quad = 5 \lim\limits_{x \to 2} x^2 - 13 \lim\limits_{x \to 2} x + \lim\limits_{x \to 2} 4$
$\quad\quad = 5 \cdot 4 - 13 \cdot 2 + 4 = -2$
f is continuous at $x = 2$.

17. $d(t) = 25 + 10 \cos \dfrac{\pi}{30} t$

18. $d'(t) = -\dfrac{\pi}{3} \sin \dfrac{\pi}{30} t$

19. $d'(70) = -0.9068\ldots$
$d(t)$ is decreasing at about 0.9 in./s.

20.

x	$(\sin x)/(x)$
0.1	0.998334166...
0.01	0.999983333...
0.001	0.999999833...

The values of $(\sin x)/x$ are getting very close to 1 as x gets closer to 0.

21. $A_{\text{small } \Lambda} \le A_{\text{sector}} \le A_{\text{large } \Delta}$
$\dfrac{1}{2} \cos x \sin x \le \dfrac{1}{2} x \le \dfrac{1}{2} \tan x$
$\cos x \le \dfrac{x}{\sin x} \le \dfrac{1}{\cos x}$
$\dfrac{1}{\cos x} \ge \dfrac{\sin x}{x} \ge \cos x \text{ (for } x > 0)$
$\cos x \le \dfrac{\sin x}{x} \le \dfrac{1}{\cos x}$, Q.E.D.

22. Squeeze theorem

23. $f'(x) = \lim\limits_{h \to 0} \dfrac{\cos (x + 0.5h) \cdot \sin 0.5h}{0.5h}$
$\quad\quad = \lim\limits_{h \to 0} \cos (x + 0.5h) \cdot \lim\limits_{h \to 0} \dfrac{\sin 0.5h}{0.5h}$
$\quad\quad = \cos x \cdot 1 = \cos x$, Q.E.D.

24. $g(x) = \sin (\pi/2 - x)$
$g'(x) = \cos (\pi/2 - x) \cdot (-1) = -\cos (\pi/2 - x)$
But $\sin (\pi/2 - x) = \cos x$, and $\cos (\pi/2 - x) = \sin x$.
$\therefore g(x) = \cos x$ and $g'(x) = -\sin x$, Q.E.D.

25. Answers will vary.

Test 9

1. $f(x) = 7e^{2x} \Rightarrow f'(x) = 14e^{2x}$

2. $g(x) = 10e^{\sin x} \Rightarrow g'(x) = 10e^{\sin x} \cdot \cos x$

3. $h(x) = 5 \cos (e^{-0.3x}) \Rightarrow$
$h'(x) = -5 \sin (e^{-0.3x}) \cdot (-0.3e^{-0.3x}) = 1.5e^{-0.3x} \sin (e^{-0.3x})$

4. $f(x) = 8 \ln 13x \Rightarrow f'(x) = \dfrac{8}{13x} \cdot 13 = \dfrac{8}{x}$

5. $y = 6 \ln x^{11} \Rightarrow y' = \dfrac{6}{x^{11}} \cdot 11x^{10} = \dfrac{66}{x}$

6. $u = 9 \ln (\cos 2x) \Rightarrow u' = \dfrac{9}{\cos 2x} \cdot (-2 \sin 2x) = -18 \tan 2x$

7. $y = 5 \ln e^x \Rightarrow y' = \dfrac{5}{e^x} \cdot e^x = 5$

8. $f(x) = 4^x \Rightarrow f'(x) = 4^x \ln 4$

9. $g(x) = 0.3^{\sin x} \Rightarrow g'(x) = 0.3^{\sin x} \cdot \ln 0.3 \cdot \cos x$

10. $\dfrac{d}{dx}(\ln 5^x) = \dfrac{1}{5^x} \cdot 5^x \ln 5 = \ln 5$

11. $y = \ln x^7 \Rightarrow y' = \dfrac{1}{x^7} \cdot 7x^6 = \dfrac{7}{x} = 7x^{-1} \Rightarrow y'' = -7x^{-2}$

12. $f(x) = 4e^{-3x} \Rightarrow f'(x) = -12e^{-3x} \Rightarrow f''(x) = 36e^{-3x}$

13. $f'(x) = 8^x \ln 8 \rightarrow f(x) = 8^x + C$

14. $y' = 15e^{3x} \Rightarrow y = 5e^{3x} + C$

15. The derivative is shown thick.

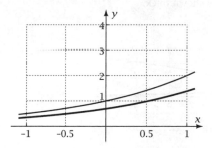

16. Constant $= \ln 2$; the graphs coincide.

17. The derivative is shown thick.

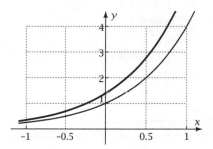

18. Constant $= \ln 4$; the graphs coincide.

19. The derivative graph coincides with the original graph.

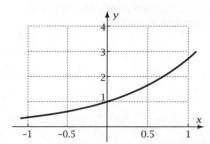

20. The derivative of e^x is $e^x \ln e$, which equals e^x.

21. $\dfrac{d}{dx}(5^x) = \lim\limits_{h\to 0} \dfrac{5^{x+h} - 5^x}{h}$

$\phantom{\dfrac{d}{dx}(5^x)} = \lim\limits_{h\to 0} \dfrac{5^x \cdot 5^h - 5^x}{h}$

$\phantom{\dfrac{d}{dx}(5^x)} = \lim\limits_{h\to 0} \dfrac{5^x(5^h - 1)}{h}$

$\phantom{\dfrac{d}{dx}(5^x)} = 5^x \cdot \lim\limits_{h\to 0} \dfrac{5^h - 1}{h}$, Q.E.D.

22.

h	$(5^h - 1)/h$
-0.002	$1.6068503...$
-0.001	$1.6081434...$
0	undefined
0.001	$1.6107337...$
0.002	$1.6120309...$

$\ln 5 = 1.609437...$, which these numbers seem to be approaching as $h \to 0$ from either side.

23. $y = \ln x$

$e^y = x$

$e^y \cdot y' = 1$

$y' = \dfrac{1}{e^y} = \dfrac{1}{x}$, Q.E.D.

24. The derivative is shown thick.

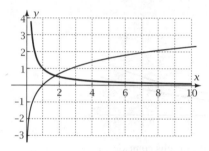

25. The graphs of y_2 and y_3 coincide, so the algebraic derivative is correct.

26. $y = \ln 0.5x \Rightarrow y' = \dfrac{1}{0.5x} \cdot 0.5 = \dfrac{1}{x}$

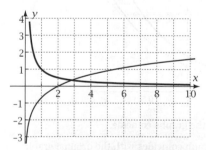

Yes, the two derivative graphs coincide. The derivative of $\ln 0.5x$ is equal to the derivative of $\ln x$.

27. Answers will vary.

Test 10

1. $f'(c) = \lim\limits_{x\to c} \dfrac{f(x) - f(c)}{x - c}$ or

$f'(x) = \lim\limits_{\Delta x\to 0} \dfrac{f(x + \Delta x) - f(x)}{\Delta x} = \lim\limits_{h\to 0} \dfrac{f(x + h) - f(x)}{h}$

2. Instantaneous rate of change of a function

3. Slope of the tangent line to the graph

4. "Differentiate" means "find the derivative."

5. Differentiate the outside function with respect to the inside function, then multiply by the derivative of the inside function with respect to x.

6. $f(x) = (x^3 + 11)^6 \Rightarrow$
$f'(x) = 6(x^3 + 11)^5 \cdot 3x^2 = 18x^2(x^3 + 11)^5$

7. $g(x) = \cos^4(x^7) \Rightarrow$
$g'(x) = 4\cos^3(x^7) \cdot [-\sin(x^7)] \cdot 7x^6$
$ = -28x^6 \cos^3(x^7) \cdot \sin(x^7)$

8. $h'(x) = x^{2001} \Rightarrow h(x) = \dfrac{1}{2002}x^{2002} + C$

9. $y = 2^{\sin x} \Rightarrow y' = 2^{\sin x} \cdot \ln 2 \cdot \cos x$

10. $\dfrac{d}{dx}\left(e^{x^3}\right) = e^{x^3} \cdot 3x^2 = 3x^2 e^{x^3}$

11. $y = \ln x^5 \Rightarrow y' = \dfrac{1}{x^5} \cdot 5x^4 = \dfrac{5}{x} = 5x^{-1} \Rightarrow y'' = -5x^{-2}$

12. $y = 6^x \Rightarrow \dfrac{dy}{dx} = 6^x \ln 6 \Rightarrow \dfrac{d^2y}{dx^2} = 6^x(\ln 6)^2$

13. $f'(x) = 10e^{5x} \Rightarrow f(x) = 2e^{5x} + C$

14. $m'(x) = 35 \sin 5x \Rightarrow m(x) = -7 \cos 5x + C$

15. $3 = -7 \cos 0 + C \Rightarrow C = 10$
$m(x) = -7 \cos 5x + 10$

16. $f(x) = 5x^3$

$f'(x) = \lim\limits_{h\to 0} \dfrac{5(x + h)^3 - 5x^3}{h}$

$ = \lim\limits_{h\to 0} \dfrac{5x^3 + 15x^2h + 15xh^2 + 5h^3 - 5x^3}{h}$

$ = \lim\limits_{h\to 0} (15x^2 + 15xh + 5h^2)$

$ = 15x^2 + 0 + 0 = 15x^2$, Q.E.D.

17. $f'(4) \approx \dfrac{5(4.01^3) - 5(3.99^4)}{0.02} = 240.0005$

$f'(4) = 15(4^2) = 240$

The numerical answer is very close!

18. The graph shows that $(\sin x)/x$ gets close to 1 as x gets close to 0.

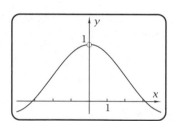

19. $f'(x) = \lim\limits_{\Delta x\to 0} \dfrac{\cos(x + 0.5\Delta x) \cdot \sin 0.5\Delta x}{0.5\Delta x}$

$ = \lim\limits_{\Delta x\to 0} \cos(x + 0.5\Delta x) \cdot \lim\limits_{\Delta x\to 0} \dfrac{\sin 0.5\Delta x}{0.5\Delta x}$

$ = \cos x \cdot 1 = \cos x$, Q.E.D.

20. The graph shows that sin′ 3x (solid line) does not equal cos 3x (dashed line).

"Mae, you neglected the chain rule."

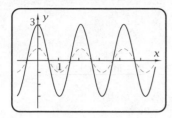

21. $\dfrac{d}{dx}(6^x) = \lim\limits_{h \to 0} \dfrac{6^{x+h} - 6^x}{h}$

$\quad = \lim\limits_{h \to 0} \dfrac{6^x \cdot 6^h - 6^x}{h}$

$\quad = \lim\limits_{h \to 0} \dfrac{6^x(6^h - 1)}{h}$

$\quad = 6^x \cdot \lim\limits_{h \to 0} \dfrac{6^h - 1}{h}$, Q.E.D.

h	$(6^h - 1)/h$
−0.002	1.7885528...
−0.001	1.7901552...
0	undefined
0.001	1.7933656...
0.002	1.7949737...

$\ln 6 = 1.7917594...$, which these numbers seem to be approaching as $h \to 0$ from either side.

22. $y = \ln x$

$e^y = x$

$e^y \cdot y' = 1$

$y' = \dfrac{1}{e^y} = \dfrac{1}{x}$, Q.E.D.

23. Let $d(t)$ = number of thousands of miles from the Sun.
t = number of hours since midnight.

$d(t) = 93000 + 4 \cos \dfrac{\pi}{12} t$

24. $d'(t) = -\dfrac{\pi}{3} \sin \dfrac{\pi}{12} t$

$d'(6) = -\dfrac{\pi}{3} \sin \dfrac{\pi}{2} = -\dfrac{\pi}{3} = -1.04719...$

The point on the equator is approaching the Sun at about 1047 mi/h.

25. $d'(12) = -\dfrac{\pi}{3} \sin \pi = 0$

The point on the equator is not moving toward or away from the Sun at noon. It is at its minimum distance from the Sun at that time.

26. $a(t) = d''(t) = -\dfrac{\pi^2}{36} \cos \dfrac{\pi}{12} t$

The maximum acceleration occurs at $t = 12$ hr, or 12:00 p.m., and is $\pi^2/36$ (thousand miles/h)/h.

27. Answers will vary.

Test 11

1. $f(1) = \dfrac{3 \cdot 1^2 - 2 \cdot 1 - 1}{1 - 1} = \dfrac{0}{0}$, which is indeterminate.

2. Removable discontinuity

3.

x	f(x)
0.995	3.985
0.996	3.988
0.997	3.991
0.998	3.994
0.999	3.997
1.000	undefined
1.001	4.003
1.002	4.006
1.003	4.009
1.004	4.012
1.005	4.015

$\lim\limits_{x \to 1} f(x) = 4$

4. $0.997 \le x \le 1.003$

5. $\lim\limits_{x \to 1} f(x) = \lim\limits_{x \to 1} \dfrac{(3x + 1)(x - 1)}{x - 1} = \lim\limits_{x \to 1} (3x + 1)$

$\quad = \lim\limits_{x \to 1} 3x + \lim\limits_{x \to 1} 1$ Limit of a sum

$\quad = 3 \lim\limits_{x \to 1} x + 1$ Limit of a constant times a function, and limit of a constant

$\quad = 3 \cdot 1 + 1$ Limit of x (identity)

$\quad = 4$ Arithmetic

6. $3.993 < 3x + 1 < 4.007$
$2.993 < 3x < 3.007$
$0.99766... < x < 1.00233...$
Maximum $\delta = 0.00233...$

7. $v(3) \approx \dfrac{2^{3.1} - 2^{2.9}}{0.2} = 5.5496... \approx 5.55 \text{ ft/s}^2$

8. Numerical derivative with tolerance 0.001 is 5.5451..., which is close to that in Problem 7.

9. $a(t) = 2^t \ln 2 \Rightarrow a(3) = 8 \ln 2 = 5.545177...$

10.

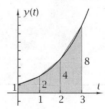

Integral $\approx 0.5(1) + 2 + 4 + 0.5(8) = 10.5 \text{ ft}$

11. $T_{50} = 10.10032085...$, $T_{100} = 10.09922919...$, $T_{500} = 10.09887984...$

12. Numerical integration gives 10.0988....
The trapezoidal approximations are approaching this value as the number of trapezoids increases.

13. $f(x) = (\sin 2x)^3$
$f'(x) = 3(\sin 2x)^3 \cdot \cos 2x \cdot 2 = 6(\sin 2x)^3 \cos 2x$

14. $f'(1) = 6(\sin 2)^2 \cos 2 = -2.0644...$
The graph shows that a line with slope $f'(1)$ is tangent at 1.

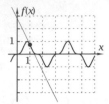

15. The graph becomes indistinguishable from the tangent line.

16. $y = t^3 - 5t^2 \Rightarrow y' = 3t^2 - 10t \Rightarrow y'' = 6t - 10$
$y'(1) = -7$, $y''(1) = -4$, $\therefore$ the object is speeding up because the velocity and acceleration are in the same direction.

17. $y' = 20e^{4x} \Rightarrow y = 5e^{4x} + C$

18. $f(0) = 3$ and $\lim_{x \to 0} f(x) = 3$ from *both* sides, so f is continuous at $x = 0$.
$\lim_{x \to 0^-} f'(x) = -2 \cdot 0 - 2 = -2$, and
$\lim_{x \to 0^+} f'(x) = \cos 0 = 1$, which does not equal -2.
Thus, $f'(0)$ does not exist, and f is not differentiable at $x = 0$, Q.E.D.

19. $g(x) = \begin{cases} -x^2 - 2x + 3, & \text{if } x < 0 \\ 3 + k \sin x, & \text{if } x \geq 0 \end{cases}$
$\lim_{x \to 0^-} g'(x) = -2$, as in Problem 18.
$\lim_{x \to 0^+} g'(x) = k \cos 0 = k$
Let $k = -2$.

20. (Instructor check.)

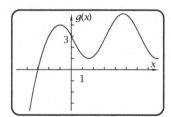

21. Answers will vary.

Test 12

1. $y = \cos^{-1} x \Rightarrow y' = -\dfrac{1}{\sqrt{1 - x^2}}$

2. $y = \tan x \Rightarrow y' = \sec^2 x$

3. $y = \tan^{-1} x \Rightarrow y' = \dfrac{1}{1 + x^2}$

4. $y = \sec^{-1} x \Rightarrow y' = \dfrac{1}{|x| \sqrt{x^2 - 1}}$

5. $y = \sec x \Rightarrow y' = \sec x \tan x$

6. $y = 3^x \Rightarrow y' = 3^x \cdot \ln 3$

7. $y = e^x \Rightarrow y' = e^x$

8. $y = \ln x \Rightarrow y' = \dfrac{1}{x}$

9. $y = e^{2x} \cos 3x \Rightarrow y' = 2e^{2x} \cos 3x - 3e^{2x} \sin 3x$

10. $y = \cot^3 (5x) \Rightarrow$
$y' = 3 \cot^2 (5x) \cdot [-\csc^2 (5x)] \cdot 5 = -15 \cot^2 (5x) \csc^2 (5x)$

11. $y = \ln (x^{1.7}) \Rightarrow y' = \dfrac{1}{x^{1.7}} \cdot 1.7 x^{0.7} = \dfrac{1.7}{x}$
or $y = \ln (x^{1.7}) = 1.7 \ln x \Rightarrow y' = \dfrac{1.7}{x}$

12. $y = \dfrac{2^x}{x^2} \Rightarrow$
$y' = \dfrac{2^x \cdot \ln 2 \cdot x^2 - 2^x \cdot 2x}{x^4} = \dfrac{2^x \cdot \ln 2 \cdot x - 2 \cdot 2^x}{x^3}$

13. $y = e^{3x} \Rightarrow \dfrac{dy}{dx} = 3e^{3x} \Rightarrow \dfrac{d^2 y}{dx^2} = 9e^{3x}$

14. $f(x) = g(x) \cdot h(x) = x^5 \cdot x^8 = x^{13}$
$\therefore f'(x) = 13x^{12}$
$g'(x) = 5x^4$ and $h'(x) = 8x^7$
$\therefore g'(x) \cdot h'(x) = 40x^{11}$, not $13x^{12}$, Q.E.D.

15. $f(x) = x^4 \sin^3 x$
$f'(x) = 4x^3 \sin^3 x + 3x^4 \sin^2 x \cos x$

16. $y = \dfrac{u}{v} \Rightarrow \dfrac{dy}{dx} = \dfrac{u'v - uv'}{v^2}$

17. $\dfrac{d}{dx} (\tan x) = \dfrac{d}{dx} \left(\dfrac{\sin x}{\cos x} \right)$
$= \dfrac{\cos x \cdot \cos x - \sin x (-\sin x)}{\cos^2 x}$
$= \dfrac{\cos^2 x + \sin^2 x}{\cos^2 x} = \dfrac{1}{\cos^2 x} = \sec^2 x$, Q.E.D.

18. $f(x) = \sec^{-1} x^3 \Rightarrow$
$f'(x) = \dfrac{1}{|x^3| \sqrt{x^6 - 1}} \cdot 3x^2 = \dfrac{3}{|x| \sqrt{x^6 - 1}}$

19. $y = x^{-3} = \dfrac{1}{x^3} \Rightarrow y' = \dfrac{0 \cdot x^3 - 1 \cdot 3x^2}{x^6} = \dfrac{-3}{x^4} = -3x^{-4}$
By the power rule, $y' = -3x^{-4}$, which is the same.

20. $y = \sin^{-1} x$
$\sin y = x = \dfrac{x}{1}$
$\cos y \cdot y' = 1$
$y' = \dfrac{1}{\cos y}$

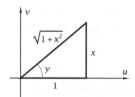

$y' = \dfrac{1}{\sqrt{1 - x^2}}$

21. $f(x) = \tan^{-1} x \Rightarrow$
$f'(x) = \dfrac{1}{1 + x^2}$
$f'(2) = \dfrac{1}{1 + 2^2} = 0.2$

Calculus: Concepts and Applications Instructor's Resource Book
©2005 Key Curriculum Press

The graph shows that the line is tangent to the graph at $(2, f(2))$.

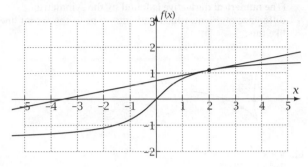

22. Answers will vary.

Test 13

1. Differentiability implies continuity.

2. $f(x) = x^3 \Rightarrow f'(x) = 3x^2 \Rightarrow f'(4) = 48$
   $\therefore f$ is differentiable at $x = 4$.
   $\therefore f$ is continuous at $x = 4$.

3. $\lim\limits_{x \to c} [f(x) - f(c)] = f'(c) \cdot 0$

   Because $f'(c)$ exists, it is a real number. By the multiplication property of zero from algebra, $f'(c) \cdot 0$ is zero. If $f'(c)$ were not a real number, no conclusion could be made about $f'(c) \cdot 0$.
   $\lim\limits_{x \to c} [f(x) - f(c)] = 0$
   $\lim\limits_{x \to c} f(x) - f(c) = 0$ Limit of a sum, limit of a constant
   $\lim\limits_{x \to c} f(x) = f(c)$ Algebra
   $\therefore f$ is continuous at $x = c$, Q.E.D.   Definition

4. $\dfrac{dx}{dt} = \sec t \tan t$

   $\dfrac{dy}{dt} = \ln t + t \cdot \dfrac{1}{t} = \ln t + 1$

   $\dfrac{dy}{dx} = \dfrac{\ln t + 1}{\sec t \tan t}$

5. $x\sqrt{y} + x^3 \sec^3 y = 3^2$

   $\sqrt{y} + \frac{1}{2}xy^{-1/2}y' + 3x^2 \sec^3 y$
   $+ x^3 \cdot 3 \sec^2 y \cdot \sec y \tan y \cdot y' = 0$

   $y'\left(\frac{1}{2}xy^{-1/2} + 3x^3 \sec^3 y \tan y\right) = -\sqrt{y} + 3x^2 \sec^3 y$

   $y' = \dfrac{-\sqrt{y} + 3x^2 \sec^3 y}{(1/2)xy^{-1/2} + 3x^3 \sec^3 y \tan y}$

6. $y = x^{11/3} \Rightarrow y^3 = x^{11}$
   $3y^2 y' = 11x^{10}$
   $y' = \dfrac{11x^{10}}{3y^2} = \dfrac{11}{3} \cdot \dfrac{x^{10}}{x^{22/3}} = \dfrac{11}{3}x^{8/3}$,

   which is the answer you would get by directly applying the derivative of a power formula, Q.E.D.

7. $y = \ln x$
   $e^y = x$
   $e^y \cdot y' = 1$
   $y' = \dfrac{1}{e^y}$
   $y' = \dfrac{1}{x}$, the reciprocal function, Q.E.D.

8. $x = 2 \sin t + \sin 2t$
   $y = 2 \cos t - \cos 2t$
   At $t = \pi/3$, $x = 1.5\sqrt{3} = 2.5980...$ and $y = 1.5$.

9. $dx/dt = 2 \cos t + 2 \cos 2t$
   $dy/dt = -2 \sin t + 2 \sin 2t$
   At $t = \pi/3$, $dx/dt = 0$ and $dy/dt = 0$.

10. The object is stopped. Because dx/dt and dy/dt are both zero, the object is not moving in either the x- or the y-direction.

11. $\dfrac{dy}{dx} = \dfrac{-\sin t + \sin 2t}{\cos t + \cos 2t}$

    At the cusp, dy/dx has the indeterminate form $0/0$. By TABLE search, dy/dx approaches $0.5773....$ (Exactly $1/\sqrt{3}$, using l'Hospital's rule.)

12. $f(x) = \begin{cases} x^3 + 1, & \text{if } x \le 1 \\ a(x-2)^2 + b, & \text{if } x > 1 \end{cases}$
    $\lim\limits_{x \to 1^-} f(x) = 1^3 + 1 = 2$
    $\lim\limits_{x \to 1^+} f(x) = a(1-2)^2 + b = a + b$
    Make $a + b = 2$.
    $\lim\limits_{x \to 1^-} f'(x) = 3 \cdot 1^2 = 3$
    $\lim\limits_{x \to 1^+} f'(x) = 2a(1-2) = -2a$
    Make $-2a = 3 \Rightarrow a = -1.5$.
    $-1.5 + b = 2 \Rightarrow b = 3.5$

13. As long as $a = -1.5$, the left and right limits of $f'(x)$ are equal. But unless $b = 3.5$ also, f is not continuous at $x = 2$. Because differentiability implies continuity, discontinuity implies that f is not differentiable.

14. $x^2 + 4xy - y^2 = 29$
    $2x + 4y + 4xy' - 2yy' = 0$
    $y'(4x - 2y) = -2x - 4y$
    $y' = \dfrac{-2x - 4y}{4x - 2y} = \dfrac{x + 2y}{y - 2x}$

15. At $(3, 2)$, $y' = \dfrac{3 + 4}{2 - 6} = -1.75$.

16. The line at $(2, 3)$ with slope -1.75 is tangent to the graph.

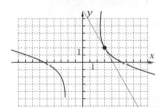

17. Amos! The answer is meaningless because the point $(5, 7)$ is not on the graph!

18. (Just for fun!) Substitute 3 for x.
    $9 + 12y - y^2 = 29$
    $y^2 - 12y + 20 = 0$
    $(y - 2)(y - 10) = 0$
    $y = 2$ or $y = 10$, and the other point is $(3, 10)$.

19. $\dfrac{dy}{dx} = \dfrac{y'(t)}{x'(t)}$

$\dfrac{d^2y}{dy^2} = \dfrac{d}{dx}\left(\dfrac{dy}{dx}\right)$

$\quad = \dfrac{y''(t) \cdot \frac{dt}{dx}\, x'(t) - y'(t) \cdot x''(t) \cdot \frac{dt}{dx}}{[x'(t)]^2}$

$\quad = \dfrac{y''(t)x'(t) - y'(t)x''(t)}{[x'(t)]^2} \cdot \dfrac{dt}{dx}$

$\quad = \dfrac{y''(t)x'(t) - y'(t)x''(t)}{[x'(t)]^2 \cdot \frac{dx}{dt}}$

$\quad = \dfrac{y''(t)x'(t) - y'(t)x''(t)}{[x'(t)]^3}$, Q.E.D.

20. Answers will vary.

Test 14

1.

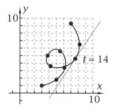

2. The tornado was at the same place at two different times.

3. $\dfrac{dx}{dt} \approx \dfrac{8.2 - 6.1}{4} = 0.525$

$\dfrac{dy}{dt} \approx \dfrac{6.5 - 3.4}{4} = 0.775$

4. $\dfrac{dy}{dx} = \dfrac{dy/dt}{dx/dt} \approx \dfrac{0.775}{0.525} = 1.4761...$

5. $\dfrac{dy}{dx} \approx \dfrac{6.5 - 3.4}{8.2 - 6.1} = 1.4761...$, which agrees.

6. See the graph in Problem 1, showing that the line at (7.6, 4.6) is tangent to the path.
   The line tells the direction of the tornado at $t = 14$.

7. Speed $= \sqrt{(dx/dt)^2 + (dy/dt)^2} \approx 0.9360...$
   ≈ 0.94 mi/min (or about 56 mi/h)

8. $x = 4\cos t + \cos 4t$
   $y = 4\sin t + \sin 4t$
   At $t = \pi/3$, $x = 1.5$ (exactly) and $y = 1.5\sqrt{3} = 2.5980....$
   The point (1.5, 2.6) is at the cusp.

9. $dx/dt = -4\sin t - 4\sin 4t$
   $dy/dt = 4\cos t + 4\cos 4t$
   At $t = \pi/3$, $dx/dt = 0$ and $dy/dt = 0$.

10. (Graph optional.)
    Slope of tangent line is $1.5\sqrt{3}/1.5 = \sqrt{3} = 1.7320...$

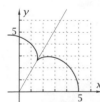

11. The parametric chain rule gives the indeterminate form 0/0 for dy/dx.

12. (Graph resembles the figure.)

13. Numerical derivative is $-0.5770...$, which is clearly wrong because it is negative, and the tangent line has positive slope. (The numerical derivative is found by the symmetric difference quotient, which finds the slope of the secant line, like this:)

14. $y = x^{13/7} \Rightarrow y^7 = x^{13}$
    $7y^6\, y' = 13x^{12}$

    $y' = \dfrac{13x^{12}}{7y^6} = \dfrac{13}{7} \cdot \dfrac{x^{12}}{(x^{13/7})^6} = \dfrac{13}{7}x^{6/7}$,

    which is the same answer as by the power rule.

15. $x^5y^3 + \tan^4 y = 10^5$
    $5x^4y^3 + 3x^5y^2 \cdot y' + 4\tan^3 y \cdot \sec^2 y \cdot y' = 0$
    $y'(3x^5y^2 + 4\tan^3 y\sec^2 y) = -5x^4y^3$
    $y' = \dfrac{-5x^4y^3}{3x^5y^2 + 4\tan^3 y\sec^2 y}$

16. $9x^2 + 25y^2 = 900$
    $x = 8$: $9 \cdot 8^2 + 25y^2 = 900$
    $25y^2 = 324$
    $y = \pm 3.6$

17. $18x + 50yy' = 0$
    $y' = \dfrac{dy}{dx} = -\dfrac{9x}{25y}$

18. At (8, 3.6), $dy/dx = -0.8$.
    At (8, -3.6), $dy/dx = 0.8$.
    The graph shows that lines with these slopes are tangent to the ellipse.

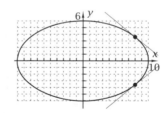

19. Answers will vary.

Test 15

1. Know: $\dfrac{da}{dt} = 7$, $\dfrac{db}{dt} = -11$

   Want: $\dfrac{dA}{dt}$

2. $A = \pi ab$
   $\dfrac{dA}{dt} = \pi \dfrac{da}{dt} \cdot b + \pi a \cdot \dfrac{db}{dt}$

3. At $a = 30$ and $b = 50$,
   $\dfrac{dA}{dt} = \pi[7(50) + (30)(-11)] = 20\pi = 62.8318...$

   Increasing at about 62.8 mm^2/s

4. At $a = 40$ and $b = 20$,
   $\dfrac{dA}{dt} = \pi[7(20) + 40(-11)] = -300\pi = -942.4777...$

   Decreasing at about 942.5 mm^2/s

Calculus: Concepts and Applications Instructor's Resource Book
©2005 Key Curriculum Press

5. $\dfrac{dA}{dt} = 0 \Leftrightarrow 7b + a(-11) = 0$

$b = \dfrac{11}{7}a$

b is larger than a by a factor of $11/7$.

6. Know: $\dfrac{dx}{dt} = 4$

Want: $\dfrac{dV}{dt}$

7. $V = \pi x^2 y$

$y = -\dfrac{120}{50}x + 120 = -2.4x + 120$

$V = \pi x^2 (-2.4x + 120) = \pi(-2.4\,x^3 + 120\,x^2)$

$\dfrac{dV}{dt} = \pi(-7.2x^2 + 240x)\dfrac{dx}{dt}$

$\qquad = \pi(-7.2x^2 + 240x)4$

$\qquad = \pi(-28.8x^2 + 960x)$

8. $\dfrac{dV}{dt}\Big|_{x=10} = \pi[-28.8(10)^2 + 960(10)] = 6720\pi$

Increasing because $dV/dt > 0$

$\dfrac{dV}{dt}\Big|_{x=50} = \pi[-28.8(50)^2 + 960(50)] = -24{,}000\pi$

Decreasing because $dV/dt < 0$

9. $\dfrac{dV}{dt} = 0 \Leftrightarrow -28.8x^2 + 960x = 0$

$x = 0 \ or \ x = 33.\overline{3}$

At $x = 0$, the volume is a minimum.

If $x = 33\frac{1}{3}$,

$V = \pi\left[-2.4\left(33\frac{1}{3}\right)^3 + 120\left(33\frac{1}{3}\right)^2\right] = 44{,}444.\overline{4}\pi$

$\qquad \approx 139{,}626.3 \text{ mm}^3$

10. Know: $\dfrac{dc}{dt} = -20$ and $\dfrac{ds}{dt} = 15$

Want: $\dfrac{dx}{dt}$

$x^2 - c^2 + s^2$

$2x\dfrac{dx}{dt} = 2c\dfrac{dc}{dt} + 2s\dfrac{ds}{dt}$

$\dfrac{dx}{dt} = \dfrac{c\frac{dc}{dt} + s\frac{ds}{dt}}{x}$

At $c = 30$ and $s = 40$, $x = 50$.

$\dfrac{dx}{dt} = \dfrac{30(-20) + 40(15)}{50} = 0$

$\therefore x$ is neither increasing nor decreasing

11. Answers will vary.

Test 16

1. $y' = \dfrac{u'v - uv'}{v^2}$

2. $\dfrac{d}{dx}\left(\dfrac{\sin 3x}{x^6}\right) = \dfrac{3\cos 3x \cdot x^6 - \sin 3x \cdot 6x^5}{x^{12}}$

$\qquad = \dfrac{3x \cdot \cos 3x - 6\sin 3x}{x^7}$

3. $\dfrac{d}{dx}(x^{-6} \cdot \sin 3x)$

$= -6x^{-7}\sin 3x + x^{-6} \cdot 3\cos 3x$

$= x^{-7}(-6\sin 3x + 3x\cos 3x)$,

which is equivalent to the answer in Problem 2.

4. $\tan y = x$

$\sec^2 y \cdot y' = 1$

$y' = \dfrac{1}{\sec^2 y}$

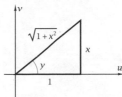

$y' = \dfrac{1}{\left(\sqrt{1+x^2}\right)^2} = \dfrac{1}{1+x^2}$, Q.E.D.

5. $x = t^2, \ y = t^5$

$\dfrac{dy}{dx} = \dfrac{5t^4}{2t} = 2.5t^3$

$\dfrac{d^2y}{dx^2} = 7.5t^2 \cdot \dfrac{dt}{dx}$

$\qquad = \dfrac{7.5t^2}{dx/dt}$

$\qquad = \dfrac{7.5t^2}{2t}$

$\qquad = 3.75t$

6. $y' = \lim\limits_{\Delta x \to 0} \dfrac{\Delta u \cdot v + u \cdot \Delta v + \Delta u \cdot \Delta v}{\Delta x}$

$\qquad = \lim\limits_{\Delta x \to 0}\left(\dfrac{\Delta u}{\Delta x} \cdot v + u \cdot \dfrac{\Delta v}{\Delta x} + \dfrac{\Delta u}{\Delta x} \cdot \Delta v\right)$

$\qquad = \dfrac{du}{dx} \cdot v + u \cdot \dfrac{dv}{dx} + \dfrac{du}{dx} \cdot 0$

$\qquad = u'v + uv'$, Q.E.D.

7. $x^3y^2 = 256$

For $(4, 2)$, $4^3 \cdot 2^2 = 256$, which checks.

For $(4, -2)$, $4^3 \cdot (-2)^2 = 256$, which checks.

8. $3x^2y^2 + 2x^3y \cdot y' = 0$

$y' = \dfrac{-3x^2y^2}{2x^3y} = -1.5x^{-1}\,y$

For $(4, -2)$, $y' = -1.5(4)^{-1}(-2) = 0.75$.

9. At $(4, -2)$, $y' = -1.5(4^{-1})(-2) = 0.75$. The graph shows that the line with slope 0.75 is tangent to the graph at $(4, -2)$.

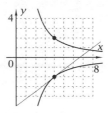

10. $x = 5\cos t$

$y = 5\sin t$

$\dfrac{dy}{dt} = 5\cos t, \dfrac{dx}{dt} = -5\sin t, \dfrac{dy}{dx} = \dfrac{5\cos t}{-5\sin t} = -\cot t$

11. $4 = 5\cos t \Rightarrow t = \cos^{-1} 0.8 = 0.6435\ldots$

$y = 5\sin 0.6435\ldots = 3 \text{ (exactly!)}$

$\therefore (4, 3)$ *is* on the graph.

12. $\dfrac{dy}{dx} = -\dfrac{1}{\tan 0.6435...} = -\dfrac{1}{0.75} = -1.3333...$

The graph shows that the line with slope $-1.3333...$ is tangent at $(4, 3)$.

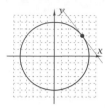

13. $f(x) = \begin{cases} x^3, & \text{if } x < 1 \\ 3x - 2, & \text{if } x \geq 1 \end{cases}$

$\lim_{x \to 1^-} f(x) = 1^3 = 1$

$\lim_{x \to 1^+} f(x) = 3 \cdot 1 - 2 = 1 = f(1)$

$\therefore f$ is continuous at $x = 1$, Q.E.D.

14. No. The fact that f is continuous at $x = 1$ is not sufficient to establish differentiability. A function can be continuous without being differentiable.

15. $\lim_{x \to 1^-} f'(x) = 3 \cdot 1^2 = 3$

$\lim_{x \to 1^+} f'(x) = 3$

$\therefore f$ is differentiable at $x = 1$ because it is continuous (from Problem 14) and the derivative approaches the same value from both sides.

16. $f(x) = (3x + 7)^8 (4x - 5)^3$

$f'(x) = 8(3x + 7)^7 \cdot 3 \cdot (4x - 5)^3 + (3x + 7)^8 \cdot 3(4x - 5)^2 \cdot 4$

$\quad = 12(3x + 7)^7 (4x - 5)^2 (8x - 10 + 3x + 7)$

$\quad = 12(3x + 7)^7 (4x - 5)^2 (11x - 3)$

$f'(x) = 0 \Leftrightarrow 3x + 7 = 0,\ 4x - 5 = 0,\ 11x - 3 = 0$

$\therefore x = -7/3,\ x = 5/4,$ or $x = 3/11$.

17. $y = \dfrac{u}{v} \Rightarrow y' = \dfrac{u'v - uv'}{v^2}$

$y = \tan x = \dfrac{\sin x}{\cos x}$

$y' = \dfrac{\cos x \cdot \cos x - \sin x \, (-\sin x)}{\cos^2 x}$

$\quad = \dfrac{\cos^2 x + \sin^2 x}{\cos^2 x} = \dfrac{1}{\cos^2 x} = \sec^2 x$

18. $\dfrac{d}{dx}(\sin^{-1} 5x^3) = \dfrac{1}{\sqrt{1 - (5x^3)^2}} \cdot 15x^2$

$\quad = \dfrac{15x^2}{\sqrt{1 - 25x^6}}$

19. Answers will vary.

Test 17

1. $g(x) = \int f(x)\, dx$ if and only if $g'(x) = f(x)$.

2. Antiderivative

3.
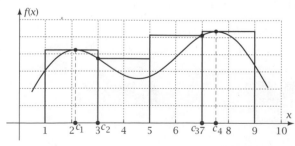

4.
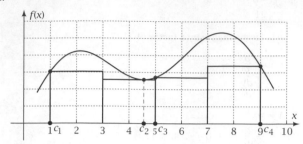

5. $\int_a^b f(x)\, dx = \lim_{\Delta x \to 0} L_n = \lim_{\Delta x \to 0} U_n$, where L_n and U_n are lower and upper Riemann sums, provided the two limits are equal.

6. $y = 5x \tan x$

$dy = (5 \tan x + 5x \sec^2 x)\, dx$

7. $dy = 72x^3\, dx$

$y = \int 72x^3\, dx = 18x^4 + C$

8.
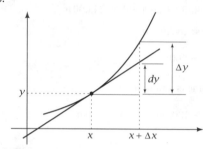

9. $\int \cos u\, du = \sin u + C$

10. $\int \cos x^3 (x^2\, dx) = \dfrac{1}{3}\int \cos x^3 (3x^2\, dx) = \dfrac{1}{3} \sin x^3 + C$

11. A *left* Riemann sum takes sample points at the lowest value of x in each interval. A *lower* Riemann sum takes sample points at the lowest value of y in each interval.

12. $f(x) = \int (\cos x)^7 \sin x\, dx = -\int (\cos x)^7 (-\sin x\, dx)$

$\quad = -\dfrac{1}{8}(\cos x)^8 + C$

$3 = -\dfrac{1}{8}(\cos 0)^8 + C \Rightarrow 3 = -\dfrac{1}{8} + C \Rightarrow C = 3\tfrac{1}{8}$

$f(x) = -\dfrac{1}{8}(\cos x)^8 + 3\tfrac{1}{8}$

13. Work = (force)(displacement). A definite integral must be used to find the work done because the force varies at different displacements.

14. $M_4 = 2[F(1) + F(3) + F(5) + F(7)]$

$\quad = 2(40 + 30 + 12.5 + 4.375) = 173.75$ ft-lb

15. $F'(x) \approx 12.2741...$ and $F(1) = 40$

$y - 40 = 12.2741...(x - 1)$

$y = 12.2741...x + 27.7258...$

16. Local linearity

17. The trapezoids would be circumscribed about the region, including more area, because the graph is concave up.

18. The rectangles would include less area than the strips because the graph is concave up.

Calculus: Concepts and Applications Instructor's Resource Book
©2005 Key Curriculum Press

19. $L_{50} = 19.4832...$
$L_{200} = 19.8702...$
$U_{200} = 20.1302...$
$U_{50} = 20.5232...$
The upper and lower sums both approach a common limit of 20, illustrating that $\int_1^3 x^3\,dx = 20$.

20. $T_{200} = 20.0002$
$M_{200} = 19.9999$
The values of T_{200} and M_{200} are both close to the limit found in Problem 19. The value of T_{200} is slightly larger than the limit, as indicated in Problem 17, and the value of M_{200} is slightly less than the limit, as indicated in Problem 18.

21. $g(x) = \int x^3\,dx = \frac{1}{4}x^4 + C$
$g(3) = \frac{81}{4} + C,\ g(1) = \frac{1}{4} + C,\ g(3) - g(1)$
$= \left(\frac{81}{4} + C\right) - \left(\frac{1}{4} + C\right) = 20$
The constant of integration is eliminated. The result of $g(3) - g(1)$ is equal to $\int_1^3 x^3\,dx$. This suggests that $\int_a^b f(x)\,dx = g(b) - g(a)$, where $g'(x) = f(x)$.

22. Answers will vary.

Test 18

1. $g(x) = \int f(x)\,dx$ if and only if $g'(x) = f(x)$.

2. Definition: $\displaystyle\int_a^b f(x)\,dx = \lim_{\Delta x \to 0} L_n = \lim_{\Delta x \to 0} U_n$

   Theorem: $\displaystyle\int_a^b f(x)\,dx = g(b) - g(a)$, where $g(x) = \int f(x)\,dx$

3. If c is differentiable on (a, b) and continuous at $x = a$ and $x = b$, then there is a number $x = c$ in (a, b) such that $f'(c) = \frac{f(b) - f(a)}{b - a}$.

4.

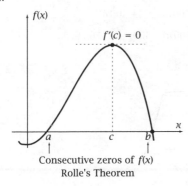

Consecutive zeros of $f(x)$
Rolle's Theorem

5. $\displaystyle\int_1^4 x^{3/2}\,dx = \frac{2}{5} x^{5/2}\Big|_1^4 = \frac{64}{5} - \frac{2}{5} = \frac{62}{5} = 12.4$

6. $\displaystyle\int_{-\pi}^{\pi} (5\cos x + 4\sin x)\,dx = (5\sin x - 4\cos x)\Big|_{-\pi}^{\pi}$
$= 0 + 4 - 0 - 4 = 0$

7. $\displaystyle\int_{20}^{50} dx = x\Big|_{20}^{50} = 50 - 20 = 30$

8. $\displaystyle\int_3^7 f(x)\,dx = -17$

9. $\displaystyle\int_7^{11} f(x)\,dx = 40 - 17 = 23$

10. $\displaystyle\int_3^{11} [f(x) - g(x)]\,dx = 40 - 10 = 30$

11.

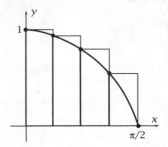

The graph shows that left endpoint of each interval is the highest valve in each interval, so the left Riemann sum is an upper sum.

12.

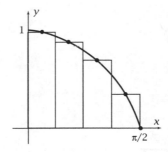

The graph shows that midpoint Riemann sum rectangles add more area than they leave out, so it is an overestimate for the area.

13. $U_{50} = 1.0156...$

14. $M_{50} = 1.00004...$

15. $\displaystyle\int_0^{\pi/2} \cos x\,dx = \sin x\Big|_0^{\pi/2} = 1 - 0 = 1$

The answers to Problems 13 and 14 are both slight overestimates of the actual integral.

16. $\displaystyle\int_1^4 (x^2 - 6x + 2)\,dx = -18$ (numerically)

The integral is negative because the curve lies below the x-axis, so the values of $f(x)$ are negative.

17. $\displaystyle\int_2^1 e^{2x}\,dx = -23.6045...$ (numerically; exactly $0.5(e^2 - e^4)$)

The integral is negative because the upper limit of integration is less than the lower limit of integration, so values of dx are negative.

18. $\displaystyle\int_{2\pi}^{\pi} \sin x\,dx = 2$

The integral is positive because the curve lies below the x-axis, so the values of $f(x)$ are negative, and the upper limit of integration is less than the lower limit of integration, so values of dx are negative, and the product of two negatives is positive.

19. $\displaystyle\int_{-3}^3 x\,dx = \frac{1}{2}x^2\Big|_{-3}^3 = \frac{9}{2} - \frac{9}{2} = 0$

The integral is zero because $y = x$ is an odd function, and it is integrated between symmetric limits. So the positive area to the right of the y-axis is canceled by the symmetric negative area to the left of the y-axis.

20.

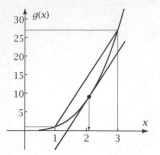

$$g'(c) = \frac{g(b) - g(a)}{b - a} \Rightarrow 3c^2 = \frac{27 - 1}{3 - 1} = 13 \Rightarrow$$

$$c = \sqrt{\frac{13}{3}} = 2.0816\ldots$$

21.

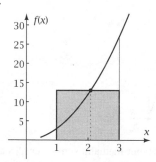

Integral $\approx 3(2.0816\ldots)^2 \cdot 2 = 13 \cdot 2 = 26$

22. $\int_1^3 3x^2\, dx = x^3 \big|_1^3 = 27 - 1 = 26$

23. Answers will vary.

Test 19

1.

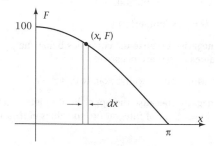

2. $dW = F\, dx \Rightarrow W = \int_0^\pi 100 \cos 0.5\, x\, dx = 200 \sin 0.5x \big|_0^\pi = 200 - 0 = 200$ ft-lb

3. $(1/3)(0.1)(4 + 4 \cdot 7 + 2 \cdot 6 + 4 \cdot 8 + 11) = 2.9$

4.

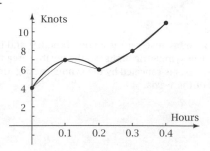

Parabolas appear to connect the data more smoothly than straight line segments.

5.

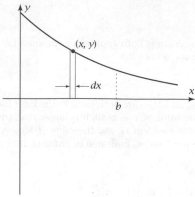

$$dA = y\, dx \Rightarrow A = \int_0^b 10e^{-0.1x}\, dx = -100e^{-0.1x} \big|_0^b = -100e^{-0.1b} + 100$$

6.

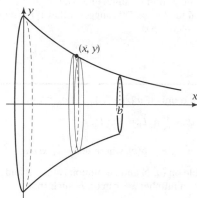

7. $dV = \pi y^2\, dx \Rightarrow V = \pi \int_0^b (10e^{-0.1x})^2\, dx = \pi \int_0^b 100e^{-0.2x}\, dx$

$= -500\pi e^{-0.2x} \big|_0^b = -500\pi e^{-0.2b} + 500\pi$

8. $\lim_{b \to \infty} (-500\pi e^{-0.2b} + 500\pi) = 500\pi = 1570.7963\ldots$

9.

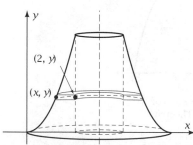

$$V = \int_0^4 \left[\pi(3 - \sqrt{y})^2 - \pi(3 - 2)^2 \right] dy = 25.1327\ldots$$

10. $V = 25.1449\ldots$

The answer is close to the answer found in Problem 9.

11. Answers will vary.

Test 20

1. $y = (3 - 4x)^7 \Rightarrow dy = -28(3 - 4x)^6\, dx$

2. $dy = \sec^2 x\, dx$

$y = \int \sec^2 x\, dx = \tan x + C$

3. $\int 24e^{3x}\, dx = 8e^{3x} + C$

4. $\int 48\tan^5 x \sec^2 x \, dx = 8\tan^6 x + C$

5. $h(x) = x^3 \ln 2x \Rightarrow h'(x) = x^3 \cdot \frac{2}{2x} + 3x^2 \ln 2x = x^2 + 3x^2 \ln 2x$

6. $\int_2^5 6x^2 \, dx = 2x^3 \big|_2^5 = 250 - 16 = 234$

7. $\int_{-\pi/2}^{\pi/2} \cos x \, dx = \sin x \big|_{-\pi/2}^{\pi/2} = 1 + 1 = 2$

8. $g(x) = \int f(x) \, dx$ if and only if $g'(x) = f(x)$.

9. $\int_a^b f(x) \, dx = \lim_{\Delta x \to 0} L_n = \lim_{\Delta x \to 0} U_n$, where L_n and U_n are lower and upper Riemann sums, provided the two limits are equal.

10. If f is integrable on $[a, b]$ and $g(x) = \int f(x) \, dx$, then $\int_a^b f(x) \, dx = g(b) - g(a)$.

11. If f is differentiable on (a, b) and continuous at $x = a$ and $x = b$, then there is a number $x = c$ in (a, b) such that $f'(c) = \frac{f(b) - f(a)}{b - a}$.

12. $x = 2$ to $x = 6$

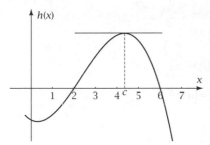

13. $\int_{-1}^1 (20x^4 + 60x^5) \, dx = 2\int_0^1 20x^4 \, dx$
$= 2 \cdot 4x^5 \big|_0^1 = 8$

14. $\int_1^4 f(x) \, dx = \int_1^4 0.3x^2 \, dx$
$= 0.1x^3 \big|_1^4 = 6.4 - 0.1 = 6.3$

15. $S_{100} = 6.3$ (exactly)

16. $M_{100} = 6.2999325$
The Simpson's rule approximation is closer.

17. $g(x) = \int 0.3x^2 \, dx = 0.1x^3 + C$
$y(0) - C - 4 \to g(x) - 0.1x^3 + 4$

18. $\frac{g(4) - g(1)}{3} = \frac{10.4 - 4.1}{3} = 2.1$
$g'(c) = f(c) = 0.3c^2 = 2.1$
$\Rightarrow c^2 = 7 \Rightarrow c = 2.6457...$, which is in $(1, 4)$.

19. The line with slope 2.1 at $x = 2.6457...$, which is parallel to the secant line, is also tangent to the graph of g.

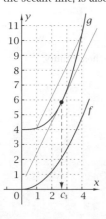

20.

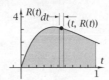

At any point in the strip the values of $R(t)$ are about the same as at the sample point.

21. $dD = R(t) \, dt = 20t(0.1)^t \, dt$

22. $D = \int_0^1 20t(0.1)^t \, dt \approx 2.5264...$ units

23.

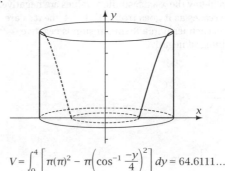

$V = \int_0^4 \left[\pi(\pi)^2 - \pi\left(\cos^{-1}\frac{-y}{4}\right)^2 \right] dy = 64.6111...$

24. Answers will vary.

Test 21

1. $\ln x = \int_1^x \frac{1}{t} \, dt$

2. If $g(x) = \int_a^x f(t) \, dt$, then $g'(x) = f(x)$.

3. $\ln' x = \frac{1}{x}$, because $\ln x = \int_1^x \frac{1}{t} \, dt$.

4. If $f'(x) = g'(x)$ for all x in the domain, and if $f(c) = g(c)$ for some $x = c$ in the domain, then $f(x) = g(x)$ for all x in the domain.

5. If two functions have identical derivatives, and a point in common, then they are the same function.

6. $y = (\cos x)^{\tan x}$
$\ln y = \tan x \cdot \ln \cos x$
$\frac{1}{y}y' = \sec^2 x \cdot \ln \cos x + \tan x \cdot \frac{1}{\cos x}(-\sin x)$
$= \sec^2 x \cdot \ln \cos x - \tan^2 x$

7. $f(x) = \int_2^{\sin x} \tan t \, dt \Rightarrow f'(x) = \tan(\sin x) \cdot \cos x$

8. $\int \frac{1}{\cos x} \sin x \, dx = -\ln|\cos x| + C = \ln|\sec x| + C$

9. $\int \tan x \, dx = -\ln|\cos x| + C = \ln|\sec x| + C$

10. $\frac{d}{dx}(\log_5 x) = \frac{1}{x\ln 5}$

11. $\int 5^x \, dx = \frac{5^x}{\ln 5} + C$

12. Prove that $\ln(ax) = \ln a + \ln x$ for all $x > 0$.
Proof:
Let $f(x) = \ln(ax)$ and let $g(x) = \ln a + \ln x$.
$f'(x) = \frac{a}{ax} = \frac{1}{x}$ and $g'(x) = 0 + \frac{1}{x} = \frac{1}{x}$
$\therefore f'(x) = g'(x)$ for all $x > 0$.
$f(1) = \ln a$ and $g(a) = \ln a + \ln 1 = \ln a$
$\therefore f(1) = g(1)$.
$\therefore f(x) = g(x)$ for all $x > 0$, which implies that
$\ln(ax) = \ln a + \ln x$ for all $x > 0$, Q.E.D.

13. $y = \ln 7x$

Directly: $y' = \dfrac{1}{7x} \cdot 7 = \dfrac{1}{x}$

Transforming: $y = \ln 7 + \ln x$

$y' = 0 + \dfrac{1}{x} = \dfrac{1}{x}$

Thus the answers are equal, Q.E.D.

14. Applying the power rule to $\int x^{-1}\,dx$ would give $\frac{1}{0}x^0$, which is undefined because of division by 0.

15. $\displaystyle\int_{-12}^{-4} \dfrac{1}{x}\,dx = \ln|x|\ \Big|_{-12}^{-4} = \ln|-4| - \ln|-12|$

$= \ln 4 - \ln 12 = -1.0986\ldots$

16. The region is below the x-axis, so the y-values are negative. Because x increases as it goes from -12 to -4, the dx's are positive. Thus each term in a Riemann sum is negative, making the integral negative.

17. $\ln 4 - \ln 12 = \ln \dfrac{1}{3} = -\ln 3$

18. Let $y = b^x$.

Then $\ln y = x \ln b$.

$\dfrac{1}{y} y' = \ln b$

$y' = y \ln b = b^x \ln b$

$\therefore \dfrac{d}{dx}(b^x) = b^x \ln b$, Q.E.D.

19. $M = M_0 (1.06^t)$

$\dfrac{dM}{dt} = M_0(1.06)^t \ln 1.06 = 1000(1.06^t) \ln 1.06$

t	dM/dt \$/yr
0	58.2689...
10	104.3507...
100	19,770.76...

20. $\displaystyle\int_{500}^{x} M^{-1}\,dM = \int_0^{20} 0.04\,dt$

$\ln|M|\ \Big|_{500}^{x} = 0.04t \Big|_0^{20}$

$\ln|x| - \ln 500 = 0.8$

$\ln|x| = 0.8 + \ln 500$

$x \approx \pm 1112.77\ldots$

The account will contain about \$1112.77.

21. Answers will vary.

Test 22

1. The graph shows the definition of $\ln x$.

$y = 1/t$

Area $= \ln x$

2. If $g(x) = \displaystyle\int_a^x f(t)\,dt$, then $g'(x) = f(x)$.

3. $y = e^{5x} \Rightarrow y' = 5e^{5x}$

4. $\displaystyle\int e^{7x}\,dx = \dfrac{1}{7}e^{7x} + C$

5. $y = \log_6 8x = \dfrac{\ln 8x}{\ln 6}$

$y' = \dfrac{1}{\ln 6} \cdot \dfrac{1}{8x} \cdot 8 = \dfrac{1}{x \ln 6}$

6. $\displaystyle\int e^{\tan x}(\sec^2 x\,dx) = e^{\tan x} + C$

7. $y = \displaystyle\int_1^{e^{2x}} x^5\,dx$

$y' = (e^{2x})^5 \cdot 2e^{2x} = 2e^{12x}$

8. $\displaystyle\int_1^{7} \dfrac{1}{p}\,dp = \ln|p|\ \Big|_1^7 = \ln 7 - \ln 1 = \ln 7$

9. $\displaystyle\lim_{x \to 4} \dfrac{3x^2 - 14x + 8}{x - 4} \to \dfrac{0}{0}$

$= \displaystyle\lim_{x \to 4} \dfrac{6x - 14}{1} = 10$

10. $\displaystyle\lim_{x \to 0} \dfrac{x^2 + \cos 5x - 1}{x^2} \to \dfrac{0}{0}$

$= \displaystyle\lim_{x \to 0} \dfrac{2x - 5 \sin 5x}{2x} \to \dfrac{0}{0}$

$= \displaystyle\lim_{x \to 0} \dfrac{2 - 25 \cos 5x}{2} = \dfrac{-23}{2} = -11.5$

11. Let $L = \displaystyle\lim_{x \to \infty} x^{1/x}$.

$\ln L = \ln\left(\displaystyle\lim_{x \to \infty} x^{1/x}\right) = \displaystyle\lim_{x \to \infty} \left(\ln x^{1/x}\right)$

$= \displaystyle\lim_{x \to \infty} \left(\dfrac{1}{x} \cdot \ln x\right) = \displaystyle\lim_{x \to \infty} \left(\dfrac{\ln x}{x}\right) \to \dfrac{\infty}{\infty}$

$= \displaystyle\lim_{x \to \infty} \left(\dfrac{1/x}{1}\right) = 0$

$\therefore L = e^0 = 1$

12. $f(x) = 10x^2 e^{-x}$

$f'(x) = 20x e^{-x} - 10x^2 e^{-x}$

13. $f'(3) = 60e^{-3} - 90e^{-3} = -1.4936\ldots$

A line at $x = 3$ with slope $-1.4936\ldots$ is tangent to the graph.

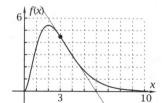

14. $f'(2) = 40e^{-2} - 40e^{-2} = 0$

The high point really is at $x = 2$ because the derivative is zero there.

15. $\displaystyle\lim_{x \to \infty} f(x) = \lim_{x \to \infty} 10x^2 e^{-x} = \lim_{x \to \infty} \dfrac{10x^2}{e^x} \to \dfrac{\infty}{\infty}$

$= \displaystyle\lim_{x \to \infty} \dfrac{20x}{e^x} \to \dfrac{\infty}{\infty}$

$= \displaystyle\lim_{x \to \infty} \dfrac{20}{e^x} \to \dfrac{20}{\infty}$

$= 0$

$f(x)$ does approach zero as x approaches infinity.

16. Let $L = \displaystyle\lim_{x \to \infty} (1 + x^{-1})^x \to 1^\infty$.

$\ln L = \displaystyle\lim_{x \to \infty} x \ln (1 + x^{-1}) \to \infty \cdot 0$

$= \displaystyle\lim_{x \to \infty} \dfrac{\ln (1 + x^{-1})}{x^{-1}} \to \dfrac{0}{0}$

$= \displaystyle\lim_{x \to \infty} \dfrac{(1 + x^{-1})^{-1}(-x^{-2})}{-x^{-2}}$

$= \displaystyle\lim_{x \to \infty} (1 + x^{-1}) = 1$

$\therefore L = e^1 = e$, Q.E.D.

Calculus: Concepts and Applications Instructor's Resource Book
©2005 Key Curriculum Press

17. $y = x$ for all $x > 0$, and y is undefined for $x \le 0$.

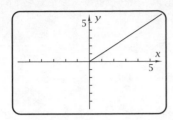

18. $\int 2^x \, dx = \dfrac{2^x}{\ln 2} + C$ (by following the pattern)

or $\int 2^x \, dx = \int e^{x \ln 2} \, dx = \dfrac{1}{\ln 2} \int e^{x \ln 2} \, (\ln 2 \, dx)$

$= \dfrac{1}{\ln 2} e^{x \ln 2} + C = \dfrac{2^x}{\ln 2} + C$

19. $\int_0^2 2^x \, dx = \dfrac{2^x}{\ln 2} \Big|_0^2 = \dfrac{4}{\ln 2} - \dfrac{1}{\ln 2} = \dfrac{3}{\ln 2} = 4.3280\ldots$

Using numerical integration, $\int_0^2 2^x \, dx = 4.3280\ldots$

The numerical answer and exact answer are the same to as many decimal places as the calculator shows.

20. Answers will vary.

Test 23

1. $y = \ln (5x - 7)^3 = 3 \ln (5x - 7)$

$y' = \dfrac{3}{5x - 7} \cdot 5 = \dfrac{15}{5x - 7}$

2. $f(x) = \ln (\cos x)$

$f'(x) = \dfrac{1}{\cos x} (-\sin x) = -\tan x$

3. $\dfrac{d}{dx}(e^{4x}) = 4e^{4x}$

4. $y = \log_9 x = \dfrac{\ln x}{\ln 9}$

$\dfrac{dy}{dx} = \dfrac{1}{\ln 9} \cdot \dfrac{1}{x} = \dfrac{1}{x \ln 9}$

5. $\dfrac{d(6^x)}{dx} = 6^x \ln 6$

6. $\int e^{7x} \, dx = \dfrac{1}{7} e^{7x} + C$

7. $\int 8^x \, dx - \dfrac{8^x}{\ln 8} + C$

8. $\int e^{x \ln 8} \, dx = \int e^{\ln 8^x} \, dx$

$= \int 8^x \, dx = \dfrac{8^x}{\ln 8} + C$ (from Problem 7)

or $\int e^{x \ln 8} \, dx = \dfrac{1}{\ln 8} \int e^{x \ln 8} \cdot (\ln 8 \, dx)$

$= \dfrac{1}{\ln 8} e^{x \ln 8} + C$

$= \dfrac{e^{x \ln 8}}{\ln 8} + C = \dfrac{8^x}{\ln 8} + C$

9. $\int x^3 e^{x^4} \, dx = \dfrac{1}{4} \int e^{x^4} (4x^3 \, dx) = \dfrac{1}{4} e^{x^4} + C$

10. $\int e^3 \, dx = e^3 x + C$

11. $f(x) = \int_1^x \dfrac{1}{1 + t^2} \, dt$

$f'(x) = \dfrac{1}{1 + x^2}$

12. $g(x) = \tan^{-1} x$

$g'(x) = \dfrac{1}{1 + x^2}$ (the same as Problem 11)

13. $f'(x) = g'(x)$ for all x. But $f(1) = 0$ and $g(1) = \tan^{-1} 1 = \pi/4$. Thus, f and g do not have a point in common, and are not the same function.

14. $(\ln x)^4 (dx/x) = \dfrac{1}{5}(\ln x)^5 + C$

15. $y = \tan x \Rightarrow y' = \sec^2 x$

16. $\int \tan x \, dx = -\ln |\cos x| + C = \ln |\sec x| + C$

17. $\int \dfrac{1}{f(x)} f'(x) \, dx = \ln |f(x)| + C$

18. $\int \dfrac{du}{u} = \ln |u| + C$

19. $\int \dfrac{\sec^2 x + \sec x \tan x}{\sec x + \tan x} \, dx$

$= \ln |\sec x + \tan x| + C$

20. $\int \sec x \, dx = \ln |\sec x + \tan x| + C$ (the same as Problem 19)

21. $\int \sec^2 x \, dx = \tan x + C$

22. $\lim\limits_{x \to \infty} \dfrac{7x^2 - 4}{3 - 4x^2} \to \dfrac{\infty}{-\infty}$

$= \lim\limits_{x \to \infty} \dfrac{14x}{-8x} = \lim\limits_{x \to \infty} \dfrac{14}{-8} - -1.75$

23. $\lim\limits_{x \to 0} \dfrac{x^2 - \cos 5x + 1}{e^x - x - 1} \to \dfrac{0}{0}$

$= \lim\limits_{x \to 0} \dfrac{2x + 5 \sin 5x}{e^x - 1} \to \dfrac{0}{0}$

$= \lim\limits_{x \to 0} \dfrac{2 + 25 \cos 5x}{e^x} \to \dfrac{27}{1}$

$= 27$

24. $L - \lim\limits_{x \to 0} (1 + 0.2x)^{1/x} \to 1^\infty$

$\ln L = \lim\limits_{x \to 0} \dfrac{1}{x} \ln (1 + 0.2x) \to \infty \cdot 0$

$= \lim\limits_{x \to 0} \dfrac{\ln (1 + 0.2x)}{x} \to \dfrac{0}{0}$

$= \lim\limits_{x \to 0} \dfrac{(1 + 0.2x)^{-1} \cdot 0.2}{1} \to 0.2$

$= 0.2$

$L = e^{0.2} = 1.2214027\ldots$

25. $(1 + 0.0002)^{1/0.001} = 1.221378\ldots$, which is close to the limit in Problem 24.

26. $\dfrac{dP}{dt} = 0.075P \Rightarrow \dfrac{dP}{P} = 0.075 \, dt$

$\int \dfrac{dP}{P} = \int 0.075 \, dt$

$\ln |P| = 0.075t + C$

27. $|P| = e^{0.075t + C} = e^{0.075t} \cdot e^C$

$P = C_1 e^{0.075t}$

$800 = C_1 e^0 \Rightarrow C_1 = 800$

$\therefore P = 800 e^{0.075t}$

28. $2000 = 800 e^{0.075t}$

$2.5 = e^{0.075t}$

$\ln 2.5 = 0.075t$

$t = \dfrac{\ln 2.5}{0.075} = 12.2172\ldots$

Incorporate in about 12.2 yr.

29. Answers will vary.

1. $f(x) = \int_2^x \cos t \, dt = \sin t \big|_2^x = \sin x - \sin 2$

   $f'(x) = \cos x - 0 = \cos x$
   This answer is the same as the integrand evaluated at the variable upper limit of integration, which is what the fundamental theorem says.

2. $g(x) = \int_3^{\tan x} \sec t \, dt$

   $g'(x) = \sec (\tan x) \cdot \sec^2 x$

3. For $\int x^{-1} \, dx$, the power rule would give $\frac{1}{0} x^0$, which is undefined because of division by zero.

4. $\ln x = \int_1^x \frac{1}{t} \, dt$

   By numerical integration, $\int_1^5 \frac{1}{t} \, dt = 1.6094... = \ln 5$

5. $\ln' x = \frac{1}{x}$

6. $\ln x$ is continuous for all $x > 0$ because it is differentiable for these values of x. Differentiability implies continuity.

7. $g(x) = \int \frac{1}{x} \, dx \Rightarrow g'(x) = \frac{1}{x}$

8. $\int \tan x \, dx = \int \frac{\sin x}{\cos x} \, dx = \int \frac{1}{\cos x} (\sin x \, dx)$

   $= -\ln |\cos x| + C = \ln |\sec x| + C$

9. $\ln 2 + \ln 7 = 2.639057...$
   $\ln 14 = 2.639057...$
   The answers are the same.

10. $(1.0001)^{10000} = 2.71814592...$
    $e = 2.71828182...$
    The numerical answer is close to e.

11. $\frac{1}{x} \log_b e$ becomes $\frac{1}{x} \log_e e = \frac{1}{x} \cdot 1 = \frac{1}{x}$. Thus algebraic calculus formulas are easier if base-e logs are used.

12. $\ln x$ and $\log_e x$ both have $1/x$ for their derivatives, and both $\ln 1$ and $\log_e 1 = 0$. Thus $\ln$ and $\log_e$ have identical derivatives and a point in common, which implies that they are the same function.

13. $f(x) = \log_{10} (\tan x) = \frac{\ln (\tan x)}{\ln 10}$

    $f'(x) = \frac{1}{(\tan x)(\ln 10)} \cdot \sec^2 x$

14. $y = 5^x \Rightarrow \ln y = x \ln 5$
    $y^{-1} y' = \ln 5$
    $y' = y \ln 5 = 5^x \ln 5$

15. $\frac{d}{dx}(10^{\sin x}) = 10^{\sin x} \cdot \ln 10 \cdot \cos x$

16. $\int 5^x \, dx = \frac{5^x}{\ln 5} + C$

17. $y = e^x \Rightarrow y' = e^x \ln e$, and $\ln e = 1$.
    Thus, $y' = e^x$.

18. $\int e^{3x} \, dx = \frac{1}{3} e^{3x} + C$

19. Let $y = e^{\ln x}$.
    $\ln y = \ln e^{\ln x} = \log_e e^{\ln x} = \ln x \cdot \log_e e = \ln x$
    Because $\ln y = \ln x$ and $\ln$ is invertible, $y = x$, and thus $e^{\ln x} = x$, Q.E.D.

20. $\lim_{x \to \infty} \frac{5x^2 - 11x + 7}{4 + 3x - 2x^2} \to \frac{\infty}{-\infty}$

    $= \lim_{x \to \infty} \frac{10x - 11}{3 - 4x} \to \frac{\infty}{-\infty}$

    $= \lim_{x \to \infty} \frac{10}{-4} \to \frac{10}{-4}$

    $= -2.5$

21. $L = \lim_{x \to 0} (1 + 5x)^{1/x} \to 1^\infty$

    $\ln L = \lim_{x \to 0} \frac{1}{x} \ln (1 + 5x) \to \infty \cdot 0$

    $= \lim_{x \to 0} \frac{\ln (1 + 5x)}{x} \to \frac{0}{0}$

    $= \lim_{x \to 0} \frac{(1 + 5x)^{-1} \cdot 5}{1} \to \frac{5}{1}$

    $= 5$

    $\therefore L = e^5 = 148.4131...$

22. $\int x e^{x^2} \, dx = \frac{1}{2} \int e^{x^2} (2x \, dx) = \frac{1}{2} e^{x^2} + C$

23. $f(x) = x^3 \ln x$
    $f'(x) = 3x^2 \ln x + x^3 \cdot \frac{1}{x} = 3x^2 \ln x + x^2$

24. $\int_{-20}^{-5} \frac{1}{x} \, dx = \ln |x| \big|_{-20}^{-5} = \ln 5 - \ln 20 = \ln 0.25 = -1.3862...$

25. $y = 5e^{\ln x^3} = 5x^3$
    $y' = 15x^2$

26. $\int \frac{(\ln x)^5}{x} \, dx = \int (\ln x)^5 (1/x \cdot dx) = \frac{1}{6} (\ln x)^6 + C$

27. Answers will vary.

Test 25

1. $f'(1) \approx \frac{2^{1.01} - 2^{0.99}}{0.02} = 1.3863...$

2. A line with slope $1.3863...$ is tangent to the graph at $x = 1$.

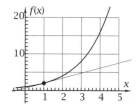

3. $f'(x)$ represents the acceleration.

4. The integral represents the displacement between the location at $t = 1$ and the location at $t = 4$.

5.

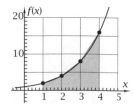

6. $A_1 = \frac{1}{2}(2 + 4) = 3$

   $A_2 = \frac{1}{2}(4 + 8) = 6$

   $A_3 = \frac{1}{2}(8 + 16) = 12$

   $T_3 = 3 + 6 + 12 = 21$

7. The trapezoids are circumscribed about the region, and thus include more area than the region.

8. $T_{100} = 20.1984583...$

9. $L = \lim_{x \to c} f(x)$ if and only if for any $\varepsilon > 0$ there is a $\delta > 0$ such that if x is within δ units of c, but not equal to c, then $f(x)$ is within ε units of L.

10. $f'(x) = \lim_{\Delta x \to 0} \dfrac{(x + \Delta x) - f(x)}{\Delta x}$

    or $f'(c) = \lim_{x \to c} \dfrac{f(x) - f(c)}{x - c}$

11. $f(x) = x^3$

    $f'(x) = \lim_{h \to 0} \dfrac{(x + h)^3 - x^3}{h}$

    $= \lim_{h \to 0} \dfrac{x^3 + 3x^2 h + 3xh^2 + h^3 - x^3}{h}$

    $= \lim_{h \to 0} (3x^2 + 3xh + h^2)$

    $= 3x^2 + 0 + 0 = 3x^2$, Q.E.D.

12. The limit of a sum property was used here:
    $\lim_{h \to 0} (3x^2 + 3xh + h^2) = 3x^2 + 0 + 0$

13. No, the power rule does not work for exponential functions such as $f(x) = 2^x$.

14. $\dfrac{\sin 0.001}{0.001} = 0.999999833...$,
    which is close to 1.

15. $\dfrac{d}{dx} [\cos (x^3 + 5)] = -3x^2 \sin (x^3 + 5)$

16. $y = x^5 \sin 2x$
    $y' = 5x^4 \cdot \sin 2x + x^5 \cdot \cos 2x \cdot 2$
    $= 5x^4 \sin 2x + 2x^5 \cos 2x$

17. $y = \tan x = \dfrac{\sin x}{\cos x}$
    $y' = \dfrac{(\cos x)(\cos x) - (\sin x)(-\sin x)}{\cos^2 x}$
    $= \dfrac{\cos^2 x + \sin^2 x}{\cos^2 x} = \dfrac{1}{\cos^2 x} = \sec^2 x$, Q.E.D.

18. $y = \tan^{-1} x \Rightarrow \tan y = x$
    $\sec^2 y \cdot y' = 1$
    $y' = \dfrac{1}{\sec^2 y}$

    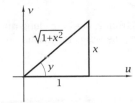

    $y' = \dfrac{1}{1 + x^2}$, Q.E.D.

19. $f(x) = \begin{cases} ax^2, & \text{if } x < 3 \\ 10 - x, & \text{if } x \geq 3 \end{cases}$
    $\lim_{x \to 3^-} f(x) = 9a, \lim_{x \to 3^+} f(x) = 7$

20. $9a = 7 \Rightarrow a = \dfrac{7}{9}$

21. $\lim_{x \to 3^-} f'(x) = 2a(3) = 6a = 6\left(\dfrac{7}{9}\right) = 4\dfrac{2}{3}$
    $\lim_{x \to 3^+} f'(x) = -1$
    Because the two limits are not equal, f is not differentiable at $x = 3$, Q.E.D.
    Differentiability implies continuity, but continuity does not imply differentiability. There is a cusp at $x = 3$.

22. $x = 5 \cos t$
    $y = 3 \sin t$
    $x' = -5 \sin t$
    At $x = 2$, $x' = -5 \sin 2 = -4.5464 \approx -4.55$ ft/s
    x is decreasing.

23. $x'' = -5 \cos t$
    At $t = 2$, $x'' = -5 \cos 2 = 2.0807...$ ft/s^2
    The pendulum is slowing down in the x-direction because the velocity and acceleration have opposite signs.

24. $\dfrac{dy}{dx} = \dfrac{dy/dt}{dx/dt} = \dfrac{3 \cos x}{-5 \sin t} = -0.6 \cot t$

25. At $t = 2$, $\dfrac{dy}{dx} = \dfrac{3 \cos 2}{-5 \sin 2} = 0.2745....$
    A line with slope 0.27... is tangent to the graph at the point when $t = 2$.

    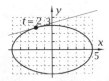

26. $g(x) = \int f(x) \, dx$ if and only if $g'(x) = f(x)$.

27. Antiderivative

28. $\int x^3 (10 - x^4)^7 \, dx = -\dfrac{1}{4} \int (10 - x^4)^7 (-4x^3 \, dx)$
    $= -\dfrac{1}{4} \cdot \dfrac{1}{8} (10 - x^4)^8 + C = -\dfrac{1}{32} (10 - x^4)^8 + C$

29.

    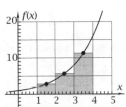

30. $M_{100} = 20.1973666...$

31. $\int_a^b f(x) \, dx = \lim_{\Delta x \to 0} L_n = \lim_{\Delta x \to 0} U_n$, where L_n and U_n are lower and upper Riemann sums, respectively, provided the two limits are equal.

32. If $g(x) = \int f(x) \, dx$, then $\int_a^b f(x) \, dx = g(b) - g(a)$.

33. $dW = F \, dx = \sin 0.2x \, dx$

    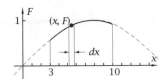

34. $W = \int_3^{10} \sin 0.2x \, dx$
    $= -5 \cos 0.2x \Big|_3^{10}$
    $= -5 \cos 2 + 5 \cos 0.6 = 6.2074...$
    ≈ 6.21 ft-lb

35. The graph shows a point c (the "mean value") between $x = a$ and $x = b$ at which the tangent line is parallel to the secant line.

    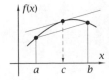

36. $f(x) = \int_1^{\sin x} t^3 \, dt$

$f'(x) = \sin^3 x \cos x$

37. $\ln x = \int_1^x \frac{1}{t} \, dt$

38. Let $f(x) = \ln x$.   Let $g(x) = \log_e x$.

$f'(x) = \frac{1}{x}$ $g'(x) = \frac{1}{x}\log_e e = \frac{1}{x}$

$\therefore f'(x) = g'(x)$ for all $x > 0$.

$f(1) = \ln 1 = 0$ $g(1) = \log_e 1 = 0$

$\therefore f$ and g have a point in common.

39. Uniqueness theorem for derivatives

40. $\int \tan x \, dx = \int \frac{\sin x}{\cos x} \, dx = \int \frac{1}{\cos x}(\sin x \, dx)$

$= -\ln|\cos x| + C = \ln|\sec x| + C$

or:

$\int \tan x \, dx = \int \tan x \cdot \frac{\sec x}{\sec x} \, dx$

$= \int \frac{1}{\sec x}(\sec x \tan x \, dx) = \ln|\sec x| + C$

or:

$\frac{d}{dx}(\ln|\sec x| + C) = \frac{1}{\sec x} \cdot \sec x \tan x = \tan x$

$\therefore \int \tan x \, dx = \ln|\sec x| + C$ by the definition of indefinite integral.

41. $f(x) = 2^x$

$\ln f(x) = x \ln 2$

$\frac{1}{f(x)} \cdot f'(x) = 1 \cdot \ln 2 = \ln 2$

$f'(x) = f(x) \ln 2 = 2^x \ln 2$

42. $\int 2^x \, dx = \frac{2^x}{\ln 2} + C$

(Pattern: For the derivative, you *multiply* 2^x by $\ln 2$. For the integral, you *divide* 2^x by $\ln 2$.)

43. $\int_1^4 2^x \, dx = \frac{2^x}{\ln 2}\Big|_1^4 = \frac{16}{\ln 2} - \frac{2}{\ln 2}$

$= \frac{14}{\ln 2} = 20.1977305\ldots$

44. Exact: $20.1977305\ldots$

T_{100}: $20.1984583\ldots$

M_{100}: $20.1973666\ldots$

M_{100} comes closer to the exact answer.

(Some students may note that the error for M_{100} is exactly half that for T_{100}, in absolute value.)

45. $\lim_{x \to 0} \frac{1 - e^x}{\sin 7x} \to \frac{0}{0}$

$= \lim_{x \to 0} \frac{-e^x}{7 \cos 7x} \to \frac{-1}{7}$

$= -\frac{1}{7}$

46. $\int_0^{24} (\text{People}) \, dt$

$\approx \frac{1}{3} \cdot 6[27 + 4(38) + 2(120) + 4(110) + 31]$

$= 2(890) = 1780$ man-hours

47. Answers will vary.

Test 26

1. $L = \lim_{x \to c} f(x)$ if and only if for any $\varepsilon > 0$ there is a $\delta > 0$ such that if x is within δ units of c, but not equal to c, then $f(x)$ is within ε units of L.

2. $f'(c) = \lim_{x \to c} \frac{f(x) - f(c)}{x - c}$ or

$f'(x) = \lim_{\Delta x \to 0} \frac{f(x + \Delta x) - f(x)}{\Delta x}$

3. $\int_a^b f(x) \, dx = \lim_{\Delta x \to 0} L_n = \lim_{\Delta x \to 0} U_n$, provided the two limits are equal.

4. $g(x) = \int f(x) \, dx$ if and only if $g'(x) = f(x)$.

5. $f(x) = 5x + 3, x \neq 2$

$5x + 3 = 12.99 \Rightarrow x = 1.998$

$5x + 3 = 13.01 \Rightarrow x = 2.002$

Keep x within 0.002 unit of 2.

6. The inflation rate is an instantaneous rate of change, which is what a derivative is.

7. The velocity varies, so you must use a definite integral to do the multiplication.

8. An indefinite integral is an antiderivative, which is an algebraic quantity. In order to find an antiderivative, you must first know how to find a derivative algebraically.

9.

x	$f(x)$
0	undefined
100	1.9949...
200	1.9956...
300	1.9966...
400	1.9978...
500	1.9990...
600	2.00007...

The values of $f(x)$ stay close to 2.

10. (The graph looks like the one on the test.)

11. The graph shows a zoom by a factor of 10. The curve is not a straight line.

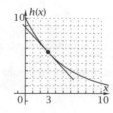

12. $f(x)$ may move toward and away from 2, but in the long run it stays *close* to 2. The larger x gets, the less is the maximum distance that $f(x)$ "strays" from 2.

13. $L = \lim_{x \to 0} x^{-1} \sin x \to \infty \cdot 0$

$= \lim_{x \to 0} \frac{\sin x}{x} \to \frac{0}{0}$

$= \lim_{x \to 0} \frac{\cos x}{1} \to \frac{1}{1}$

$= 1$

14. $g'(x) \approx \frac{5^{2.01} - 5^{1.99}}{0.02} = 40.237684\ldots$

15. $g'(x) = 5^x \ln 5$

$g'(2) = 25 \ln 5 = 40.235947\ldots$ Close!

16. $h'(3) \approx -1.1$

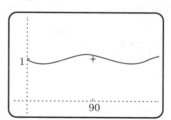

Calculus: Concepts and Applications Instructor's Resource Book
©2005 Key Curriculum Press

17. Integral $\approx$ 22.5 or 22.6

18. $\displaystyle\int_0^3 10e^{-0.2x}\,dx = -50e^{-0.2x}\big|_0^3$
$= -50e^{-0.6} + 50e^0 = 22.5594...$

19. $\displaystyle\ln x = \int_1^x \frac{1}{t}\,dt$

20. Numerical derivative with tolerance of 0.001 is about 0.3333333457, which is close to 1/3.

21. Let $f(x) = \ln x$ and $g(x) = \log_e x$.
$f'(x) = 1/x$
$g'(x) = (1/x)\log_e e = 1/x$
$f(1) = 0$ and $g(1) = 0$
Because f and g have identical derivatives and a point in common, $f(x) = g(x)$ for all $x > 0$.
$\therefore \ln x$ and $\log_e x$ are the same function.

22. $\displaystyle f'(x) = 3x^2 \sin^{-1} x + x^3 \cdot \frac{1}{\sqrt{1 - x^2}}$

23. $y = 2^x$
$\ln y = x \ln 2$
$\dfrac{1}{y}y' = \ln 2$
$y' = y \ln 2 = 2^x \ln 2$

24. $y^5 = x^7$
$5y^4 y' = 7x^6$
$y' = \dfrac{7x^6}{5y^4} = \dfrac{7}{5}\dfrac{x^6}{(x^{7/5})^4} = \dfrac{7}{5}x^{2/5}$,
which is what you would get from the derivative of a power formula.

25. $\dfrac{dy}{dx} = \dfrac{dy/dt}{dx/dt} = \dfrac{\sec t \tan t}{\sec^2 t} = \sin t$
At $t = 1$, $\dfrac{dy}{dx} = \sin 1 = 0.8414....$

The graph shows a slope of about 0.8, so this answer is reasonable.

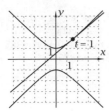

26. $\displaystyle\int (10x - 7)^5\,dx = \frac{1}{10}\int (10x - 7)^5(10\,dx)$
$= \dfrac{1}{60}(10x - 7)^6 + C$

27. $\displaystyle\int \frac{1}{\sin x}\cos x\,dx = \ln|\sin x| + C$

28. $\displaystyle\int e^{\tan x}\sec^2 x\,dx = e^{\tan x} + C$

29. $\displaystyle\int 3^x\,dx = \frac{1}{\ln 3} \cdot 3^x + C$

30. $v(t) = 200t \cdot e^{-t}$
$a(t) = v'(t) = 200e^{-t} + 200t(-e^{-t}) = 200e^{-t}(1 - t)$
$a(3) = -400e^{-3} = -19.9148... \approx -19.9$ ft/s^2
The object is slowing down.

31. Distance $= \displaystyle\int_1^5 (200t \cdot e^{-t})\,dt \approx 139.066...$

About 139.1 ft.

32. $f'(x) = \begin{cases} 3x^2, & \text{if } x \le 1 \\ 2a(x - 2), & \text{if } x > 1 \end{cases}$
$\displaystyle\lim_{x \to 1^-} f'(x) = 3$. $\displaystyle\lim_{x \to 1^+} f'(x) = 2a(1 - 2) = -2a$
Let $-2a = 3$. Thus, $a = -1.5$.

33. $\displaystyle\lim_{x \to 1^-} f(x) = 1$. $\displaystyle\lim_{x \to 1^+} f(x) = -1.5(1 - 2)^2 = -1.5$
$\therefore f$ is discontinuous at $x = 1$ because the left and right limits are unequal.
Note: This fact does not contradict that differentiability implies continuity. Just because the left and right limits of the derivative are equal does not imply that the function is differentiable at $x = 1$.

34.

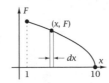

35. $dW = F\,dx = (10 - x)^{0.5}\,dx$

36. $W = \displaystyle\int_1^{10} (10 - x)^{0.5}\,dx = -\int_1^{10} (10 - x)^{0.5}\,(-dx)$
$= -\dfrac{1}{1.5}(10 - x)^{1.5}\Big|_1^{10} = \dfrac{27}{1.5} = 18$ ft-lb

37. $W = \dfrac{1}{3}(5)(35 + 4 \cdot 41 + 2 \cdot 50 + 4 \cdot 44 + 23) = \dfrac{5}{3}(498)$
$= 830$ ft-lb

38. $F'(x) = -0.5(10 - x)^{-0.5}$
$F(1) = 9^{0.5} = 3$ and $F(10) = 0$, so the slope is $-\dfrac{1}{3}$.
$-0.5(10 - c)^{-0.5} = -\dfrac{1}{3} \Rightarrow (10 - c)^{-0.5} = \dfrac{2}{3} \Rightarrow$
$10 - c = \dfrac{9}{4} \Rightarrow c = 7.75$

39. $\dfrac{dP}{dt} = 0.04P \Rightarrow \dfrac{dP}{P} = 0.04\,dt$
$\displaystyle\int \frac{dP}{P} = \int 0.04\,dt \Rightarrow \ln|P| = 0.04t + C$
$\Rightarrow |P| = e^{0.04t + C} \Rightarrow P = C_1 e^{0.04t}$
$100 = C_1 e^0 \Rightarrow C_1 = 100$
$\therefore P = 100e^{0.04t}$
$t = 10$: $P = 100e^{0.4} = 149.182...$
About \$149.18

40. Answers will vary.

Test 27

1. $\dfrac{dy}{dx} = 10xy^2$, with initial condition (3, 0.2)
$\displaystyle\int y^{-2}\,dy = \int 10x\,dx$
$-y^{-1} = 5x^2 + C$
$-0.2^{-1} = 5 \cdot 3^2 + C \Rightarrow C = -50$
$-y^{-1} = 5x^2 - 50$
$y = -\dfrac{1}{5x^2 - 50}$

2. $\dfrac{dy}{dx} = ky$
$\displaystyle\int \frac{dy}{y} = \int k\,dx$
$\ln|y| = kx + C$
$|y| = e^{kx+C} = e^{kx} \cdot e^C$
$y = C_1 e^{kx}$
$\therefore y$ varies exponentially with x, Q.E.D.

3. Let M = number of g. Let t = number of mo.

$\dfrac{dM}{dt} = kM \Rightarrow M = Ce^{kt}$ from Problem 2.

$70 = Ce^0 \Rightarrow C = 70$

$200 = 70e^{3k}$

$k = \dfrac{1}{3} \ln \dfrac{200}{70} = 0.3499407\ldots$ (Store without rounding.)

$\therefore M = 70e^{0.34\ldots t}$.

4. $50{,}000 = 70e^{0.34\ldots t}$

$0.34\ldots t = \ln \dfrac{50{,}000}{70}$

$t = 18.7782\ldots$

After about 19 months

5.

Years	t	Mass (g)
1	12	4,665
2	24	310,852
3	36	20,714,836

6. $\dfrac{M(12)}{M(0)} = 66.63\ldots$

$\dfrac{M(24)}{M(12)} = 66.63\ldots$

$\dfrac{M(36)}{M(24)} = 66.63\ldots$

$\therefore$ the tree appears to grow by a constant factor each year, Q.E.D.

7. Eventually the tree would slow down or stop growing. The mathematical model predicts continued, unrestricted growth.

8. $\dfrac{dW}{dt} = F - kW$

9. $\displaystyle\int \dfrac{dW}{F - kW} = \int dt \Rightarrow -\dfrac{1}{k} \int \dfrac{1}{F - kW}(-k\,dW) = \int dt$

$-\dfrac{1}{k} \ln|F - kW| = t + C$

$\ln|F - kW| = -kt + C_1$

$|F - kW| = e^{-kt + C_1} = e^{-kt} \cdot e^{C_1}$

$F - kW = C_2 e^{-kt}$

Substitute $(t, W) = (0, 0)$.

$F = C_2 e^0 \Rightarrow C_2 = F$

$F - kW = Fe^{-kt}$

$W = \dfrac{F}{k}(1 - e^{-kt})$

10. $k = 0.002$ and $F = 300{,}000$:

$W = \dfrac{300{,}000}{0.002}(1 - e^{-0.002t}) = 150{,}000{,}000(1 - e^{-0.002t})$

When $t = 100$, $W = 150{,}000{,}000(1 - e^{-0.2})$

$= 27{,}190{,}387.0\ldots \approx 27{,}190$ thousand ft^3

11. $\displaystyle\lim_{t \to \infty} W = 150{,}000{,}000$

The lake will hold about 150 million ft^3.

12. Answers will vary.

Test 28

1.

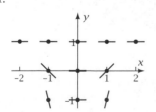

2. All the slope lines at $y = 1$ are horizontal. The proposed solution has slopes that are not zero where $y = 1$, and thus could not be a valid solution.

3. $\displaystyle\int (y - 1)^{-2}\,dy = \int x\,dx$

$-(y - 1)^{-1} = 0.5x^2 + C$

$-(-1 - 1)^{-1} = 0.5(0) + C$

$0.5 = C$

$\therefore -(y - 1)^{-1} = 0.5x^2 + 0.5$

$\dfrac{2}{1 - y} = x^2 + 1$

$1 - y = \dfrac{2}{x^2 + 1}$

$y = 1 - \dfrac{2}{x^2 + 1}$ or $y = \dfrac{x^2 - 1}{x^2 + 1}$

4. $\dfrac{dy}{dt} = ky \cdot \dfrac{m - y}{m}$

5.

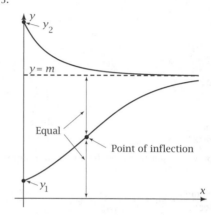

6. See the graph in Problem 5.

7. m is called the carrying capacity.

8. $dy = x(y - 1)^2\,dx = x(y - 1)^2(0.5)$

$x = 0$, $y = -1$: $dy = 0(-1 - 1)^2(0.5) = 0$, new $y \approx -1 + 0 = -1$

$x = 0.5$, $y = -1$: $dy = 0.5(-1 - 1)^2(0.5) = 1$, new $y \approx -1 + 1 = 0$

$x = 1$, $y = 0$: $dy = 1(0 - 1)^2(0.5) = 0.5$, new $y \approx 0 + 0.5 = 0.5$

$x = 1.5$, $y = 0.5$: $dy = 1.5(0.5 - 1)^2(0.5) = 0.1875$,

new $y \approx 0.5 + 0.1875 = 0.6875$

Points: $(0.5, -1)$, $(1, 0)$, $(1.5, 0.5)$, $(2, 0.6875)$

9.

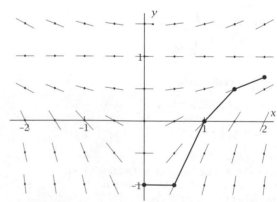

The figure shows line segments approximating the graph. Note that each segment follows the slope line.

Calculus: Concepts and Applications Instructor's Resource Book
©2005 Key Curriculum Press

10. $x = 2$: $y = 1 - \dfrac{2}{2^2 + 1} = 0.6$

The Euler's 0.6875 is close to this.

11. Slope $= -2(-20) - 32 = 8$, which is positive, and reasonable because the vertical scale is compressed by a factor of 10 on the graph.

12.

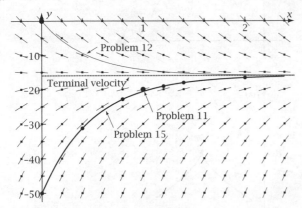

See the curve with initial condition $(0, 0)$, showing the skydiver speeding up in the negative direction, approaching a terminal velocity.

13. $\displaystyle\int \dfrac{dv}{v + 16} = -2 \int dt$

$\ln|v + 16| = -2t + C$

$|v + 16| = e^{-2t+C} = e^C \cdot e^{-2t}$

$v + 16 = \pm e^C \cdot e^{-2t} = C_1 e^{-t}$

$-50 + 16 = C_1 e^0 \Rightarrow C_1 = -34$

$\therefore v = -16 - 34e^{-2t}$

14.

t	v
0.0	-50
0.4	-31.3
0.8	-22.9
1.2	-19.1
1.6	-17.4
2.0	-16.6

15. See the graph in Problem 12.

16. By Euler's method, $v(2) \approx -16.3919...$, which is reasonable because it is close to, and slightly larger than, the actual -16.6, because the convex side of the graph is upward.

17. Answers will vary.

Test 29

1. $\dfrac{dy}{dx} = ky$

$\displaystyle\int \dfrac{dy}{y} = \int k \, dx$

$\ln|y| = kx + C$

$|y| = e^{kx+C} = e^{kx} \cdot e^C$

$y = C_1 e^{kx}$

2. The graph shows the populations starting at $(C, P) = (12, 9)$, and progressing clockwise in a cyclical pattern.

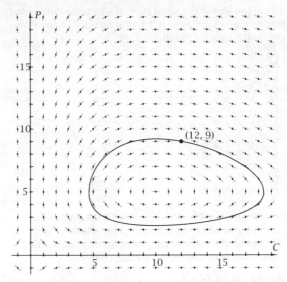

3. $\dfrac{dC}{dt} = 0 \Leftrightarrow -0.1C + 0.02PC = 0$

$C = 0$ or $P = \dfrac{0.1}{0.02} = 5$

Whenever $P = 5$, C is not changing, no matter what C equals.

4. $\dfrac{dP}{dt} = 0 \Leftrightarrow 0.1P - 0.01PC = 0$

$P = 0$ or $C = \dfrac{0.1}{0.01} = 10$

The fixed point is $(C, P) = (10, 5)$. (Also $(0, 0)$.)

5. $\dfrac{dD}{dt} = kt \Rightarrow D = Ce^{kt}$ from Problem 1.

$130 = Ce^0 \Rightarrow C = 130$

$117 = 130e^{3k}$

$k = \dfrac{1}{3} \ln \dfrac{117}{130} = -0.03512...$ (Store without rounding.)

$D = 130e^{-0.03512...t}$

6. $t = 15$: $D = 130e^{(-0.03512...)(15)} = 76.7637$

The coffee is still drinkable after 15 minutes.

or:

$50 = 130e^{-0.03512...t}$

$t = \dfrac{\ln(50/130)}{-0.03512...} = 27.2069...$

The coffee is drinkable for about 27 minutes, so it is still drinkable after 15 minutes.

7. $\dfrac{dy}{dx} = 1 - 0.2y$

$\displaystyle\int \dfrac{dy}{1 - 0.2y} = \int dx \Rightarrow -5 \int \dfrac{1}{1 - 0.2y}(-0.2 \, dy) = \int dx$

$-5 \ln|1 - 0.2y| = x + C$

$|1 - 0.2y| = e^{-0.2x-0.2C}$

$1 - 0.2y = C_1 e^{-0.2x}$

Substitute $(0, 0)$ for (x, y).

$1 = C_1 e^0 \Rightarrow C_1 = 1$

$1 - 0.2y = e^{-0.2x}$

$y = 5(1 - e^{-0.2x})$

8. If y were ever greater than 5, dy/dx would be negative, meaning that the population would be decreasing (due to overcrowding, perhaps).

9. $\dfrac{dy}{dx} = 0.35y - 0.05y^2$

$\dfrac{dy}{dx} = 0 \Leftrightarrow 0.05y(7 - y) = 0 \Leftrightarrow y = 0$ or $y = 7$

The population will be increasing between $y = 0$ and $y = 7$ because dy/dx is positive for these values.

10. The graph shows the point (5, 9) at which the differential equation gives $dy/dx = -0.9$, which agrees with the slope of about -1 on the graph.

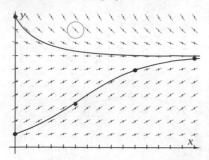

11. See the graph in Problem 10, showing the graph of the particular solution starting at (0, 1) rising toward an asymptote at $y = 7$, and the particular solution starting at (0, 10) falling toward the same asymptote.

12. $dy = (0.35y - 0.05y^2) \, dx$
    For (0, 1), with $dx = 0.5$,
    $dy = (0.35 - 0.05)(0.5) = 0.15$.
    $\therefore y = 1 + 0.15 = 1.15$.

13.

x	y
0	1
5	3.3169...
10	5.9194...
15	6.8129...

See the graph in Problem 7, showing that these points lie close to the plotted curve.

14. Answers will vary.

Test 30

1. A critical point at $x = c$ is a point where $f(c)$ exists and $f'(c)$ is either zero or undefined.

2.

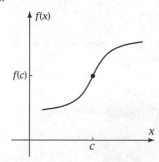

3.

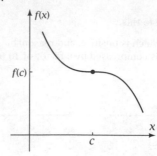

4.

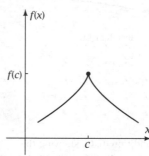

5.

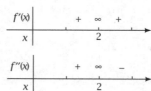

6. (Note: This problem duplicates Example 2 in Section 8-2.)

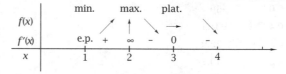

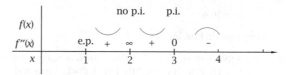

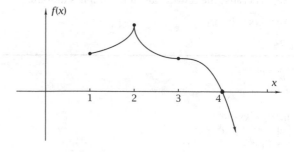

7. $f(x) = 5x^{2/3} - x^{5/3}$

$f'(x) = \frac{10}{3}x^{-1/3} - \frac{5}{3}x^{2/3} = \frac{5}{3}x^{-1/3}(2 - x)$

$f''(x) = -\frac{10}{9}x^{-4/3} - \frac{10}{9}x^{-1/3} = -\frac{10}{9}x^{-4/3}(1 + x)$

$f'(x) = 0 \Leftrightarrow x = 2$

$f'(x)$ is infinite $\Leftrightarrow x = 0$

$f''(x) = 0 \Leftrightarrow x = -1$

$f''(x)$ is infinite $\Leftrightarrow x = 0$

8. The tangent line is vertical at $x = 0$, so its slope is infinite there; so there is no value of the derivative there.

9. There is no point of inflection at the cusp because $f''(x)$ does not change signs there. There is a point of inflection at $x = -1$ because $f''(x)$ goes from positive to negative there.

10. $f(x) = ax^3 + bx^2 + cx + d$

$f'(x) = 3ax^2 + 2bx + c$

$f''(x) = 6ax + 2b$

$f(6) = 30 \Rightarrow 216a + 36b + 6c + d = 30$

$f(4) = 14 \Rightarrow 64a + 16b + 4c + d = 14$

$f'(6) = 0 \Rightarrow 108a + 12b + c = 0$

$f''(4) = 0 \Rightarrow 24a + 2b = 0$

The matrix solution of this system is shown here.

$$\begin{bmatrix} 216 & 36 & 6 & 1 \\ 64 & 16 & 4 & 1 \\ 108 & 12 & 1 & 0 \\ 24 & 2 & 0 & 0 \end{bmatrix}^{-1} \begin{bmatrix} 30 \\ 14 \\ 0 \\ 0 \end{bmatrix} = \begin{bmatrix} -1 \\ 12 \\ -36 \\ 30 \end{bmatrix}$$

$\therefore f(x) = -x^3 + 12x^2 - 36x + 30$

11. Let the sample point shown be (x, y).

Domain of x is $[0, 1]$.

$V = \pi x^2 y = \pi x^2(1 - x^4) = \pi(x^2 - x^6)$

$V' = \pi(2x - 6x^5) = 2\pi x(1 - 3x^4)$

$V' = 0 \Leftrightarrow x = 0$ or $x = \pm(1/3)^{1/4}$

There is a maximum at $x = (1/3)^{1/4}$ because V' goes from positive to negative there.

$V = 0$ at the endpoints $x = 0$ and $x = 1$.

Maximum V is $\pi(1/3)^{1/2}(1 - 1/3) = \frac{2\pi\sqrt{3}}{9} = 1.2091\ldots$

12. Let x = width of a room. $0 < x \le 10$

Let y = depth of a room.

Let L = total length of walls.

$L = 6x + 4y$

$xy = 360 \Rightarrow y = 360x^{-1}$

$L = 6x + 1440x^{-1}$

$L' = 6 - 1440x^{-2}$

$L' = 0 \Leftrightarrow 6 - 1440x^{-2} = 0$

$\Leftrightarrow x^2 = 240 \Leftrightarrow x = \pm15.4919\ldots$

Both values are out of the domain.

As $x \to 0$, $L \to \infty$.

At $x = 10$, $L = 204$.

The minimum total wall length is 204 ft.

13. Steps in solving max-min problems:

• Write an equation for the variable to be maximized or minimized. Specify a domain for the independent variable(s).

• Get the equation in terms of one variable.

• Differentiate, and find critical points where the derivative is zero or undefined.

• Check each critical point and any endpoints to find the global (absolute) maximum or minimum.

• Answer the question that was asked.

14. Answers will vary.

Test 31

1. $dV = 2\pi a(w_1 - w_2)\, du$

2. $V = 2\pi \int_a^b x(y_1 - y_2)\, dx$

3. $V = \pi \int_c^d (x_1{}^2 - x_2{}^2)\, dy$

4. The graph shows the back half of the solid.

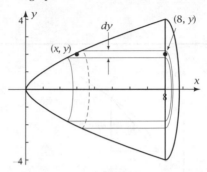

5. $dV = 2\pi y(8 - x)\, dy = 2\pi y(8 - y^{3/2})\, dy$

$V = 2\pi \int_0^4 (8y - y^{5/2})\, dy$

$= 2\pi\left(4y^2 - \frac{2}{7}y^{7/2}\right)\Big|_0^4$

$= 2\pi\left(64 - \frac{2}{7} \cdot 128\right) - 2\pi(0)$

$= 128\pi\left(1 - \frac{4}{7}\right)$

$= \frac{384\pi}{7}$

6. $dV = 2\pi(5 - x)(y)\, dx = 2\pi(5 - x)(2x)\, dx$

$V = \int_0^3 4\pi x(5 - x)\, dx = 169.6460\ldots$

(Exact: 54π)

7. $V = V_{\text{big cone}} - V_{\text{small cone}} - V_{\text{cylinder}}$

$= \frac{1}{3}\pi(5^2)(10) - \frac{1}{3}\pi(2^2)(4) - \pi(2^2)(6)$

$= 54\pi$, which agrees with Problem 6.

8. Slicing parallel to the x-axis would make the length of the strip a *piecewise* function of y.

9. $dA = |(x + 4) - x^{3/2}|\, dx$

$A = \int_1^4 (x + 4 - x^{3/2})\, dx = 7.1$ (Exact)

10.

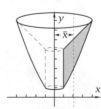

$dV = 2\pi x\, dA = 2\pi x(x + 4 - x^{3/2})\, dx$

$V = \int_1^4 2\pi x(x + 4 - x^{3/2})\, dx = 92.4525\ldots$

(Exact: $29\frac{3}{7}\pi$)

11. $2\pi\bar{x}(7.1) = 92.4525\ldots$

$\bar{x} = 2.0724\ldots$

See the graph in Problem 10, showing $\bar{x}$.

12. $dV = yz\, dx$

13. The line in the xy-plane contains $(0, 1)$ and $(8, 3)$.
   Slope is 0.25. Equation is $y = 0.25x + 1$.
   The line in the xz-plane contains $(0, 2)$ and $(8, 6)$.
   Slope is 0.5. Equation is $z = 0.5x + 2$.
   $dV = (0.25x + 1)(0.5x + 2)\,dx$

14. $V = \int_0^8 (0.25x + 1)(0.5x + 2)\,dx = 69\frac{1}{3}$ ft^3

15. $(69.3333...)(7.5) = 520$ gallons

16. Answers will vary.

Test 32

1.
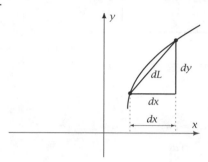

The graph shows a right triangle with legs dx and dy and hypotenuse dL, the approximate length of the section of the curve.
By the Pythagorean theorem, $dL = \sqrt{dx^2 + dy^2}$.

2.
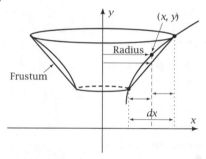

The graph shows the frustum and the sample point with radius equal to the average of the radii of the upper and lower bases of the frustum.
$dS = 2\pi x\,dL = 2\pi x\sqrt{dx^2 + dy^2}$

3.
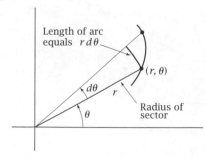

Area of whole circle $= \pi r^2$.

Fraction of circle $= \dfrac{\text{arc length}}{\text{circumference}} = \dfrac{r\,d\theta}{2\pi r}$.

$\therefore dA = \dfrac{r\,d\theta}{2\pi r} \cdot \pi r^2 = \dfrac{1}{2}r^2\,d\theta$.

4.
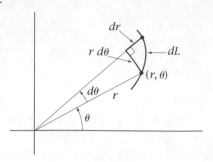

If the graph of $f(\theta)$ is locally linear everywhere, then as $d\theta$ approaches zero, dL approaches the hypotenuse of a right triangle with legs dr and $r\,d\theta$. By the Pythagorean theorem, $dL = \sqrt{dr^2 + (r\,d\theta)^2}$.

5.

6.
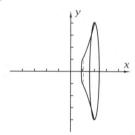

7. Conjecture: The surface in Problem 6 has greater area because the curve being rotated goes farther from the axis of rotation.

8. $y = x^2 \Rightarrow dy = 2x\,dx$
   $dL = \sqrt{dx^2 + dy^2} = \sqrt{dx^2 + 4x^2\,dx^2} = \sqrt{1 + 4x^2}\,dx$
   Problem 5:
   $dS = 2\pi x \cdot dL = 2\pi x\sqrt{1 + 4x^2}\,dx$
   $S = \int_1^2 2\pi x\sqrt{1 + 4x^2}\,dx = 30.8464...$
   Problem 6:
   $dS = 2\pi y \cdot dL = 2\pi x^2\sqrt{1 + 4x^2}\,dx$
   $S = \int_1^2 2\pi x^2\sqrt{1 + 4x^2}\,dx = 49.4162...$
   The answers confirm the conjecture in Problem 7.
   49.4... is greater than 30.8....

9. $x = y^{0.5} \Rightarrow dx = 0.5y^{-0.5}\,dy$
   $dL = \sqrt{dx^2 + dy^2} = \sqrt{0.25y^{-1} + 1}\,dy$
   $dS = 2\pi x \cdot dL = 2\pi y^{0.5}\sqrt{0.25y^{-1} + 1}\,dy$
   $S = \int_1^4 2\pi y^{0.5}\sqrt{0.25y^{-1} + 1}\,dy = 30.8464...$, which agrees with the answer to Problem 8 for the surface in Problem 5.

10. $L = \int_1^2 \sqrt{1 + 4x^2}\,dx = 3.1678...$

11. $30.8464... = 2\pi\bar{x} \cdot 3.1678...$
    $\bar{x} = 1.5497...$

12. Spiral makes 5 revolutions, so $0 \le \theta \le 10\pi$.
$r = 0.2\theta \Rightarrow dr = 0.2\,d\theta$
$dL = \sqrt{dr^2 + r^2\,d\theta^2} = \sqrt{0.04 + 0.04\theta^2}\,d\theta$
$\int_0^{10\pi} \sqrt{0.04 + 0.04\theta^2}\,d\theta = 99.1601\ldots$

Check: Five circles with radii 0.2π, $0.2 \cdot 3\pi$, $0.2 \cdot 5\pi$, $0.2 \cdot 7\pi$, and $0.2 \cdot 9\pi$ have total length $2\pi[0.2\pi(1 + 3 + 5 + 7 + 9)] = 10\pi^2 = 98.6964\ldots$, which is close to the actual length of $99.1601\ldots$.

13. $dA = 0.5r^2\,d\theta = 0.02\theta^2\,d\theta$
Area swept out in the fifth cycle is
$A_5 = \int_0^{10\pi} 0.02\theta^2\,d\theta = 206.7085\ldots$
Area swept out in the fourth cycle is
$A_4 = \int_0^{8\pi} 0.02\theta^2\,d\theta = 105.8347\ldots$
Area of band is $A_5 - A_4 = 100.8737\ldots$
(Exact: $244\pi^3/75$)

14. Answers will vary.

Test 33

1.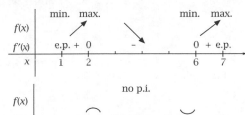
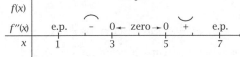
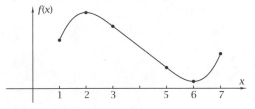

2. $dL = \sqrt{dx^2 + dy^2}$

3. $dL = \sqrt{dr^2 + (r\,d\theta)^2}$

4. $dA = \frac{1}{2}r^2\,d\theta$

5. $dS = 2\pi(\text{radius})\,dL = 2\pi r\sqrt{dx^2 + dy^2}$

6. $V = \int_a^b 2\pi(c - x)(y_2 - y_1)\,dx$

7. $f(x) = (x - 2)^5 + x + 20$
$f'(x) = 5(x - 2)^4 + 1$
$f'(x) = 0 \Leftrightarrow (x - 2)^4 = -0.2$
No real solutions.
$\therefore$ no local maxima or minima.

8. $f''(x) = 20(x - 2)^3$
$f''(2) = 20(2 - 2)^3 = 0$
$\therefore$ the graph is "straight" at $x = 2$.
$f'(2) = 5(2 - 2)^4 + 1 = 1$, not zero.
$\therefore$ the graph is not horizontal at $x = 2$, Q.E.D.

9. Solving $e^{0.5b} - x^2 = 0$ gives $b = 1.4296\ldots$

10.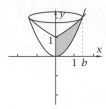

11. Slice parallel to the y-axis, generating cylindrical shells.
$dV = 2\pi x(e^{0.5x} - x^2)\,dx$
$V = \int_0^b 2\pi x(e^{0.5x} - x^2)\,dx = 3.9221\ldots$

12. $y = e^{0.5x} \Rightarrow dy = 0.5e^{0.5x}\,dx$
$dL = \sqrt{dx^2 + dy^2} = \sqrt{1 + 0.25e^x}\,dx$
$L = \int_0^b \sqrt{1 + 0.25e^x}\,dx = 1.7784\ldots$

13. $y = x^2 \Rightarrow dy = 2x\,dx$
$dL = \sqrt{dx^2 + dy^2} = \sqrt{1 + 4x^2}\,dx$
$dS = 2\pi x\,dL = 2\pi x\sqrt{1 + 4x^2}\,dx$
$S = \int_0^b 2\pi x\sqrt{1 + 4x^2}\,dx = 14.0282\ldots$

14. $A = (8 - x)(y) = (8 - x)(x^{2/3}) = 8x^{2/3} - x^{5/3}$
$A' = \frac{16}{3}x^{-1/3} - \frac{5}{3}x^{2/3} = \frac{1}{3}x^{-1/3}(16 - 5x)$
A' is undefined $\Leftrightarrow x = 0$.
$A' = 0 \Leftrightarrow 16 - 5x = 0 \Rightarrow x = 3.2$
Critical points are at $x = 0$ and $x = 3.2$.
At $x = 3.2$, A' goes from positive to negative, indicating a local maximum. However, 3.2 is out of the domain. Checking the endpoints,
$A(4) = 4^{5/3} = 10.0793\ldots$ and $A(8) = 0$
Maximum area is $10.0793\ldots$ at the endpoint $x = 4$.

15. $r = 5 + 15\cos\theta$
$r = 0 \to \theta = \arccos(-1/3) = 1.9106\ldots + 2\pi n$
The inner loop starts at $\theta = 1.9106\ldots$ and ends at $\theta = -1.9106\ldots + 2\pi = 4.3725\ldots$

16. $dA = 0.5r^2\,d\theta = 0.5(5 + 15\cos\theta)^2\,d\theta$
$A = \int_{1.9106\ldots}^{4.3725\ldots} 0.5(5 + 15\cos\theta)^2\,d\theta = 63.1909\ldots$

17. The outer loop starts at $\theta = -1.9106\ldots$ and ends at $\theta = 1.9106\ldots$.
$dr = -15\sin\theta\,d\theta$
$dL = \sqrt{dr^2 + r^2\,d\theta^2}$
$\quad = \sqrt{(-15\sin\theta)^2 + (5 + 15\cos\theta)^2}\,d\theta$
$L = \int_{-1.9106\ldots}^{1.9106\ldots} dL = 68.4422\ldots$

18. Answers will vary.

1. $\int u\,dv = uv - \int v\,du$

2. $\int x^2 \cos x\,dx$

$$\begin{array}{cc} u & dv \\ x^2 & \cos x \\ 2x & \sin x \\ 2 & -\cos x \\ 0 & -\sin x \end{array}$$

$= x^2 \sin x + 2x \cos x - 2\sin x + C$

3. $\int x^2 \ln x\,dx$

$$\begin{array}{cc} u & dv \\ \ln x & x^2 \\ 1/x & \frac{1}{3}x^3 \\ \hline 1 & \frac{1}{3}x^2 \\ 0 & \frac{1}{9}x^3 \end{array}$$

$= \frac{1}{3}x^3 \ln x - \frac{1}{9}x^3 + C$

4. For $\int x^2 \cos x\,dx$, dv can be $\cos x\,dx$ because you can integrate it. For $\int x^2 \ln x\,dx$, dv can't be $\ln x\,dx$ because you don't know how to integrate it.

5. The primary consideration is that dv must be something you know how to integrate. The secondary consideration is that when u is differentiated and dv is integrated, the result should be simpler than the original integral, or at least not more complicated.

6. $\int e^{2x} \cos 3x\,dx$

$$\begin{array}{cc} u & dv \\ e^{2x} & \cos 3x \\ 2e^{2x} & \frac{1}{3}\sin 3x \\ 4e^{2x} & -\frac{1}{9}\cos 3x \end{array}$$

$= \frac{1}{3}e^{2x} \sin 3x + \frac{2}{9}e^{2x} \cos 3x - \frac{4}{9}\int e^{2x} \cos 3x\,dx$

$\frac{13}{9}\int e^{2x} \cos 3x\,dx = \frac{1}{3}e^{2x} \sin 3x + \frac{2}{9}e^{2x} \cos 3x + C_1$

$\int e^{2x} \cos 3x\,dx = \frac{3}{13}e^{2x} \sin 3x + \frac{2}{13}e^{2x} \cos 3x + C$

7. $\int \cos 5x \sin 3x\,dx$

$$\begin{array}{cc} u & dv \\ \cos 5x & \sin 3x \\ -5\sin 5x & -\frac{1}{3}\cos 3x \\ -25\cos 5x & -\frac{1}{9}\sin 3x \end{array}$$

$= -\frac{1}{3}\cos 5x \cos 3x - \frac{5}{9}\sin 5x \sin 3x + \frac{25}{9}\int \cos 5x \sin 3x\,dx$

$\frac{34}{9}\int \cos 5x \sin 3x\,dx$

$= -\frac{1}{3}\cos 5x \cos 3x - \frac{5}{9}\sin 5x \sin 3x + C_1$

$\int \cos 5x \sin 3x\,dx$

$= -\frac{3}{34}\cos 5x \cos 3x - \frac{5}{34}\sin 5x \sin 3x + C$

8. $\int \sin^8 x\,dx$

$$\begin{array}{cc} u & dv \\ \sin^7 x & \sin x \\ 7\sin^6 x \cos x & -\cos x \end{array}$$

$= -\sin^7 x \cos x + 7\int \sin^6 x \cos^2 x\,dx$

$= -\sin^7 x \cos x + 7\int \sin^6 x(1 - \sin^2 x)\,dx$

$= -\sin^7 x \cos x + 7\int \sin^6 x\,dx - 7\int \sin^8 x\,dx$

$8\int \sin^8 x\,dx = -\sin^7 x \cos x + 7\int \sin^6 x\,dx$

$\int \sin^8 x\,dx = -\frac{1}{8}\sin^7 x \cos x + \frac{7}{8}\int \sin^6 x\,dx$

Conjecture:

$\int \sin^n x\,dx = -\frac{1}{n}\sin^{n-1} x \cos x + \frac{n-1}{n}\int \sin^{n-2} x\,dx$

9. $\int \sec^5 x\,dx = \frac{1}{4}\sec^3 x \tan x + \frac{3}{4}\int \sec^3 x\,dx$

$= \frac{1}{4}\sec^3 x \tan x + \frac{3}{4}\left(\frac{1}{2}\sec x \tan x + \frac{1}{2}\int \sec x\,dx\right)$

$= \frac{1}{4}\sec^3 x \tan x + \frac{3}{8}\sec x \tan x + \frac{3}{8}\ln|\sec x + \tan x| + C$

10. $\int \ln dx$

$$\begin{array}{cc} u & dv \\ \ln x & 1 \\ 1/x & x \end{array}$$

$= x\ln x - \int 1\,dx = x\ln x - x + C,\ \text{Q.E.D.}$

11. $y = 7\cos\frac{\pi}{6}x$

$dV = 2\pi x \cdot \left(-7\cos\frac{\pi}{6}x\right) \cdot dx = -14\pi x \cos\frac{\pi}{6}x\,dx$

(The "−" is because the curve is below the x-axis.)

$V = \int_3^9 -14\pi x \cos\frac{\pi}{6}x\,dx$

$$\begin{array}{cc} u & dv \\ -14\pi x & \cos\frac{\pi}{6}x \\ -14\pi & \frac{6}{\pi}\sin\frac{\pi}{6}x \\ 0 & -\frac{36}{\pi^2}\cos\frac{\pi}{6}x \end{array}$$

$= \left(-84x \sin\frac{\pi}{6}x - \frac{504}{\pi}\cos\frac{\pi}{6}x\right)\Big|_3^9$

$= -756(-1) - \frac{504}{\pi}(0) + 252(1) + \frac{504}{\pi}(0)$

$= 1008\ \text{cm}^3$

Integrating numerically also gives $1008\ \text{cm}^3$.

12. Answers will vary.

Test 35

1. $\dfrac{4x - 26}{x^2 + 2x - 8} = \dfrac{4x - 26}{(x + 4)(x - 2)}$

$\qquad = \dfrac{A}{x + 4} + \dfrac{B}{x - 2}$

$A = [(4)(-4) - 26]/(-6) = 7$

$B = [(4)(2) - 26]/6 = -3$

$\therefore \dfrac{4x - 26}{x^2 + 2x - 8} = \dfrac{7}{x + 4} - \dfrac{3}{x - 2}$

2. $\int \dfrac{4x - 26}{x^2 + 2x - 8}\,dx$

$= \int \left(\dfrac{7}{x + 4} - \dfrac{3}{x - 2}\right)dx$

$= 7\ln|x + 4| - 3\ln|x - 2| + C$

3. $\int \dfrac{x^2 + 3x - 37}{x - 5}\,dx$

$$\underline{5\big|}\quad \begin{array}{rrr} 1 & 3 & -37 \\ & 5 & 40 \\ \hline 1 & 8 & 3 \end{array}$$

$\int \dfrac{x^2 + 3x - 37}{x - 5}\,dx$

$= \int \left(x + 8 + \dfrac{3}{x - 5}\right) dx$

$= \dfrac{1}{2}x^2 + 8x + 3 \ln|x - 5| + C$

4. $\int \dfrac{2x + 10}{x^2 + 10x + 13}\,dx = \ln|x^2 + 10x + 13| + C$

(The numerator is the differential of the denominator.)

5. $\int \dfrac{8}{(x - 1)(x - 3)(x - 5)}\,dx$

$= \int \left(\dfrac{A}{x - 1} + \dfrac{B}{x - 3} + \dfrac{C}{x - 5}\right) dx$

$A = 8/[(-2)(-4)] = 1$
$B = 8/[(2)(-2)] = -2$
$C = 8/[(4)(2)] = 1$

$= \int \left(\dfrac{1}{x - 1} - \dfrac{2}{x - 3} + \dfrac{1}{x - 5}\right) dx$

$= \ln|x - 1| - 2\ln|x - 3| + \ln|x - 5| + C$

6. $\dfrac{4x - 26}{x^2 + 2x - 8} = \dfrac{A(x - 2) + B(x + 4)}{x^2 + 2x - 8}$

$= \dfrac{(A + B)x + (-2A + 4B)}{x^2 + 2x - 8}$

$\therefore A + B = 4$ and $-2A + 4B = -26$

$$\begin{array}{rcr} A + B &=& 4 \\ -A + 2B &=& -13 \\ \hline 3B &=& -9 \\ B &=& -3 \end{array}$$

$A + (-3) = 4 \Rightarrow A = 7$

$\therefore \dfrac{4x - 26}{x^2 + 2x - 8} = \dfrac{7}{x + 4} - \dfrac{3}{x - 2}$, Q.E.D.

7. $\dfrac{dP}{dt} = 0.038(P)(10.5 - P)$

$\int \dfrac{dP}{P(10.5 - P)} = \int 0.038\,dt$

$\int \left(\dfrac{1/10.5}{P} + \dfrac{1/10.5}{10.5 - P}\right) dP = \int 0.038\,dt$

$\dfrac{1}{10.5} \ln|P| - \dfrac{1}{10.5} \ln|10.5 - P| = 0.038t + C$

8. $\ln\left|\dfrac{P}{10.5 - P}\right| = 0.399t + 10.5C$

$\left|\dfrac{P}{10.5 - P}\right| = e^{0.399t + 10.5C}$

$\dfrac{P}{10.5 - P} = C_1 e^{0.399t}$

$P = 1$ when $t = 0$:

$\dfrac{1}{10.5 - 1} = C_1 \cdot e^0 \Rightarrow C_1 = \dfrac{1}{9.5}$

$\therefore \dfrac{P}{10.5 - P} = \dfrac{1}{9.5} \cdot e^{0.399t}$

$9.5P = 10.5e^{0.399t} - Pe^{0.399t}$

$P(e^{0.399t} + 9.5) = 10.5e^{0.399t}$

$P = \dfrac{10.5e^{0.399t}}{e^{0.399t} + 9.5}$

$P = \dfrac{10.5}{1 + 9.5e^{-0.399t}}$, Q.E.D.

9.

t	P	t	P	t	P
0	1	7	6.63...	14	10.13...
1	1.42...	8	7.55...	15	10.25...
2	1.98...	9	8.32...	16	10.33...
3	2.71...	10	8.93...	17	10.38...
4	3.58...	11	9.39...	18	10.42...
5	4.58...	12	9.73...	19	10.44...
6	5.62...	13	9.97...	20	10.46...

The graph shows that the data points fit the slope field.

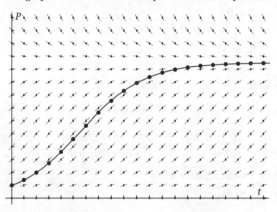

10. Answers will vary.

Test 36

1. $\int \cos^2 5x\,dx = \dfrac{1}{2}\int (1 + \cos 10x)\,dx$

$= \dfrac{1}{2}x + \dfrac{1}{20} \sin 10x + C$

2. $\int \sin^5 x\,dx = \int (1 - \cos^2 x)^2 \sin x\,dx$

$= \int \sin x\,dx - 2\int \cos^2 x \sin x\,dx + \int \cos^4 x \sin x\,dx$

$= -\cos x + \dfrac{2}{3}\cos^3 x - \dfrac{1}{5}\cos^5 x + C$

3. $\int \sec^6 x\,dx = \int (1 + \tan^2 x)^2 \sec^2 x\,dx$

$= \int \sec^2 x\,dx + 2\int \tan^2 x \sec^2 x\,dx + \int \tan^4 x \sec^2 x\,dx$

$= \tan x + \dfrac{2}{3}\tan^3 x + \dfrac{1}{5}\tan^5 x + C$

4. $\int \sin^6 x\,dx$

$= -\dfrac{1}{6}\sin^5 x \cos x + \dfrac{5}{6}\int \sin^4 x\,dx$

$= " + \dfrac{5}{6}\left(-\dfrac{1}{4}\sin^3 x \cos x + \dfrac{3}{4}\int \sin^2 x\,dx\right)$

$= " - \dfrac{5}{24}\sin^3 x \cos x + \dfrac{5}{8}\int \sin^2 x\,dx$

$= " - " + \dfrac{5}{8}\left(-\dfrac{1}{2}\sin^1 x \cos x + \dfrac{1}{2}\int \sin^0 x\,dx\right)$

$= " - " - \dfrac{5}{16}\sin x \cos x + \dfrac{5}{16}\int dx$

$= -\dfrac{1}{6}\sin^5 x \cos x - \dfrac{5}{24}\sin^3 x \cos x - \dfrac{5}{16}\sin x \cos x + \dfrac{5}{16}x + C$

5. $\int \dfrac{1}{\sqrt{81 + x^2}}\,dx$

$x = 9\tan\theta$, $dx = 9\sec^2\theta\,d\theta$, $\sqrt{81 + x^2} = 9\sec\theta$

$\therefore \int \dfrac{1}{\sqrt{81 + x^2}}\,dx = \int \dfrac{1}{9\sec\theta} \cdot 9\sec^2\theta\,d\theta$

$= \int \sec\theta\,d\theta = \ln|\sec\theta + \tan\theta| + C$

$$= \ln \left| \frac{1}{9} x + \frac{1}{9} \sqrt{81 + x^2} \right| + C$$

$$= \ln \left| x + \sqrt{81 + x^2} \right| + C_1$$

6. For $\int \sqrt{x^2 - 100} \, dx$, use $x = 10 \sec \theta$.

7. $\int \frac{2x - 22}{x^2 + 2x - 8} \, dx = \int \frac{2x - 22}{(x + 4)(x - 2)} \, dx$

$$= \int \left(\frac{5}{x + 4} + \frac{-3}{x - 2} \right) dx$$

$$= 5 \ln |x + 4| - 3 \ln |x - 2| + C$$

8. $\int \sin^{-1} x \, dx$

$$\begin{array}{cc} u & dv \\ \sin^{-1} x & \searrow + \quad 1 \\ (1 - x^2)^{-1/2} & \xleftarrow{-} \quad x \end{array}$$

$$= x \sin^{-1} x - \int (1 - x^2)^{-1/2} x \, dx$$

$$= x \sin^{-1} x + \frac{1}{2} \int (1 - x^2)^{-1/2} (-2x \, dx)$$

$$= x \sin^{-1} x + (1 - x^2)^{1/2} + C$$

9. $x^2 + y^2 = 25 \Rightarrow y = \sqrt{25 - x^2}$ (upper branch)

$$dA = 2y \, dx = 2 \sqrt{25 - x^2} \, dx$$

$$A = \int_{-2}^{1} 2 \sqrt{25 - x^2} \, dx$$

Let $x = 5 \sin \theta$, $dx = 5 \cos \theta \, d\theta$, $\sqrt{25 - x^2} = 5 \cos \theta$

$$\therefore A = 2 \int_{x=-2}^{x=1} 5 \cos \theta \cdot 5 \cos \theta \, d\theta$$

$$= 50 \int_{x=-2}^{x=1} \cos^2 \theta \, d\theta$$

$$= 25 \int_{x=-2}^{x=1} (1 + \cos 2\theta) \, d\theta = (25\theta + 12.5 \sin 2\theta) \Big|_{x=-2}^{x=1}$$

$$= (25\theta + 25 \sin \theta \cos \theta) \Big|_{x=-2}^{x=1}$$

$$= \left(25 \sin^{-1} \frac{x}{5} + x \sqrt{25 - x^2} \right) \Big|_{-2}^{1}$$

$$= 25 \sin^{-1} 0.2 + \sqrt{24} - 25 \sin^{-1} (-0.4) + 2\sqrt{21}$$

Evaluating the exact answer, $A = 29.3860\ldots$
Integrating numerically gives $A \approx 29.3960\ldots$, which agrees with the exact answer.

10. $r = 0.2\theta \Rightarrow dr = 0.2 \, d\theta$

$$dL = \sqrt{dr^2 + r^2 d\theta^2} = \sqrt{0.04 + 0.04\theta^2} \, d\theta$$

$$= 0.2 \sqrt{1 + \theta^2} \, d\theta$$

$$L = 0.2 \int_0^{10\pi} \sqrt{1 + \theta^2} \, d\theta$$

Let $\theta = \tan \phi$, $d\theta = \sec^2 \phi \, d\phi$, $\sqrt{1 + \theta^2} = \sec \phi$

$$L = 0.2 \int_{\phi=0}^{\phi=10\pi} \sec^3 \phi \, d\phi$$

$$= \left(0.1 \sec \phi \tan \phi + 0.1 \ln |\sec \phi + \tan \phi| \right) \Big|_{\phi=0}^{\phi=10\pi}$$

$$= \left(0.1\theta \sqrt{1 + \theta^2} + 0.1 \ln |\sqrt{1 + \theta^2} + \theta| \right) \Big|_0^{10\pi}$$

$$= \pi \sqrt{1 + 100\pi^2} + 0.1 \ln |\sqrt{1 + 100\pi^2} + 10\pi|$$

$$- 0 - 0.1 \ln 1$$

Evaluating the exact answer, $L = 99.1601\ldots$
Integrating numerically gives $L \approx 99.1601\ldots$, which agrees with the exact answer.

11. Answers will vary.

Test 37

1. $\cosh x = \frac{1}{2}(e^x + e^{-x})$

   $\sinh x = \frac{1}{2}(e^x - e^{-x})$

2. $\tanh x = \frac{\sinh x}{\cosh x}$

   $\operatorname{sech} x = \frac{1}{\cosh x}$

3. Catenary (from "chain")

4. $y = \cosh 5x \Rightarrow y' = 5 \sinh 5x$

5. $\int \sinh 3x \, dx = \frac{1}{3} \cosh 3x + C$

6. $y = \tanh^3 x \Rightarrow y' = 3 \tanh^2 x \operatorname{sech}^2 x$

7. $\int \cosh^5 x \sinh x \, dx = \frac{1}{6} \cosh^6 x + C$

8. $\cosh^2 x - \sinh^2 x = 1$ for hyperbolics.
   ($u^2 - v^2 = 1$ is the equation of a hyperbola.)
   $\cos^2 x + \sin^2 x = 1$ for trigs or circulars.
   ($u^2 + v^2 = 1$ is the equation of a circle.)

9. $y = \cosh^{-1} x$
   $\cosh y = x$
   $\sinh y \cdot y' = 1$
   $$y' = \frac{1}{\sinh y}$$
   $$y' = \frac{1}{\sqrt{\cosh^2 y - 1}}$$
   $$y' = \frac{1}{\sqrt{x^2 - 1}}$$

10. $\int \sinh^{-1} x \, dx$

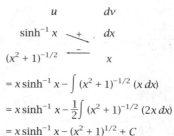

$$= x \sinh^{-1} x - \int (x^2 + 1)^{-1/2} (x \, dx)$$

$$= x \sinh^{-1} x - \frac{1}{2} \int (x^2 + 1)^{-1/2} (2x \, dx)$$

$$= x \sinh^{-1} x - (x^2 + 1)^{1/2} + C$$

11. $\cosh x = \frac{1}{2}(e^x + e^{-x})$

   $\cosh 3 = \frac{1}{2}(e^3 + e^{-3}) = 10.0676\ldots$

   The graph shows that the point $(3, 10.06\ldots)$ is on the graph of $y = \cosh x$.

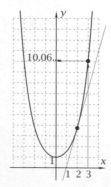

12. $dy/dx = \sinh x$

At $x = 2$, $dy/dx = \sinh 2 = 3.6268....$

The graph, at Problem 11, shows that a line at $x = 2$ with slope 3.62... is tangent to the graph.

13. Area ≈ 13.6 by counting squares.

14. $A = \int_{-2}^{3} \cosh x\, dx = \sinh x \Big|_{-2}^{3}$

$= \sinh 3 - \sinh(-2) = 13.6447...$

This result confirms that the answer by counting squares in Problem 13 is reasonably accurate.

15. $y = k \cosh \frac{1}{k}x + C$

Substitute (0, 3) and (15, 50) for (x, y).

$3 = k\cosh 0 + C \Rightarrow C = 3 - k$

$50 = k\cosh \frac{1}{k}(15) + C = k\cosh \frac{1}{k}(15) + 3 - k$

$k\cosh \frac{1}{k}(15) - k - 47 = 0$

Solving numerically gives $k \approx 4.9234....$

(Store without rounding.)

$C = 3 - k = -1.9234...$

Equation is

$y = 4.9234...\cosh(0.2311...\ x) - 1.9234...$

16. $dy = \sinh \frac{1}{k}x$

$dL = \sqrt{dx^2 + dy^2} = \sqrt{1 + \sinh^2 \frac{1}{k}x}\ dx = \cosh \frac{1}{k}x\, dx$

$L = \int_{-15}^{15} \cosh \frac{1}{k}x\, dx = k\sinh \frac{1}{k}x \Big|_{-15}^{15}$

$= k\sinh(15/k) - k\sinh(-15/k) = 2k\sinh(15/k)$

$= 103.3789... \approx 103.4$ ft

17. $w = 6$ lb/ft

Weight of chain is $6(103.3789...) = 620.2737...$

≈ 620.3 lb

$k = h/w$ and $w = 6$ lb/ft, so $h = 6k = 29.5405...$

≈ 29.5 lb

18. $A = \int_{0}^{5} x^{-0.99}\, dx = \lim_{a \to 0^+} \int_{a}^{5} x^{-0.99}\, dx$

$= \lim_{a \to 0^+} 100x^{0.01} \Big|_{a}^{5} = \lim_{a \to 0^+} (100 \cdot 5^{0.01} - 100a^{0.01})$

$= 101.6224... - 0 = 101.6224...$

$\therefore A$ approaches a finite limit, Q.E.D.

19. $A = \int_{0}^{5} x^{-1}\, dx = \lim_{a \to 0^+} \int_{a}^{5} x^{-1}\, dx$

$= \lim_{a \to 0^+} \ln|x| \Big|_{a}^{5} = \lim_{a \to 0^+} (\ln 5 - \ln a)$, which diverges.

$\therefore$ the area of the region is infinite, Q.E.D.

20. $dV = 2\pi x \cdot y \cdot dx = 2\pi x(1/x)\, dx = 2\pi\, dx$

$V = \int_{0}^{5} 2\pi\, dx = \lim_{a \to 0^+} \int_{a}^{5} 2\pi\, dx$

$= \lim_{a \to 0^+} 2\pi x \Big|_{a}^{5} = \lim_{a \to 0^+} (10\pi - 2\pi a) = 10\pi$

$\therefore$ the volume approaches a finite limit, Q.E.D.

21. Answers will vary.

Test 38

1. $\int x^5 e^{-x}\, dx$

u		dv
x^5	+	e^{-x}
$5x^4$	−	$-e^{-x}$
$20x^3$	+	e^{-x}
$60x^2$	−	$-e^{-x}$
$120x$	+	e^{-x}
120	−	$-e^{-x}$
0	+	e^{-x}

$= -e^{-x}(x^5 + 5x^4 + 20x^3 + 60x^2 + 120x + 120) + C$

2. $\int e^x \cos 0.5x\, dx$

u		dv
e^x	+	$\cos 0.5x$
e^x	−	$2\sin 0.5x$
e^x	+	$-4\cos 0.5x$

$= 2e^x \sin 0.5x + 4e^x \cos 0.5x - 4\int e^x \cos 0.5x\, dx$

$5\int e^x \cos 0.5x\, dx = 2e^x \sin 0.5x + 4e^x \cos 0.5x + C_1$

$\int e^x \cos 0.5x\, dx = 0.4e^x \sin 0.5x + 0.8e^x \cos 0.5x + C$

3. $\int_{1}^{3} e^x \cos 0.5x\, dx$

$= 0.4e^3 \sin 1.5 + 0.8e^3 \cos 1.5 - 0.4e \sin 0.5 - 0.8e \cos 0.5$

$= 6.7210...$

4. Numerical integration gives about 6.7210..., which agrees with the exact answer in Problem 3.

5. $\int \sin^6 x\, dx$

u		dv
$\sin^5 x$	+	$\sin x$
$5\sin^4 x \cos x$	−	$-\cos x$

$= -\sin^5 x \cos x + 5\int \sin^4 x \cos^2 x\, dx$

$= -\sin^5 x \cos x + 5\int \sin^4 x (1 - \sin^2 x)\, dx$

$= -\sin^5 x \cos x + 5\int \sin^4 x\, dx - 5\int \sin^6 x\, dx$

$6\int \sin^6 x\, dx = -\sin^5 x \cos x + 5\int \sin^4 x\, dx$

$\int \sin^6 x\, dx = -\frac{1}{6}\sin^5 x \cos x + \frac{5}{6}\int \sin^4 x\, dx$

This answer fits the pattern of the given reduction formula.

6. $\int \sin^6 x\, dx = -\frac{1}{6}\sin^5 x \cos x + \frac{5}{6}\int \sin^4 x\, dx$

$= -\frac{1}{6}\sin^5 x \cos x + \frac{5}{6}\left(-\frac{1}{4}\sin^3 x \cos x + \frac{3}{4}\int \sin^2 x\, dx\right)$

$= -\frac{1}{6}\sin^5 x \cos x - \frac{5}{24}\sin^3 x \cos x + \frac{5}{8}\left(-\frac{1}{2}\sin x \cos x + \frac{1}{2}\int dx\right)$

$= -\frac{1}{6}\sin^5 x \cos x - \frac{5}{24}\sin^3 x \cos x - \frac{5}{16}\sin x \cos x + \frac{5}{16}x + C$

7. $\int \sin^7 x\, dx = \int (1 - \cos^2 x)^3 \sin x\, dx$

$= \int (1 - 3\cos^2 x + 3\cos^4 x - \cos^6 x)(\sin x\, dx)$

$= -\cos x + \cos^3 x - \frac{3}{5}\cos^5 x + \frac{1}{7}\cos^7 x + C$

8. $\int \sin^2 x\, dx = \frac{1}{2}\int (1 - \cos 2x)\, dx = \frac{1}{2}x - \frac{1}{4}\sin 2x + C$

9. $\int \dfrac{1}{\sqrt{1+x^2}}\,dx$

$\qquad\qquad x = \tan\theta$

$\qquad\qquad dx = \sec^2\theta\,d\theta$

$\qquad\qquad \sqrt{1+x^2} = \sec\theta$

$= \int \dfrac{1}{\sec\theta}\,(\sec^2\theta\,d\theta) = \int \sec\theta\,d\theta$

$= \ln|\sec\theta + \tan\theta| + C = \ln\left|\sqrt{1+x^2} + x\right| + C$

10. $\int \dfrac{1}{1+x^2}\,dx = \tan^{-1}x + C$

11. $x = \sqrt{51}\,\sec\theta$

12. $x = \sin\theta$

13. $\int \dfrac{40x - 72}{(x-1)(x-5)(x+3)}\,dx$

$= \int \left(\dfrac{2}{x-1} + \dfrac{4}{x-5} + \dfrac{-6}{x+3}\right)dx$

$= 2\ln|x-1| + 4\ln|x-5| - 6\ln|x+3| + C$

14. $\int \sin^{-1}x\,dx$

$\qquad\qquad u \qquad\qquad dv$

$\qquad \sin^{-1}x \quad\searrow^{+}\quad 1$

$\quad (1-x^2)^{-1/2} \quad\xleftarrow{-}\quad x$

$= x\sin^{-1}x - \int (1-x^2)^{-1/2}\,x\,dx$

$= x\sin^{-1}x + \dfrac{1}{2}\int (1-x^2)^{-1/2}(-2x\,dx)$

$= x\sin^{-1}x + (1-x^2)^{1/2} + C$

$= x\sin^{-1}x + \sqrt{1-x^2} + C,\ \text{Q.E.D.}$

15. $y = \cosh 3x$

$dA = \cosh 3x\,dx$

$A = \displaystyle\int_{-2}^{2} \cosh 3x\,dx = \dfrac{1}{3}\sinh 3x\,\Big|_{-2}^{2}$

$= \dfrac{1}{3}\sinh 6 - \dfrac{1}{3}\sinh(-6) = 134.4754\ldots$

16. $\displaystyle\int_{1}^{\infty} x^{-1.001}\,dx = \lim_{b\to\infty}\int_{1}^{b} x^{-1.001}\,dx$

$= \displaystyle\lim_{b\to\infty}(-1000x^{-0.001})\Big|_{1}^{b}$

$= \displaystyle\lim_{b\to\infty}(-1000b^{-0.001} + 1000)$

$= 0 + 1000 = 1000$

17. $\int \dfrac{x\,dx}{x^2 - 1}$

   a. Use the secant trig substitution.

   b. Factor the denominator and use partial fractions.

   c. Write as the integral of the reciprocal function.

18. Answers will vary.

Test 39

1. $v(t) = t^2 - 5t + 4$

$a(t) = 2t - 5$

$v(2) = -2$

$a(2) = -1$

The object is speeding up because v and a have the same sign.

2. Displacement $= \displaystyle\int_{2}^{5} (t^2 - 5t + 4)\,dt$

$= \dfrac{1}{3}t^3 - \dfrac{5}{2}t^2 + 4t\,\Big|_{2}^{5}$

$= \dfrac{125}{3} - \dfrac{125}{2} + 20 - \dfrac{8}{3} + \dfrac{20}{2} - 8$

$= \dfrac{117}{3} - \dfrac{105}{2} + 12 = 39 - 52.5 + 12$

$= -1.5$ furlongs

The negative sign indicates displacement in the negative direction.

3. Average velocity $= \dfrac{-1.5}{(5-2)} = -0.5$ furlong/min

4. Distance $= -\displaystyle\int_{2}^{4}(t^2 - 5t + 4)\,dt + \int_{4}^{5}(t^2 - 5t + 4)\,dt$

$= -\dfrac{64}{3} + \dfrac{80}{2} - 16 + \dfrac{8}{3} - \dfrac{20}{2} + 8$

$\quad + \dfrac{125}{3} - \dfrac{125}{2} + 20 - \dfrac{64}{3} + \dfrac{80}{2} - 16$

$= \dfrac{5}{3} + \dfrac{15}{2} - 4 = 1 + \dfrac{2}{3} + 7 + \dfrac{1}{2} - 4$

$= 4 + \dfrac{7}{6} = 5\dfrac{1}{6}$ furlongs

5. Let $y = x - x^3$.

$y' = 1 - 3x^2$

$y' = 0 \Leftrightarrow 3x^2 = 1 \Leftrightarrow x = \sqrt{1/3}$, for $x \geq 0$

y' changes from positive to negative at $\sqrt{1/3}$.

$\therefore y$ is a maximum at $x = \sqrt{1/3}$.

6. $\sin\theta = 55/70$

7. Let $x =$ distance from closest point to bridge end.

Let $t =$ number of hours to make the one-way trip.

$t = \dfrac{1}{70}(10 - x) + \dfrac{1}{55}(16 + x^2)^{1/2}$

$t' = -\dfrac{1}{70} + \dfrac{1}{55}x(16 + x^2)^{-1/2}$

$t' = 0 \Leftrightarrow \dfrac{1}{55}x(16 + x^2)^{-1/2} = \dfrac{1}{70}$

$70x = 55(16 + x^2)^{1/2}$

$4900x^2 = 3025(16 + x^2)$

$1875x^2 = 48400$

$x = \pm 5.0806\ldots$

Build the bridge about 5.1 miles closer to the field office than the closest point of approach.

Alternative solution:

Let θ be the angle of incidence of the bridge.

$\sin\theta = 55/70 \Rightarrow \theta = 51.7687\ldots°$

$x = 4\tan 51.7687\ldots° = 5.0806\ldots$

8. $t(5.0806\ldots) = 0.1878\ldots$ h

$t(0) = 0.2155\ldots$ h

Difference is $0.02773\ldots$ h

For round-trip, difference is $0.05547\ldots$ h, or about 3.3 min.

9. Total time saved is

$(0.05557\ldots)(30)(365) = 607.4827\ldots$ h

Total savings is $20(607.4827\ldots) = 12149.65\ldots$, or about $12,150 per year.

10.

t	a	Av. a	v	Av. v	Disp.
0	3	—	6	—	0
5	12	7.5	43.5	24.75	123.75
10	4	8.0	83.5	63.5	441.25
15	-7	-1.5	76	79.75	840
20	-15	-11.0	21	48.5	1082.5

Net displacement ≈ 1082.5 ft.

Calculus: Concepts and Applications Instructor's Resource Book
©2005 Key Curriculum Press

11. $y = x + 2 \sin x$

$\bar{y} = \dfrac{1}{5} \displaystyle\int_2^7 (x + 2 \sin x)\, dx = 4.0319...$

Average of $y(2)$ and $y(7)$ is
$0.5(3.8185... + 8.3139...) = 6.0662...$, which does not
equal the average value of y.

The graph shows that the area of the rectangle with altitude
4.0319... is the same as the area of the region under the
graph, and that the area of the region above $y = 4.0319...$
equals the area left out below $y = 4.0319...$.

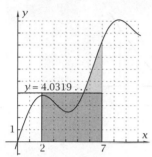

12. $s_c(t) = t^3 \Rightarrow s_c{}'(t) = 3t^2 \Rightarrow s_c{}''(t) = 6t \Rightarrow s_c{}''(0) = 0$
$s_p(t) = e^t - 1 \Rightarrow s_p{}'(t) = e^t \Rightarrow s_p{}''(t) = e^t \Rightarrow s_p{}''(0) = 1$
Phoebe has the greater acceleration at $t = 0$, as shown above.

13. The graphs of s_c and s_p are shown here. From the graph, the
first positive time the distances are equal is close to $t = 1.5$ s.
Solving $t^3 = e^t - 1$ numerically for t close to 1.5 gives
$t \approx 1.5450...$.

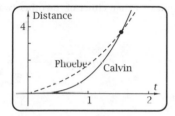

Maximize $y = e^t - 1 - t^3$ on $[0, 1.54...]$.
$y' = e^t - 3t^2$
On $[0, 1.54...]$, $y' = 0$ at $t \approx 0.9100...$
$s_p(0.91...) - s_c(0.91...) = 0.7307...$
Phoebe's car was ahead by a maximum of about 0.73 ft, or a
bit less than 9 in.

14. Maximize $y = s_p{}'(t) - s_c{}'(t) = 3t^2 - e^t$
$y' = 6t - e^t$
$y' = 0 \Leftrightarrow t = 0.2044...$
$y(0.2044...) = -1.101...$, meaning a difference of about 1.1 ft/s.
$y(0) = -1$ and $y(1.5450...) = 2.4731...$
Thus the difference in velocities is greatest at the endpoint,
$t = 1.54...$, as Calvin's car passes Phoebe's car. The maximum
difference in velocities does not occur at the maximum
separation. In fact, at the maximum separation, the
difference in velocities is zero since the cars are going the
same speed.

15. Phoebe's car eventually gets back ahead of Calvin's car.
Widening the window on the graph in Problem 13 shows this
to be true when t is close to 4.5. Solving $t^3 = e^t - 1$ for t close
to 4.5 gives $t \approx 4.5670...$.

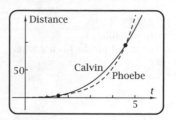

16. Answers will vary.

Test 40

1.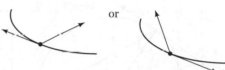

2.

3.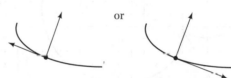

4. $\vec{v}(t) = (-4 \sin 0.5t + 4 \sin 2t)\vec{i} + (4 \cos 0.5t - 4 \cos 2t)\vec{j}$
$\vec{a}(t) = (-2 \cos 0.5t + 8 \cos 2t)\vec{i} + (-2 \sin 0.5t + 8 \sin 2t)\vec{j}$

5. $\vec{r}(1) \approx 7.853\vec{i} + 2.017\vec{j}$
$\vec{v}(1) \approx 1.719\vec{i} + 5.175\vec{j}$
$\vec{a}(1) \approx -5.084\vec{i} + 6.316\vec{j}$

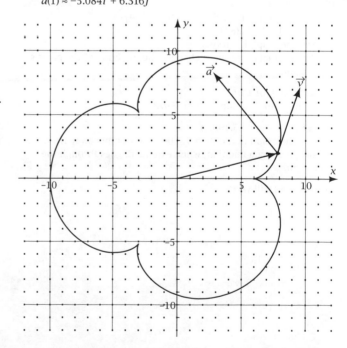

6. The point is speeding up because the angle between $\vec{v}$ and $\vec{a}$ is acute.

7. The point is slowing down because the angle between $\vec{v}$ and $\vec{a}$ is obtuse.

8. $\vec{v} \cdot \vec{a} \approx (-5.108)(7.540) + (-3.558)(-4.230)$
   $= -23.4639...$ (precisely $-23.4607...$)
   The angle is obtuse because the dot product is negative.

9. $\vec{a}_t = \left(\dfrac{\vec{v} \cdot \vec{a}}{|\vec{v}|}\right)\left(\dfrac{\vec{v}}{|\vec{v}|}\right) = \left(\dfrac{\vec{v} \cdot \vec{a}}{|\vec{v}|^2}\right)\vec{v}$

   $\approx \dfrac{-23.4639...}{(-5.108)^2 + (-3.558)^2}(-5.108\vec{i} - 3.558\vec{j})$
   $= (-0.6055)(-5.108\vec{i} - 3.558\vec{j})$
   $\approx 3.093\vec{i} + 2.154\vec{j}$
   (precisely $3.0927...\vec{i} + 2.1542...\vec{j}$)

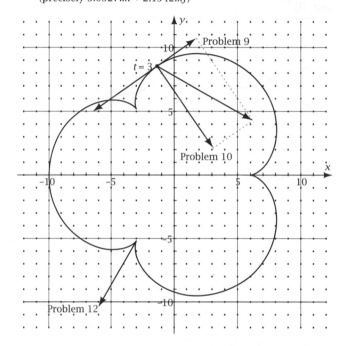

The tangential component changes the speed of the point.

10. $\vec{a}_n = \vec{a} - \vec{a}_t$
    $\approx (7.540\vec{i} - 4.230\vec{j}) - (3.093\vec{i} + 2.154\vec{j})$
    $= 4.447\vec{i} - 6.384\vec{j}$
    See the graph in Problem 9.
    The normal component changes the direction of the point's motion.

11. $\vec{v}(8\pi/3) = 0\vec{i} + 0\vec{j}$
    $\therefore$ the point is stopped at $t = 8\pi/3$.

12. $\vec{a}(8\pi/3) = -3\vec{i} - 5.196...\vec{j}$
    See the graph in Problem 9. The vector points away from the origin along a line that, when extended, goes through the origin.

13. Answers will vary.

Test 41

1. $t = -3$: Speeding up
   $t = 2$: Slowing down
   $t = 8$: Speeding up
   $t = 13$: Slowing down

2. $\bar{v} = \dfrac{72}{8 - 2} = 12$ cm/s

   The graph shows equal areas above and below the line at $v = 12$.

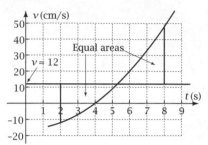

3. Distance from $t = 2$ to $t = 4$ is $85\frac{1}{3} - 72 = 13\frac{1}{3}$

   Total distance $= 85\frac{1}{3} + 13\frac{1}{3} = 98\frac{2}{3}$ cm

4. For the roadway as shown, the bridge is 5 mi long.
   Cost $= 5(250) + 7(100) = \$1950$ thousand
   Shortest bridge:
   Cost $= 4(250) + 10(100) = \$2000$ thousand
   Direct bridge:
   $10.8(250) = \$2700$ thousand
   $\therefore$ roadway as shown is cheaper than either of the other two.

5.

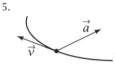

6.

7. $v = e^t \cos t$

   Distance $= \displaystyle\int_0^5 |e^t \cos t|\, dt = 65.5193... \approx 65.5$ ft

8. Displacement $= \displaystyle\int_0^5 e^t \cos t\, dt = -50.6088... \approx -50.6$ ft

9. $v_{av} = \dfrac{1}{5}(-50.6088...) = -10.1217... \approx -10.1$ ft/s

10. $a = v' = e^t \cos t - e^t \sin t$
    At $t = 3$, $a = e^3 \cos 3 - e^3 \sin 3 = -22.7910...$
    ≈ -22.8 ft/s^2
    $v = e^3 \cos 3 = -19.8845...$
    The object is speeding up since the acceleration and velocity have the same sign.

11. Let x = distance from closest point to bridge end.
Let m = no. of thousands of dollars.
$t = 100(10 - x) + 250(16 + x^2)^{1/2}$
$t' = -100 + 250x(16 + x^2)^{-1/2}$
$t' = 0 \Leftrightarrow 250x(16 + x^2)^{-1/2} = 100$
$250x = 100(16 + x^2)^{1/2}$
$62500x^2 = 10000(16 + x^2)$
$52500x^2 = 160000$
$x = \pm 1.7457...$
Build the bridge about 1.75 mi closer to the field office than the closest point of approach.
Alternative solution:
Let θ be the angle of incidence of the bridge.
$\sin \theta = 100/250 \Rightarrow \theta = 23.5781...°$
$x = 4 \tan 23.5781...° = 1.7457...$

12. $v(t) = 3(t - 1)(t - 3) = 3t^2 - 12t + 9$
$a(t) = v'(t) = 6t - 12$
$a'(t) = 6$
Because $a'(t)$ is never zero, the minimum acceleration occurs at an endpoint of the domain.
$a(0) = -12$ and $a(5) = 18$.
Minimum acceleration is -12 m/s at $t = 0$.

13. $\vec{r}(t) = (7 \sin 0.5t)\vec{i} + 3(1 + \cos t)\vec{j}$
$\vec{v}(t) = (3.5 \cos 0.5t)\vec{i} + (-3 \sin t)\vec{j}$
$\vec{a}(t) = (-1.75 \sin 0.5t)\vec{i} + (-3 \cos t)\vec{j}$
$\vec{v}(4.5) = -2.1986... \, \vec{i} + 2.9325... \, \vec{j} \approx -2.2\vec{i} + 2.9\vec{j}$
$\vec{a}(4.5) = -1.3616... \, \vec{i} + 0.6323... \, \vec{j} \approx -1.4\vec{i} - 0.6\vec{j}$

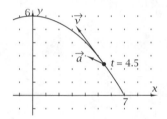

14. The velocity vector is tangent to the path.
The acceleration vector is on the concave side.

15. Geometrically, the angle between the velocity and acceleration vectors is acute, indicating the acceleration has a component in the same direction as the velocity.
Algebraically, $\vec{v}(4.5) \cdot \vec{a}(4.5)$
$= (-2.1986...)(-1.3616...) + (2.9325...)(0.6323...)$
$= 4.8482...$
Because the dot product is positive, the angle is acute and thus the acceleration has a component in the same direction as the velocity.

16. $|\vec{v}(4.5)|^2 = (-2.1986...)^2 + (2.9325...)^2 = 13.4339...$
The factor by which to multiply $\vec{v}(4.5)$ to get $\vec{a}_t(4.5)$ is $(4.8482...)/(13.4339...) = 0.3608...$
$\vec{a}_t(4.5) = (0.3608...)(-2.1986...\vec{i} + 2.9325...\vec{j})$
$= -0.7934...\vec{i} + 1.0583...\vec{j} \approx -0.8\vec{i} + 1.1\vec{j}$
$\vec{a}_n(4.5) = \vec{a}(4.5) - \vec{a}_t(4.5)$
$= -0.5681...\vec{i} - 0.4259...\vec{j} \approx -0.6\vec{i} - 0.4\vec{j}$

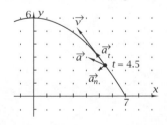

17. From Problem 16, $|\vec{v}(4.5)|^2 = 13.4339....$
$|\vec{v}(4.5)| = 3.6652...$
The object is going about 3.7 cm/s.

18. Answers will vary.

Test 42

1. Draw x- and y-axes through the end of the tank.

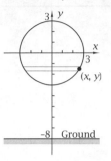

$dW = F \cdot (8 + y)$
The force to lift a horizontal slice is
$F = 44 \, dV = 44 \cdot 2x \cdot 10 \cdot dy = 880x \, dy$
$x^2 + y^2 = 9 \Rightarrow x = (9 - y^2)^{1/2}$
$F = 880(9 - y^2)^{1/2} \, dy$
$dW = 880(9 - y^2)^{1/2}(8 + y) \, dy$
$W = \int_{-3}^{0} dW = 41842.8276...$
≈ 41.8 thousand foot-pounds

2. $dF = p \, dA = 44(3 - y) \cdot 2(9 - y^2)^{1/2} \, dy$
$F = \int_{-3}^{3} 88(3 - y)(9 - y^2)^{1/2} \, dy$
$= 3732.2120... \approx 3732$ lb

3. $dM = y \, dF = y \cdot 88(3 - y)(9 - y^2)^{1/2} \, dy$
$M = \int_{-3}^{3} dM = -2799.1590...$
≈ -2800 lb-ft

4. $F\bar{x} = M \Rightarrow \bar{x} = \dfrac{M}{F} = \dfrac{-2799.15...}{3732.21...}$
$= -0.75$ ft (exactly)
The center of pressure is slightly below the center of the circle because the gasoline in the bottom hemisphere is at a higher average pressure than the gasoline in the top hemisphere.

5. $dm = \rho \, dV = \rho A \, dx$, where x is the depth to a sample point in the compost heap.
$m = \int_{0}^{40} \rho A \, dx$
Evaluate using the trapezoidal rule.
$m \approx 10\left[\dfrac{1}{2}(0.7)(10000) + 0.9(9000) + 1.2(8000) \right.$
$\left. + 1.6(4000) + \dfrac{1}{2}(2.2)(1000)\right]$
$= 287,000$ g, or about 287 kg
$\text{Volume} = \int_{0}^{40} A \, dx$
$\approx 10\left[\dfrac{1}{2}(10,000) + 9000 + 8000 + 4000 + \dfrac{1}{2}(1000)\right]$
$= 265,000$ g
$\text{Density} \approx \dfrac{287000}{265000} = 1.0830... \approx 1.08$ g/cm^3

6. Let c = cost.
   $dc = p\,dx = (200 \cdot 1.0003^x)\,dx$
   $c = \displaystyle\int_{1000}^{4000} (200 \cdot 1.0003^x)\,dx = 1313344.56\ldots$
   ≈ 1.31 million dollars

7. Answers will vary.

Test 43

1. • $f(x) = \displaystyle\sum_{n=0}^{\infty} \frac{1}{(2n)!}x^{2n}$

   • $f(x) = \cosh x$

2. • $f(x) = x - \dfrac{1}{3!}x^3 + \dfrac{1}{5!}x^5 - \dfrac{1}{7!}x^7 + \cdots$

   • $f(x) = \sin x$

3. $e^x = 1 + x + \dfrac{1}{2!}x^2 + \dfrac{1}{3!}x^3 + \dfrac{1}{4!}x^4 + \cdots$

   $e^x = 1 - x + \dfrac{1}{2!}x^2 - \dfrac{1}{3!}x^3 + \dfrac{1}{4!}x^4 - \cdots$

4. $\dfrac{d}{dx}\left(x - \dfrac{1}{3}x^3 + \dfrac{1}{5}x^5 - \dfrac{1}{7}x^7 + \cdots\right) = 1 - x^2 + x^4 - x^6 + \cdots$

   Common ratio $r = -x^2$

5. If $|r| < 1$ then $\lim\limits_{n \to \infty} r^n = 0$, and thus
   $\lim\limits_{n \to \infty} S_n = t_1 \cdot \dfrac{1}{1-r} = \dfrac{t_1}{1-r}$.

6. • $f(5) = 3 = c_0$
     $f'(5) = -4 = c_1$
     $f''(5) = 0.4 = 2!c_2 \Rightarrow c_2 = 0.2$
     $f'''(5) = -0.12 = 3!c_3 \Rightarrow c_3 = -0.02$
     $f^{(4)}(5) = 0.0024 = 4!c_4 \Rightarrow c_4 = 0.0001$
     $\therefore f(x) = 3 - 4(x-5) + 0.2(x-5)^2 - 0.02(x-5)^3$
     $\qquad + 0.0001(x-5)^4 + \cdots$

   • S_3 is the fourth partial sum because the term index starts at $n = 0$, not $n = 1$. Thus the first partial sum is S_0.

7.

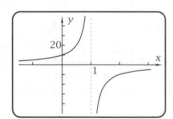

8.

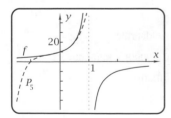

9. From the graph in Problem 8, P_5 seems to fit f reasonably well for $-0.7 \le x \le 0.6$.

10. Sixth partial sum is $10 \cdot \dfrac{1 - 0.95^6}{1 - 0.95} = 52.9816\ldots$
    ≈ 53.0 mg.
    The limit is $10 \cdot \dfrac{1}{1 - 0.95} = 200$ mg.

11. $\cos x = 1 - \dfrac{1}{2!}x^2 + \dfrac{1}{4!}x^4 - \dfrac{1}{6!}x^6 + \cdots$

12. The graph shows a reasonably good fit for $-3 \le x \le 3$.

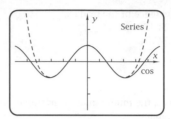

13. $\ln x = \displaystyle\sum_{n=1}^{\infty} (-1)^{n+1} \dfrac{1}{n}(x-1)^n$

14. $T_5(1.3) = 0.3 - \dfrac{1}{2}(0.3)^2 + \dfrac{1}{3}(0.3)^3 - \dfrac{1}{4}(0.3)^4 + \dfrac{1}{5}(0.3)^5$
    $T_5(1.3) = 0.262461$ (exactly)
    $\ln 1.3 = 0.262364264\ldots$
    $T_5(1.3)$ is close to $\ln 1.3$.
    $T_5(4) = 3 - \dfrac{1}{2}(3)^2 + \dfrac{1}{3}(3)^3 - \dfrac{1}{4}(3)^4 + \dfrac{1}{5}(3)^5$
    $T_5(4) = 35.85$ (exactly)
    $\ln 4 = 1.3862\ldots$
    $T_5(4)$ is not close to $\ln 4$.

15. $\sinh x = x + \dfrac{1}{3!}x^3 + \dfrac{1}{5!}x^5 + \dfrac{1}{7!}x^7 + \cdots$
    $\sinh' x = 1 + \dfrac{1}{3!} \cdot 3x^2 + \dfrac{1}{5!} \cdot 5x^4 + \dfrac{1}{7!} \cdot 7x^6 + \cdots$
    $\qquad = 1 + \dfrac{1}{2!}x^2 + \dfrac{1}{4!}x^4 + \dfrac{1}{6!}x^6 + \cdots = \cosh x$

16. $\displaystyle\int \sinh x\,dx = \dfrac{1}{2}x^2 + \dfrac{1}{4 \cdot 3!}x^4 + \dfrac{1}{6 \cdot 5!}x^6 + \dfrac{1}{8 \cdot 7!}x^8 + \cdots + C$
    $\qquad = \dfrac{1}{2!}x^2 + \dfrac{1}{4!}x^4 + \dfrac{1}{6!}x^6 + \dfrac{1}{8!}x^8 + \cdots + C,$
    which equals $\cosh x$ if $C = 1$, Q.E.D.

17. $x^2 \sinh 3x = x^2\left[(3x) + \dfrac{1}{3!}(3x)^3 + \dfrac{1}{5!}(3x)^5 + \dfrac{1}{7!}(3x)^7 + \cdots\right]$
    $\qquad = 3x^3 + \dfrac{3^3}{3!}x^5 + \dfrac{3^5}{5!}x^7 + \dfrac{3^7}{7!}x^9 + \cdots$

18. Answers will vary.

Test 44

1. A sequence converges if and only if $\lim_{n \to \infty} t_n$ is a finite real number.

2. A series converges if and only if the sequence of partial sums converges.

Calculus: Concepts and Applications Instructor's Resource Book
©2005 Key Curriculum Press

3. If $|r| < 1$, then $\lim_{n \to \infty} r^n = 0$. Thus, S_n converges to $\frac{t_1}{1-r}$, a finite real number.

4. The sequence converges because the terms approach 2 as a limit. The partial sums do not converge because larger and larger numbers are being added to the partial sums.

5. The series diverges because t_n does not approach 0 as n approaches infinity.

6. Check the limit of t_n. If it doesn't equal zero, then the series does not converge.

7. $\int_1^\infty \frac{1}{x}\,dx = \lim_{b \to \infty} \left(\ln|x| \big|_1^b \right) = \lim_{b \to \infty} \left(\ln|b| - \ln 1 \right) = \infty$

   $\therefore$ the series can be bounded below by a divergent improper integral, and thus the series diverges, even though the terms are decreasing in value and approach zero as a limit.

8. The series converges because (1) the signs are strictly alternating, (2) the terms are strictly decreasing in absolute value, and (3) the term values approach zero as a limit as n approaches infinity. The series does not converge absolutely because the series of absolute values is the divergent harmonic series in Problem 6.

9. The p-series is $\displaystyle\sum_{n=1}^\infty \frac{1}{n^p}$.
   The p-series converges if $p > 1$.

10. $\displaystyle\sum_{n=1}^\infty \frac{1}{n^2}(5x-7)^n$

    $L = \lim_{n \to \infty} \left| \frac{(5x-7)^{n+1}}{(n+1)^2} \cdot \frac{n^2}{(5x-7)^n} \right|$

    $= |5x-7| \lim_{n \to \infty} \left(\frac{n}{n+1} \right)^2 = |5x-7| \cdot 1 = |5x-7|$

    Make $L < 1$.
    $|5x-7| < 1 \Leftrightarrow -1 < 5x-7 < 1 \Leftrightarrow 6 < 5x < 8$
    $\Leftrightarrow 1.2 < x < 1.6$

11. At $x = 1.2$, the series is $-1 + \frac{1}{4} - \frac{1}{9} + \frac{1}{16} - \cdots$,
    which is a convergent alternating series.
    At $x = 1.6$, the series is $1 + \frac{1}{4} + \frac{1}{9} + \frac{1}{16} + \cdots$,
    which is a convergent p-series with $p = 2$.
    The series converges at both endpoints.

12.

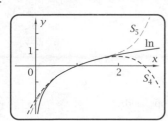

13. $\displaystyle\sum_{n=1}^\infty n^{-1.01}$

    For the tail, $R_{50} = \displaystyle\sum_{n=51}^\infty n^{-1.01} < \int_{50}^\infty x^{-1.01}\,dx$

    $= \lim_{b \to \infty} \left(-100x^{-0.01} \big|_{50}^b \right)$

    $= \lim_{b \to \infty} \left(-100b^{-0.01} + 100 \cdot 50^{-0.01} \right) = 96.1635...$

    $\therefore$ the tail is bounded above.
    With the other hypothesis, that the sequence of partial sums is bounded above, this is sufficient to prove that the tail (and thus the series) converges.

14. $R_{50} > \displaystyle\int_{51}^\infty x^{-1.01}\,dx = 100 \cdot 51^{-0.01} = 96.1444...$

    $\therefore 96.1444 < R_{50} < 96.1635...$
    $S_{50} = 4.4240188...$
    $\therefore \lim_{n \to \infty} S_n \approx 4.4240... + \frac{1}{2}(96.1444 + 96.1636...) = 100.5780...$
    (Note that the S_{50} is nowhere close to the limit.)

15. Hypotheses:
    • The terms strictly alternate in sign.
    • The terms strictly decrease in absolute value.
    • The limit of t_n is zero as n approaches infinity.

16. $1 - \frac{1}{2} + \frac{1}{3} - \cdots$

    $|R_{20}| < |t_{21}| = \frac{1}{21}$

17. $f(x) = e^x = \displaystyle\sum_{n=0}^\infty \frac{1}{n!}x^n$

    $R_5(2) = \frac{1}{6!} f^{(6)}(c) \cdot 2^5 = \frac{1}{6!} e^c \cdot 2^5$ for c in $(0, 2)$.

    $e^c < e^2 < 3^2 = 9$

    $\therefore R_5(2) < \frac{1}{6!} \cdot 9 \cdot 2^5 = 0.4$

    $S_5(2) = 1 + 2 + \frac{1}{2!}(2^2) + \frac{1}{3!}(2^3) + \frac{1}{4!}(2^4) + \frac{1}{5!}(2^5) = 7.2666...$

    $R_5(2) = e^2 - 7.2666... = 0.1223...$, which is less than the upper bound 0.4.

18. Answers will vary.

Test 45

1. $f(x) = \ln x \Rightarrow f(1) = 0 \Rightarrow c_0 = 0$
   $f'(x) = x^{-1} \Rightarrow f'(1) = 1 \Rightarrow c_1 = 1$
   $f''(x) = -x^{-2} \Rightarrow f''(1) = -1 \Rightarrow c_2 = -1/2! = -\frac{1}{2}$
   $f'''(x) = 2x^{-3} \Rightarrow f'''(1) = 2 \Rightarrow c_3 = 2/3! = \frac{1}{3}$
   $f^{(4)}(x) = -6x^{-4} \Rightarrow f^{(4)}(1) = -6 \Rightarrow c_4 = -6/4! = -\frac{1}{4}$
   $\therefore \ln x = (x-1) - \frac{1}{2}(x-1)^2 + \frac{1}{3}(x-1)^3 - \frac{1}{4}(x-1)^4 + \cdots$

2. $\ln x = \displaystyle\sum_{n=0}^\infty (-1)^{n+1} \cdot \frac{1}{n}(x-1)^n$

3. $L = \lim_{n \to \infty} \left| \frac{(x-1)^{n+1}}{n+1} \cdot \frac{n}{(x-1)^n} \right|$

   $= |x-1| \lim_{n \to \infty} \frac{n}{n+1} = |x-1| \cdot 1$

   Make $L < 1$.
   $|x-1| < 1 \Leftrightarrow -1 < x-1 < 1 \Leftrightarrow 0 < x < 2$, Q.E.D.

4. The graph shows that the fit is good between $x = 0$ and $x = 2$, and not good elsewhere.

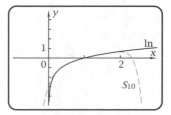

5. $x = 2$: $1 - \frac{1}{2} + \frac{1}{3} - \frac{1}{4} + \cdots$
   Converges by the alternating series test.

   $x = 0$: $-1 - \frac{1}{2} - \frac{1}{3} - \frac{1}{4} - \cdots$
   Divergent harmonic series.
   $\therefore$ the series converges at $x = 2$ but diverges at $x = 0$, Q.E.D.

6. $S_9(1.8) = 0.594012875\ldots$
   $\ln 1.8 = 0.587786664\ldots$
   $S_9(1.8) \approx \ln 1.8$

7. Tail: $\frac{1}{11}(0.8)^{11} - \frac{1}{12}(0.8)^{12} + \frac{1}{13}(0.8)^{13} - \cdots$
   $= 0.0078090\ldots - 0.0057266\ldots + 0.004228\ldots - \cdots$

8. $R_{10}(1.8) = \ln 1.8 - S_{10}(1.8) = 0.00451120\ldots$

9. $t_{11}(1.8) = \frac{1}{11}(0.8)^{11} = 0.0078090\ldots > R_{10}(1.8)$, Q.E.D.

10. $S_{10}(0.3) = -1.198859887\ldots$
    $R_{10}(0.3) = \ln 0.3 - S_{10}(0.3) = -0.00511291\ldots$
    $t_{11}(0.3) = \frac{1}{11}(-0.7)^{11} = -0.001797\ldots$
    $\therefore |t_{11}(0.3)|$ is not an upper bound for $|R_{10}(0.3)|$.

11. $\ln(x+1) = x - \frac{1}{2}x^2 + \frac{1}{3}x^3 - \frac{1}{4}x^4 + \cdots$

12. $\displaystyle\sum_{n=0}^{\infty} (-1)^n \frac{1}{(2n+1)!} x^{2n+1}$
    Write out the first few terms.
    $x - \frac{1}{3!}x^3 + \frac{1}{5!}x^5 - \cdots$
    The series is for $\sin x$.

13. $L = \lim\limits_{n\to\infty} \left| \dfrac{x^{2n+3}}{(2n+3)!} \cdot \dfrac{(2n+1)!}{x^{2n+1}} \right|$
    $= x^2 \lim\limits_{n\to\infty} \dfrac{(2n+1)!}{(2n+3)(2n+2)(2n+1)!} = x^2 \cdot 0$
    $\therefore L < 1$ for all real x.
    $\therefore$ the interval of convergence is {real nos.}, Q.E.D.

14. $f(x) = x^3 \cos 2x$
    $= x^3 \left[1 - \frac{1}{2!}(2x)^2 + \frac{1}{4!}(2x)^4 - \cdots \right]$
    $= x^3 - \frac{2^2}{2!}x^5 + \frac{2^4}{4!}x^7 - \cdots$

15. $f(x) = \dfrac{1}{1-x} = 1 + x + x^2 + x^3 + x^4 + \cdots$
    This is a geometric series.

16. $g(x) = \dfrac{1}{1+x^2} = 1 - x^2 + x^4 - x^6 + x^8 - \cdots$

17. $\tan^{-1} x = \int (1 - x^2 + x^4 - x^6 + x^8 - \cdots) \, dx$
    $= x - \frac{1}{3}x^3 + \frac{1}{5}x^5 - \frac{1}{7}x^7 + \frac{1}{9}x^9 - \cdots + C$
    Because $\tan^{-1} 0 = 0$, $C = 0$.
    $\therefore \tan^{-1} x = x - \frac{1}{3}x^3 + \frac{1}{5}x^5 - \frac{1}{7}x^7 + \frac{1}{9}x^9 - \cdots$

18. $\sinh x = x + \frac{1}{3!}x^3 + \frac{1}{5!}x^5 + \cdots$
    $\cosh x = 1 + \frac{1}{2!}x^2 + \frac{1}{4!}x^4 + \cdots$
    $\sinh x + \cosh x = 1 + x + \frac{1}{2!}x^2 + \frac{1}{3!}x^3 + \cdots$
    This is the series for e^x. By definition,
    $\sinh x = \frac{1}{2}(e^x - e^{-x})$
    $\cosh x = \frac{1}{2}(e^x + e^{-x})$
    $\sinh x + \cosh x = \frac{1}{2}(2e^x + 0) = e^x$,
    which confirms that the series are consistent with the definitions, Q.E.D.

19. Each denominator is a power of n, hence the name p-series.

20. $R_4 = \displaystyle\sum_{n=5}^{\infty} n^{-2} < \int_4^{\infty} x^{-2} \, dx = \lim\limits_{b\to\infty} \left(-x^{-1} \big|_4^b \right)$
    $= \lim\limits_{b\to\infty} (-b^{-1} + 4^{-1}) = 0.25$
    Upper bound for the tail is 0.25.

21. Answers will vary.

Test 46

1. $dV = 2\pi xy \, dx = 2\pi x^2 e^{-x} \, dx$
   $V = 2\pi \displaystyle\int_0^b x^2 e^{-x} \, dx$

u	dv
x^2 $\quad+$	e^{-x}
$2x$ $\quad-$	$-e^{-x}$
2 $\quad+$	e^{-x}
0 $\quad-$	$-e^{-x}$

   $= 2\pi(-x^2 e^{-x} - 2xe^{-x} - 2e^{-x}) \big|_0^b$
   $= 2\pi[e^{-b}(-b^2 - 2b - 2) + 2]$

2. $b = 3 \Rightarrow V = 2\pi[e^{-3}(-9 - 6 - 2) + 2]$
   $= 2\pi(2 - 17e^{-3}) = 7.2480721\ldots$
   Numerical integration gives $7.2480721\ldots$, which agrees with the algebraic answer.

3. The fundamental theorem of calculus allows one to evaluate definite integrals. Integration by parts is the technique in this problem.

4. Improper

5. $\bar{y} = \dfrac{1}{2a} \displaystyle\int_{-a}^{a} (a^2 - x^2) \, dx$
   $= \dfrac{1}{2a} \cdot 2\left(a^2 x - \frac{1}{3}x^3 \right) \Big|_0^a = \dfrac{1}{a} \cdot \dfrac{2}{3}a^3 = \dfrac{2}{3}a^2$
   $\therefore$ the average value of y is 2/3 of the maximum value of y, Q.E.D.

6. $I = \displaystyle\int (49 - x^2)^{-1/2} \, dx$
   Let $x = 7\sin\theta$, $dx = 7\cos\theta \, d\theta$, $(49 - x^{1/2}) = 7\cos\theta$.
   $\therefore I = \displaystyle\int [1/(7\cos\theta)](7\cos\theta \, d\theta) = \int d\theta$
   $= \theta + C = \sin^{-1} \dfrac{x}{7} + C$

7. $\dfrac{dM}{dt} = 0.06M \Rightarrow \dfrac{dM}{M} = 0.06 \, dt$
   $\displaystyle\int \dfrac{dM}{M} = \int 0.06 \, dt$
   $\ln|M| = 0.06t + C$
   $|M| = e^{0.06t+C} = e^{0.06t} \cdot e^C$
   $M = C_1 e^{0.06t}$
   $\therefore M$ increases exponentially with t, Q.E.D.

8. $M = 80e^{0.06t}$

t	M (rounded)
5	107.99
10	145.77
15	196.77

   The graph follows the slope field.

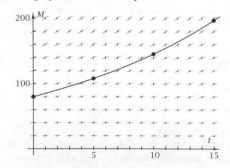

9. Know: dr/dt. Want: dA/dt
$A = \pi r^2$
$$\frac{dA}{dt} = 2\pi r \frac{dr}{dt}$$
Because $2\pi r$ is the circumference of the circle, dA/dt equals the circumference times the rate of change of the radius, Q.E.D.

10. $\vec{r}(t) = (\cosh 2t)\vec{i} + (\sin^{-1} t)\vec{j}$
$\vec{v}(t) = (2\sinh 2t)\vec{i} + (1 - t^2)^{-1/2}\vec{j}$

11. $\ln x = (x-1) - \frac{1}{2}(x-1)^2 + \frac{1}{3}(x-1)^3 - \cdots$
$$L = \lim_{n\to\infty}\left|\frac{(x-1)^{n+1}}{n+1} \cdot \frac{n}{(x-1)^n}\right|$$
$$= |x-1|\lim_{n\to\infty}\frac{n}{n+1} = |x-1| \cdot 1$$
$L < 1 \Leftrightarrow |x-1| < 1 \Leftrightarrow -1 < x-1 < 1 \Leftrightarrow 0 < x < 2.$
∴ the open interval of convergence is $0 < x < 2$, Q.E.D.

12. Answers will vary.

Test 47

1. $f(x) = \dfrac{4\ln x}{x-1}$

x	$f(x)$
0.97	4.0612...
0.98	4.0405...
0.99	4.0201...
1.00	undefined
1.01	3.9801...
1.02	3.9605...
1.03	3.9411...

Conjecture: $\lim_{x\to 1} f(x) = 4$

2. Distance $\approx \frac{1}{3}(4)(25 + 4 \cdot 30 + 2 \cdot 37 + 4 \cdot 43$
$\qquad + 2 \cdot 47 + 4 \cdot 50 + 52)$
$= \frac{4}{3}(737) = 982\frac{2}{3}$ ft

3. $v' \approx \dfrac{47 - 37}{16 - 8} = 1.25$ ft/s^2

4. Acceleration

5. $y = e^x \Rightarrow dy = e^x\, dx$
$dS = 2\pi x\sqrt{dx^2 + dy^2} = 2\pi x\sqrt{1 + e^{2x}}\, dx$
$S = \int_1^2 dS = 47.4474...$

6. Hypotheses:
   1. f is differentiable for all x in (a, b).
   2. f is continuous at $x = a$ and $x = b$.

7. The graph shows a tangent line at $x = c$ parallel to secant line, where c is between a and b.

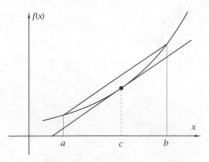

8. a. Local maximum: $x = 5$
   b. Local minimum: $x = 1$, $x = 9$
   c. Point of inflection: $x = 3$, $x = 7$

9. $\dfrac{dy}{dx} = 0.5y(1 - 0.15y)$
   At $(2, 3)$, $\dfrac{dy}{dx} = 0.5(3)(1 - 0.45) = 0.825$.
   The graph shows that the slope is a bit less than 1 at $(2, 3)$.

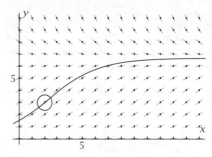

10. See the graph in Problem 9, showing the particular solution subject to the initial condition $(2, 3)$.

11.

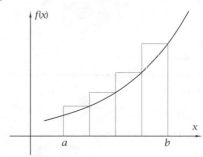

12. Counting squares
    (or trapezoidal rule)

13. $f(x) = \sqrt{100 - x^2} = (100 - x^2)^{1/2}$
    $f'(x) = \frac{1}{2}(100 - x^2)^{-1/2}(-2x) = -x(100 - x^2)^{-1/2}$
    $f'(6) = -6(100 - 36)^{-1/2} = -\frac{3}{4}$

14. (Slice the region parallel to the y-axis, generating cylindrical shells.)
    $dV = 2\pi x \cdot y \cdot dx = 2\pi x e^x\, dx$
    $V = 2\pi\displaystyle\int_1^2 x e^x\, dx$

u		dv
x	$+$	e^x
1	$-$	e^x
0	$+$	e^x

    $= 2\pi(xe^x - e^x)\big|_1^2 = 2\pi(2e^2 - e^2 - e + e)$
    $= 2\pi e^2$
    (Answer equals 46.4268..., which checks with the answer by numerical integration.)

15. $\lim_{x\to 1}\dfrac{4\ln x}{x-1} \to \dfrac{0}{0}$
    $= \lim_{x\to 1}\dfrac{4/x}{1} \to \dfrac{4}{1}$
    $= 4$, which confirms the conjecture in Problem 1.

16. $f(x) = \int_0^x \dfrac{\sin t}{t}\, dt$

$\qquad = \int_0^x \left(1 - \dfrac{1}{3!}t^2 + \dfrac{1}{5!}t^4 - \dfrac{1}{7!}t^6 + \cdots\right) dt$

$\qquad = x - \dfrac{1}{3 \cdot 3!}x^3 + \dfrac{1}{5 \cdot 5!}x^5 - \dfrac{1}{7 \cdot 7!}x^7 + \cdots$

17. Ratio technique

18. $\vec{r}(t) = (e^{0.5t})\vec{i} + (\sin t)\vec{j}$
$\vec{v}(t) = (0.5e^{0.5t})\vec{i} + (\cos t)\vec{j}$
$\vec{a}(t) = (0.25e^{0.5t})\vec{i} + (-\sin t)\vec{j}$
$\vec{a}(1) = 0.4121\ldots\, \vec{i} - 0.8414\ldots\, \vec{j}$
The graph shows that $\vec{a}(1)$ forms an obtuse angle with $\vec{v}(1)$, implying that the object is slowing down.

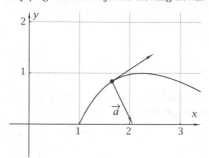

19. Answers will vary.

Test 48

1. $dA = y\, dx = 3 \sin x\, dx$

$A = \displaystyle\int_0^\pi 3 \sin x\, dx = -3 \cos x \Big|_0^\pi$

$\qquad = -3 \cos \pi + 3 \cos 0 = 3 + 3 = 6$, Q.E.D.

2. $dM_y = x \cdot 3 \sin x\, dx$

$M_y = \displaystyle\int_0^\pi 3x \sin x\, dx = 9.4247\ldots$ (Exact: 3π)

3. $\bar{x} = \dfrac{9.4247\ldots}{6} = 1.5707\ldots$ (Exact: $\pi/2$)

4. (Slice the region parallel to the y-axis, generating cylindrical shells.)
$dV = 2\pi x \cdot y \cdot dx = 6\pi x \sin x\, dx$
$V = \displaystyle\int_0^\pi 6\pi x \sin x\, dx = 59.2176\ldots$ (Exact: $6\pi^2$)

5. $2\pi \bar{x} A = 2\pi(\pi/2)(6) = 6\pi^2 = 59.2176\ldots$,
which agrees with the answer to Problem 4, Q.E.D.

6. (Slice the region perpendicular to the x-axis, generating plane disks.)
$dV = \pi y^2\, dx = 9\pi \sin^2 x\, dx$
$V = \displaystyle\int_0^\pi 9\pi \sin^2 x\, dx = 44.4132\ldots \left(\text{Exact: } \dfrac{9}{2}\pi^2\right)$

7. $2\pi \bar{y} A = V$
$\bar{y} = \dfrac{44.4132\ldots}{2\pi \cdot 6} = 1.17809\ldots \left(\text{Exact: } \dfrac{3}{8}\pi\right)$

8. $x = t^2 \Rightarrow dx = 2t\, dt$
$y = t^3 \Rightarrow dy = 3t^2\, dt$
$dL = \sqrt{dx^2 + dy^2} = \sqrt{4t^2 + 9t^4}\, dt$
$dS = 2\pi x\, dL = 2\pi t^2 \sqrt{4t^2 + 9t^4}\, dt$
$S = \displaystyle\int_0^2 dS = 131.1568\ldots$

9. The graph shows a curved "right triangle" with legs dr and $r\, d\theta$, and hypotenuse dL, showing that $dL = \sqrt{(dr)^2 + (r\, d\theta)^2}$.

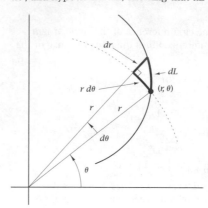

10. $r = \theta,\ dr = d\theta$
$dL = \sqrt{d\theta^2 + \theta^2\, d\theta^2} = \sqrt{1 + \theta^2}\, d\theta$
$L = \displaystyle\int_0^{6\pi} \sqrt{1 + \theta^2}\, d\theta = 179.7178\ldots$
$\left(\text{Exact: } 3\pi\sqrt{1 + 36\pi^2} + \dfrac{1}{2}\ln\left|\sqrt{1 + 36\pi^2} + 6\pi\right|\right)$

11. Let x = distance from closest point of approach to cut-off point.
Let C = cost.
$C = 5\sqrt{100^2 + x^2} + 3(400 - x)$
$C' = 5x(100^2 + x^2)^{-1/2} - 3$
$C' = 0 \Leftrightarrow 5x(100^2 + x^2)^{-1/2} = 3$
$25x^2 = 9(100^2 + x^2) \Leftrightarrow 16x^2 = 9 \cdot 100^2$
$x = \pm 75$
Cut across 75 ft from the closest point of approach (or 325 ft from the well).
or:
Let θ = angle of incidence of diagonal pipe for the minimal cost path.
$\sin \theta = \dfrac{3}{5} \Rightarrow \theta = 36.8698\ldots°$
$x = 100 \tan 36.8698\ldots° = 75$ ft, and so on

12. $y = \cosh x$

$\bar{y} = \dfrac{1}{2}\displaystyle\int_0^2 \cosh x\, dx = \dfrac{1}{2} \sinh x \Big|_0^2 = \dfrac{1}{2} \sinh 2 - 0 = 1.8134\ldots$

The graph shows that a horizontal line drawn across the graph at $y = 1.8134\ldots$ forms a rectangle whose area equals the area of the region under the graph, or that the area of the part of the region outside the rectangle equals the area of the part of the rectangle outside of the region.

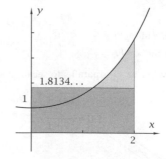

Calculus: Concepts and Applications Instructor's Resource Book
©2005 Key Curriculum Press

13. $\frac{dy}{dx} = 0.2(y - 5)(y - 1)$

At $(1, 4)$, $\frac{dy}{dx} = 0.2(-1)(3) = -0.6$.

The graph shows a slope of about -0.6 at $(1, 4)$.

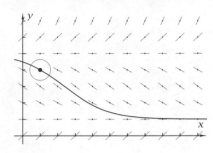

14. See the graph in Problem 13, showing the particular solution containing $(1, 4)$.

15. $\int \frac{1}{(y - 5)(y - 1)} \, dy = \int \left(\frac{1/4}{y - 5} + \frac{-1/4}{y - 1} \right) dy$

$= \frac{1}{4} \ln |y - 5| - \frac{1}{4} \ln |y - 1| + C$

16. $\int \sqrt{1 + x^2} \, dx \qquad x = \tan \theta, \ dx = \sec^2 \theta \, d\theta$

$\sqrt{1 + x^2} = \sec \theta$

$= \int \sec \theta \cdot \sec^2 \theta \, d\theta = \int \sec^3 \theta \, d\theta$

$= \frac{1}{2} \sec \theta \tan \theta + \frac{1}{2} \ln |\sec \theta + \tan \theta| + C$

$= \frac{1}{2} x \sqrt{1 + x^2} + \frac{1}{2} \ln \left| \sqrt{1 + x^2} + x \right| + C$

17. $\int x \sin x \, dx$

u		dv
x	$+$	$\sin x$
1	$-$	$-\cos x$
0	$+$	$-\sin x$

$= -x \cos x + \sin x + C$

18. $y = x^2 \, e^{-x}$

$y' = 2xe^{-x} - x^2 e^{-x}$

$y'' = 2e^{-x} - 2xe^{-x} - 2xe^{-x} + x^2 e^{-x} = e^{-x}(2 - 4x + x^2)$

$y'' = 0 \Leftrightarrow 2 - 4x + x^2 = 0$

$x = \frac{4 \pm \sqrt{16 - 4 \cdot 1 \cdot 2}}{2} = 2 \pm \sqrt{2}$

(Approx.: $3.4142...$ or $0.5857...$)

There are points of inflection at both points since y'' changes sign at both points.

19. Let $L = $ length, $W = $ width, and $A = $ area.

Know: $\frac{dL}{dt} = 5$ and $\frac{dW}{dt} = -3$

Want: $\frac{dA}{dt}$

$A = LW$

$\frac{dA}{dt} = \frac{dL}{dt} W + L \frac{dW}{dt}$

$= 5(50) + 100(-3) = -50$

The area is decreasing at 50 cm^2/s.

20. $\cos x = 1 - \frac{1}{2!}x^2 + \frac{1}{4!}x^4 - \frac{1}{6!}x^6 + \cdots$

$\int x \cos x \, dx = \int \left(x - \frac{1}{2!}x^3 + \frac{1}{4!}x^5 - \frac{1}{6!}x^7 + \cdots \right) dx$

$= \frac{1}{2}x^2 - \frac{1}{4 \cdot 2!}x^4 + \frac{1}{6 \cdot 4!}x^6 - \frac{1}{8 \cdot 6!}x^8 + \cdots + C$

21. $\sum_{n=1}^{\infty} \frac{(-1)^n}{2^n}(x - 1)^n$

$= -\frac{1}{2}(x - 1) + \frac{1}{4}(x - 1)^2 - \frac{1}{8}(x - 1)^3 + \frac{1}{16}(x - 1)^4 - \cdots$

$L = \lim_{n \to \infty} \left| \frac{(x - 1)^{n+1}}{2^{n+1}} \cdot \frac{2^n}{(x - 1)^n} \right|$

$= |x - 1| \lim_{n \to \infty} \frac{1}{2} = \frac{1}{2}|x - 1|$

$L < 1 \Leftrightarrow \frac{1}{2}|x - 1| < 1 \Leftrightarrow -2 < x - 1 < 2$

$\Leftrightarrow -1 < x < 3$

Open interval of convergence is $(-1, 3)$.

22. $\int_1^{\infty} x^{-1.02} \, dx = \lim_{b \to \infty} \int_1^b x^{-1.02} \, dx$

$= \lim_{b \to \infty} \left(-50x^{-0.02} \big|_1^b \right) = \lim_{b \to \infty} (-50b^{-0.02} + 50) = 50$

$\therefore$ the integral converges, Q.E.D.

23. $\vec{r}(t) = (5t - 12 \sin t)\vec{i} + (15 + 12 \cos t)\vec{j}$

$\vec{v}(t) = (5 - 12 \cos t)\vec{i} + (-12 \sin t)\vec{j}$

$\vec{v}(2.5) = 14.61...\vec{i} - 7.18...\vec{j}$

$\vec{a}(t) = (12 \sin t)\vec{i} + (-12 \cos t)\vec{j}$

$\vec{a}(2.5) = 7.18...\vec{i} + 9.61...\vec{j}$

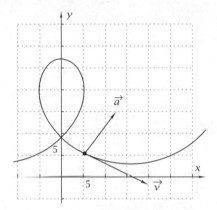

24. $|\vec{v}(2.5)| = \sqrt{(14.61...)^2 + (7.18...)^2} = 16.2830...$

Coaster is going about 16.3 m/s.

It is speeding up because the angle between the velocity and acceleration vectors is acute.

[Note: $\vec{v}(t) \cdot \vec{a}(t)$

$= (5 - 12 \cos t)(12 \sin t) + (-12 \sin t)(-12 \cos t)$

$= 60 \sin t$.

Thus, $\vec{v}(2.5) \cdot \vec{a}(2.5) = 60 \sin 2.5 = 35.9083...$, which is positive, confirming that the angle between the velocity and acceleration vectors is acute.]

25. Answers will vary.

Programs for Graphing Calculators

From time to time, various problem sets call upon students to write or download programs for their graphing calculators. The programs listed and described in this *Instructor's Resource Book* are relatively simple versions of what students might do. They are specific to the TI-83 and TI-84 graphing calculators, but can be adapted to other graphers.

It is instructive to have your students write their own programs for specific purposes. If there is time, the writing of such programs can be excellent learning activities, and can support students' understanding of the calculus concepts the programs address. You will find that some of your students—not necessarily the ones who make the best grades—can quickly come up with remarkably insightful and useful programs! Often, however, you may want to download a program you have written or adapted from the ones that follow so that students' attention will not be distracted from the topic at hand. In this case it is recommended that you have students work "by hand" a simple example, such as a trapezoidal rule problem. The first thing they do after receiving the downloaded program is to work the same example and show that the answers agree. From that time on, they will have confidence in the program and can use it for more complicated examples, such as exploring the limit a Riemann sum seems to approach as the number of increments increases.

You are invited to explore the publisher's Web page, www.keypress.com, for updated information on graphing calculator programs. You are encouraged to share with other instructors, via the publisher, any highly effective programs you or your students have written. Contact Key Curriculum Press at editorial@keypress.com or 1-800-338-7638.

Here, in the order that they are first used in the text, are listings of the programs.

TRAPRULE, Problem Set 1-4, Problem 5 (pages 22–23)

This program evaluates the definite integral of a given function between lower and upper limits of integration using the trapezoidal rule with any desired number of increments. Before you run the program, store the function for the integrand as Y_1. When you run the program, the grapher will prompt you to enter the lower and upper limits of integration, A and B, and the number of increments, N. The grapher then computes and sums the successive y-values, using half the first and half the last, and saves the sum as S. The grapher displays the approximate value of the integral, which it has saved internally as the variable I. Along the way the grapher displays the successive y-values to give students a sense of how rapidly it is calculating. You may want to omit this instruction so that the program will run faster, particularly for larger numbers of increments.

TRAPRULE (TI-83, TI-83+, and TI-84+)

```
:Prompt A
:Prompt B
:Prompt N
:A→X
:0→S
:(B-A)/N→D
:0→C
:Lbl 1
:Y1+S→S
:X+D→X
:Y1+S→S
:IS>(C,N-1)
:Goto 1
:SD/2
:Disp "INTEGRAL"
:Disp Ans
```

TRAPRULD, Problem Set 1-4, Problem 6 (page 23)

The name comes from "trapezoidal rule from data." This program evaluates an integral of a function for which y-values are given, assuming that the x-values are evenly spaced. Before running the program, store the given y-values in list L1. Upon running the program, the grapher will prompt you to enter the number of increments (which must be one less than the number of data points). Then it will prompt you to enter the width of each increment, DX. The grapher then runs the program and displays the approximate integral, which it has stored in its memory as I. Note that the x-values themselves appear nowhere in the program.

TRAPRULD (TI-83, TI-83+, and TI-84+)

```
:Disp "INCREMENTS"
:Input N
:Disp "DX"
:Input D
:(D/2)*(2*sum(L1)-L1(1)-L1(N+1))→I
:Disp I
```

NEWTON, Problem Set 4-10, Problem C1 (pages 182–183)

This program finds zeros of a given function. Before running the program, store the equation for the function in Y1. Upon running the program, the grapher pauses to ask for the initial value of x, giving the prompt "FIRST X." The grapher then displays the next approximation for x. Press ENTER repeatedly for successive iterations. The current value is stored as X in the grapher's memory. The program as presently written has no elegant way of getting out of the loop. So simply press ON when you are ready to exit the program. Then clear the resulting "error" message.

NEWTON (TI-83, TI-83+, and TI-84+)

```
:Disp "FIRST X"
:Input X
:Lbl 1
:X-Y1/nDeriv(Y1,X,X)
:Ans→X
:Disp "NEXT X IS"
:Disp X
:Pause
:Goto 1
```

RIEMANN, Problem Set 5-4, Problem 12 (page 210)

This program finds a Riemann sum for a definite integral of a given function between $x = A$ and $x = B$. Before running the program, store the integrand function in Y1. The grapher will prompt you to enter the limits of integration, A and B; the number of increments, N; and the percent of the way through each interval at which the sample points are to be taken, PCT. By entering 0 for PCT, the grapher finds a left Riemann sum. By entering 50, it finds a midpoint sum. By entering 100, it finds a right Riemann sum. At the end of the run, the grapher will display S, the sum of the y-values before multiplying by Δx, and the approximate value of the integral, I. The integral is stored as I in the grapher's memory.

RIEMANN (TI-83, TI-83+, and TI-84+)

```
:Prompt A
:Prompt B
:Prompt N
:Disp "PCT?"
:Input P
:(B-A)/N→D
:A+P/100*D→X
:0→S
:1→K
:Lbl 1
:Y1+S→S
:Disp X
:K+1→K
:X+D→X
:If K≤N
:Goto 1
:S*D→I
:Disp S
:Disp I
```

SIMPSONE, Problem Set 5-10, Problem 16 (page 259)

The name comes from "Simpson's rule from equation." The program evaluates an integral of a function from $x = A$ to $x = B$, for which an equation is given. Before running the program, store the equation for the function as Y1. Upon running the program, the grapher will prompt you to enter the limits of integration, A and B, and the number of increments, N. The grapher runs the program and displays the approximate integral, which it has stored in its memory as I. The weighted sum of the data, before multiplying by $\Delta x/3$, is stored as S. Note also that the program, as currently written, does not protect against students entering an odd number of increments.

SIMPSONE (TI-83, TI-83+, and TI-84+)

```
:Disp "A"
:Input A
:Disp "B"
:Input B
:Disp "INCREMENTS"
:Input N
:(B-A)/N→D
:0→S
:2→K
:A+D→X
:Lbl 1
:Y₁(X-D)+4Y₁(X)+Y₁(X+D)
:Ans+S→S
:X+2D→X
:K+2→K
:If K≤N
:Goto 1
:S/3*D→I
:Disp I
```

SIMPSOND, Problem Set 5-10, Problem 16 (page 259)

The name comes from "Simpson's rule from data." The program evaluates an integral of a function for which y-values are given, assuming that the x-values are regularly spaced. Before running the program, store the given y-values in list L1. Upon running the program, the grapher will prompt you to enter the number of increments (which must be one less than the number of data points). Then it will prompt you to enter the width of each increment, DX. The grapher runs the program and displays the approximate integral, which it has stored in its memory as I. The weighted sum of the data, before multiplying by $\Delta x/3$, is stored as S. Note that the x-values themselves appear nowhere in the program. Note also that the program, as currently written, does not protect against students entering an odd number of increments.

SIMPSOND (TI-83, TI-83+, and TI-84+)

```
:Disp "INCREMENTS"
:Input N
:Disp "DX"
:Input D
:0→S
:2→K
:Lbl 1
:L1(K-1)+4L1(K)+L1(K+1)
:Ans+S→S
:K+2→K
:If K≤N
:Goto 1
:S/3*D→I
:Disp I
```

SLOPEFLD, Problem Set 7-4, Problem 14 (page 343)

The program plots a slope field for a given differential equation. Before running the program, store the differential equation in Y1 in terms of both x and y. Upon running the program, the grapher prompts you to select the window by asking, "Same as last?" If you choose to change the window, be sure to remember that the number of x- and y-values must take into account a beginning and an end data point. For instance, a window of [0, 10] would require 11 values if the slope lines were to be spaced 1 unit apart. The grapher also asks if you want to "square" the window, using the same scales on both axes. The grapher then proceeds to draw the slope field. Note that as presently written, the program does not correctly compensate for slope fields where there are different scales on the two axes.

SLOPEFLD (TI-83, TI-83+, and TI-84+)

```
:((Ymax-Ymin)/Yscl)→L
:((Xmax-Xmin)/Xscl)→W
:(W*(.5^(W/10)))→G
:(L*(.5^(L/10)))→A
:(Ymax-Ymin)/L→V
:(Xmax-Xmin)/W→H
:ClrDraw
:FnOff
:0→R
:Ymin→Y
:Lbl 1
:R+1→R
:0→C
:Xmin→X
:If Y=0:.0000001→Y
:Lbl 2
:If X=0:.0000001→X
:If Y=0:.0000001→Y
:C+1→C
:Y1→M
: -M*H/A+Y→S
:M*H/A+Y→T
```

```
:X-H/G→P
:X+H/G→Q
:If abs((T-S))>V
:Goto 3
:Lbl 4
:Y→Z
:Line(P,S,Q,T)
:Z→Y
:X+H→X
:If C-1<W
:Goto 2
:Y+V→Y
:If R-1<L
:Goto 1
:Stop
:Lbl 3
:Y+V/A→T
:Y-V/A→S
:(T-Y)/M+X→Q
:(S-Y)/M+X→P
:Goto 4
```

SLOPEDRW, Problem Set 7-4, Problem 14 (page 343)

This program, written by the author's student Robert "Trae" Sawyer in 1994, plots a particular solution for a given differential equation on a slope field that has already been drawn by the program SLOPEFLD, described above. The differential equation in terms of x and y should already be stored as Y1 in the grapher. Upon running the program, the grapher prompts you to enter the initial condition and the direction (right or left) to begin. Then it asks you to enter a factor, which is used to determine the step size in Euler's method of solving the differential equation. Entering 3 for the factor gives reasonable accuracy. The grapher will draw successive steps, including cyclical paths, until you stop it by pressing the ON key, or until the curve goes off-screen.

SLOPEDRW (TI-83, TI-83+, and TI-84+)

```
:ClrHome
:FnOff 1
:Disp "   SLOPEFIELD","DRAWER",""
:Input "INITAL X? ",X
:Input "INITAL Y? ",Y
:Disp "START GOING TO","THE (0=LEFT OR"
:Input "1=RIGHT?= ",L
:Input "FACTOR?=",F
:F*(Xmax-Xmin)/94→S
:F*(Ymax-Ymin)/62→T
:While ((X≥Xmin) and (X≤Xmax) and (Y≥Ymin)
and (Y≤Ymax))
:((abs(Y1)≤1)→A
:((abs(Y1)≠Y1)→B
:(abs((L-1))→C
:If B:Then
:If C:Then
: -1→U:1→V
:Else
:1→U:-1→V
:End
:Else
:If C:Then
: -1→U:-1→V
:Else
:1→U:1→V
:End:End
:If A:Then
:Line(X,Y,X+U*S,Y+V*T*(abs(Y1))
:Y1→P:(X+U*S)→X
:(Y+V*T*(abs (Y1))→Y:Y1→Q
:Else
:Line(X,Y,X+U*S/(abs (Y1),Y+V*T)
:Y1→P:(X+U*S/(abs (Y1))→X
:(Y+V*T)→Y:Y1→Q
:End
:If (((abs (P)=P) and ((abs (P))>1) and ((abs (Q)≠Q)
and ((abs (Q))>1)):Then
:(abs ((L-1))→L
:End:End
```

EULER, Problem Set 7-5, Problem 6 (page 348)

The program calculates successive values of y for a given differential equation. Before running the program, store the differential equation in Y1 in terms of both x and y. Upon running the program, the grapher will ask you to enter the initial condition and increment size by asking for First x, First y, and Delta x. The grapher then displays the next x-value and the corresponding (approximate) y-value. To calculate subsequent values, press ENTER repeatedly. The program as presently written has no elegant way of getting out of the loop. So simply press ON when you are ready to exit the program. Then clear the resulting "error" message.

EULER (TI-83, TI-83+, and TI-84+)

```
:Disp "FIRST X"
:Input X
:Disp "FIRST Y"
:Input Y
:Disp "DELTA X"
:Input D
:Lbl 1
:Y+Y₁D→Y
:X+D→X
:Disp "X"
:Disp X
:Disp "Y"
:Disp Y
:Pause
:Goto 1
```

ARCSUM, Problem Set 8-5, Problem 33 (page 407)

This program calculates the approximate arc length of a plane curve by summing the lengths of the chords for any chosen partition. Before running the program, store the equation for the curve in Y1. Upon running the program, the grapher will ask you to enter A (the lower limit of integration), B (the upper limit of integration), and N (the number of increments). The grapher then sums the chord lengths and displays the sum. The answer is also stored as S in the grapher's memory.

ARCSUM (TI-83, TI-83+, and TI-84+)

```
:Disp "A?"
:Input A
:Disp "B?"
:Input B
:Disp "N?"
:Input N
:(B-A)/N→D
:A→X
:0→S
:1→K
:Lbl 1
:Y₁→V
:X+D→X
:S+√((Y₁-V)²+D²)→S
:IS>(K,N)
:Goto 1
:Disp "SUM"
:Disp S
```

ACVELDIS, Section 10-2, Example 2 (pages 504–505)

The name comes from ACceleration, VELocity, DISplacement. The program, written by the author's student Patrick "P. J." Stevens in 1995, calculates numerically the approximate displacement of a moving object, using a table of time and acceleration data. Before running the program, store the times in list L1 and the corresponding accelerations in L2. Upon running the program, the grapher will pause for you to enter the number of data points and the initial velocity. The program then computes the displacements under the assumption that the acceleration varies linearly throughout each time interval. The displacements are obtained from the ordinary physics formula $s = v_0 t + 0.5at^2$. (The same result could be computed by averaging the initial and final velocities in each time interval and multiplying by the time.) The results are stored in other lists. The grapher will direct you to the appropriate lists, as follows:

L3 has the average acceleration for the time interval.
L4 has velocity at the time in L1.
L5 has the total displacement at the time in L1.

ACVELDIS (TI-83, TI-83+, and TI-84+)

```
:Disp "NO. DATA PTS."
:Input N
:N→dim(L3)
:0→L3(1)
:N→dim(L4)
:0→L4(1)
:N→dim(L5)
:0→L5(1)
:Disp "INIT. V"
:Input V
:V→L4(1)
:For(A,2,N,1)
:L1(A)-L1(A-1)→T
:(L2(A-1)+L2(A))/2→L3(A)
:L3(A)*T+L4(A-1)→L4(A)
:.5L3(A)*(T²)+L4(A-1)*T+L5(A-1)→L5(A)
:End
:Disp "PRESS STAT."
:Disp "L1: TIME"
:Disp "L2: ACCELERATION"
:Disp "L3: AV. ACCEL."
:Disp "L4: VELOCITY"
:Disp "L5: DISPLACEMENT"
```

SERIES, Section 12-2 (page 590)

This program calculates a partial sum of a series where the formula for the xth term is given. Before running the program, store the formula for the xth term in Y1. Upon running the program, the grapher prompts you to enter the final value, N, of the term index and the initial value of the term index, which it stores as A. Then it calculates and displays each partial sum so that students can see what is happening as x increases. The display is particularly effective for a convergent series if you set the grapher to show a fixed number of decimal places. As more and more terms are displayed, more and more decimal places remain constant. Thus, students develop a practical sense of what it means for a series to converge.

SERIES (TI-83, TI-83+, and TI-84+)

```
:0→S
:Disp "HOW MANY TERMS?"
:Prompt N
:For(X,1,N)
:S+Y1(X)→S
:Disp S
:End
:Disp "NO. OF TERMS ="
:Disp N
:Disp "PARTIAL SUM ="
:Disp S
```

Technology Projects:
The Geometer's Sketchpad®

Teachers and students who are beginners with Sketchpad may wish to consult the reference guide that comes with the software. You can also visit The Geometer's Sketchpad Resource Center at www.keypress.com/sketchpad/.

The projects in this section provide a technology-enhanced method of introducing the calculus concepts of Chapter 1. They cover essentially the same material as Chapter 1, can be completed in approximately five days, and can be assigned in conjunction with the homework assignments suggested in the *Instructor's Resource Book*. Alternatively, *Limits with Tables* and *Limits with Delta and Epsilon* can be used with Chapter 2.

All required sketches can be found in the project folder in the GSP Sketches folder in the *Instructor's Resource Book* CD-ROM. Activity Notes are provided on pages 380–382.

Instantaneous Rate

Consider a door equipped with an automatic closer. When you push it, it opens quickly, and then the closer closes it again, more and more slowly until it finally closes completely.

A: Door Angle as a Function of Time

1. Open the sketch **InstantaneousRate.gsp** in the **GSP Sketches** folder. Press the *Open Door* button to operate the door. Observe the door opening and closing, and the graph showing the angle of the door as a function of time.

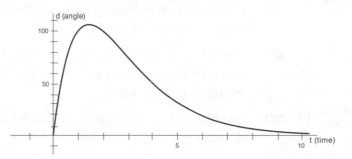

2. Drag Point t back and forth along the time axis, and watch how the angle of the door changes and how the point on the graph corresponds to the door's angle. Observe the values of the t and d measurements as you drag.

Q1 For what values of t is the angle increasing? How can you tell?

Q2 What is the maximum angle the door reaches? At what time does this occur?

B: The Door at Two Different Times

The value h is the separation between the two values of time (t and t_1).

3. To find the rate of change of the angle of the door, you need to look at the door's position at two different times. Press the *Show t1* button to see a second point on the graph, slightly separated from Point t. Drag Point t back and forth, and observe the behavior of the new points on the graph. To change the separation of the two times, press the button labeled *1.0* and then the button labeled *0.1*.

4. Make the separation of the two points smaller than 0.1. Can you still see two distinct points on the graph? Can you see the values of t_1 and d_1 change as you make h smaller? Experiment with dragging the h slider to change the separation of the two values of time directly.

Q3 What is the largest separation you can get by moving the slider? What's the smallest separation you can actually observe on the graph?

Q4 As you make h smaller, can you observe changes in the numeric values of t_1 and d_1 even when you can no longer observe any changes on the graph?

Instantaneous Rate (continued)

C: The Rate of Change of the Door's Angle

Hint: Divide the change in the angle by the change in the time. →

5. Set h to 0.1, and then use the numeric values of t, d, t_1, and d_1 to calculate the rate of change of the door's angle at any particular time. (Use Sketchpad's calculator to do this calculation.)

Q5 What are the units of the rate of change? What does the rate of change tell you about the door's motion?

When you press this button, a dotted line appears connecting the two points on the graph. →

6. Press the *Show Rate* button to check your result.

Q6 What is the relationship between the dotted line and the rate of change you calculated?

Q7 Move t back and forth. How can you tell from the rate of change whether the door is opening or closing? How can you tell whether its rate is fast or slow?

The value of t_1 should now be exactly *1.10000*. →

Q8 Use the buttons to set t to *1.0* and h to *0.1*. What's the rate of change?

You should now have two rows of numbers in the table, with the first row permanent and the second row changing as the measurements themselves change. →

7. Select the numeric values of t, d, t_1, d_1, h, and the rate of change. With these six measurements selected, choose **Graph | Tabulate**. Double-click the table to make the current entries permanent.

D: The Limit of the Rate of Change

You may want to press the 0.1 button and then the 0.01 button again to check the motion of the dotted line. →

8. Set the time interval (h) to exactly *0.01*. Note the new value of the rate of change. Could you see the dotted line move as you reduced the time interval? With the interval set to *0.01*, double-click the table to permanently record these new values.

Q9 How does this rate of change compare to the value when h was *0.1*?

9. Similarly, record in the table the values for intervals of *0.001*, *0.0001*, *0.00001*, and *0.000001*.

Q10 What do you notice about the value of the rate of change as the time interval becomes smaller and smaller? What value does the rate of change seem to be approaching?

Q11 Can you see the dotted line move as h changes from *0.001* to *0.0001*?

10. Set the value of t to *3* seconds (by pressing the $t \rightarrow 3$ button), and collect more data on the rate of change of the door's angle. Collect one row of data for each time interval from *0.1* second to *0.000001* second.

Calculus: Concepts and Applications Instructor's Resource Book
©2005 Key Curriculum Press

Instantaneous Rate (continued)

The *average rate of change* is the rate of change between *two* different values of t. The *instantaneous rate of change* is the exact rate of change at *one* specific value of t. Because you must have two different values to calculate the rate of change, one way of measuring the instantaneous rate of change is by making the second value closer and closer to the first, and finding the *limit* of the average rate of change as the interval gets very small.

The instantaneous rate of change of a function—that is, the limit of the average rate of change as the interval gets close to zero—is called the *derivative* of the function.

Q12 What is the derivative of the door's angle when t is 3 seconds?

One Type of Integral

Consider starting up when driving a car. The speed increases for a while and then levels off at 60 ft/s. From a graph of the speed, how could you determine the distance the car has traveled?

Recall that *distance = rate · time*. Because the speed is constant in the shaded part on the right, from $t = 70$ s to $t = 100$ s, you can multiply rate by time (60 ft/s · 30 s) to find that the car travels 1800 ft during this period of time.

The distance traveled from $t = 70$ s to $t = 100$ s is equal to the area of the shaded rectangle on the right, because rate · time is equal to height · width.

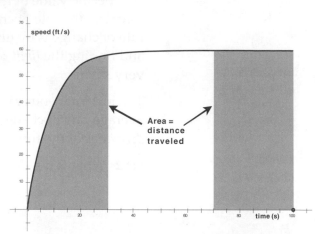

Determining how far the car travels during the time from $t = 0$ s to $t = 30$ s is harder, because the speed is changing. The process of finding this distance, when the speed is changing, is called finding the *definite integral*.

The definite integral of a function corresponds to the area under the graph of the function.

A: The Distance a Car Travels

1. Open the sketch **DefiniteIntegral.gsp** in the **GSP Sketches** folder. Press the button labeled *Drive Car* to start the car. Observe how the car's speed behaves, starting from 0 and ending up at 60 ft/s.

2. To find the total distance the car travels during any period of time, you'll have to estimate the area under the curve. Press the button labeled *Show Grid* to display a grid you can use in estimating the area.

Q1 How wide is each square of the grid? What are the units?

Q2 How high is each square of the grid? What are the units?

Q3 What's the area of each square of the grid? What are the units?

Q4 How many squares are in the right-hand shaded region? How can you use this result to find the distance traveled from $t = 70$ s to $t = 100$ s?

Now you'll count squares to find the area (distance traveled) for the left-hand region.

To keep track, you can use the Point Tool to put a point inside each square you count.

3. Count the number of complete squares that are totally contained within the left-hand shaded region.

4. Now estimate the area of the squares that are partially within the shaded region. For each such square, estimate whether it is more than half shaded or less than half shaded. Count only the squares that are more than half shaded. Add this number to the number of complete squares you counted in Step 3.

Calculus: Concepts and Applications Instructor's Resource Book
©2005 Key Curriculum Press

One Type of Integral (continued)

Remember to multiply the number of squares by the value represented by each square.

Q5 What is your estimate of the number of squares in the left-hand shaded region?

Q6 What is the distance the car traveled from $t = 0$ s to $t = 30$ s?

5. Select the *Square Size* parameter, and then press the minus sign on the keyboard to change the size of the squares to *2.0*.

Count the complete squares first, and then count all the partial squares that are more than half shaded.

6. Count the squares in the left-hand shaded region.

Q7 How many squares do you get this time?

Q8 Based on this count, what is the distance the car traveled?

Q9 Do you think this estimate is more or less accurate than the previous one? Why? How could you make it still more accurate?

Q10 Estimate the area from $t = 30$ s to $t = 70$ s, and add your results for the three areas to find the total distance the car traveled. This area is called the *definite integral*.

B: Definite Integrals for Other Functions

7. On page 2 of the sketch, you'll find another function, $y = 8 \cdot 0.7^x$. Estimate the definite integral for this function, using the domain from $x = 1.00$ to $x = 7.00$.

Q11 What is your estimate of the definite integral for this function?

Q12 Double-click the *Square Size* parameter, and change the value of the parameter to *0.5*. What is your new estimate of the definite integral for this function?

Q13 Change the value of the parameter to *0.1*. If you had to count such small squares, what kind of function would you prefer to have? Why?

C: Explore More

Be careful to determine the area of each rectangle correctly.

Use several different-size rectangles to estimate the definite integral for the function on page 3 of the sketch.

Using the grid on page 4 of this sketch, plot some other functions of your choice and estimate the definite integrals. (Choose **Graph | Plot New Function** to graph a function.) You'll need to adjust the parameters to position the grid appropriately. Here are some possible function choices:

$f(x) = \sin(x)$ from $x = 0$ to $x = \pi$

$f(x) = \sin(x)$ from $x = \pi$ to $x = 3\pi/2$ (What should you do about squares that are below the x-axis?)

$g(x) = x^2 - 2x - 1$ from $x = 1$ to $x = 2$

$g(x) = x^2 - 2x - 1$ from $x = 2$ to $x = 3$

Rectangular and Trapezoidal Accumulation

As you've discovered, it is time-consuming to use squares to accurately estimate a definite integral. An accurate estimate requires small squares, so there are a lot of them to count.

A quicker method is to count all the squares in a column at once, by calculating the area of a rectangle or a trapezoid.

A: Definite Integrals by Rectangles

Note that this sketch has six rectangular columns that can be used to estimate the definite integral.

1. Open the sketch **TrapezoidalAccumulation.gsp** in the **GSP Sketches** folder.

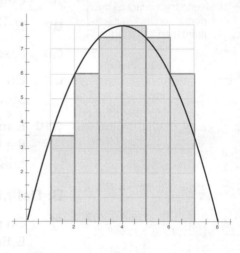

Q1 What is the sum of the areas of the rectangles?

Q2 Do you think this sum is a good estimate of the definite integral? Why or why not?

2. Press the button labeled *Animate Grid* to change the number of rectangles used in estimating the definite integral.

Q3 As the animation progresses, watch the sum measurement. What is the largest estimate for the definite integral? What's the smallest?

3. Stop the animation, and choose **Undo Animate Parameters** from the Edit menu to return the number of rectangles to 6.

4. Select two measurements: *width* and *Sum of Rectangle Areas*. Choose **Tabulate** from the Graph menu to create a table.

5. With the table selected, choose **Add Table Data** from the Graph menu. Select the option to add 10 entries as values change, and then click **OK**.

6. Press the *Animate Grid* button again. This time the various total area estimates are recorded in the table.

Q4 Which of the estimates recorded in the table do you think is the most accurate? Why?

B: Constructing Your Own Rectangles

7. Go to page 2 of the sketch. On this page you will construct rectangles of your own.

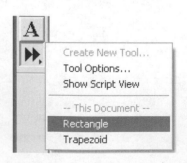

8. Press and hold the Custom Tool icon. From the menu that appears, choose the Rectangle Tool.

Rectangular and Trapezoidal Accumulation
(continued)

9. You'll use the tool to construct three rectangles. First, click on the *x*-axis at the start of the domain, exactly where *x = 1.0*. This should produce a single rectangle, along with an area measurement.

*If you haven't done it right, choose **Undo** from the Edit menu as many times as necessary, choose the Rectangle Tool again, and then try again from step 9.*

10. Click on the bottom right corner of the rectangle you just constructed to make a second rectangle. Click on the bottom right corner of the second rectangle to make the third. If you've done it correctly, the last rectangle ends exactly at *x = 7.0*.

Q5 Each time you used the Rectangle Tool, a measurement appeared with the area of that rectangle. What is the sum of the three areas?

You can use Parameter Properties to determine the amount by which the parameter will change when you press the plus or minus key on the keyboard.

11. Select both the width and height measurements, and press the minus key on the keyboard twice. This will change both values from *2.0* to *1.0*, so the widths of your rectangles are now *1.0*. Now you need more rectangles.

12. Use the Rectangle Tool again to make the three more rectangles required to cover the entire domain to *x = 7.0*. Add the six area measurements for the six rectangles.

Use Sketchpad's calculator to add the area measurements.

Q6 Now that you have six rectangles, what is the sum of their areas? Is this more or less accurate than your previous result?

C: Definite Integrals by Trapezoids

Rectangles don't measure the area at the top of each column very well.

Rectangles don't do a very good job of estimating the squares that are only partially within the area you want to find. Using trapezoids will give a more accurate result.

13. Go to page 3 of the sketch. Choose the Trapezoid Tool from the Custom Tool menu.

This should produce a single trapezoid, along with an area measurement.

14. Click the Trapezoid Tool on the *x*-axis at the start of the domain, exactly where *x = 1.0*.

15. Click again to construct five more trapezoids, ending at *x = 7.0*.

Q7 Use Sketchpad's calculator to add the areas of the trapezoids. What is the sum?

Q8 How does this area compare with the area of the rectangles from the previous page? Which do you think is more accurate?

The more accurately you measure the area, the closer you come to the exact value of the definite integral. The definite integral can be defined as the *limit* of the total area as the width of the approximating rectangles or trapezoids decreases.

Limits with Tables

The definition of both derivative and integral involves the concept of a limit. In this activity you'll explore the mathematical meaning of the limit of the value of a function. You'll do so by making a table of values using values closer and closer to the x-value at which you want to find the limit.

A: A Table of Values

1. Open the sketch **LimitsByTable.gsp** in the **GSP Sketches** folder. Note that this sketch contains the function $f(x) = \frac{0.4x^2 - 10}{x - 5}$.

To calculate $f(5)$, choose **Calculate** from the Measure menu, then click on the function $f(x)$ in the sketch, press 5 on the calculator's keypad, and finally click OK.

2. Use Sketchpad's calculator to evaluate $f(5)$.

Q1 What is the result? Why do you think you get this result?

3. The sketch contains a parameter x. Double-click this parameter to change its value. First change it to 4 and record below the value of the function $f(x)$. Then change x to 5 and record the function's value. Finally change it to 6 and record the value again.

Q2 What is $f(4)$? _____ $f(5)$? _____ $f(6)$? _____

4. Change the value of the parameter x to 4.5, and click the button labeled *Animate By 0.1*.

Q3 What happens? What values does x take on? When does it stop?

Make sure the value of x is reset to exactly 4.5 before collecting table data.

5. You can collect the changing values in the table on the right side of the screen. Select the table and choose **Add Table Data** from the Graph menu. Click the button to add 10 entries as the values change, and click OK.

6. For you to actually collect the values in the table, the values must be changing. Click the *Animate By 0.1* button to change the parameter and add values to the table.

Q4 What does the table show for $f(5)$? Can you see a pattern in the values of $f(x)$ before and after $f(5)$? If you followed that pattern, what would be the value for $f(5)$? (This value is the *limit* of $f(x)$ as x approaches 5.)

B: Getting Closer to the Limit

If your table gets too large, create a second table, or select the existing table and choose **Graph|Remove Table Data.**

7. To get values of $f(x)$ that are closer to this limit, you need to use values of x that are closer to 5. Double-click the x parameter and change its value to 4.95. Then add 10 more entries to the table, and click the *Animate By 0.01* button to actually add entries.

Q5 Does the pattern still indicate the same limit as x approaches 5? How close do the new values actually come to the limit?

You may have to drag the table vertically to see the new entries.

8. To get values even closer to the limit, change x to 4.995, and add 10 more entries, using the *Animate By 0.001* button.

Q6 Does the pattern still indicate the same limit as x approaches 5? How close do these new values actually come to the limit?

Calculus: Concepts and Applications Instructor's Resource Book
©2005 Key Curriculum Press

Limits with Tables (continued)

Consult your table to answer the next questions.

Q7 Approximately how close must x be to 5 so that the value of $f(x)$ will be within *0.01* of the limit?

Q8 Approximately how close must x be to 5 so that the value of $f(x)$ will be within *0.001* of the limit?

C: Explore More

If you need to remove entries from a table, select the table and choose **Graph|Remove Table Data.**

→ Change the function to one of the following, and collect similar data. For each function, describe your findings, tell whether or not the function has a limit L, and give a value of L (if possible).

$$f(x) = \frac{1}{x - 5} \text{ at } x = 5$$

$$f(x) = 2 + \frac{|x - 5|}{x - 5} \text{ at } x = 5$$

To change a button's properties, select the button by clicking on its handle. Then choose **Edit|Properties.**

→ The animation buttons in this sketch are set to animate x on both sides of the value *5.0*. You can change the properties of the buttons to use a different domain. (Go to the Animate panel of the Properties dialog to do so.) Modify the buttons to investigate one or more of the following limits.

$$f(x) = |x - 2| \text{ at } x = 2$$

$$f(x) = \frac{1}{x^2 - 1} \text{ at } x = 1$$

$$f(x) = 0.5x + \frac{|x - 3|}{x - 3} \text{ at } x = 3$$

$$f(x) = \sin(x) \text{ at } x = \pi/4$$

$$f(x) = \tan(x) \text{ at } x = \pi/2$$

Limits with Delta and Epsilon

The formal definition of a limit is:

> L is the limit of $f(x)$ as x approaches c if and only if:
>   For any $\varepsilon > 0$, no matter how small,
>   there exists a positive number δ such that,
>   when x is within δ of c,
> $f(x)$ is within ε of L.

In this activity you'll determine the limit L of a function, and you'll adjust the value of δ to satisfy the definition above. For some functions and values of c this will work, because the limit exists. For other functions and values of c this won't work, because there is no such limit.

A: First Function

1. Open the sketch **LimitsEpsilonDelta.gsp** in the **GSP Sketches** folder. Note that this sketch contains the function $f(x) = \frac{0.4x^2 - 10}{x - 5}$.

2. Double-click the parameter c and set its value to 5. Drag point x along the axis, and observe the values of x and of the function.

Q1 Use the *Move x→c* button to move x to the exact value of c. What happens? What is the value of $f(c)$?

3. Drag x back and forth near c, and observe the values of x and $f(x)$.

Q2 What do you think is the limit of the value of the function when x is close to c?

4. Double-click the parameter L and change its value to this limit.

5. Click the *Show Epsilon* button. This button shows in green a range above and below L on the y-axis. Use the ε slider to change the value of epsilon, and observe the results. Manipulate the slider so that ε is approximately *0.25*.

To confirm numerically, observe the value of $|f(x) - L|$. |→ **Q3** Drag x back and forth. For what values of x is the value of the function within ε of L? (In other words, for what values of x does the horizontal red segment touch the green portion of the y-axis?)

6. Click the *Show Delta* button. Drag the δ slider back and forth, and observe the effect on the horizontal blue portion of the x-axis.

7. Click the *Restrict x* button, and drag x back and forth. Observe that the value of x is now restricted to the blue area.

Your job now is to set δ so that the value of $f(x)$ is always within ε of L.

Q4 What value of δ is required to keep $f(x)$ within ε of L?

8. Now try a smaller value of ε. Set $\varepsilon = 0.15$, and determine the value of δ required to keep $f(x)$ within ε of L.

Q5 What value of δ is now required to keep $f(x)$ within ε of L?

Limits with Delta and Epsilon (continued)

Q6 Do you think you can find an appropriate value of δ, even if ε is very small? Justify your answer.

B: Second Function

For this function, the values of *c* and *L* are already set for you.

9. Go to page 2 of the sketch. On this page you'll investigate the limit of a different function.

10. Click the *Show Epsilon* button, and make sure that ε is close to *1.0*. Also click the *Show Delta* and *Show Segments* buttons.

Q7 Can you adjust δ to keep $f(x)$ within ε of *L*? What value of δ must you use?

11. Now choose a smaller value of ε, by setting ε = 0.50. Try to adjust δ to keep $f(x)$ within ε of *L*.

Q8 What happens when you try to adjust δ to keep $f(x)$ within ε of *L*? Does it help to use a smaller value of δ? Can you make this work by choosing a different value of *L*?

C: Other Functions

12. Go to page 3, containing the function $f(x) = 1 + \frac{x}{x-3}$. Set the value of *c* to *3.0*. Click *Show Epsilon* and set ε = *1.00*. Experiment with various settings of *L* and δ.

Q9 Are there any values of *L* and δ that keep $f(x)$ within ε of *L*? If so, what values did you use? If not, why not?

Try to find the indicate limits of these functions:

$$f(x) = \frac{1}{x^2 - 1} \text{ at } x = 1 \text{ and at } x = 0$$

$$f(x) = 0.5x + \frac{|x-3|}{x-3} + 1 \text{ at } x = 0.5 \text{ and at } x = 3$$

$$f(x) = \tan(x) \text{ at } x = \frac{\pi}{4} \text{ and at } x = \frac{\pi}{2}$$

Activity Notes

Instantaneous Rate

Activity Time: 45 minutes

Required Sketch: InstantaneousRate.gsp

General Notes: Use this activity to

- make a connection between instantaneous rate and slope of the tangent to the graph.

- get students to see the instantaneous rate as a limit of the slope between two points, just as the tangent represents the limit of a secant line.

- introduce the concept and definition of the derivative.

Q1 The angle increases from $t = 0$ to approximately $t = 1.45$. You can tell because the maximum value of the angle occurs at approximately $t = 1.45$.

Q2 The maximum angle is approximately $106°$, at $t = 1.45$.

Q3 The slider has a maximum value of 1. It uses a logarithmic scale, so it's easy to achieve very small values—values that are much smaller than can be observed on the graph.

Q4 Yes, the displayed values (to 5 decimal digits) continue to show the changes.

Q5 The units are degrees per second. The rate of change tells you by how many degrees the door is opening or closing for every second.

Q6 The rate of change is the slope of the dotted secant line. As the secant line approaches tangency, the calculated rate of change approaches the instantaneous rate of change.

Q7 When the rate of change is positive, the door is opening; when the rate is negative, it's closing. When the rate of change is close to zero, the door is moving slowly; when the absolute value of the rate of change is large, it's moving quickly.

Q8 When $t_1 = 1$ and $\Delta t = 0.1$, the calculated rate of change is 26.33629 degrees/second.

Q9 The average rate of change is higher (over 30 degrees/second) and appears to be a more accurate value for $t_1 = 1.0$.

Q10 The rate of change seems to be approaching a limit; the differences are less and less. The rate of change seems to be approaching 30.685... degrees/second.

Q11 No, the change is too small to observe on the graph.

Q12 The derivative (that is, the limit of the rate of change) seems to be about $-26.986...$ degrees/second. The negative sign means that the door is closing.

One Type of Integral

Activity Time: 45 minutes

Required Sketch: DefiniteIntegral.gsp

General Notes: This activity and the following one introduce the concept of definite integral—the concept of accumulating the value of a function over a particular domain of values of the independent variable. The practical application, in which we use the speed function to determine distance traveled, helps to suggest the usefulness of the definite integral.

Q1 Each grid square is 5 s wide.

Q2 Each grid square is 5 ft/s high.

Q3 Each grid square represents 25 ft of travel.

Q4 The right-hand region has $6 \cdot 12 = 72$ squares. Because each square represents 25 ft of travel, the car travels $72 \cdot 25 = 1800$ ft during this period of time.

Q5 Answers will vary. There are approximately 44 whole squares and 7 squares that are more than half shaded, for a total of 51 squares in the left region.

Q6 Answers will vary. The car traveled approximately 1275 ft.

Q7 Answers will vary. There are approximately 320 or 330 squares in the left region.

Q8 Answers will vary. A count of 325 squares corresponds to 1300 ft of travel.

Q9 This estimate is more accurate. The smaller squares allow a more accurate measurement, because they fit the curve better. You could have a more accurate result by making the squares still smaller.

Q10 There are about 597 squares between $t = 30$ s and $t = 70$ s, representing a distance of 2388 ft. The total distance traveled is about 1300 ft + 2388 ft + 1800 ft = 5488 ft.

Q11 Based on 14 squares, the definite integral is about 14.

Q12 Based on 55 squares, the definite integral is about 13.75.

Q13 If the function were constant, we could just find the area of the rectangle instead of counting. If the function were a linear function, we could find the area of a trapezoid. Either method is much easier than trying to count every single square.

Rectangular and Trapezoidal Accumulation

Activity Time: 45 minutes

Required Sketch: TrapezoidalAccumulation.gsp

Optional Sketch: TrapezoidalAccumulationTool. gsp

General Notes: This activity builds on the last by developing a more accurate and more efficient way of accumulating values.

The first page of this sketch shows a trapezoidal accumulation in which the number of trapezoids can be varied. This construction is provided as a tool, and is explained in detail, in the sketch **TrapezoidalAccumulationTool.gsp**.

Q1 The sum of the areas is approximately 38.5.

Q2 It's a better estimate than using rectangles. Still, it's not great, because the shapes of the trapezoids don't match the function very well.

Q3 The largest is 40.32, the smallest is 38.50.

Q4 The last estimate uses the smallest trapezoids, so is more accurately fitted to the graph.

Q5 The sum of the three rectangles is 19.38.

Q6 The sum of the three rectangles is 16.47. This is significantly closer, although by looking at the rectangles it's clear that it still overstates the true value.

Q7 The sum of the areas of the three trapezoids is 14.00.

Q8 The result is smaller and eliminates most of the excess of the rectangles. The trapezoids give a far more accurate result.

Limits with Tables

Activity Time: 45 minutes

Required Sketch: LimitsByTable.gsp

General Notes: This activity introduces the fundamental concept of a limit numerically, by looking at values in a table. The formal definition and manipulation of delta and epsilon are left for a later activity.

Q1 The result is undefined, because the divisor is $(x - 5)$ and division by zero is undefined.

Q2 $f(4) = 3.60$, $f(5)$ is undefined, and $f(6) = 4.40$.

Q3 The parameter changes from 4.5 up to 5.5 in steps of 0.1 and then returns to its original value.

Q4 The table shows an undefined value for $f(5)$. Values before $f(5)$ are increasing regularly by 0.04, and values after $f(5)$ are also increasing by the same amount. If the pattern were followed, the value of $f(5)$ would be 4.000.

Q5 The pattern indicates the same limit as before. The values of $f(x)$ now come within 0.004 of 4.000.

Q6 Yes, these values are even closer, within 0.0004 of 4.0000.

Q7 If x is within about 0.02 of 5, $f(x)$ is within 0.01 of 4. (More precisely, x must be within 0.025 of 5.)

Q8 If x is within about 0.002 of 5, $f(x)$ is within 0.001 of 4. (More precisely, x must be within 0.0025 of 5.)

Limits with Delta and Epsilon

Activity Time: 45 minutes

Required Sketch: LimitsEpsilonDelta.gsp

General Notes: This activity introduces the formal definition of a limit and reinforces it by asking the student to choose values of L (to determine the limit itself) and to manipulate values of δ and ε (so that the definition actually makes sense).

By manipulating the sliders for δ and ε, students get a much clearer sense of the meanings of these two values, and a clearer understanding of the formal definition of a limit.

Q1 The point x on the axis moves to c. The red point on the graph and the connecting segments disappear. The value of the function is undefined.

Q2 When x is close to c, the value of $f(x)$ is close to 4, so the limit is 4.

Q3 When x is between 4.5 and 5.5, the value of the function is within ε of L.

Q4 A value of 0.5 keeps $f(x)$ within ε of L.

Q5 A value of approximately 0.35 keeps $f(x)$ within ε of L.

Q6 Yes. No matter how small ε is, you can just make δ smaller as needed.

Q7 Yes, a value of δ that's less than 2.0 will keep $f(x)$ within ε of L.

Q8 Now there's no way to choose an appropriate δ. Any value we pick allows the value of $f(x)$ to be taken from either of the two branches of the graph, both of which are outside the ε range.

Q9 No, there's no other value of L that will work, because the function takes a jump from 2 to 4 at $x = 4$, and any limit cannot be close to both of those values.

Calculus: Concepts and Applications Instructor's Resource Book
©2005 Key Curriculum Press

Technology Projects: Fathom

For students and teachers who are beginners to Fathom, the learning guide that comes with Fathom is an excellent resource, as is *Data in Depth: Exploring Mathematics with Fathom*, by Tim Erickson and published by Key Curriculum Press. You can also visit the Fathom resource center at www.keypress.com/fathom/.

All required Fathom files can be found in the project folder in the Fathom Files folder in the *Instructor's Resource Book* CD-ROM. Instructor's Notes follow each activity.

Here is a list of the projects in this section, in the order of the chapters they are meant to accompany.

Chapter 3 Derivatives, Antiderivatives, and Indefinite Integrals

The Fathom project *Creating Change* uses Fathom to explore the calculus of numerical data. Students are asked to find formulas that will calculate both rate of change (derivative) and accumulation (antiderivative). These ideas are linked to velocity, acceleration, and displacement. Students explore the relationships among the graphs of function, derivative, and antiderivative, and can investigate how changes in one graph affect the others. This activity is recommended for use with Section 3-5.

Chapter 5 Definite and Indefinite Integrals

The Fathom project *The Mean Value Theorem* uses Fathom to help students explore the mean value theorem and discover some interesting patterns that occur when the theorem is applied to quadratic, cubic, power, and sinusoidal functions. This activity is recommended for use with Section 5-5.

Chapter 7 The Calculus of Growth and Decay

The Fathom project *Euler's Method* explores Euler's method numerically and is recommended for use with Section 7-5.

Chapter 8 The Calculus of Plane and Solid Figures

The Fathom project *Arc Length* uses Fathom to explore how segments can be used to approximate the length of an arc and to see that smaller Δx's result in better approximations. The project provides experimentation with rectangular, parametric, and polar equations. This activity is recommended for use with Sections 8-5 and 8-7.

Chapter 12 The Calculus of Functions Defined by Power Series

The Fathom project *Taylor Polynomials* uses Fathom to explore how series can be used as approximations for various functions. Students practice increasing the number of terms of a series to see how that affects the radius of convergence. This activity is recommended for use with Section 12-5.

Creating Change

Adapted from *Change Playground*, by Tim Erickson

Part 1

1. In a new Fathom document, make a new case table (by dragging it from the shelf or choosing **Case Table** from the **Insert** menu).

2. Make a new attribute, **T**, and give it seven cases with the values {1, 2, 3, 4, 5, 6, 7}.

3. Make a second new attribute, **V**, and give it seven cases with the values {0, 2, 4, 6, 8, 10, 12}.

4. Make a third new attribute, **A**. Choose **Show Formulas** from the **Display** menu. Double-click on the gray box that appears below **A** to enter a formula for **A**. Enter the formula **V − prev(V, "")**. ("" means that if there is no previous value of **V**, no value of **A** will be calculated.) Click the **OK** button to close the formula editor. **A** now has values. Your case table should look like the one shown here.

5. Make two graphs. In one, put **T** on the horizontal axis and **V** on the vertical axis; in the other, put **T** on the horizontal axis and **A** on the vertical axis. Make both graphs line plots by choosing **Line Scatter Plot** from the pop-up menu in the graph itself. The two graphs should look like the ones shown here.

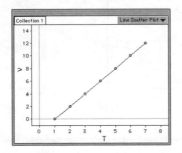 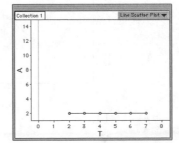

6. If you think of **T** as time, **V** as velocity, and **A** as acceleration, why does the formula for **A** make sense? Why do the graphs make sense?

7. In the **V** graph, grab the third point and drag it vertically. (Try to keep the **T**-value close to 3.) You will see the values changing in the case table. Describe the effect this has on the **A** graph. Why does this make sense?

8. Now make a new attribute, **D**, representing distance. Enter the formula **prev(D) + V · (T − prev(T))**.

9. Make a new graph, with **T** on the horizontal axis and **D** on the vertical axis. Make the graph a line plot. How is the graph of **D** related to the graph of **V**?

Creating Change (continued)

10. Highlight all the points in the **V** graph. Then grab one point and drag it up or down. (Try not to change the **T**-values.) What happens to the graphs of **A** and **D**? Why? What if you drag only one value on the **V** graph up or down?

11. Why can you drag only values of **V**, not values of **A** or **D**? How can you adjust the values of **V** to make the graph of **D** a straight line that increases at a constant rate? How can you adjust the values of **V** to make the graph of **D** a horizontal line?

12. The formula you entered for **D** assumes that the initial value of **D** is zero. Create a slider to control the initial value of **D**. Make a slider by dragging it from the shelf or choosing **Slider** from the **Insert** menu. Change the name of the slider to **initial_D**. Change the formula for **D** to **prev(D, initial_D) + V · (T − prev(T))**. Now use the slider to change the value of **initial_D**. How do the graphs of V, A, and D change?

Part 2

For each of the following graphs of **V**, **A**, or **D**, sketch possibilities for the two missing graphs. You may wish to use the Fathom document you created in Steps 1–12 to help you. If the graph of **D** is not given, assume an initial value of 0. Be sure to notice the scale given.

13.

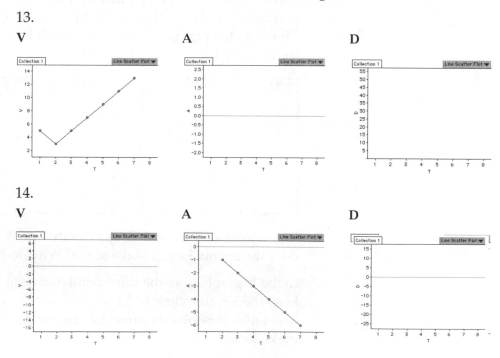

14.

15.

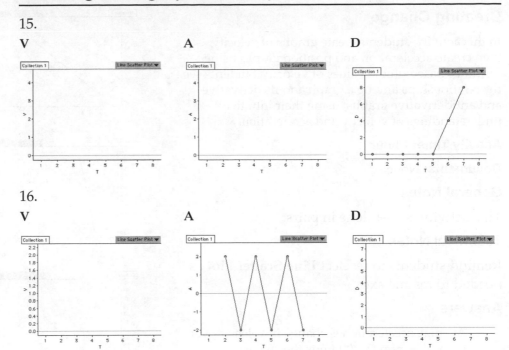

V   A   D

16.

V   A   D

Instructor's Notes

Creating Change

In this activity, students create graphs of velocity, then create acceleration and position graphs using formulas based on the values of velocity. Students see the relationships among a graph and its derivative and antiderivative graphs, using their intuitive understandings of velocity and acceleration.

Activity Time: 1 hour

Documents: None

General Notes

This activity is best done in pairs.

Technical Notes

Remind students to reselect **Line Scatter Plot** as needed to rescale axes.

Answers

6. Average acceleration is change in velocity over time. **V − prev(V, "")** finds the change in velocity over the previous 1 unit of time interval. Because the time interval is 1, it is not necessary to divide by the change in time. The first graph shows that velocity increases at a constant rate of 2. The second graph shows that acceleration is a constant, 2, which is consistent with the velocity graph.

7. The **A** graph is no longer constant. If the value of **V** at **T** = 3 is increased, then the value of **A** is increased also, because the acceleration must be larger than it was. Then the value of **A** at **T** = 4 is decreased, because the velocity must decrease to return to where it was. The opposite is also true.

9. The graph of **D** is the accumulation of the area under **V**.

10. The graph of **A** remains the same, whereas the graph of **D** gets steeper as **V**-values are increased.

11. You cannot drag values of **A** or **D** because they are calculated by formula based on the values of **V**.

12. The graphs of **V** and **A** are not affected. The graph of **D** is translated vertically.

13.

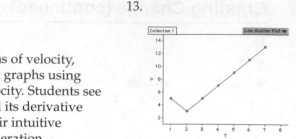

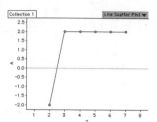

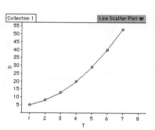

14.

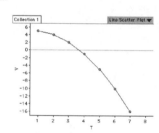

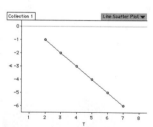

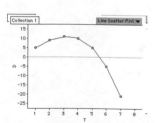

Calculus: Concepts and Applications Instructor's Resource Book
©2005 Key Curriculum Press

Extensions

For students who finish early, you may wish to have them draw **V**, **A**, or **D** graphs, trade with another student, and sketch the missing graphs.

15.

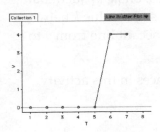

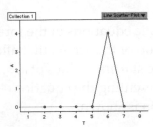

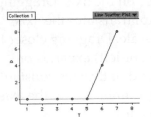

16.

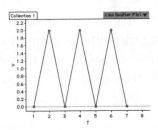

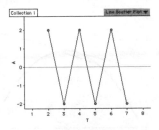

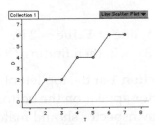

The Mean Value Theorem

The mean value theorem states that if $f(x)$ is continuous on $[a, b]$ and differentiable on (a, b), there exists some value k on $[a, b]$ such that $f'(k) = \frac{f(b) - f(a)}{b - a}$. In other words, there must be some value k between a and b such that the tangent line at k and the secant line from a to b are parallel.

You'll explore this property and its consequences in this activity.

Part 1: Quadratic Functions

1. Open the file **MVTquadratic**.

2. In this activity you will work with quadratic equations in the form $y = ax^2 + bx + c$. There are sliders at the top of the screen that allow you to change the values of a, b, and c. The starting values of a, b, and c are 2, -1, and -6, respectively, representing the equation $y = 2x^2 - x - 6$. The graph of this equation is shown.

    To adjust axes in Fathom, drag the numbers on the axis. Dragging in the middle (when the hand is straight up) translates the axis, changing the range without changing the scale. Dragging closer to the ends (when the hand points to the right or left) expands or contracts the range, keeping the opposite end of the axis constant. You can think of this action as pulling new numbers onto the axis (zooming out) or pulling them off (zooming in).

    Play with the axes and get comfortable changing them.

3. Now change the values of a, b, and c. Click on a slider to make it active. It will then have a gray border. Drag the slider's thumb to a new position on the number scale. Or double-click the blue numeric value and type in a new one. How does changing the values of a, b, and c change the graph?

4. Change the values of a to -1, b to 3, and c to 2. Your graph should look like the one shown here. Now look at the slider called **Value** at the bottom of your screen. This represents the location of a line tangent to the curve $y = -x^2 + 3x + 2$. Change this slider's value and notice the change in location of the tangent line.

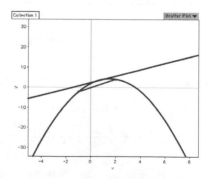

5. Set **Value** $= 2$. Find the slope of the tangent line at **Value** $= 2$ by calculating the derivative of $f(x) = -x^2 + 3x + 2$, then finding $f'(2)$.

6. Double-click on the gold box called **Collection 1** at the top left of the screen. You will see the collection's inspector appear on the bottom of the screen. The value of **mtan** shown in the inspector should match your answer to Problem 5. Move the **Value** slider and watch the value of **mtan** change.

The Mean Value Theorem (continued)

7. The case table near the top left of the screen indicates two points, (x, y). When $x = -1$, $y = f(-1) = -2$, and when $x = 2$, $y = f(2) = 4$. The secant line between these two points is shown on the graph. Find the slope of this line. This value should match the current value of **msec** in the inspector chart.

8. Now adjust the **Value** slider to make the tangent line parallel to the secant line, as shown here. If necessary, rescale the graph. At what x-value are the two lines parallel? How can you determine that the tangent and secant lines are exactly parallel?

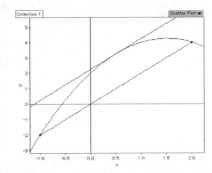

9. Use the mean value theorem to verify your answer to Problem 8 analytically.

10. Now you'll repeat this process with a different secant line. In the case table, change the values of x to $x = -4$ and $x = 9$. (You must put the smaller value of x first in the case table.) Note that the y-value adjusts automatically, as do the value of **msec** in the inspector and the location of the secant line in the graph.

11. Adjust the **Value** slider to find the x-value that makes the tangent line parallel to the secant line. Rescale the graph if necessary. Verify your solution by checking that the values of **msec** and **mtan** are equal. Solve the problem algebraically using the mean value theorem.

12. Use Fathom to find the value of k guaranteed by the mean value theorem for $f(x) = 3x^2 - 5x + 8$ on the interval $[3, 7]$, and verify analytically.

13. Use Fathom to find the value of k guaranteed by the mean value theorem for $f(x) = 0.5x^2 - 4x + \frac{13}{2}$ on the interval $[-1.5, 3.5]$, and verify analytically.

14. Use Fathom to find the value of k guaranteed by the mean value theorem for $f(x) = \frac{2x^2}{3} - \frac{5}{7}x - \frac{7}{5}$ on the interval $[-2, 4]$, and verify analytically.

15. Look for a relationship between the value of k and the endpoints of the intervals for Problems 8, 11, 12, 13, and 14. Using the equation given in Problem 14, change the values of a, b, and c using the sliders. Animate your graph by clicking on the arrows in each slider. Does the relationship still appear to be true? Prove that this relationship holds for any quadratic equation and for any interval.

The Mean Value Theorem (continued)

Part 2: Cubic Functions

16. Open the file **MVTcubic**.

17. In this activity you will work with cubic equations in the form $y = ax^3 + bx^2 + cx + d$. At the top of the screen, there are sliders that allow you to change the values of a, b, c, and d. The starting values of a, b, c, and d are $1, 0, 0$, and -1, respectively, representing the equation $y = x^3 - 1$. The graph of this equation is shown. How does changing the values of a, b, c, and d affect the graph?

18. Return the values of a, b, c, and d to $1, 0, 0$, and -1, respectively. Look at the slider called **Value**, representing the location of a line tangent to the curve $y = x^3 - 1$. Set **Value** = 2. Find the slope of the tangent line by calculating the derivative of $f(x) = x^3 - 1$, then finding $f'(2)$.

19. Double-click on the gold box called **Collection 1** at the top left of the screen. The collection's inspector will appear at the bottom left of the screen.

20. The case table near the top left of the screen shows the points $(0, -1)$ and $(1, 0)$. Find the slope of the secant line between these points (shown on the graph). This should match the value of **msec** in the inspector chart.

21. Now adjust the **Value** slider to make the tangent line appear parallel to the secant line. If necessary, rescale the graph. At approximately what x-value are the two lines parallel? How can you determine whether they are exactly parallel?

22. You will probably not be able to get the values of **msec** and **mtan** in the inspector to be exactly equal. Change the scale of the **Value** slider as shown below, to try to get closer values of **msec** and **mtan**. You can rescale a slider in the same way that you rescale axes on a graph.

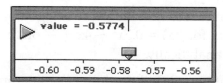

Measure	Value
msec	1
mtan	1.00017

23. Use the mean value theorem to verify your answer to Problem 21 analytically. You get two answers. Use Fathom to determine why.

24. Use Fathom to find the value of k guaranteed by the mean value theorem for $f(x) = 2x^3 + 3x^2 - 3x - 5$ on the interval $[-1, 2]$. Verify your solution analytically. (Use the quadratic formula or a grapher to solve the quadratic equation that results.)

25. Use Fathom to find the value of k guaranteed by the mean value theorem for $f(x) = -3x^3 - 3x^2 + 3x - 6$ on the interval $[-1, 1]$. Verify analytically. How is this problem different from Problem 24?

Calculus: Concepts and Applications Instructor's Resource Book
©2005 Key Curriculum Press

The Mean Value Theorem (continued)

26. Use Fathom to find the value of k guaranteed by the mean value theorem for $f(x) = -4x^3 - 8x^2 + 5$ on the interval $[-3, 2]$. Verify analytically. How is this problem different from Problem 25?

27. Starting with the equation and interval given in Problem 26, change the value of d using your slider. Describe what happens. Why? Does the same phenomenon occur if you change the values of a, b, and c? Can you determine why this occurs?

Part 3: Sinusoidal Functions

28. Open the file **MVTsinusoid**.

29. In this activity, you will work with sinusoidal equations in the form $f(x) = a \sin(bx + c) + d$. Use the sliders to change the values of a, b, c, and d. How does changing the values of a, b, c, and d change the graph?

30. Change the values of a to 1, b to 1, c to 0, and d to -1, to graph $f(x) = \sin x - 1$. Then look at the slider called **Value**, representing the location of the tangent line. Set **Value** = 0. Find the slope of the tangent line at **Value** = 0 by calculating the derivative of $f(x) = \sin x - 1$, then finding $f'(0)$.

31. Double-click on the gold box called **Collection 1** to show the collection's inspector.

32. The case table shows two points: $(0, -1)$ and $(3.14159, -0.999997)$. The graph shows the secant line between these two points. Find the slope of this line algebraically. Your answer will not be exactly the same as the value of **msec** in your inspector chart. Why?

33. Adjust the **Value** slider to find the x-value that makes the tangent and secant lines appear approximately parallel. You will probably be unable to get the values of **msec** and **mtan** to be exactly equal. Change the scale of the **Value** slider to get a more accurate approximation for x.

34. Use the mean value theorem to verify your answer to Problem 33 analytically. You get more than one answer. Use Fathom to determine why.

35. Use Fathom to find the value of k guaranteed by the mean value theorem for $f(x) = 3 \sin(2x + \pi) - 2$ on the interval $[0, \pi/3]$. Verify your solution analytically. (Use a grapher to solve the sinusoidal equation that results.)

36. Use Fathom to find the value of k guaranteed by the mean value theorem for $f(x) = 5 \sin\left(\frac{1}{2}x + \frac{\pi}{4}\right) + 1$ on the interval $[0, 3\pi]$. Verify analytically. How is this problem different from Problems 34 and 35?

37. Starting with the equation and interval given in Problem 36, change the value of d using the slider. What do you notice? Does the same phenomenon occur if you change the values of a, b, and c?

38. Can you determine why changing the value of a, b, c, or d will or will not affect the results of the mean value theorem?

39. What change to c does not affect the solution(s) to the mean value theorem?

Part 4: Power Functions

40. Open the file **MVTpower**.

41. In this activity you will work with equations in the form $f(x) = a|x|^b$. At the top of the screen, there are sliders that allow you to change the values of a and b. The starting values of a and b are 2 and 3, respectively, representing the equation $y = 2|x|^3$. How does changing the values of a and b affect the graph?

42. Change the values of a to 3 and b to -1. Set **Value** = 3. Find the slope of the tangent line at **Value** = 3 by calculating the derivative of $y = \frac{3}{|x|}$, then finding $f'(3)$.

43. Double-click on the gold box called **Collection 1** to show the collection's inspector.

44. Set **Value** = 0. Find the slope of the tangent line at **Value** = 0 by calculating the derivative of $y = \frac{3}{|x|}$, then finding $f'(0)$.

45. The case table shows two points: $(-1, 3)$ and $(1, 3)$. Find the slope of the secant line between these two points. Your answer should match the value of **msec** in the inspector chart.

46. Adjust the **Value** slider to find the x-value that makes the tangent and secant lines appear approximately parallel. Will you ever be able to make the lines parallel?

47. Does your answer to Problem 46 contradict the mean value theorem? Explain.

48. Use Fathom to find the value of k guaranteed by the mean value theorem for $f(x) = 3|x|^{2/3}$ on the interval $[-2, 2]$. If the theorem doesn't apply, explain why, and use Fathom to show why k does not exist.

49. Using the equation and interval given in Problem 48, show algebraically why $f'(0)$ does not exist. Determine $\lim_{x \to 0} f'(x)$ and confirm using Fathom.

50. Find the value of k guaranteed by the mean value theorem for $f(x) = 5|x|$ on the interval $[1, -3]$. If the theorem doesn't apply, explain why, and use Fathom to show why k does not exist.

Instructor's Notes

The Mean Value Theorem

The goal of this activity is to give the student a visual impression of what the mean value theorem says. Students analyze quadratic, cubic, sinusoidal, and power functions in order to find the value of k that satisfies the mean value theorem for each function. (Note: k is used in place of the more common c because the constants a, b, c, and so on, are used as coefficients for the functions, e.g., $y = ax^2 + bx + c$.) Students are encouraged to use Fathom not only to visually determine the value for which the secant line is parallel to the tangent line, but also to verify the results analytically. Students will also discover how changing some coefficients in these functions does not alter the solution to the mean value theorem.

Activity Time: 1.5 hours

Documents: MVTquadratic.ftm, MVTcubic.ftm, MVTsinusoid.ftm, MVTpower.ftm, CubicAnalysis.ftm (optional)

General Notes

The four parts of this activity increase in complexity, both analytically and algebraically. The quadratic form allows for a very simple analysis of the mean value theorem. Solving the mean value theorem for a cubic function requires the use of the quadratic equation and may yield more than one answer. Sinusoidal functions require the use of a graphing utility to determine solutions, and power functions elicit the observation that the mean value theorem does not apply when functions are not continuous and differentiable.

Technical Notes

In the case table for each file, it is important that the two values between which you want your secant line must be input in increasing order. The first value of x should be the smaller number; if it isn't, the secant line will not show.

The inspector that shows the values of **msec** and **mtan** will not show on the screen automatically. Students will need to double-click on the gold collection box called **Collection 1** at the top left of the screen to show the inspector.

Answers

3. As $|a|$ increases, the parabola narrows; as $|a|$ decreases, the parabola widens. If $a < 0$, the parabola opens downward; if $a > 0$, the parabola opens upward. If $a = 0$, the result is a line. Changing b changes the position of the vertex of the parabola, while keeping the width of the parabola constant. The variable c controls the vertical translation of the parabola.

5. $f'(x) = -2x + 3 \Rightarrow f'(2) = -1$

7. Slope $= \dfrac{4 - (-2)}{2 - (-1)} = 2$

8. The lines are parallel when $x = 0.5$. The lines are exactly parallel when the values of **msec** and **mtan** are the same.

9. $-2k + 3 = 2 \Rightarrow k = 1/2$

11. The lines are parallel when $x = 2.5$.
$$-2k + 3 = \frac{f(9) - f(-4)}{9 - (-4)} = \frac{-52 - (-26)}{13} = -2$$
$$\Rightarrow k = 5/2$$

12. $6k - 5 = 25 \Rightarrow k = 5$

13. $k - 4 = -3 \Rightarrow k = 1$

14. $\dfrac{4k}{3} - \dfrac{5}{7} = \dfrac{13}{21} \Rightarrow k = 1$

15. For any quadratic equation, the value of k that satisfies the mean value theorem is the midpoint of the interval. This can be proven as follows:

Let x be the value guaranteed by the mean value theorem for $f(x) = ax^2 + bx + c$ between x_1 and x_2.

$$f'(x) = 2ax + b = \frac{ax_2^2 + bx_2 + c - ax_1^2 - bx_1 - c}{x_2 - x_1}$$

$$x = \frac{\dfrac{ax_2^2 + bx_2 + c - ax_1^2 - bx_1 - c}{x_2 - x_1} - b}{2a}$$

$$= \frac{a(x_2^2 - x_1^2) + b(x_2 - x_1)}{2a(x_2 - x_1)} - \frac{b}{2a}$$

$$= \frac{x_2 + x_1}{2} + \frac{b}{2a} - \frac{b}{2a} = \frac{x_2 + x_1}{2}$$

The value of x guaranteed by the mean value theorem is the average of the endpoints of the interval and is not dependent on the values of a, b, and c.

The Mean Value Theorem Instructor's Notes *(continued)*

17. As $|a|$ increases, the curve gets steeper; as $|a|$ decreases, the curve flattens. If $a < 0$, the curve increases from left to right; if $a > 0$, the curve decreases from left to right. The point $(0, -1)$ is a point of inflection of $y = x^3 - 1$. If $b > 0$, the curve will have a local maximum in the second or third quadrant. If $b < 0$, the curve will have a local minimum in the fourth quadrant. As c increases from 0, the curve becomes more linear. As c decreases, the local maximum and minimum become more extreme. The variable d controls the vertical translation.

18. $f'(x) = 3x^2 \Rightarrow f'(2) = 12$

20. Slope $= \dfrac{0 - (-1)}{1 - 0} = 1$

21. The lines are parallel when $x \approx 0.58$. The lines are exactly parallel when the values of **msec** and **mtan** are the same. In this case, you can't make them exactly the same, so just make them as close as possible.

23. $f'(k) = 3k^2 = 1 \Rightarrow k = \pm\sqrt{\dfrac{1}{3}}$

    There are two values of k for which the slope of the curve is 1, but only one of these values is in the specified interval.

24. $6k^2 + 6k - 3 = 6 \Rightarrow k = \dfrac{\sqrt{7} - 1}{2}$,

    $k = \dfrac{-\sqrt{7} - 1}{2} \Rightarrow k = 0.8228...$

25. $-9k^2 - 6k + 3 = 0 \Rightarrow k = \frac{1}{3}, k = -1$. One of the solutions is an endpoint; k must be *between* -1 and 1, so an endpoint does not satisfy the mean value theorem. So, $k = 1/3$.

26. $-12k^2 - 16k = -20 \Rightarrow$

    $k = \dfrac{\sqrt{19} - 2}{3}, k = \dfrac{-\sqrt{19} - 2}{3}$

    For this problem, there are two values of k in the given interval that satisfy the mean value theorem.

27. The variables c and d have no impact on the solution to the mean value theorem. The variables a and b do have an impact. (The impact of a is slight and might be difficult to observe.) You can prove this as follows:

    Let x be the value guaranteed by the mean value theorem for $f(x) = ax^3 + bx^2 + cx + d$ between x_1 and x_2.

$f'(x) = 3ax^2 + 2bx + c$

$= \dfrac{ax_2^3 + bx_2^2 + cx_2 + d - ax_1^3 - bx_1^2 + -x_1 - d}{x_2 - x_1}$

$= \dfrac{a(x_2^3 - x_1^3) + b(x_2^2 - x_1^2) + c(x_2 - x_1)}{x_2 - x_1}$

$\therefore 3ax^2 + 2bx = a(x_2^2 + x_1 x_2 + x_1^2) + b(x_2 - x_1)$

It is not necessary to solve for x to see that the solution of this equation is dependent on the values of a and b.

29. a controls the amplitude, b controls the period, c controls the horizontal translation (phase shift), and d controls the vertical translation.

30. $f'(x) = \cos x \Rightarrow f'(0) = 1$

32. Slope $= \dfrac{-0.999997 - (-1)}{3.14159 - 0} = -0.00000095....$
    This value is different from **msec** because the y-value -0.999997 in the case table is rounded. **msec** is calculated using the unrounded value. The exact slope value for $[0, \pi]$ is 0.

33. $k \approx 1.5708$

34. $\cos k = 0 \Rightarrow k = \dfrac{\pi}{2}, \dfrac{3\pi}{2}, \dfrac{5\pi}{2}, \ldots, \dfrac{(2n + 1)\pi}{2}$, where n is an integer. There are infinite values of k that make the slope of the curve zero. In the indicated interval, however, there is only one: $k = \dfrac{\pi}{2}$.

35. $f'(x) = 6\cos(2x + \pi)$
    $\Rightarrow 6\cos(2k + \pi)$

    $= \dfrac{3\sin(5\pi/3) - 3\sin\pi}{\pi/3}$

    $= -2.4809...$

    $\Rightarrow k = 0.5722...$

36. $f'(x) = \dfrac{5}{2}\cos\left(\dfrac{1}{2}x + \dfrac{\pi}{4}\right)$
    $\Rightarrow \dfrac{5}{2}\cos\left(\dfrac{1}{2}k + \dfrac{\pi}{4}\right)$

    $= \dfrac{5\sin(7\pi/4) - 5\sin(\pi/4)}{3\pi - 0}$

    $= -0.7502...$

    $\Rightarrow k = 2.1819...$ and $7.2428...$

    There are two solutions to the mean value theorem in the given interval.

37. Changing a and d does not change the solution to the mean value theorem.

Calculus: Concepts and Applications Instructor's Resource Book
©2005 Key Curriculum Press

The Mean Value Theorem Instructor's Notes (continued)

38. The mean value theorem gives

$$ab\cos(bx+c)$$
$$= \frac{a[\sin(bx_2+c)+d-\sin(bx_1+c)+d]}{x_2-x_1}$$

The variable d cancels. And you can divide both sides by a, canceling a as well. Thus the solution to the mean value theorem is not dependent on the value of a or d.

39. c represents the horizontal translation. Adding any multiple of the period, $\frac{2\pi}{b}$, will not change the solution to the mean value theorem.

41. If $a > 0$, the curve is above the x-axis, and if $a < 0$, the curve is below the x-axis. As $|a|$ increases, the steepness of the curve increases. If $b > 0$, the curve has a vertex at $(0, 0)$, and as b increases, the curve flattens out more around the origin. If $b < 0$, the curve has a vertical asymptote at $x = 0$, and as b decreases, the curve flattens out closer to $x = \pm 1$.

42. $f'(x) = \begin{cases} \dfrac{-3}{x^2}, & \text{if } x \geq 0 \\ \dfrac{3}{x^2}, & \text{if } x < 0 \end{cases} \Rightarrow f'(3) = -1/3$

44. $f'(x)$ is given in Problem 42. $f'(0)$ does not exist.

45. Slope $= \dfrac{3-3}{1-(-1)} = 0$

46. It is not possible to find a tangent line parallel to the secant line.

47. This does not contradict the mean value theorem because the function is not continuous on $[-1, 1]$.

48. $f(x)$ is not differentiable on $(-2, 2)$, so the mean value theorem doesn't apply. There is no value of k on the interval $[-2, 2]$ that has slope 0, because there is a cusp.

49. $f'(x) = \begin{cases} \dfrac{2}{x^{1/3}}, & \text{if } x \geq 0 \\ \dfrac{-2}{x^{1/3}}, & \text{if } x < 0 \end{cases}$

$\lim_{x\to 0^-} f'(x) = -\infty$ and $\lim_{x\to 0^+} f'(x) = \infty$, so $\lim_{x\to 0} f'(x)$ does not exist.

50. Slope $= \dfrac{15-5}{3-1} = 2; f'(x) = \begin{cases} 5, & \text{if } x \geq 0 \\ -5, & \text{if } x < 0 \end{cases}$

so for the interval $[1, 3]$, $f'(x) = 5$. So the mean value theorem is satisfied by every value of x in the interval $(1, 3)$.

Extensions

Explore algebraically how changing the value of a in the cubic equation $f(x) = ax^3 + bx^2 + cx + d$ changes the conclusion of the mean value theorem only very subtly. For instance, find the solutions to the mean value theorem for $f(x) = x^3 + x^2 + x + 1$ and $f(x) = 100x^3 + x^2 + x + 1$ on the interval $[0, 1]$.

$3x^2 + 2x + 1 = (4-1)/(1-0) \Rightarrow 3x^2 + 2x - 2 = 0$
$\Rightarrow x = 0.54858\ldots$

$300x^2 + 2x + 1 = (104-1)/(1-0) \Rightarrow$
$300x^2 + 2x - 102 = 0 \Rightarrow x = 0.57977\ldots$

So the solutions to the mean value theorem are very close. You can take this analysis further by asking, "What is the limit of the solution to the mean value theorem for $f(x) = kx^3 + x^2 + x + 1$ on the interval $[0, 1]$, as k approaches infinity?" The Fathom file **CubicAnalysis.ftm** explores this question. Here is the algebraic analysis:

$$f(x) = kx^3 + x^2 + x + 1$$
$$f'(x) = 3kx^2 + 2x + 1 = (k+3-1)/(1-0) \Rightarrow$$
$$3kx^2 + 2x + (-k-1) = 0$$
$$x = \frac{-2 + \sqrt{4-4(3k)(-a-1)}}{6k}$$
$$= \frac{-2 + \sqrt{4+12k^2+12k}}{6k}$$
$$= \frac{-1 + \sqrt{3k^2+3k+1}}{3k}$$
$$\lim_{k\to\infty} \frac{-1 + \sqrt{3k^2+3k+1}}{3k} = \frac{\sqrt{3}}{3}$$

More advanced students might wish to analyze the conclusion of the mean value theorem for $f(x) = kx^3 + mx^2 + x + 1$ on the interval $[x_1, x_2]$. (Note: In the activity, students learned that the coefficients of x and the constant make no difference in the solution to the mean value theorem.)

Euler's Method

Euler's method is used to approximate y-values for a particular solution of a differential equation. In this activity you'll use Fathom to compare Euler's method and the trapezoidal rule to analytical solutions of differential equations.

1. Let $\frac{dy}{dx} = 2x$, containing the point $(x, y) = (0, 0)$. Complete this chart for Euler's method with $\Delta x = dx = 0.5$.

$x_{new} = x_{old} + dx$	$y_{new} = y_{old} + dy$	$\frac{dy}{dx}$	$dy = \frac{dy}{dx}\, dx$
0.0	0	0	0
0.5	0	1	0.5
1.0	0.5		
1.5			
2.0			
2.5			
3.0			
3.5			
4.0			

2. Now complete the chart for the trapezoidal rule using the same differential equation and increment of x from Step 1. The accumulated area of the trapezoids from 0 to any point x is equal to y. Mathematically, $y = \int_0^x 2t\, dt$.

$x_{new} = x_{old} + dx$	$\frac{dy}{dx} = 2x$	Area of Trapezoid	y = Accumulated Area
0.0	0		
0.5	1	0.25	0.25
1.0			
1.5			
2.0			
2.5			
3.0			
3.5			
4.0			

3. Finally, find the equation of y analytically. Make a table with x, y_{new} from Step 1, y from Step 2, and the analytical solution. Which approximation method appears more accurate?

Calculus: Concepts and Applications Instructor's Resource Book
©2005 Key Curriculum Press

Euler's Method (continued)

4. On this graph, plot the points for Euler's method using circles, the points for the trapezoidal method in squares, and the graph of your analytical solution. Does your conclusion from Step 3 hold?

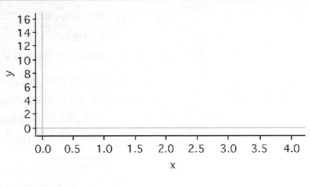

5. Open the Fathom file **Euler**, which shows the results of Steps 1–4. The graph on the bottom left shows the results of the Euler's method, trapezoidal rule, and analytical solutions. The graph on the bottom right shows the original differential equation, $\frac{dy}{dx} = 2x$.

6. The sliders on the top left allow you to change the starting value of x, the starting value of y, the end value of x, and the increment $dx = \Delta x$. Click on the slider **dx**. Experiment with different values of **dx**. Describe the changes you see in the case table on the right. What happens to the accuracy of Euler's method when **dx** is smaller? Larger? What happens to the accuracy of the trapezoidal rule?

7. Now try changing the differential equation. Let $\frac{dy}{dx} = y$, containing the point $(x, y) = (0, 2)$, and let $dx = 0.5$. To change the differential equation, click on **dydx** in the case table. From the **Edit** menu, choose **Edit Formula** and simply type **y**. Press **OK**. Use your sliders to change the variables. Make **startx** = 0, **starty** = 2, **endx** = 6, and **dx** = 0.5. (Make sure to rescale your graph.)

8. The equation for y is now incorrect. Solve the differential equation $\frac{dy}{dx} = y$, containing the point $(x, y) = (0, 2)$.

9. Click on the formula shown at the bottom of the left graph. In the equation editor, enter the equation you found in Step 8. Your graph should look like the one here. (Hint: There is no "e" button, so use the value of e to five decimal places.)

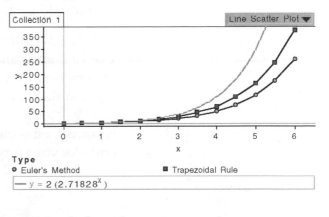

10. Click on the arrow of the **dx** slider to animate the slider. As dx changes, does the accuracy of the approximation methods follow the same trend you observed previously? If not, how does their accuracy differ?

Euler's Method (continued)

11. Now let $\frac{dy}{dx} = \frac{-x}{2y}$ containing the point $(x, y) = (0, 3)$ and let $dx = 0.5$, from $x = 0$ to $x = 7$. Change your slider values: **startx** = 0, **starty** = 3, **endx** = 7, and **dx** = 0.5. Rescale the graph.

12. Solve the differential equation $\frac{dy}{dx} = \frac{-x}{2y}$ with initial condition $(x, y) = (0, 3)$, and change the formula shown on the left graph. Your graph should look like the one here. At approximately what x-value do Euler's method and the trapezoidal rule fail? Why does this occur?

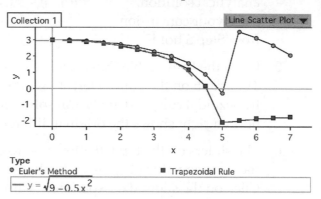

Extensions

13. Now apply what you have learned to a real-world example. Let $y(t)$ represent the temperature, in degrees Fahrenheit, of a cup of coffee at time t, in minutes. The initial temperature of the coffee, $y(0)$, is 190°. The coffee's temperature is described by the differential equation $\frac{dy}{dx} = -0.1(y - 70)$. Start with 10-min increments. Remember that in **Euler** the dependent variable is in terms of x. According to the approximation methods, at what time will the coffee be 100°? Reduce the increment to 2 min and then 1 min to see the effects on the graphs. At what temperature does the coffee temperature appear to level off? What do you call this temperature? Solve the problem analytically to check your answers.

16. Consider the differential equation $\frac{dy}{dx} = 1 + 3x - 2y$ with $y(0) = 2$. Use Fathom to analyze the problem for $x = 0$ to $x = 10$ with increments of 1. Reduce the increments and describe the effect. The solution to the differential equation $\frac{dy}{dx} = 1 + 3x - 2y$ is $y = Ce^{-2x} + \frac{3x}{2} - \frac{1}{4}$. Differentiate y to show that the given derivative is correct. Find the value of C for the initial condition $y(0) = 2$ and plot your function.

Calculus: Concepts and Applications Instructor's Resource Book
©2005 Key Curriculum Press

Instructor's Notes

Euler's Method

You can assign this activity to students after discussing Euler's method. Students work with Euler's method and the trapezoidal rule to understand how numerical techniques approximate the accumulated area under the curve and, therefore, the analytical solution to a differential equation.

Activity Time: 1 hour

Document: Euler.ftm

General Notes

You may wish to assign Steps 1–4 for homework the night before so that students can compare their answers to the Fathom portion of the activity. For students to appreciate Euler's method, they must have experience working with it. Fathom crunches the numbers for Euler's method, saving considerable time, especially with small values of dx. This allows students to focus on the solution rather than the repetitive steps.

You may want to discuss with students why the trapezoidal rule exactly matched the analytical solution to the linear differential equation for all values of dx, but introduced error with the more complicated differential equations.

Most of this activity involves separable differential equations, which students are expected to know how to solve. Step 14, however, involves a differential equation that is not separable, so the solution is given and students are asked to verify that the stated differential equation indeed has the given solution. However, if students have had more experience in solving first-order differential equations, these can be assigned as an activity as well without telling the student the solution. Whether you use separable or more advanced differential equations, having students actually solve the differential equations in conjunction with the Fathom activity will allow them to verify their work.

Technical Notes

Remind students to rescale their graphs when they change an equation or the starting and ending values. When extreme accuracy is needed, students may add cases. If a graph seems incomplete, it is because there are not enough cases. Students can add 1000 cases at a time in Fathom. However, remind them that saving files with too many cases will use a lot of memory.

Answers

1. See **Euler.ftm**. Answers are on the odd rows of the case table.

2. See **Euler.ftm**. Answers are on the even rows of the case table.

3. $y = x^2$. The trapezoidal method appears to give the better approximation.

$x_{new} = x_{old} + dx$	$y_{new} = y_{old} + dy$	$y =$ Accumulated Area	Analytical Solution
0.0	0	0	0
0.5	0	0.25	0.25
1.0	0.5	1.00	1.00
1.5	1.5	2.25	2.25
2.0	3.0	4.00	4.00
2.5	5.0	6.25	6.25
3.0	7.5	9.00	9.00
3.5	10.5	12.25	12.25
4.0	14.0	16.00	16.00

4. See **Euler.ftm**. The graph is on the bottom left of the screen.

6. As dx increases, Euler's method becomes less accurate. As dx decreases, Euler's method becomes more accurate. The trapezoidal rule appears to give exact answers no matter what the value of dx is.

8. $\frac{dy}{dx} = y \Rightarrow y = Ce^x$. Because the function passes through $(0, 2)$, $C = 2$. Therefore, $y = 2 \cdot e^x$.

10. Euler's method follows the same trend as previously. The trapezoidal rule, which was exact for all values of dx previously, follows the same trend as Euler's method this time.

12. $2y\,dy = -x\,dx \Rightarrow y^2 = \frac{-x^2}{2} + C$. Because the function passes through $(0, 3)$, $C = 9$. Therefore, $y = \pm\sqrt{9 - \frac{x^2}{2}}$. For this particular problem, $y = \sqrt{9 - \frac{x^2}{2}}$. The domain of the function is $[-\sqrt{18}, \sqrt{18}]$. All values obtained by the numerical methods greater than $\sqrt{18}$ are useless.

13. According to Euler's method, the temperature hit 100° after about 13 min. According to the trapezoidal rule, the temperature appears to hit 100° after about 14 min. The coffee appears to level off at about 70°. This is called room temperature.

$$\frac{dy}{y - 70} = -0.1\, dt \Rightarrow \ln|y - 70| = -0.1t + C$$

$$y - 70 = Ce^{-0.1t} \Rightarrow y = 70 + Ce^{-0.1t}$$

$$120 = 70 + C \Rightarrow C = 120$$

$$y = 70 + 120e^{-0.1t}$$

14. As the increments get smaller, the approximations become more and more accurate.

$$y = Ce^{-2x} + \frac{3x}{2} - \frac{1}{4} \Rightarrow Ce^{-2x} = y - \frac{3x}{2} + \frac{1}{4}$$

$$\frac{dy}{dx} = -2\left(y - \frac{3x}{2} + \frac{1}{4}\right) + \frac{3}{2} = -2y + 3x + 1$$

$$2 = C - \frac{1}{4} \Rightarrow C = \frac{9}{4}$$

$$y = \frac{9}{4}e^{-2x} = \frac{3}{2}x - \frac{1}{4}$$

This graph uses an increment of 0.5.

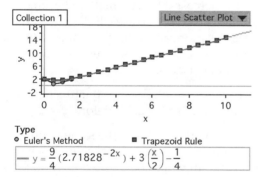

Collection 1 — Line Scatter Plot ▼

Type
○ Euler's Method   ■ Trapezoid Rule

$$- \quad y = \frac{9}{4}(2.71828^{-2x}) + 3\left(\frac{x}{2}\right) - \frac{1}{4}$$

Arc Length

An arc can be approximated with straight-line segments whose lengths are given by the distance formula, $d = \sqrt{(x_2 - x_1)^2 + (y_2 - y_1)^2}$. As x_1 and x_2 become closer, the estimated arc length becomes more accurate. In the activity that follows, the variable **Inc** (representing "Increment") that is generated by a slider will represent the distance between any two consecutive x-values.

1. Open the file **Arclength1**. Note that this collection has a case table and three sliders: **Startx**, **Endx**, and **Inc**. You'll first use this file to approximate the arc length of $y = 2x - 3$ from $x = -1$ to $x = 4$.

2. To graph $y = 2x - 3$, click on the attribute **y** in the case table so that the entire column is highlighted. Then choose **Edit | Edit Formula**. In the editor box, enter the right side of the equation, **2x − 3**, and click **OK**. Next, change the value of the **Startx** slider to -1, and change the value of **Endx** to 4. For now, set the increment, **Inc**, to 0.5.

3. When you change the formula for **y** or change **Startx** or **Endx**, you must rescale your graph. You can do this by dragging the attribute **x** from the case table to the horizontal axis of the graph or by selecting **Graph | Rescale Graph Axes**.

4. In the case table, there is an attribute called **Length**. This represents the straight-line distance between each two successive points. Notice that the first length is zero. Why? What do you notice about the other values of **Length**? Why does this occur? Double-click on the gold box called **Collection 1** at the top left of the screen and the inspector will appear. The inspector shows the sum of all the lengths, **TotalLength**. Record the total length.

5. Change the value of **Inc** to 0.25 and then to 0.1. What do you notice? Why does this occur?

6. Explain why changing the value of **Inc** does not affect the arc length of this function.

7. Use a geometric method to find the arc length of this function.

8. Find the exact arc length of the function using the formula $L = \int_a^b \sqrt{1 + [f'(x)]^2} \, dx$. How close is the Fathom approximation to the exact solution?

9. Use Fathom to approximate the arc length of the function $y = x^{3/2}$ from $x = 0$ to $x = 4$. Select the **y** attribute in the case table and choose **Edit | Edit formula**. You may enter $x^{1.5}$ by using the $\boxed{x^?}$ key or ^ to generate a superscript. Change **Startx** to 0 and **Inc** to 0.5. Remember to rescale the graph.

10. What do you notice about each successive length? Why does this occur? What is the approximation of total length given for an increment of 0.5?

11. Use calculus to find the exact arc length of this function. What is the error in Fathom's approximation for an increment of 0.5?

12. Decrease the value of **Inc** and notice that **TotalLength** approaches your answer to Problem 11. What value of **Inc** makes the Fathom approximation accurate within three decimal places?

13. Use Fathom to find the length of $y = \sin x$ from $x = 0$ to $x = 2\pi$, accurate to two decimal places. When you enter the formula for $y = \sin x$, you must type **sin (x)**, with x enclosed in parentheses. Remember to rescale the graph. If the graph appears incomplete, click on the gold collection box and choose **New Cases** (from the **Data** menu in version 1 or the **Collection** menu in version 2). Add 100 cases at a time until you get the accuracy you need. Use calculus to verify your answer. You may use the numerical integration feature of your grapher.

14. The diagram shows a suspension bridge with a center span of length 4200 ft. The center suspension cables hang in parabolic arcs from towers 749.2 ft above the water's surface. The

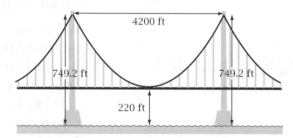

cables are 220 ft above the water at the center of the span. Write a quadratic function expressing the distance of the cables from the water as a function of the horizontal distance from the center of the span. Use Fathom to determine the length of the cables, using an increment of 1 ft. You will have to add cases as described in Problem 13. You can create 1000 new cases at a time and repeat as many times as necessary. Use calculus to find the exact arc length. How does it compare to the Fathom approximation?

15. Open the file **Arclength2**. This application allows you to determine the arc length of a parametric equation in the form $x = f(t)$ and $y = g(t)$. The application has the same features as the previous one. Approximate the arc length of the curve generated by $x = \sqrt{t}$ and $y = 3t - 1$ from $t = 0$ to $t = 2$, using a t-increment of 0.1. Input the formulas in the same way as before, except write them in terms of t. Rescale the axes as you did before. Click on the gold collection box to show the total length. Record the total length.

Calculus: Concepts and Applications Instructor's Resource Book
©2005 Key Curriculum Press

16. What rectangular equation is determined by the equations in Problem 15, and on what interval? Reopen the file **Arclength1** and confirm your answer using an x-increment of 0.1. What is the approximate arc length given by the rectangular equation? Why are the two approximations different?

17. Use Fathom to approximate the arc length of $x = 4\cos t$ and $y = 4\sin t$ from $t = 0$ to $t = 2\pi$, using an increment of 0.5. Decrease **Inc** to increase the accuracy of your approximation. You may have to add cases as described in Problem 13. What do you think the exact arc length is? Confirm your answer geometrically and with calculus. The formula for arc length given by parametric equations is

$$L = \int_a^b \sqrt{\left(\frac{dx}{dt}\right)^2 + \left(\frac{dy}{dt}\right)^2}\,.$$

18. A *cycloid* is the curve traced by a point on the circumference of a circle rolling along a straight line. Use Fathom to graph the cycloid generated by $x = 4(t - \sin t)$ and $y = 4(1 - \cos t)$ from $t = 0$ to $t = 6\pi$. Determine the length of one arc of the cycloid.

19. A circle of radius 1 rolls around the circumference of a bigger circle of radius 4. A point on the circumference of the smaller circle traces an *epicycloid* given by the equations $x = 5\cos t - \cos 5t$ and $y = 5\sin t - \sin 5t$. Graph the epicycloid from $t = 0$ to $t = 2\pi$ and determine the arc length of the curve. Compare this number to the circumference of a circle with radius 6. Graph a circle with radius 6 by choosing **Graph | Plot Function**, and entering $\sqrt{36 - x^2}$, then $-\sqrt{36 - x^2}$. Explain why the circle and epicycloid have similar arc lengths, but one is clearly greater.

20. Next, open the file **Arclength3**. This application allows you to determine the arc length of a polar equation in the form $r = f(\theta)$. The application has the same features as the previous one. Approximate the arc length of the curve generated by $r = 2 + 2\cos\theta$ for $\theta = 0$ to $\theta = 2\pi$. Use a θ-increment of 0.1. To graph this equation, enter **2 + 2 cos(theta)**. As always, rescale the axes. Double-click on the gold collection box to show the total length. Record the total length.

21. Use calculus to confirm your answer. The formula for arc length given by a polar equation is $L = \int_a^b \sqrt{\left[\left(\frac{dr}{d\theta}\right)^2 + r^2\right]}\,d\theta$. You may use your grapher's numerical integration feature.

22. A race is to be held on a course in the shape of the *limaçon* generated by $r = 1 - 5\sin\theta$ for $\theta = 0$ to $\theta = 2\pi$, with axes measured in kilometers. The varsity teams will run the outer loop and the junior varsity teams will run the inner loop. Graph the expression with **Inc** = 0.025. Find the lengths of the varsity and junior varsity courses by first determining the total length of both courses. Then use guess-and-check to find the approximate minimum and maximum θ-values that generate the inner loop. You can find the value of a particular point on the graph by clicking on it, then scrolling through the case table to find the value that has been highlighted. Change **Starttheta** and **Endtheta** to these values to find the length of the junior varsity loop. Subtract to find the length of the varsity loop.

23. Find the length of one petal of the rose curve $r = 4\sin 2\theta$.

24. If you walk a path determined by the spiral $r = \theta$, starting at $\theta = 0$, how far would you have to walk to return to the positive x-axis? (The axes are measured in kilometers.)

Instructor's Notes

Arc Length

This activity deals with finding the arc length of curves given in rectangular, parametric, and polar form. Fathom is used to divide the curves into segments that approximate it. Fathom then calculates the length of each of these segments, and sums the lengths to estimate the total arc length. Students decrease the length of each segment, creating more segments and greater accuracy. In some cases, students are asked to verify arc lengths analytically using calculus methods.

Activity Time: 1 hour

Documents: Arclength1.ftm, Arclength2.ftm, Arclength3.ftm

General Notes

This activity explores arc length of functions in rectangular, parametric, and polar form. You may wish to do only the portion of the activity dealing with functions in rectangular form with Section 8-5, and perhaps follow up by doing the remainder of the activity with Section 8-7. Or you can assign the entire activity after Section 8-7.

When working with functions in rectangular form, you are encouraged to come up with your own problems for which students can determine arc length.

There are several functions for which the student can analytically determine the arc length (the hyperbolic cosine function is one in particular), but students can use the numerical integration feature of their graphers to determine how accurate their Fathom solution is.

Technical Notes

Remind students to rescale their graphs when they change the equation or the starting and ending values. When extreme accuracy is needed, students may add cases. If a graph seems incomplete, it is because there are not enough cases. Students can add 1000 cases at a time in Fathom. However, remind them that saving a file with many cases will use a lot of memory.

Because most graphs students examine are curves, it follows that the arc length approximations found by Fathom will be less than the actual lengths, because the length of a segment between two points will be the shortest path between the two points. However, there are cases when the Fathom solution is greater than the analytical solution. This occurs

when the increment value is not a multiple of the difference between the starting x-value and the ending x-value (or t- or θ-values). For instance, finding the arc length of some function between $x = 0$ and $x = 1$ with an increment of 0.15 will create the last segment from $x = 0.90$ to $x = 1.05$. Many of the problems use an interval of length 2π, so this phenomenon will occur frequently. However, if the increment is small, the difference will be minute.

Answers

4. The first length is 0 because there is no point before it. All other lengths are equal because they are the lengths of congruent segments. The approximate total length is 11.1803.

5. As **Inc** decreases, there are more points. The lengths between consecutive points are equal, and the total length remains the same as for **Inc** = 0.5.

6. For this equation, we are determining the "arc" length of a line. No matter how many segments are generated, the length of the line stays constant.

7. $d = \sqrt{5^2 + 10^2} = \sqrt{125} = 11.1803\ldots$

8. $L = \int_{-1}^{4}\sqrt{1 + 4}\,dx = 5\sqrt{5}$. The Fathom approximation is the same as the exact arc length to four decimal places.

10. The successive lengths are increasing because the slope of the curve is increasing; 0.06264

11. $L = \int_0^4 \sqrt{1 + (1.5x^{0.5})^2}\,dx = \int_0^4 \sqrt{1 + \frac{9x}{4}}\,dx =$

    $\int_0^4 \left(1 + \frac{9x}{4}\right)^{0.5} dx = \frac{8}{27}\left(1 + \frac{9}{4}x\right)^{1.5}\Big|_0^4$

    $= \frac{8}{27}(10\sqrt{10} - 1) = 9.07342\ldots$. The error is $9.06264 - 9.07342 = -0.01078$.

12. Approximately 0.025

13. 7.64; $\int_0^{2\pi}\sqrt{1 + \cos^2 x}\,dx = 7.6403\ldots$

14. Set the origin at the water's surface below the center of the span and determine the parabola with points $(0, 220)$, $(-2100, 749.2)$, and $(2100, 749.2)$. The equation is $y = 0.00012x^2 + 220$. Each cable has length 4371.58 ft.

    $\int_{-2100}^{2100}\sqrt{1 + 0.00024x}\,dx = 4371.5844\ldots$

    The Fathom approximation is very close to the exact answer.

15. 6.25783

16. The equation is $y = 3x^2 - 1$, on the interval $x = 0$ to $x = \sqrt{2}$. The arc length approximation using the rectangular equation is 7.03017. The approximations are different because the increments are based on t for the parametric equation and on x for the rectangular equation.

17. These equations describe a circle with radius 4. The circumference is $8\pi = 25.1327....$

$$L = \int_0^{2\pi} \sqrt{(-4\sin t)^2 + (4\cos t)^2} \, dt = 8\pi$$

18. The arc length seems to be 32.

19. The Fathom approximation is close to 40. (The answer found using calculus is exactly 40.) The circumference of a circle with radius 6 is $12\pi = 37.6991....$ The two shapes are similar, but at each quadrant the epicycloid has an indented cusp. So its arc length will be slightly larger than that of the circle.

20. 16.0488

21. $L = \int_0^{2\pi} \sqrt{(-2\sin\theta)^2 + (2 + 2\cos\theta)^2} \, d\theta = 16$

22. The total length is approximately 31.8 km. The varsity race is about 20.1 km, and the junior varsity race is about 11.7 km. The **theta** values that define the junior varsity race are $0.2 \leq \theta \leq 2.925$.

23. Approximately 9.6884

24. Approximately 21.2562 km

Extensions

The application investigates an epicycloid, the path traced by a fixed point on a circle of radius B as it rolls along the *outside* of a circle of radius A. Another interesting curve is the hypocycloid, the path traced by a fixed point on a circle of radius B as it rolls along the *inside* of a circle of radius A. The general form for an epicycloid is $x = (A + B)\cos t - B\cos\left(\frac{A + B}{B}\right)t$ and $y = (A + B)\sin t - B\sin\left(\frac{A + B}{B}\right)t$. The general form for a hypocycloid is $x = (A - B)\cos t + B\cos\left(\frac{A - B}{B}\right)t$ and $y = (A - B)\sin t - B\sin\left(\frac{A - B}{B}\right)t$.

Students who know how to create sliders can create sliders for A and B to examine the behavior of these interesting curves.

Taylor Polynomials

In this series of Fathom activities, you will investigate how taking successive derivatives of a function can create Taylor polynomials that will approximate that function.

Part 1

1. Open the file **Taylor1**. This file investigates the behavior of functions in the form

$$x - \frac{x^3}{3!} + \frac{x^5}{5!} - \frac{x^7}{7!} + \frac{x^9}{9!} - \cdots + \frac{(-1)^n x^{2n+1}}{(2n+1)!} \quad \text{(which we will call "odd powers") and}$$

$$1 - \frac{x^2}{2!} + \frac{x^4}{4!} - \frac{x^6}{6!} + \frac{x^8}{8!} - \cdots + \frac{(-1)^n x^{2n}}{(2n)!} \quad \text{(which we will call "even powers")}$$

2. At the start of the application, the value of **P** (shown on the slider on the left) is set to zero. **P** represents the highest possible power of x in each of the two series above. So the odd-power graph has a value of 0 for all x-values and the even-power graph has a value of 1 for all x-values.

3. Change the slider value to **P** = 1 by double-clicking on the blue slider value and changing it. Why does only one of the graphs change? What function is now graphed?

4. Change the slider value to **P** = 2. Why does only one of the graphs change? What function is now graphed?

5. Change the value of **P** to each integer from 3 through 11, and explain what occurs. You may wish to examine the case table as you change the value of **P**. What two familiar curves are approximated by these series?

6. Graph $y = \cos x$ and $y = \sin x$. To do this, click on the graph, then choose **Plot Function** from the **Graph** menu. Type **cos (x)** and click **OK**. Repeat the process for $y = \sin x$. Does this confirm your answer to Problem 5? If necessary, change the values of **P** from 3 through 11 again.

7. The slider called **Startx** is set to −4.9. Change it to −6.30. Single-click on the gold collection box called **Collection 1**, then choose **New Cases** (from the **Data** menu in version 1 and the **Collection** menu in version 2). Add 50 cases. Describe what happens. What could you do to make the graphs converge to the graphs of $y = \sin x$ and $y = \cos x$?

Taylor Polynomials (continued)

Part 2

8. Open the file **Taylor2**. This file investigates the behavior of functions in the form

$$1 + x + \frac{x^2}{2!} + \frac{x^3}{3!} + \frac{x^4}{4!} + \frac{x^5}{5!} + \cdots + \frac{x^n}{n!} \quad \text{(which we will call "type 1") and}$$

$$1 - x + \frac{x^2}{2!} - \frac{x^3}{3!} + \frac{x^4}{4!} - \frac{x^5}{5!} + \cdots \frac{(-1)^n x^n}{n!} \quad \text{(which we will call "type 2")}$$

9. At the start of the application, the value of **P** (shown on the slider) is set to zero. **P** represents the highest power of x in each of the two series above. So both the "type 1" and "type 2" graphs, shown in the graph on the left, have a value of 1 for all x-values. (You'll work with the graph on the right later in this activity.)

10. Change the slider value to **P** = 1. How does the graph change? What equations are now graphed?

11. Change the slider value to **P** = 2. Now which equations are graphed?

12. Change the value of **P** to each integer from 3 through 10, and explain what occurs. What familiar curves are approximated by these series?

13. Graph $y = e^x$ and $y = e^{-x}$. To do this, click on the graph, then choose **Plot Function** from the **Graph** menu. Type **2.71828^x** or **exp(x)** and click **OK**. Repeat the process for $y = e^{-x}$. Does this confirm your answer to Problem 12? If necessary, change the values of **P** from 3 through 10 again.

14. The graph on the right is determined by summing the values of the two curves on the left and dividing by 2. What important mathematical function is this? Confirm that the Taylor series that is the sum of the type-1 and type-2 series approximates the original curve on the right as **P** increases from zero. Explain why the graph changes only on even values of **P**.

Part 3

15. Open the file **Taylor3**. This file investigates the behavior in functions in the form $f(x) = \frac{a}{x-b}$. These functions can be expressed as a summation:

$$\frac{a}{x-b} = -\frac{a}{b-c} \sum_{n=0}^{\infty} \left(\frac{x-c}{b-c}\right)^n \quad \text{centered at } c$$

The initial values of a, b, and c are 5, –2, and 0, respectively. What function is approximated, and where is it centered?

Calculus: Concepts and Applications Instructor's Resource Book
©2005 Key Curriculum Press

Taylor Polynomials (continued)

16. At the start of the application, the value of **P** is set to zero. **P** represents the highest value of n. So the graph plotted is $y = -\frac{5}{-2-0}\sum_{n=0}^{0}\left(\frac{x-0}{-2-0}\right)^n = \frac{5}{2}\left(\frac{x}{-2}\right)^0 = \frac{5}{2}$, which has a value of 2.5 for every value of x. Change the value of **P** to 1. What function is now graphed? Change **P** to 2. Now what function is graphed?

17. Gradually increase the value of **P** to 10. What happens to the graph as **P** increases?

18. The graph of $y = \frac{a}{x-b}$, in this case, $y = \frac{5}{x+2}$, is graphed in red. For what values of x does the series approximation appear to diverge from the graph? For a center of $c = 0$, what is the radius of convergence? Double-click on the gold collection box called **Collection 1** and the inspector will open. The radius of convergence and the left and right endpoints of convergence should confirm your answers. Note that Fathom will not tell you whether the approximation is convergent at the endpoints.

19. Use Fathom to create an approximation centered at $c = -1$ of the function $y = \frac{-3}{x-4}$. To graph it, drag x from the case table to the horizontal axis of the graph. Observe the behavior of the function as **P** increases from 0 to 10. Approximate the radius and interval of convergence visually, and confirm using the collection inspector.

20. Repeat Problem 19 with the function $y = \frac{2}{4x-1}$. What are the values of a and b for this function? (Be careful.) Keep the approximation centered at $c = -1$.

21. Why won't Fathom graph an approximation of $y = \frac{1}{x}$ centered at $c = 0$?

Part 4

22. The files **Taylor4**, **Taylor5**, **Taylor6**, and **Taylor7** contain graphs of approximations to familiar functions. For each file, investigate the behavior of the approximation as **P** increases from 0 to 8. Then approximate the radius of convergence and the interval of convergence. If you believe you know what function the graphs approximate, graph the function to verify your conjecture.

Instructor's Notes

Taylor Polynomials

This is an activity that can be given to students after an initial discussion of Taylor series. It will lead students toward a deeper understanding of the manner in which well-known functions can be approximated by series, and approximated better by adding more and more terms of a series. The actual act of adding successive terms by finding first, second, and third derivatives, and beyond, is handled by Fathom and is not the focus of this activity. Students should experiment with graphing more and more terms to see the convergence of data points to well-known functions, and to observe the interval and radius of convergence.

Activity Time: 1 hour

Documents: Taylor1.ftm, Taylor2.ftm, Taylor3.ftm, Taylor4.ftm, Taylor5.ftm, Taylor6.ftm, Taylor7.ftm

General Notes

Taylor1 focuses on sine and cosine graphs. The window given shows the behavior of the series from $x = -4.9$ to $x = 4.9$. When the graphs of $y = \sin(x)$ and $y = \cos(x)$ are displayed, students will begin to see divergence of their data from these graphs. They are asked to add more cases to their case table, graphing from $x = -2\pi$ to $x = 2\pi$, where the divergence will be even more apparent. Enterprising students can add new attributes **der12**, **der13**, and so on, which will give more terms. To set up a formula for these attributes, edit the formulas for the other attributes to get a feel for the programming of it. Also edit the formula for the **y** attribute to add these new terms.

Taylor2 focuses on exponential graphs. It mentions the hyperbolic function $y = \cosh(x)$, which students may or may not be acquainted with.

Taylor3 focuses on geometric power series, and it is recommended that students be familiar with these series before they attempt this activity. Several geometric series examples are explored, but teachers should feel free to make up their own. An interesting aspect of this activity is that Fathom will choose the appropriate x-values to show convergence and where the series begins to diverge.

The four files **Taylor4–Taylor7** examine functions with which the student should be familiar. Even if they are not familiar with the given functions, students should be able to determine the interval and radius of convergence by increasing the value of **P**. If they are unable to determine a function (the last one is difficult), you may wish to tell them the function and ask them to graph it and identify the radius and interval of convergence.

Answers

3. The odd-power function changes to $y = x$. The even-power function will not change because it has no powers of x greater than or equal to 1.

4. The even-power function changes to $y = 1 - \frac{x^2}{2}$. The odd-power function will not change because it has no powers of x greater than or equal to 2.

5. The odd-power function approximates $y = \sin x$ and the even-power function approximates $y = \cos x$. As you increase the number of terms of the series, the sine and cosine graphs are better approximated.

6. The graphs of $y = \cos x$ and $y = \sin x$ should confirm the answer to Problem 5.

7. The graphs of the two series are shown for a larger domain (about $[-2\pi, 2\pi]$). They are close approximations to $y = \cos x$ and $y = \sin x$ for the interval $[-5, 5]$. To make the odd-power and even-power graphs converge to $y = \cos x$ and $y = \sin x$, you could add more terms to the series (increase the value of **P**).

10. Both graphs change. The type-1 graph is $y = 1 + x$ and the type-2 graph is $y = 1 - x$.

11. $y = 1 + x + \frac{x^2}{2}$ and $y = 1 - x + \frac{x^2}{2}$.

12. Both curves are becoming asymptotic to the x-axis and appear exponential; $y = e^x$ and $y = e^{-x}$

13. The graphs of e^x and $y = e^{-x}$ should confirm the answer to Problem 12.

14. $y = \cosh(x)$; as **P** increases, the graph approximates the red curve better. For odd values of **P**, the sum of the two newly added terms of the series is 0, thus the sum of the series does not change. (For example, for $\mathbf{P} = 3$, the new terms are $x^3/3!$ and $-x^3/3!$, which sum to 0.)

Calculus: Concepts and Applications Instructor's Resource Book
©2005 Key Curriculum Press

15. $y = \dfrac{5}{x-2}$, centered at $c = 0$

16. For $\mathbf{P} = 1$, $y = \dfrac{5}{2}\left(1 - \dfrac{x}{-2}\right)$. For $\mathbf{P} = 2$,

    $y = \dfrac{5}{2}\left(1 - \dfrac{x}{-2} + \dfrac{x^2}{4}\right)$.

17. As $\mathbf{P}$ increases, the plotted values of the series approximate the red curve better.

18. The approximation diverges for approximately $x > 2$ and $x < -2$. The radius of convergence is about 2.

19. Use $a = -3$, $b = 4$, $c = -1$; radius of convergence $= 5$; interval of convergence: $(-6, 4)$

20. $a = 0.5$, $b = 0.25$; radius of convergence $= 1.25$; interval of convergence: $(-2.25, 0.25)$

21. At $c = 0$, the function does not exist because of division by 0.

22. **Taylor4.** $y = \dfrac{1}{x}$, radius of convergence $= 1$, interval of convergence: $(0, 2)$

    Taylor5: $y = \sin^{-1}(x)$; radius of convergence $= 1$; interval of convergence: $[-1, 1]$

    Taylor6: $y = \ln x$; radius of convergence $= 1$; interval of convergence: $(0, 2]$

    Taylor7: $y = (x + 1)^n$; radius of convergence $= 1$; interval of convergence: $(-1, 1)$, with the convergence at the endpoints dependent on n.

Technology Projects: CBL™

Teachers and students who are new to the Calculator Based Laboratory (CBL) can download the CBL Guidebook from the Texas Instruments Web site, http://education.ti.com/downloads/guidebooks/eng/cblguide.pdf.

Here is a list of the projects in this section, in order of the chapters they are meant to accompany.

Chapter 2 Properties of Limits

The Limit of a Function at a Point: The Effect of Exercise on Pulse uses CBL to gather data and explore the concepts of limit and continuity in a real-world context. It is recommended for use as a fun resolution to Chapter 2.

Chapter 3 Derivatives, Antiderivatives, and Indefinite Integrals

Graphical Differentiation: Walking a Motion Plan uses CBL to gather motion data and analyze graphs of position, velocity, and acceleration. This activity can be used to strengthen students' understanding of the relationships between the graphs of a function, its first and second derivatives, and its antiderivative. This activity is recommended for use with Section 3-5.

Chapter 4 Products, Quotients, and Parametric Functions

Parametric Differentiation: How Fast Does pH Change with Hydrogen Concentration? uses CBL to gather data and analyze a chemistry application of parametric derivatives. This activity is recommended for use with Section 4-7.

Related Rates: Environmental Parameters in a Grass Ecosystem uses CBL to gather data and explore the relationship between change in light intensity and change in relative humidity. This activity is recommended for use with Section 4-9.

Chapter 7 The Calculus of Growth and Decay

The Logistic Model: Simulating the Spread of Disease uses the grapher's random number generator to simulate the spread of disease in a closed environment. Students then use logistic regression to model the data and to analyze and interpret their results. They also derive a differential equation and solve it using partial fractions. You may wish to use this project to deepen understanding of logistic growth situations, and connect this topic to other calculus topics. This activity is recommended for use with Section 7-6.

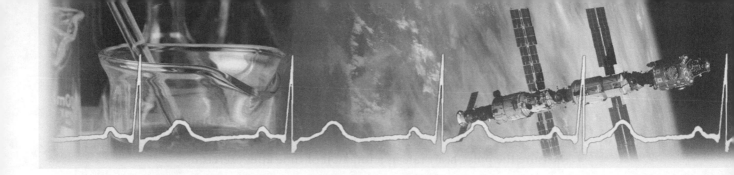

The Limit of a Function at a Point

The Effect of Exercise on Pulse

INTRODUCTION

One of the most important functions of the cardiovascular system during exercise is to deliver oxygen and other nutrients to the working muscles. The major role of the heart is to maintain an adequate level of blood flow throughout the cardiovascular system by pumping blood under pressure into the system. The amount of blood pumped out of the left ventricle and into the aorta during a period of 1 minute is defined as the *cardiac output*. The average cardiac output for a man at rest is 5 liters per minute.

Each beat of the heart, or cardiac cycle, involves a number of highly coordinated events that generate the blood flow. The number of cardiac cycles per minute is called the *heart rate* (or *pulse*) and is measured in beats per minutes (bpm). The heart rate of an average teenager at rest may vary between 55 and 80 bpm.

During heavy exercise, blood flow in the muscle can increase approximately 25 times. During exercise, cardiovascular regulation provides an adequate cardiac output to ensure an adequate oxygen and nutrient supply to the working muscles. As work output increases during light or moderate exercise, there is a proportional increase in oxygen consumption, which dilates the muscles' arteries. This dilation increases the volume of blood returning through the veins, resulting in a linear increase in cardiac output, which, in turn, causes a significant increase in the heart rate.

FIGURE 1.1

Because of the greater pumping effectiveness of the heart, a trained athlete can achieve the same cardiac output with a lower heart rate both at rest and during exercise. So a trained athlete has a significantly lower heart rate than the average person.

This lab will involve each of you exercising (doing calisthenics) for a specific time period and then recording your pulse as a function of time after the exercise.

OBJECTIVES

- Measure the pulse/heart rate as a function of time after exercising.
- Analyze this function and determine its properties.
- Find the mathematical model that best describes this function.
- Determine the limit of the function at a given moment of time using the mathematical model.

EQUIPMENT REQUIRED

- ☐ TI graphing calculator with unit-to-unit cable
- ☐ LabPro or CBL 2 interface
- ☐ Vernier exercise heart rate monitor

- ☐ TI-Graph Link cable
- ☐ Saline solution

PROGRAMS

DataMate

TI-Graph Link

SAFETY

- Do not exceed the amount of exercise you would usually engage in while working out or tax your own level of fitness.

EQUIPMENT SETUP PROCEDURE

1. Connect the LabPro or CBL 2 to the calculator with the unit-to-unit cable using the input/output ports located on the bottom edge of each unit. Press the cable ends in firmly.

2. Connect the heart rate monitor to the CH 1 port of the LabPro or CBL 2.

3. Turn on the calculator.

4. Run DataMate on the calculator. Press Clear, and the program will automatically identify the exercise heart rate monitor connected to CH 1.*

5. The calculator is now ready for data collection.

---

*If you are using an old sensor (ear-lobe model), it will not be identified by the interface. In this case set up the sensor manually by selecting the channel, pressing 1: Setup, and then pressing Enter. Select the appropriate sensor from the menu provided.

EXPERIMENTAL PROCEDURE

Note: The person whose heart rate is being measured should initially be at rest.

1. Make sure that the belt of the heart rate monitor fits snugly but not too tightly. The receiver module of the exercise heart rate monitor will receive signals from the closest transmitter source. To avoid confusion or erroneous readings, make sure that students being tested by different lab teams stay at least 2 meters apart.

2. Because of possible electromagnetic interference, the students being tested should be at least 2 meters away from the electronic equipment (including computers).

3. Measure the pulse before exercise by observing the sensor readings in the upper right corner of the calculator Main Screen. Record it in beats per minute (bpm) in the data section below. Do not store this data.

4. Have the person whose pulse is being measured exercise for a total of 30–60 seconds. The exercise could include but is not limited to jumping jacks, running up and down stairs, push-ups, and other calisthenics.

5. Press 2: Start on the calculator immediately after the exercise. Make sure that the person whose pulse is being measured does not talk or move during data collection. The total time of data collection is 15 minutes.

DATA

Pulse before the exercise: _____ bpm

Time measured in seconds is stored in List 1, and pulse data in beats per minute are stored in List 2.

DATA ANALYSIS

1. Use StatPlot to plot the pulse as a function of time. Describe the behavior of this function. Is this a continuous function? Why?

2. Choose the best-fit mathematical model for this function. Graph your data along with the regression equation of the model. Analyze the residuals. Use TI Graph Link to print the graph data with the regression equation and include them with your lab report.

3. What is the limit of this function when $t = 15$ min? 20 min? Why? Calculate these limits using the mathematical model you found and explain your results.

4. Explain your choice of the mathematical model based on the physical situation and properties of the pulse as a function of time.

The Limit of a Function at a Point
The Effect of Exercise on Pulse

BEFORE THE EXPERIMENT

1. If LabPro or CBL 2 have not been used before this experiment, ask students to bring their calculators to class in advance and download the DataMate program from LabPro or CBL 2 to the calculators.

2. Announce this lab in advance and ask students to wear comfortable clothes and shoes.

3. Make sure that both electrodes are wet with either saline solution or contact lens solution. If needed, prepare a 5% salt solution by adding 5 grams of salt per 100 ml of distilled water. (This equipment requires the belt to be placed on the bare chest, so students must be volunteers.)

SAFETY

- Do not allow/require students to exercise beyond their apparent level of fitness. Not every student's pulse needs to be measured for a successful outcome.

TEACHING OBJECTIVES

Students will be able to

- analyze experimental data and make reasonable conclusions about the behavior of pulse as a function of time

- use the definition of continuity of functions to analyze pulse as a function of time

- choose the regression equation that best describes the behavior of pulse as a function of time, not only within the experimental range of values but also for a longer time

- evaluate the limit of the equation they found at given instants of time

ACTIVITY NOTES

You could introduce this activity before you introduce the concept of limit of a function at a point. Then questions in the data analysis will lead to the discussion of limit and continuity.

Students should have a clear understanding that the pulse will reach its normal (resting) value some time after the exercise. This helps them analyze pulse as a function of time.

The concept of continuity is very important and sometimes hard for students to verbalize. In this activity they need to use all three points of the definition of continuity of the function to justify that pulse is a continuous function of time. Because the pulse as a function of time is continuous, they can use the fact that the limit of the function approaching a particular instant of time will be equal to the value of the function at that instant.

Students are forced to consider the main trend of the function in order to choose a regression equation. They cannot simply use collected data and find the best-fitting line because the expression that defines the function should approach the normal (resting) pulse value at longer time intervals.

Experimental Procedure Notes

Students need to make sure that the at-rest pulse readings are within the correct range of values (usually between 55 and 80 bpm for teenagers). The student whose pulse is being measured should, before exercising, be seated and avoid moving and talking to ensure that he or she is in a state of complete rest. Athletic students may need to choose harder exercise or exercise for a longer period of time to see significant change in their pulse rates. Sometimes the final pulse value after exercise is less than the pulse value measured before exercise. That could happen if the student whose pulse was measured right after he or she came to class did not calm down completely. Students could always take resting pulse measurements again at the end of the class.

Electronic equipment can cause electromagnetic interference that may affect the data collection using the exercise heart rate monitors. Avoid using this sensor near computers, exercise equipment, and the like.

The default settings for the heart rate monitor allow 15 minutes of data collection with 5 seconds between samples. That gives students 180 data points. Some calculators may not have enough memory for default time settings. In this case you may change time settings for this experiment to allow a smaller number of data points, longer interval between samples, and a shorter total time for the experiment. Sample data with different time settings are provided later in these notes.

Using the exercise heart rate monitor might present a problem in some classrooms because it involves removing outer clothing. In this case, or if the heart rate monitor is not available, a stopwatch could be used to measure the pulse. If a stopwatch is used, students can measure the number of heartbeats per 10 seconds and take these data in 20-second intervals for 5 minutes. That will result in 15 data points.

For some people, the pulse after exercise may change nonmonotonically. In this case it is better to adjust time settings to take the pulse in longer time intervals (20 seconds, for example). Even if pulse values do not decrease monotonically, the general behavior of the function will still be decreasing.

Data Analysis Notes

1. Students should use Stat options to view the data, describe the properties of the function, and choose an appropriate regression equation.

2. Students should use the definition of continuity of a function on a closed interval to answer the first question: Pulse is defined at all times within its domain, and it is approaching its value at each instant of time, so it is a continuous function of time.

3. To find the best-fit model, students should not simply use the data for the given time interval but also consider the end behavior of the function for large values of time: With time, pulse values should be decreasing to the normal at-rest pulse value, reaching the value measured prior to the exercise. Thus, students should reduce the options for the regression equation to exponential equations.

4. Students will have to adjust their experimental data by subtracting the normal resting pulse value before they can use exponential regression because this regression provides a function that asymptotically approaches zero for large values of the independent variable.

5. Students should be able to write an equation for pulse as a function of time using adjusted values in the regression equation. Then they can calculate limits at particular instants using the equation they found.

Sample Data

Sample data were collected with the ear-lobe model of the heart rate monitor. The time settings were changed to collect a total of 10 data points every 10 seconds to measure heart rate after exercise. A 17-year-old male student did jumping jacks for 30 seconds.

Pulse before exercise was 54 bpm.

Time (s)	10	20	30	40	50	60	70	80	90	100
Pulse (bpm)	148	140	127	120	111	108	98	90	87	84

Sample Graph

This is the graph of heart rate as a function of time viewed in DataMate:

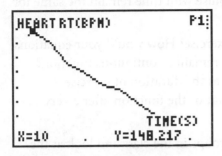

Expected Calculations

Exponential regression equation using the adjusted pulse:
$y = 109.8(0.987)^x$ $(r^2 = 0.99)$
Residuals for the exponential regression:

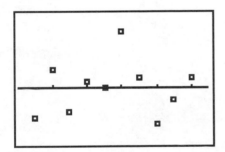

Collected data along with the equation for the pulse as a function of time adjusted from the exponential regression equation:
$p = 54 + 109.8(0.987)^t$

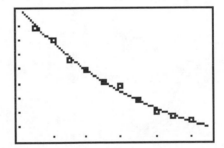

Because the function is continuous,

$$\lim_{t \to 900} P(t) = P(900) = 54 \text{ and } \lim_{t \to 1200} P(t) = P(1200) = 54$$

The pulse as a function of time must be defined at zero, must approach resting pulse for large values of time, and must decrease with time after the exercise. Linear, quadratic, cubic, and quartic regressions do not have horizontal asymptotes. The power regression equation does not allow the function to be defined at zero. The only option that is close to the properties of the data is exponential regression because it is defined at zero, strictly decreases when the base is less than 1, and approaches constant value (horizontal asymptote).

FURTHER EXPLORATIONS

1. Compare pulse as a function of time for athletes and non-athletes. Would your conclusions about behavior of the pulse with time remain the same for both cases?

2. What if you extend the duration of the exercise? How would your equations change? Does pulse as a function of time remain a continuous function? How does the shape of the graph change as the duration of exercise increases? What can you say about the limit of the function after a very long time?

3. Compare the pulse data from different groups in the class and look at the similarities and differences.

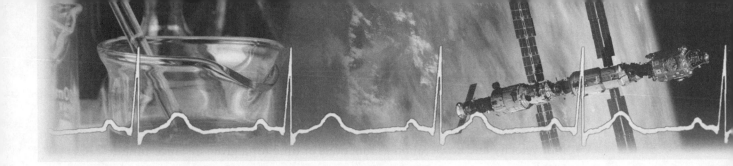

Graphical Differentiation

Walking a Motion Plan

INTRODUCTION

Bobsleighing, or bobsledding as it is commonly known, is a dramatically exciting and demanding sport. Competitions are run down ice tracks that are at least 1500 m long with at least 15 banked curves. A modern bobsled reaches speeds greater than 90 mph.

The object of bobsledding is to get to the finish line in the shortest time. The passengers' role at the start is vital; they must push the sled so that it attains maximum speed in a very short period of time. Once everyone is in the sled, it is the pilot's responsibility to steer it down the track in the most time-efficient way. Teamwork is the essential ingredient.

Bobsled teams must plan all their moves from start to the finish. Track conditions and

preparation of the sled affect its speed, but a fast start and a clean drive are crucial. Bobsledders study each curve and angle of the track. They have to plan each small movement. Slight motion by one person could cause an acceleration that would change the speed of the sled. Safety is also a concern. Planning, team coordination, and practice are the keys to success.

In your experiment you will have a similar but much simpler task. Some students will develop a written plan of walking motion for other students to follow, such that the graph of their distance from the motion detector with respect to time matches a given graph. You can describe the linear motion of an object with the help of several basic quantities—displacement, velocity, and acceleration. These quantities are functions of time. By definition, the displacement of an object, Δx, is the distance from its initial position to its final position. The velocity of the object, v, is defined as the rate of change of its displacement, $v = \frac{dx}{dt}$, and the acceleration of the object is defined as the rate of change of its velocity, $a = \frac{dv}{dt}$. Comparing the definitions of acceleration and velocity, we see that acceleration is the second derivative of displacement with respect to time, $a = \frac{d^2x}{dt^2}$. In SI the units of displacement are meters (m), the units of velocity are meters per second (m/s), and the units of acceleration are meters per second per second (m/s²).

FIGURE 2.1 *Four-man bobsled start*

OBJECTIVES

- Plot velocity and acceleration as functions of time for a given distance-time graph.

- Develop a written plan of motion to match a given distance-time graph.

- Compare the experimental distance-time graph generated by walking with the given graph.

- Analyze graphs of functions and graphs of derivatives. Make connections between the behavior of a function and its first and second derivatives.

BEFORE THE EXPERIMENT

1. Plot the given distance-time graph in the indicated place in the Data section.

2. In the Data section, plot a qualitative graph of the first derivative (velocity) as a function of time and a qualitative graph of the second derivative (acceleration) as a function of time.

3. Looking at the graphs of velocity and acceleration, plan the motion to match the given distance-time graph. Describe the motion in terms of speed, acceleration, and direction. Assume that 10 seconds is the total duration of the motion.

4. Record your motion plan on a separate piece of paper. Exchange it with another group without showing them your distance-time graph.

EQUIPMENT REQUIRED

- ☐ TI graphing calculator with unit-to-unit cable
- ☐ LabPro or CBL 2
- ☐ Vernier motion detector or CBR

- ☐ TI-Graph Link cable (optional)
- ☐ Piece of cardboard approximately 20 cm by 30 cm

PROGRAMS

DataMate

TI-Graph Link

EQUIPMENT SETUP PROCEDURE

1. Position the Vernier motion detector and tape it on a flat table about 15 cm above the waist level of a walking person.

2. Aim the motion detector toward an area that is free from objects that might reflect the ultrasound waves.

3. Connect the LabPro or CBL 2 to the calculator with the unit-to-unit cable using the input/output ports located on the bottom edge of each unit. Press the cable ends in firmly.

4. Connect the motion detector to the DIG/Sonic 1 port on the LabPro or CBL 2.

5. Turn on the calculator.

6. Run the DataMate program on the calculator. Press Clear, and the program will automatically identify the motion detector connected to the sonic port.*

EXPERIMENTAL PROCEDURE

1. Choose 1: Setup. Move the Up Arrow to get the cursor to Mode. Press Enter.

2. Select 2: Time Graph, and the calculator will display the Time Graph Settings window. Press 2: Change Time Settings.

3. Enter 0.2 seconds as the time between samples. Press Enter. Enter 50 for the number of samples. Press Enter. Press 1: OK to return to the Setup menu.

4. Press 1: OK, and the calculator will return to the Main Menu ready for data collection.

5. Press 2: Start, and as soon as you hear a clicking sound produced by the motion detector, walk the path according to the motion plan given to your group.

6. For better results,
   - hold a piece of cardboard at waist level
   - take small steps and keep your upper body still while walking
   - do not approach the motion detector more closely than 0.5 m

---

*If you are using an old sensor, it will not be identified by the interface. In this case set up the sensor manually by selecting the channel, pressing 1: Setup, and then pressing Enter. Select the appropriate sensor from the menu provided.

DATA ANALYSIS

Time is stored in List 1, distance is in List 6, velocity is in List 7, and acceleration is in List 8.

1. Exchange the Data section page with the group that you exchanged the motion plans with.

2. Display the "walked" distance-time graph on the calculator. Did it correctly match the given distance-time graph?

3. Analyze the plan of motion that you received. Did the other group's plot of the velocity-time and acceleration-time graphs correspond to the distance-time graph? Explain. If necessary, make corrections and add missing details. Record your changes in the Data section. This page must be included with your lab report.

4. If needed, walk again according to your revised plan and see if you now match the given distance-time graph.

5. Use TI-Graph Link to print the "walked" distance-time graph and corresponding velocity-time and acceleration-time graphs and include them with your lab report.

6. Compare the walked distance-time graph with the velocity-time and acceleration-time graphs provided by the calculator. (Because of the errors in calculations produced by the calculator and the imperfections in real motion, the velocity-time and acceleration-time graphs will look different from the theoretically predicted graphs. However, you should be able to find a correspondence between experimental velocity and distance, and between acceleration and velocity, that reflects the correspondence between the derivative of a function and the function itself.) Looking at your experimental graphs, provide at least three reasons that support the fact that velocity is the first derivative of displacement and acceleration is the second derivative of displacement.

DATA

Names of the group members who developed the motion plan for the distance-time graph given below:

Names of the group members who walked the distance-time graph given below:

Revised plan of motion:

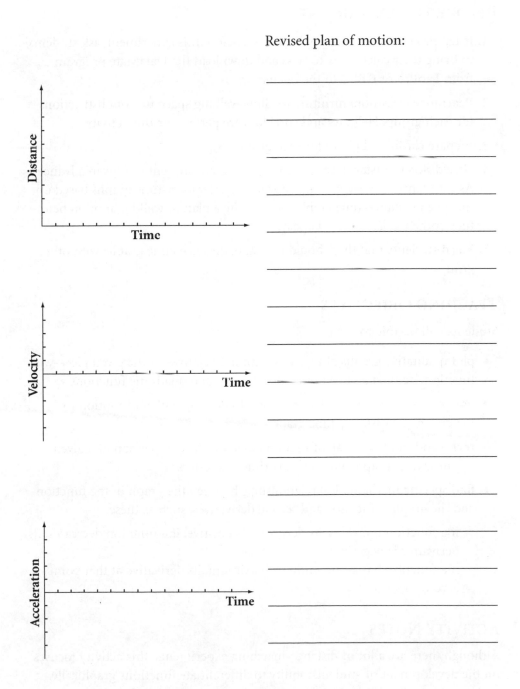

_____

_____

_____

_____

_____

_____

_____

_____

_____

_____

_____

_____

_____

_____

Graphical Differentiation

Walking a Motion Plan

BEFORE THE EXPERIMENT

1. If LabPro or CBL 2 have not been used before this experiment, ask students to bring their calculators to class and download the DataMate program from LabPro or CBL 2 to the calculators.

2. Rearrange classroom furniture to allow walking space free of obstructions for each group. Hallways and corridors are perfect for this activity.

3. Prepare cardboard pieces for each group.

4. Give different distance-time graphs to different student groups in advance. Ask students to make velocity-time and acceleration-time graphs based on the given distance-time graph and to write a plan of walking motion before they come to class on the lab day.

5. Warn students that they should not share distance-time graphs with other groups.

TEACHING OBJECTIVES

Students will be able to

- plot qualitative graphs of first and second derivatives of the given piece-wise function, defined as a combination of linear and quadratic functions

- use graphs of velocity and acceleration to develop a plan of motion to match a given distance-time graph

- revise and modify a plan of motion based on the comparison of a given distance-time graph and their experimental results

- find specific mathematical relationships between the graph of the function and the graphs of its first and second derivatives, such as these:

  ○ if a function increases, its derivative is positive; if a function decreases, its derivative is negative

  ○ if a function has a minimum or maximum, its derivative at that point is zero

ACTIVITY NOTES

Although there are a lot of distance-matching experiments, this activity focuses on the development of students' ability to differentiate functions graphically and to analyze the graphs of a function and its derivatives qualitatively.

When students plot the first and second derivatives of the given distance-time function, they will get functions that are discontinuous unless they have "smoothed out" the corners of the distance-time graph before taking the derivatives. In reality, velocity and acceleration are always continuous functions of time, and their theoretical graphs are ideal.

Looking at the graphs of velocity and acceleration, students should be able to identify the direction of motion (direction of velocity), changes in velocity (in terms of speeding up, slowing down, or remaining constant), and the relative magnitudes of velocities (for constant velocities) or accelerations (for constant accelerations). Students use their conceptual understanding of velocity and acceleration to develop a written plan of walking motion based on the graphs of the first and second derivatives of a given distance-time graph.

In this activity students associate everyday concepts of speeding up, slowing down, moving at a constant pace, direction of motion, and so forth with mathematical concepts such as concavity, positive or negative slope of the graph, and increasing or decreasing behavior of the function.

The purpose of having student groups exchange their plans of motion is to put more responsibility on them for developing clear and detailed plans of motion. Students "walk" the distance-time graph using only a plan of motion written in terms of velocity, acceleration, and direction without seeing the distance-time graph. Only then do groups exchange their graphs and compare their experimental graph to the given distance-time graph. The Data section of the student worksheet is prepared on a separate sheet of paper for that reason.

Students are expected to analyze graphs of the first and second derivatives plotted by another group for the assigned distance-time graph and, if necessary, improve the plan of motion given to them. There should be significant collaboration between student groups.

The given distance-time graph can be a combination of quadratic and linear (in particular, constant) functions. Several samples of the distance-time graphs you can assign follow.

In the following graphs, distance is measured from the CBL motion sensor to the walking person. Each graph is a piece-wise function that consists of segments representing these functions:

- Constant
- Linear (not constant)
- Quadratic

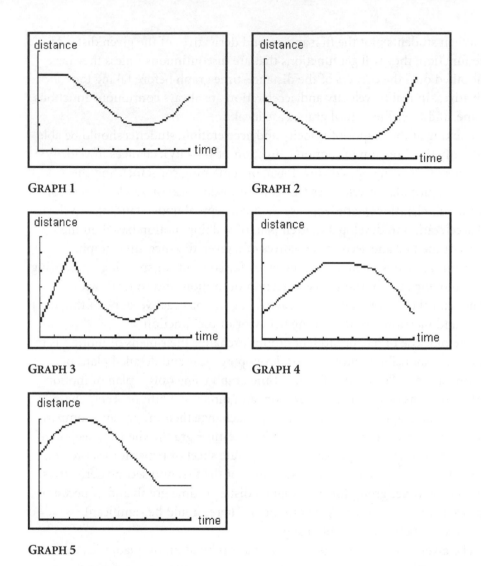

GRAPH 1

GRAPH 2

GRAPH 3

GRAPH 4

GRAPH 5

Experimental Procedure Notes

A CBR can be used instead of a motion detector. However, in order to get experimental velocity-time and acceleration-time graphs, the CBR should be connected to LabPro or CBL 2 as a motion detector.

Advise students to walk keeping their upper body still to get as smooth a signal as possible for the motion detector. The cardboard should be kept at about 15 cm above waist level. The motion detector should be aligned at the same height and facing the walker at all times.

If reflections from external objects occurred during the experiment, the resulting graph will be discontinuous and have extraneous points. Students will need to align the motion detector before data collection is started and verify that signals reflect from the walking person by observing the readings of the motion detector in the upper corner of the calculator screen. Students can also get a good graph by walking with the motion detector facing the wall. Students should repeat the experimental procedure until the graph displayed on the calculator screen is smooth.

Data Analysis Notes

1. Students will need to compare the shapes of the given and experimental distance-time graphs. If the plan of motion was correctly and clearly stated, they should get a graph that is qualitatively the same as the given distance-time graph. If the experimental distance-time graph is different from the given distance-time graph, students should follow these steps:
   a. Analyze the theoretical graphs of velocity and acceleration borrowed from a different group and make necessary corrections.
   b. Analyze the written plan of motion they got from the other group, compare it to the theoretical velocity-time and acceleration-time graphs, and make necessary corrections to the plan.
   c. Walk the revised plan of motion and confirm their corrections by producing the experimental distance-time graph they expected.

2. Students will need to verify the differential relationships between distance, velocity, and acceleration on the experimental graphs. Because of the errors in calculations produced by the calculator and the irregularities in real motion, the velocity-time and acceleration-time graphs will look different from the theoretically predicted graphs. However, students should be able to find a correspondence between experimental velocity and distance, and between acceleration and velocity, that reflects the correspondence between the derivative of a function and the function itself.

3. Students will need to compare slopes and concavities of lines in each segment, as well as the correspondence of graphs at critical points on the distance-time, velocity-time, and acceleration-time graphs. Students compare experimental distance-time, velocity-time, and acceleration-time graphs to analyze their mathematical relationships—the maximum on a distance-time graph should correspond to the zero of the velocity-time graph, increasing distance should correspond to positive velocity, the maximum on the velocity-time graph should correspond to zero acceleration, and so forth. Despite the irregularities in the graphs, the correspondence of graphs at critical points should hold true, and students should be able to confirm differential relationships.

4. You will need to discuss with the students the role of the calculator in the interpretation of data. Although the distance-time graph is a result of direct measurements from the motion detector, the velocity-time and acceleration-time graphs result from the calculator-based program. These calculations must be reasonably interpreted.

Expected Calculations

Sample theoretical graphs for Graph 1:

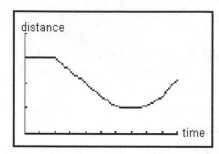

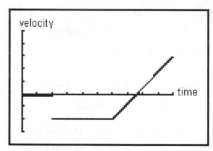

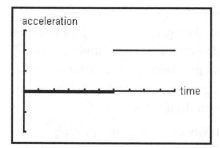

Sample plan of motion to match the given distance-time graph (final version):

1. Stand still for 2 seconds at a distance of about 4 meters from the motion detector facing you.

2. Move toward the motion detector with constant speed for 4 seconds.

3. Slow down for 1 second until reaching a complete stop.

4. Immediately start moving away from the detector, slowly gaining speed for 3 seconds.

Students are expected to analyze the distance-time graph as the one above and make these conclusions:

Mathematical reasoning	Interpretation
1. On the first segment, distance is constant, the first derivative (velocity) is zero, and the second derivative (acceleration) is zero.	Stand still.
2. On the second segment, distance is linearly decreasing, the first derivative (velocity) is negative and constant, and the second derivative (acceleration) is zero.	Move toward the detector with constant speed.

Mathematical reasoning	Interpretation
3. On the third segment, distance is a parabola concave upward, the first derivative (velocity) is a linear function changing sign, and the second derivative (acceleration) is positive and constant.	Slow down as you move toward the detector, stop, then change the direction of motion, speeding up as you move away from the detector.

Sample Data

These data were collected by having the student walk in front of the motion detector following the sample written plan of motion without seeing the assigned distance-time graph.

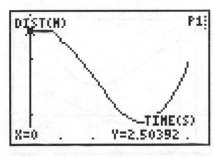
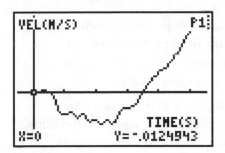
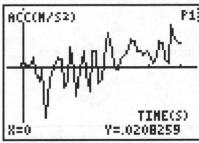

As is clear from the experimental graphs, the distance-time graph matches the given theoretical graph very well. The velocity graph has three separate segments representing the behavior of the function, as illustrated on the theoretical graph of velocity:

1. There is a segment with zero velocity.

2. There is a segment with negative velocity, which can be considered horizontal on average.

3. There is a close-to-linear segment that represents the change in velocity with constant acceleration.

The acceleration-time graph does not look at all like the theoretical graph. However, it is possible to reason about some features of the acceleration within experimental error:

1. The first segment, where acceleration is zero at the very beginning of the graph, corresponds to the first segment of the theoretical graph.

2. The second segment, where average acceleration is zero, corresponds to the motion with constant velocity.

3. The third segment, where average acceleration is positive, corresponds to the motion with constant acceleration.

Expected Analysis

Distance-Time vs. Velocity-Time

1. In segment A, the horizontal slope of the distance-time function corresponds to the zero of the velocity-time function.

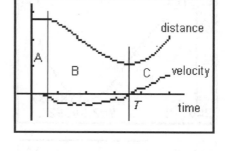

2. In segment B, the distance-time function is decreasing and the slope is negative—the same as velocity.

3. At point T, the distance-time graph has a minimum and the velocity is zero.

4. In segment C, the distance-time function is increasing and the slope is positive—the same as velocity.

Velocity-Time vs. Acceleration-Time

1. At point A, the acceleration changes sign from negative to positive and the velocity has a local minimum.

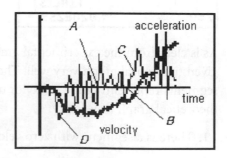

2. At point B, the acceleration changes sign from positive to negative and the velocity has a local maximum.

3. At point C, the acceleration is positive and the velocity is increasing. At point D, the acceleration is negative and the velocity is decreasing.

FURTHER EXPLORATIONS

1. Analyze what really happens at the points where the theoretical velocity-time or acceleration-time graph is discontinuous. Make adjustments in these graphs to make them closer to realistic functions.

2. Analyze the differences in the experimental and theoretical graphs, describe sources of error, and suggest possibilities to improve the experimental results.

3. If you teach anti-differentiation at the same time as differentiation, a good further exploration for students is to have them predict the shape of the distance-time graph from the shape of the velocity-time graph, using a step-like velocity function.

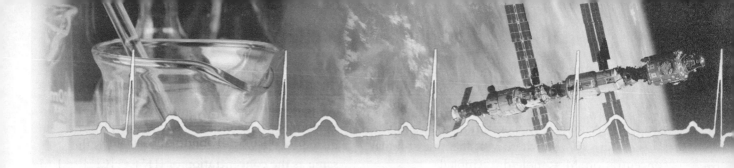

Parametric Differentiation

How Fast Does pH Change with Hydrogen Concentration?

INTRODUCTION

Water does not have a taste, and we think of it as neutral. Lemon juice and vinegar are sour, or *acidic*. If you drank them, you would need something *alkaline*, like bicarbonate of soda or milk of magnesia, to neutralize the acidity in your stomach. Instead of sour, let's use the term "hydrogen ions," and instead of alkaline, let's use the term "hydroxyl ions." Vinegar has many more hydrogen ions than hydroxyl ions. Conversely, soda

ash and bicarbonate, being alkaline, or basic, have more hydroxyl ions than hydrogen ions. In summary, acids produce hydrogen ions, and alkalis produce hydroxyl ions. This is how pH was introduced as a scale measuring the acidity or alkalinity of a solution: pH is the power (German *Potenz*) of a solution to yield hydrogen ions $[H^+]$. Scientifically, pH is defined as the negative logarithm of the hydrogen ion concentration: $pH = -\log[H^+]$. The square brackets are used in

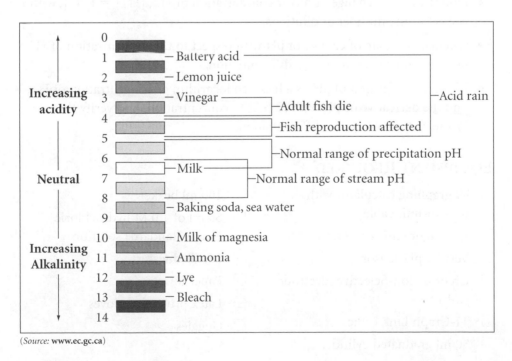

(*Source:* **www.ec.gc.ca**)

FIGURE 13.1 *The pH scale*

---

chemistry to indicate concentration, for example, $[H^+] = 2.5 \cdot 10^{-9}$ M, where M is the unit of molar concentration, M = mole/dm^3 (mole/l).

The pH scale was defined because the enormous range of hydrogen ion concentrations found in aqueous solutions makes using H^+ molarity awkward. For example, in a typical acid-base *titration*, $[H^+]$ may vary from about 0.01 M to 0.0000000000001 M. It is easier to write "the pH varies from 2 to 13." The pH scale runs from 0 (highly acidic) to 14 (highly alkaline), with distilled water being neutral at pH 7. The more hydrogen ions there are, the lower the pH. Because the pH scale is logarithmic, pH 8 is 10 times more alkaline than pH 7 and pH 9 is 100 times more alkaline than pH 7.

Consider hydrochloric acid (HCl) with concentration 1 M. In water, hydrochloric acid exists as ions of H^+ and Cl^- that completely dissociate. So the concentration of HCl is the same as the concentration of $[H^+] = [Cl^-] = 1$ M, which results in pH = 0 for this acid solution. If you dilute HCl with distilled water, you will change the concentrations of both ions and also increase pH.

In this experiment, you will take measurements of pH and of the concentration of Cl^- as functions of the number of dilutions. You'll determine the rate of change of pH with respect to the concentration by the method of parametric differentiation. You will use the scientific definition of pH as a base-ten logarithm of the hydrogen-ion concentration and directly differentiate this function with respect to the concentration to confirm the equation for the rate of change of pH.

OBJECTIVES

- Measure pH and the concentration of Cl^- of an HCl solution while diluting the acid with distilled water in the ratio 1:10.

- Find the rate of change of pH with respect to the number of dilutions.

- Find the rate of change of molar concentration of H^+, $[H^+] = [Cl^-]$, with respect to the number of dilutions.

- Calculate the rate of change of pH with respect to the concentration of H^+, using formulas of parametric differentiation.

- Using the definition of pH as a base-ten logarithm of concentration of H^+, find the derivative of pH with respect to concentration, and verify the formulas for parametric differentiation.

EQUIPMENT REQUIRED

- ☐ TI graphing calculator with unit-to-unit cable
- ☐ LabPro or CBL 2 interface
- ☐ Vernier pH sensor
- ☐ Chloride Ion-Selective Electrode (ISE)
- ☐ TI-Graph Link cable
- ☐ 50 ml graduated cylinder
- ☐ 100 ml beaker
- ☐ 50 ml of 1.0 M hydrochloric (High Standard) solution
- ☐ Distilled water
- ☐ Paper towels
- ☐ Latex protective gloves
- ☐ Goggles

PROGRAMS

DataMate

TI-Graph Link

SAFETY

1. Wear protective latex gloves and goggles when working with acid solution.

2. Avoid splashing the acid solution. Keep it away from your face.

3. After the experiment is completed, dispose of the solution in the sink.

EQUIPMENT SETUP PROCEDURE

1. Connect the LabPro or CBL 2 to the calculator with the unit-to-unit cable using the input/output ports located on the bottom edge of each unit. Press the cable ends in firmly.

2. Connect the ISE to the CH 1 port of the LabPro or CBL 2.

3. Connect the pH sensor to the CH 2 port on the LabPro or CBL 2.

4. Turn on the calculator.

5. Run the DataMate program on the calculator. Press Clear, and the program will automatically identify the ISE connected to CH 1 and the pH sensor connected to CH 2.* Select 1: Setup. Move the cursor to CH 1. Select 2: Calibrate. Select 2: Calibrate Now.

6. The ISE should have been soaking in the High Standard solution, provided with the ISE, for half an hour. Wait until the reading is stable, and press Enter. At the prompt, enter the concentration value for the High Standard Calibration Point, "1000" for 1000 mg/L. Press Enter.

7. Remove the ISE from the High Standard solution, rinse well with distilled water from the wash bottle, and gently blot dry with a paper towel or lab wipe. Place the electrode into the Low Standard solution (included with the ISE). **Important:** Make sure the ISE is not resting on the bottom of the container and that the small white reference contact is immersed. Make sure no air bubbles are trapped below the ISE. Hold the ISE still, and wait for the voltage reading to stabilize. Press Enter, and at the prompt, enter the concentration value for the Low Standard solution, "10" for 10 mg/L. Select 1: OK twice to return to the Setup menu.

---

*If you are using an old sensor, it will not be identified by the interface. In this case, set up the sensor manually by selecting the channel, pressing 1: Setup, and then pressing Enter. Select the appropriate sensor from the menu provided.

8. Use the up arrow to select Mode, and press Enter. Select 3: Events with Entry. Press 1: OK to return to the Setup menu.

9. Press 1: OK, and the calculator will return to the Main menu, ready for data collection.

EXPERIMENTAL PROCEDURE

1. After calibrating, rinse off the end of the ISE, and blot it dry with a paper towel or lab wipe.

2. Remove the pH sensor from the storing solution, and rinse with distilled water.

3. Press 2: Start on the calculator.

4. Pour 50 ml of HCl solution into the beaker.

5. Insert the tip of the ISE into the solution. Make sure the ISE is not resting on the bottom of the container and that the small white reference contact is immersed. Make sure no air bubbles are trapped below the ISE. Hold the ISE still, and wait for the reading displayed on the calculator to stabilize.

6. Place the pH sensor in the solution. Wait for the reading displayed on the calculator to stabilize.

7. Record the concentration and pH values in the data table. Press Enter to store this data point. At the prompt, enter 0. Remove sensors from the solution.

8. Pour 45 ml of distilled water into the graduated cylinder, and add 5 ml of HCl solution from the beaker to the graduated cylinder so that the total volume of the new solution is 50 ml. Mix well. Empty the beaker, and pour the solution from the graduated cylinder into the beaker. Repeat steps 5–7. Record the concentration and pH values in the data table. Press Enter, and at the prompt, enter 1 as the number of times you diluted the given HCl solution.

9. Repeat step 8 four more times by mixing 45 ml of distilled water and 5 ml of the HCl solution you created in the previous step. Each time at the prompt, record the concentration and pH values in the data table and the number of times you diluted the HCl solution.

10. When you are finished, press STO on the calculator to store all data. The number of dilutions will be stored in List 1, chloride concentration in List 2, and pH in List 3.

11. After you finish the experiment, rinse both sensors with distilled water, and dry them. Store the pH sensor in the buffer storage solution provided. Store the ISE in long-term storage (for longer than 24 hours) or in short-term storage (less than 24 hours)—check with your teacher for detailed instructions.

DATA

| | \multicolumn{6}{c}{n = **Number of dilutions**} |
	0	1	2	3	4	5
y = pH						
Mass concentration of $[Cl^-]$ (mg/L)						
x = Molar concentration of $[H^+]=[Cl^-]/35500$ (mole/L)						

DATA ANALYSIS

1. Calculate the molar concentration of hydrogen ions using the measured concentration of $[Cl^-]$, and record these values in the data table. Store these values in List 4 of your calculator.

2. Using the data stored in your calculator, graph the molar concentration (List 4) as a function of n (List 1).

3. Use the exponential regression option to find the best-fitting curve for this graph. Analyze the residuals.

4. Record the equation of the best-fitting curve for the concentration as a function of the number of dilutions:

   $x(n) = $ _____

5. Use TI-Graph Link to print data points along with the regression curve for inclusion with the lab report.

6. Using the data stored in your calculator, graph pH (List 3) as a function of n (List 1).

7. Use the linear regression option to find the best-fitting curve for this graph. Analyze the residuals.

8. Record the equation of the best-fitting line for the pH as a function of the number of dilutions:

   $y(n) = $ _____

9. Use TI-Graph Link to print data points along with the regression line for inclusion with the lab report.

10. Using the equations you found in steps 4 and 8, find derivatives $\frac{dx}{dn}$ and $\frac{dy}{dn}$:

$$\frac{dx}{dn} = \underline{\hspace{2cm}}$$

$$\frac{dy}{dn} = \underline{\hspace{2cm}}$$

11. Find the rate of change of pH with respect to concentration, using parametric differentiation: $\frac{dy}{dx} = \frac{\frac{dy}{dn}}{\frac{dx}{dn}}$. Express your answer in terms of x:

$$\frac{dy}{dx} = \underline{\hspace{2cm}}$$

12. Find $\frac{dy}{dx}$ using the equation that defines pH as a function of hydrogen molar concentration.

13. Compare the experimental and theoretical results.

Parametric Differentiation

How Fast Does pH Change with Hydrogen Concentration?

BEFORE THE EXPERIMENT

1. If LabPro or CBL 2 have not been used before this experiment, ask students to bring their calculators to class in advance and download the DataMate program from LabPro or CBL 2 to the calculators.

2. Prepare enough 1.0 M hydrochloric solution in advance. It can be stored in a tightly closed, marked container.

3. We recommend that you pour equal amounts of HCl solution into separate containers, one for each group, before the experiment. Allow extra solution for mistakes.

4. Have a separate container with distilled water for each group.

5. The Ion-Selective Electrode (ISE) must be soaked in the High Standard solution (included with the ISE) for approximately 30 minutes.
   Important: Make sure the ISE is not resting on the bottom of the container and that the small white reference contact is immersed. Make sure that no air bubbles are trapped below the ISE.

SAFETY

1. Highly concentrated acids are poisonous. Hydrochloric acid of 2.0 M concentration or lower could be dangerous in contact with the eye, so students should be wearing protective gloves and goggles while working with this acid.

2. Warn students to avoid splashing solutions.

3. Dispose of the acid solution in the sink.

TEACHING OBJECTIVES

Students will be able to
- determine regression equations for molar concentration of H^+ and pH as functions of number of dilutions

- evaluate regressions using residuals

- differentiate general exponential and logarithmic functions

---

- calculate the rate of change of pH with respect to the hydrogen molar concentration using parametric differentiation

- compare the rate of change of pH with respect to the hydrogen molar concentration found using parametric differentiation and directly

ACTIVITY NOTES

In this activity, students collect experimental data that illustrate parametric differentiation. The parameter is the number of dilutions, and pH and hydrogen molar concentration both depend on the parameter. The definition of pH provides the exact formula for the pH as a function of hydrogen concentration, so the experimental derivative they find by parametric differentiation can be easily verified by direct differentiation.

You can use this activity to explore parametric differentiation. Students can first find the rate of change of pH with respect to the hydrogen molar concentration using the definition of pH. Then they can differentiate both parametric equations for $pH(n)$ and $[H^+](n)$ and try to determine how to combine these derivatives to get the theoretical result. Then parametric differentiation can be introduced at a more formal level.

Diluting the given concentrated acid solution with distilled water while keeping the total volume of the solution constant allows the concentration of acid to be considered as an exponential function of the number of dilutions. Thus, students need to know how to differentiate the general exponential function. For convenience, the diluting factor is 1/10 in this experiment.

pH is defined as the negative base-ten logarithm of the concentration, so students need to know how to differentiate the general logarithmic function.

When the solution is diluted with the same ratio, the concentration of the solution is represented by the exponential function of the number of dilutions having the ratio as base. In this experiment, the dilutions occur at a 1:10 ratio, so the base is $\frac{1}{10}$ and the exponential function is 10^{-n}. Thus, pH is proportional to $-\log_{10} 10^{-n} = n$, which means that pH is a linear function of the number of dilutions.

Experimental Procedure Notes

1. High school chemistry labs should have 1.0 M or 2.0 M hydrochloric solutions. Check with the chemistry teacher. If needed, ask him or her to prepare the solutions. Safety precautions include use of goggles and gloves while working with this acid.

2. The ISE probe has a range of 1.8–35,500 mg/L, which puts an upper limit of 1.0 M on the concentration and allows for a maximum of four or five dilutions with the factor of $\frac{1}{10}$. At the same time, the pH sensor cannot measure precisely near the neutral points, so precision drops significantly when pH $\geq$ 6. That allows for only five data points (with the initial point taken for the 1.0 M HCl solution).

3. Expected ideal values for concentrations and pH are provided in the table below. The concentration of hydrochloric acid available in high school chemistry labs is not necessarily 1.0 M even if so labeled. Concentration and pH measurements may show slightly different values than expected. That would not affect the mathematical results of the lab.

Concentration (mg/L)	35,500	3,550	355	35.5	3.55	0.355
Concentration (M)	1	0.1	0.01	0.001	0.0001	0.00001
pH	0	1	2	3	4	5

4. Students may forget to store data in their calculators and to dilute solutions. Recommend to students that they record experimental data in the data table as a backup. If the values of pH and concentration are recorded, they will not need to re-do a whole experiment but can add this data point later during data analysis.

Data Analysis Notes

1. When the experiment is completed, events are stored in List 1, concentration in mg/L is stored in List 2, and pH is stored in List 3. Students should quit the DataMate program and use StatPlot for data analysis and plotting graphs along with the regression equations.

2. Students should convert mass concentration to molar concentration as suggested in the Data Analysis section of the lab.

3. Students should use exponential and linear regression equations for concentration and pH, respectively, as functions of the number of dilutions.

4. Students should analyze the residuals after each regression is calculated. If residuals are randomly scattered around the horizontal axis, the regression line is the best-fitting line. Then the data along with the regression equation should be plotted on the same screen and printed using TI-Graph Link.

5. When students calculate the derivative using parametric differentiation, they need to express the final answer in terms of concentration rather than in terms of the number of dilutions. This permits comparison of the derivatives of pH with respect to the concentration found from the experiment and from theory.

The derivative should be in the form of $-\frac{a}{x}$, where a is a constant and x is concentration. To compare the derivatives, students can find the percentage error between the experimental and theoretical values of the coefficient a in the equation for the derivative.

Sample Data

The solution labeled 2.0 M HCl was diluted with water at a 1:1 proportion to make an initial 1.0 M solution. As is clear from the experimental data, the initial solution was not a 1.0 M solution but about a 0.5 M solution.

	$n =$ **Number of dilutions**					
	0	**1**	**2**	**3**	**4**	**5**
$y =$ pH	0.3415	1.15177	2.03342	2.87756	3.75921	4.49079
Mass concentration of $[Cl^-]$ (mg/L)	16106.8	2284.59	368.087	51.6742	7.7688	1.84165
$x =$ **Molar concentration of $[H^+] =$ $[Cl^-]/35500$ (mole/L)**	0.45647	0.06435	0.01037	0.00146	0.000218	0.0000518

Sample Graphs

Viewed in DataMate

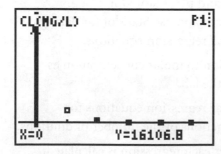

Concentration versus number of dilutions

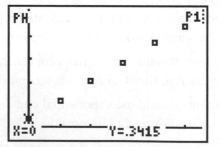

pH versus number of dilutions

Calculus: Concepts and Applications Instructor's Resource Book
©2005 Key Curriculum Press

Expected Calculations

1. Exponential regression—molar concentration of [H$^+$] versus number of dilutions:

$$x(n) = 0.414(0.159)^n, \quad (r^2 = 0.9981)$$

2. Linear regression—pH versus number of dilutions:

$$y(n) = 0.840n + 0.341, \quad (r^2 = 0.9994)$$

3. Derivatives:

$$\frac{dx}{dn} = 0.414 \times \ln(0.159) \times 0.159^n = -0.76(0.159)^n$$

$$\frac{dy}{dn} = 0.84$$

4. The rate of change of pH with respect to concentration:

$$\frac{dy}{dx} = \frac{0.84}{-0.76(0.159)^n} = -\frac{1.1}{0.159^n}$$

From the exponential regression equation, we get $0.159^n = \frac{x}{0.414}$. Substituting that into the equation for the derivative, we finally get

$$\frac{dy}{dx} = -\frac{1.1}{\frac{x}{0.414}} = -\frac{.046}{x}$$

5. Theoretically, $y = -\log x$. Differentiating, we get

$$\frac{dy}{dx} = -\frac{1}{x \ln 10} = -\frac{0.43}{x}$$

6. The percentage error between coefficients 0.46 and 0.43 can be calculated as

$$\frac{|0.46 - 0.43|}{0.43} \cdot 100\% \approx 7\%$$

Comments: We see from the residuals that all regression lines are good choices for the given sets of data. The only "bad" data point is the first value of concentration. This can be explained by the fact that measurements were taken very close to the upper threshold of the ISE sensor.

StatPlot graphs viewed with regression curves and residuals for each function

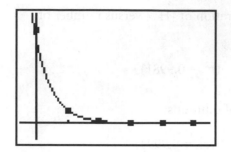

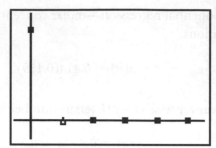

Concentration versus number of
dilutions with regression, $x(n)$

Residuals

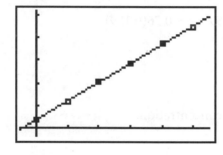

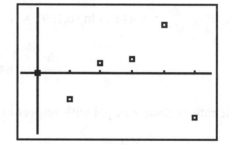

pH versus number of dilutions with
regression, $y(n)$

Residuals

FURTHER EXPLORATIONS

1. It is possible to choose a different dilution factor and to analyze the effect of
dilution factor on the pH-concentration relationship.

2. Students can explore the role of the parameter on the derivative. They can
change the parameter in the experiment, for example, by increasing the
volume of the solution and measuring pH and concentration as functions
of volume. Then they can check to see if the parametric differentiation
method still works and gives the same result.

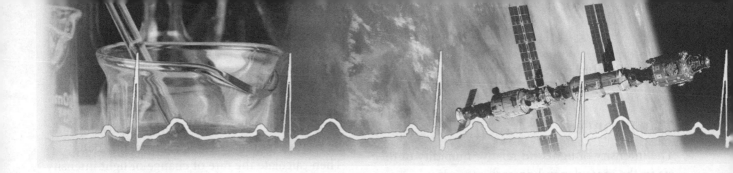

Related Rates

Environmental Parameters in a Grass Ecosystem

INTRODUCTION

An *ecosystem* consists of a community of living organisms and their local physical environment. The richness and variety of living organisms and their habitats is called *biodiversity*. The living and nonliving elements of an ecosystem are connected through the flow of energy and the cycling of chemical elements. No single organism, population, or species is able to produce all of its own food and recycle all of its metabolic products. Life requires the interaction of several species in an environment that includes air and/or water to transport materials and energy.

There are no absolute boundaries between ecosystems—actually, the *biosphere* is one big ecosystem in which everything is connected to everything else in some way or another. Some ecosystem borders are, however, quite well defined. For example, there is a relatively clear transition from a rocky ocean coast to the forest along its edge or from a pond to the woods that surround it. Other borders are much more vague, as is the case with the gradual transition from deciduous woodland to coniferous forest in some parts of the world.

Ecosystems change continuously over time according to certain recognizable, repeatable patterns and in response to environmental changes

FIGURE 11.1

such as shifts in climate. An area's biodiversity has a profound effect upon the physical and biological makeup of an ecosystem. Change in the biodiversity of a particular area would have an immediate effect on physical parameters such as air temperature, relative humidity, and light intensity. On the other hand, changes in one of these parameters would immediately cause change in the others.

In this experiment, you will explore the relationship between light intensity and relative humidity in a simple ecosystem—a grassy field. Your goal is to determine how changes in one of the physical parameters affect changes in another one.

THE PROBLEM

The intensity of light and relative humidity of the air in the grass depend on each other. It is important to know how fast the intensity of light changes with the height if we know how fast the relative humidity is changing. For a given ecosystem, determine how light intensity depends on relative humidity using experimental data. Then calculate the rate of change of light intensity at the heights 20 cm, 40 cm, and 80 cm using experimental data for the relative humidity. Verify the calculated rate of change of light intensity by finding it experimentally.

EQUIPMENT REQUIRED

☐ TI-83 calculator with unit-to-unit cable

☐ LabPro or CBL 2

☐ Vernier relative humidity sensor

☐ TI light probe

☐ Vernier CBL-DIN adapter cable

☐ TI-Graph Link cable

☐ Meterstick

☐ Rubber band

PROGRAMS

DataMate

TI-Graph Link

EQUIPMENT SETUP PROCEDURE

1. Connect the LabPro or CBL 2 to the calculator with the unit-to-unit cable, using the input/output ports located on the bottom edge of each unit. Press the cable ends in firmly.

2. Connect the relative humidity sensor to Channel 1 and the light sensor to Channel 2 of the LabPro or CBL 2. Wrap both sensors with the rubber band so that one person can manage them together.

3. Turn on the calculator and run the DataMate program. Press Clear, and the program will automatically identify both sensors connected to the LabPro or CBL 2.*

4. On the main screen, choose 1: Setup. Use the up arrow to select Mode, press Enter, and then select 3: Events with Entry.

5. Select 1: OK, and the calculator will return to the Main menu, ready for data collection.

---

*If you are using an old sensor, it will not be identified by the interface. In this case, set up the sensor manually by selecting the channel, pressing 1: Setup, and then pressing Enter. Select the appropriate sensor from the menu provided.

Calculus: Concepts and Applications Instructor's Resource Book
©2005 Key Curriculum Press

EXPERIMENTAL PROCEDURE

1. Find a place where the height of the grass is at least 20 cm. Hold a meterstick vertically with zero mark at the ground, directly on the dirt. Record the height of the grass.

2. Press 2: Start on the calculator.

3. Place the relative humidity sensor and the light probe at the 0 cm mark. Make sure that the light probe is pointing directly toward the ground. When readings have stabilized, record all the displayed values in Table 2, and then press Enter.

4. At the prompt, enter the value of the height above the ground measured in centimeters. In this case, it is 0.

5. Move the sensors up to the 10 cm mark, and when readings have stabilized, record the displayed values in Table 1, and press Enter. At the prompt, enter 10.

6. Repeat this procedure, changing the height by 10 cm until you reach the 100 cm mark. When you are finished, press STO on the calculator to store all data.

7. Quit the DataMate program.

DATA

The collected height data are stored in List 1, relative humidity in List 2, and light intensity in List 3.

TABLE 1 *Experimental Data*

Height, h (cm)	Relative humidity, R (%)	Relative light intensity, I
0		
10		
20		
30		
40		
50		
60		
70		
80		
90		
100		

DATA ANALYSIS

1. Display relative humidity as a function of height. In order to use the exponential regression option to find the equation that best fits these data, you will need to transform the data before you run the regression. Record the final equation for $R(h)$ in Equations.

2. Use TI-Graph Link to print these data along with the equation you found for inclusion with your lab report.

3. Display light intensity versus relative humidity on the screen. Find the best-fitting regression curve that describes this relationship. (If you can't recognize the relationship, try to plot light intensity versus the reciprocal of relative humidity.) Record the equation that you found in Equations.

4. Display the regression equation you found along with the data points. Use TI-Graph Link to print this graph, and include it with your lab report.

5. Differentiate the equation for $I(R(h))$ to determine the rate of change of light intensity, $\frac{dI}{dh}$, as a function of the relative humidity rate, $\frac{dR}{dh}$, based on your regression equation. Show the details of your calculations, and record the final equation.

6. Calculate the rate of change of light intensity at the given points. In order to do that, use experimental values of $R(h)$ at the given points, and calculate $\frac{dR}{dh}$ at the given points using the regression equation you found. This is the theoretical value of the rate of change of light intensity. Record the data in Table 2.

7. In order to verify your calculations, display light intensity as a function of height. Use the logistic regression option to find the equation that best fits these data. Record the final equation for $I(h)$.

8. Use TI-Graph Link to print these data along with the equation you found, and include it with your lab report.

9. Calculate the rate of change of the light intensity at the given points using the equation you found. This is the experimental value of the rate of change of the light intensity. Record these data in Table 2.

10. Compare the theoretical and experimental results.

EQUATIONS

$R(h) = $ _____

$I(R(h)) = $ _____

$dR/dh = $ _____

$dI/dh = $ _____

$I(h) = $ _____

TABLE 2 *Comparison of Experimental and Calculated Rates of Change*

Height, h (cm)	R (%)	$\dfrac{dR}{dh}$ (%/cm)	Rate of change of light intensity, $\left(\dfrac{1}{cm}\right)$ $\dfrac{dI}{dh}$ (theoretical)	$\dfrac{dI}{dh}$ (experimental)	Percentage error
		Relative humidity data			
20					
40					
80					

Related Rates

Environmental Parameters in a Grass Ecosystem

BEFORE THE EXPERIMENT

1. Find a field with homogeneous growth of grass of at least 20 cm high. The less diverse the growth, the closer the relationship between relative humidity and light intensity will be to the inversely proportional relationship.

2. If LabPro or CBL 2 have not been used before this experiment, ask students to bring their calculators to class in advance and download the DataMate program from LabPro or CBL 2 to the calculator.

3. Bring extra batteries for the LabPro or CBL 2 to the site.

4. Announce in advance that the experiment will be conducted outside so that students wear appropriate clothes and shoes and bring sunscreen or hats.

5. Students will need to use logistic regression on their data. If you have not already discussed logistic functions in class, spend some time explaining the properties of these functions. You may use Experiment 12 from this book to study the behavior of logistic functions.

TEACHING OBJECTIVES

Students will be able to

- find the best-fitting regression equations for the relative humidity and light intensity as functions of height

- calculate experimental rates of change based on the regression equations

- analyze experimental data and find an equation that establishes a mathematical relationship between relative humidity and light intensity as functions of height above the ground

- differentiate this equation to determine the mathematical relationship between rates of change of relative humidity and light intensity with height

- calculate the theoretical rate of change of light intensity from the regression equation

- compare experimental and theoretical results for the rate of change of light intensity

456 / CBL™ Projects

Calculus: Concepts and Applications Instructor's Resource Book
©2005 Key Curriculum Press

ACTIVITY NOTES

This is an engaging outdoor activity that makes related-rates problems more applicable to their experiences and links it to the biology that the majority of students have previously studied. The statement of the problem, similar to standard textbook problems on related rates, gives the objectives of this lab. For a textbook problem, students have to find a mathematical relationship between two functions. However, in this activity, they find an equation that links these two functions experimentally by taking simultaneous measurements of the relative humidity and light intensity at the site. This activity is open-ended because the equation will depend on the ecosystem of the site, the time of day, the weather, and so forth. For a simple grassy field, expect the light intensity to be inversely proportional to the relative humidity.

Students have to use the chain rule to differentiate the equation they found. This will give them an equation that links the rates of change of the two functions.

In order to calculate the theoretical rate of change of light intensity at given heights of the grass, students need to know the relative humidity and rate of change of relative humidity at given heights. Students can use their experimental data to find the best-fitting equation for relative humidity as a function of height and calculate the rate of change of relative humidity from this equation. On the other hand, they can also use the experimental data for the light intensity to determine the best-fitting equation for the light intensity and find the rate of change of light intensity at given heights directly from this regression equation. This allows verification of the related-rates equation.

Experimental Procedure Notes

If possible, collect data on a warm, dry day. If you cannot find a site with tall enough grass, adjust the experimental procedure so that data are collected at 5 cm intervals.

When binding the light sensor and relative humidity sensor together, make sure that the sensors are aligned at the data collection end so that the measurements are always taken at the same height.

Use a plumb line to ensure that the meterstick is perpendicular to the ground.

Data Analysis Notes

1. The relative humidity as a function of time is close to the exponential function that is shifted up to the value of humidity above the grass. Students have to shift all data down, run the exponential regression, and then add the relative humidity above the grass in order to find a final equation for the relative humidity, $R(h)$.

2. The light sensor measures irradiance using a relative scale from 0 to 1. For a simple grassy field, the light intensity is practically inversely proportional to the relative humidity. That allows you to graph light intensity against the reciprocal of relative humidity. Students can easily recognize linear regression from this graph.

3. When differentiating the regression equation they got for light intensity as a function of relative humidity, students may need to be reminded that both functions, $I(h)$ and $R(h)$, depend on height, so the chain rule is necessary to complete the calculations.

4. Students can use the numeric derivative option of the calculator to determine the rate of change of relative humidity $\frac{dR}{dh}$ necessary to find numeric values for the rate of change of light intensity, $\frac{dI}{dh}$, at given heights.

5. Light intensity as a function of height is close to the logistic function with the horizontal asymptote $y = 1$ (maximum light intensity). Because exponential regression is used for relative humidity, $R(h)$ has the form $a + be^{kh}$. Then the reciprocal function should have the form $\frac{c}{a + be^{kh}}$, which is a logistic equation.

6. Students can use the numeric derivative option of the calculator to find the rate of change, $\frac{dI}{dh}$, at given heights and compare these values with the ones they found theoretically.

7. The exponential and logistic regressions may not necessarily be the best-fitting equations for the given sets of data. However, both regressions have asymptotic behavior at their extremes, which corresponds to the behavior of measured parameters. Relative humidity as a function of height asymptotically decreases to a constant value, whereas light intensity as a function of height asymptotically increases to a constant value. Because asymptotic behavior of both parameters will be observed at all sites, these two regressions are suggested as best-fitting equations for the data. For a given sample of experimental data, the exponential regression fits relative humidity best, whereas logistic regression fits the light intensity function best.

8. The results of calculations will produce large percentage errors between calculated and experimental rates of change of light intensity. Still, they demonstrate a fairly good correlation between the calculated and experimental data. The activity allows you to discuss with students the role of a mathematical model to simplify a complex real-world situation to determine the trends and major features of a specific phenomenon.

Sample Data

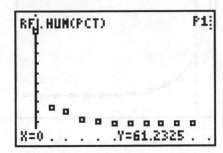
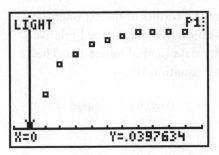

Relative humidity and light intensity as functions of height above the ground, viewed in the DataMate program

TABLE 1 *Experimental Data (Rounded)*

Height, h (cm)	Relative humidity, R (%)	Relative light intensity, I
0	61.2	0.04
10	22.0	0.35
20	20.3	0.63
30	16.7	0.73
40	15.4	0.84
50	14.2	0.87
60	14.1	0.92
70	14.0	0.96
80	14.0	0.96
90	14.0	0.96
100	14.0	0.96

Expected Calculations

Here are the results of the exponential regression on the transformed relative humidity data (actual minus 14). The resulting equation is

$$R(h) = 23.07(0.92)^h + 14(r^2 = 0.94)$$

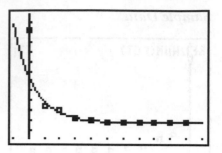

Relative humidity data with the regression equation

The equation for the light intensity versus the reciprocal of relative humidity is

$$I(h) = 17.03\left[\frac{1}{R(h)}\right] - 0.28$$

$$= \frac{17.03}{R(h)} - 0.28(r^2 = 0.96)$$

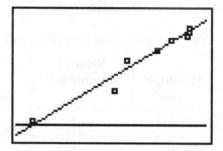

Differentiating the equation for the light intensity, you get this related-rates equation:

$$\frac{dI}{dh} = -\frac{17.03}{R^2(h)}\frac{dR}{dh}$$

Light intensity versus the reciprocal of relative humidity with the linear regression

Calculated rates of change of light intensity are given in Table 2.

Here is the resulting logistic regression equation on the light intensity data:

$$I(h) = \frac{0.93}{1 + 6.22e^{-0.12h}}$$

Using this equation, experimental values of the rate of change, $\frac{dI}{dh}$, are calculated.

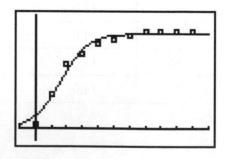

The light intensity data with the logistic regression equation

TABLE 2 *Comparison of Experimental and Calculated Rates of Change*

Height, h (cm)	Relative humidity data			Rate of change of light intensity, $\left(\dfrac{1}{cm}\right)$		Percentage error
	R (%)	$\dfrac{dR}{dh}$ (%/cm)	$\dfrac{dI}{dh}$ (theoretical)	$\dfrac{dI}{dh}$ (experimental)		
10	22.0	−0.83	0.029	0.024		17%
20	20.3	−0.38	0.016	0.025		36%
40	15.4	−0.08	0.0057	0.0059		4%
60	14.1	−0.016	0.0014	0.00007		50%

Although the percentage error between these values is high, they are within the measurement error.

The relationship between factors such as relative humidity and light intensity in an ecosystem is a function much more complex than the one students used in this activity. However, even though you did simplify the situation, you found a correlation between the theoretical and experimental rates of change. The comparison of the logistic curve for light intensity with the curve based on the reciprocal equation and the exponential regression for relative humidity, $R(h)$ (shown in the graph at right), supports this conclusion.

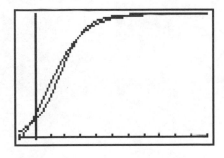

In addition, the corresponding rates of change of light intensity are shown in the graph at right—one that is found by direct differentiation of the logistic equation for $I(h)$ and another based on the related-rates equation. The curves are very similar in shape and behavior, with a slight shift from one to the other.

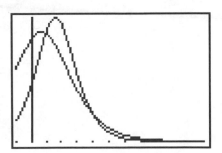

FURTHER EXPLORATIONS

1. Investigate the relationship between the rates of change of
   a. relative humidity and temperature
   b. light intensity and temperature

2. Investigate the relationship between the rates of change of the same functions in different ecosystems.

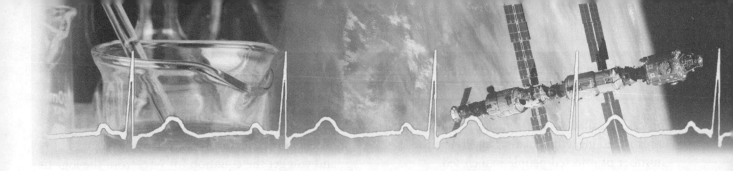

The Logistic Model

Simulating the Spread of Disease

INTRODUCTION

There are many contagious diseases. Smallpox
and polio are severe and often fatal, whereas the
common cold and flu are usually relatively mild.
You can get some diseases, like chicken pox, only
once, but you can catch the flu again and again.
A contagious disease can spread to thousands and
thousands of people. When that happens, the
outbreak is called an *epidemic* (from the Greek
words *epi*, upon + *demos*, the people). When the
disease affects several geographic regions at the
same time, reaching populations worldwide, it is
called a *pandemic* (in Greek, *pan* means all).

   Epidemiology is the scientific study of
contagious diseases. It deals with the essential
features of diseases, how they spread, and the
mathematics that describes the phenomenon
symbolically. The mathematical description of a
disease and its features is called a *model*. The model
helps us understand how a contagious disease
spreads through a population and predict what
fraction of the population might fall ill and when.

   In this activity, you will simulate the spread of
a contagious disease in a confined population that
is fixed in size. You will build a mathematical
model for this simulation and solve it to make
predictions. Assume that you and your classmates
represent a population that is fixed in size. Because
of the process of disease spread, the larger the size
of the statistical sample population, the better the

FIGURE 12.1

mathematical model describes the experimental
results. However, even in the case of a small group,
such as your class, you can still do a simulation and
model the experimental process, but you will need
to repeat the simulation several times to get good
data for the model.

   Suppose there is a contagiously "infected"
person in the class. Every time this person makes
contact with another person, he or she passes on
the infection unless the other person is already
infected. Of course, if two people are infected, they
are both sources of the disease, and so on.

   Your goal is to record how the number of
infected people depends on time and to analyze
this function. The mathematical model of this

process is called a *logistic model,* which describes a restricted growth process. Let $N(t)$ be the number of infected people in a closed environment at instant t. Then the logistic model can be described by this differential equation, where A and k are constant parameters:

$$\frac{dN}{dt} = kN(A - N)$$

Assuming that only one person is infected initially provides the *initial condition* $N(0) = 1$, and you get the equation for $N(t)$ from the logistic model:

$$N(t) = \frac{A}{1 + Be^{-kAt}}$$

OBJECTIVES

- Analyze the behavior of the function of the number of infected people over time in a closed environment. Verify that the experimental results correspond to the logistic model.

- Interpret the meaning of the coefficients A and B in the logistic function.

- Analyze the behavior of the rate of change of the logistic function.

- Derive and solve the differential equation for the logistic function.

EQUIPMENT REQUIRED

☐ TI-83 graphing calculator

PROGRAMS

Random integer generator

TI-Graph Link

EXPERIMENTAL PROCEDURE

There is one "infected" student in the class, so the whole class is put under quarantine. The environment is closed, so each "infected" student can only infect people who are in the classroom and are not yet "infected" (the teacher does not count).

1. Record the total number of students as A in the Data section. Assign each student in the classroom a number from 1 to A.

2. The teacher will choose one student randomly to be initially "infected." The "infected" student should move to an "infected" table. Record 1 for day 0 in the data table.

3. If you are an "infected" person, set up the random generator to generate integers between 1 and A, except your own number.

4. Run the random generator once. Use the number you generated to select the next "infected" person. Record 2 for day 2 in the data table.

5. A new "infected" student moves to the "infected" table. Now both "infected" students use the random generator, and each produces a number to represent the next "infected" person.

6. The new "infected" person moves to the designated table and starts using the random generator, and so on. All "infected" people should use the random generator at the same time, and each time the random generator is used counts as one day.

7. Count the number of people at the "infected" table each time before the random generator is used to find the next "infected" person(s). Record the data in the data table.

8. If the random generator produced a number that is assigned to an already "infected" person, then no one is added to the group of "infected" people.

9. Continue this procedure until all students are "infected" (or when the teacher asks you to stop the experiment).

10. Repeat this procedure at least four more times to build the statistical sample. Record your data for each trial in the data table.

DATA

A (total number of students in the class) = _____

		Days									
		0	1	2	3	4	5	6	7	8	9
	Trial #1										
	Trial #2										
	Trial #3										
Number of "infected" people	Trial #4										
	Trial #5										
	Average number of "infected" people										

DATA ANALYSIS

Part 1: The Logistic Function and Its Properties

1. Calculate the average number of "infected" students per day, and record it in the data table.

2. Enter days in List 1 and the average number of "infected" students in List 2.

3. Use StatPlot to plot the average number of "infected" people as a function of time (days).

4. Describe this function qualitatively. Analyze its behavior at infinity.

5. This function is close to the logistic function, which describes processes of restricted growth. Use the logistic regression option for your data. Record the logistic function that describes your data. Analyze the residuals.

6. Use StatPlot to plot your data along with the regression function, and use TI-Graph Link to print the graph of your data and regression equation for inclusion with the lab report.

7. Using the spread-of-disease simulation and the logistic model, explain the meaning of the coefficients A and B in the logistic function $N(t) = \dfrac{A}{1 + Be^{-kAt}}$.

Part 2: Rate of Change of the Logistic Function and the Logistic Differential Equation

1. Calculate the growth rate (rate of change) of the function that you found experimentally for the average number of "infected" students. Find $\dfrac{dN}{dT} \approx \dfrac{\Delta N}{\Delta t}$ for each interval, and fill in the table below. Use half-day points for the time variable.

Days	0.5	1.5	2.5	3.5	4.5	5.5	6.5	7.5	8.5
Growth rate									

Enter these data in List 3 and List 4.

2. Use StatPlot to plot the rate of change as a function of time, and use TI-Graph Link to print the graph of the numeric derivative for inclusion with the lab report.

3. Explain the properties of the rate of change of the function based on the spread-of-disease simulation.

4. The rate of change of the number of "infected" people is directly proportional to the number of "infected" and number of "not-infected" people at each instant. Find the product of $N(t)$ and $A - N(t)$, and enter these data in List 5. Delete the last data point from List 5 to adjust the dimensions of List 4 and List 5.

5. Use StatPlot to plot $\frac{dN}{dt}$ (List 4) as a function of $N(A - N)$ (List 5). What is the mathematical relationship between these quantities? Use the appropriate regression option, and determine the regression equation. Analyze the residuals.

6. Use TI-Graph Link to print the graph and regression equation for inclusion with the lab report.

7. Based on your findings in step 5, derive a differential equation for the function $N(t)$. Solve this differential equation with the initial condition $N(0) = 1$. Show all the steps of your solution.

8. Plot the function $N(t)$ you found as the solution of the differential equation along with the experimental data. Use TI-Graph Link to print the graph for inclusion with the lab report.

The Logistic Model

Simulating the Spread of Disease

BEFORE THE EXPERIMENT

1. Familiarize yourself with the use of the random integer generator on the calculator so that you can assist students in using this program.

2. Before class starts, draw a table on the board to keep track of the number of "infected" students as a function of the number of days.

TEACHING OBJECTIVES

Students will be able to

- simulate the spread of disease in a closed environment using the rules provided and represent it with experimental data on the number of infected people as a function of time

- use logistic regression on the experimental data

- analyze a logistic function in terms of behavior, concavity, and asymptotes

- interpret the real meaning of the coefficients in terms of the size of the population and initial conditions

- analyze the rate of change of the function graphically

- calculate the rate of change of the function defined by a table

- derive a differential equation for the logistic model based on given information and experimental data

- recognize and solve the differential equation for the logistic model using the method of separation of variables and integration by partial fractions

ACTIVITY NOTES

This activity is a simulation game. It allows students to evaluate the restricted growth process and understand the shape of the logistic function based on the experimental data. With a large enough group of students, the function is very close to the actual logistic function. The number of possible infected people is restricted, so students will get a very good conceptual understanding of the boundaries of the function and its horizontal asymptotes. Because the assumption is made that no one is treated for the infection, the monotonically increasing behavior of the function will be well understood. Students can analyze the rate of change of the function as a function of time, which allows them to analyze the concavity of the function.

Students can derive a differential equation for the logistic model from the data and get a conceptual understanding of the process of disease spread. They can use the experimental procedure and data to interpret the meaning of the differential equation. Then they can solve the differential equation and compare their solution to the experimental data.

Experimental Procedure Notes

In this activity, the random generator program on the calculator is used to select the person to whom the infection is passed. You can help students set up the random integer generator to exclude their own numbers using this method:

1. Enter numbers from 1 to A in a list, for example, List 1.

2. Delete a particular number from List 1.

3. Set $L_1(\text{randInt}(1, A - 1))$.

Keep all "infected" students together at the same table for easy counting of the number of infected people as a function of time. It is useful to assign a student at this table to facilitate the simultaneous counts of days.

The process of an infection's spread is statistical, so a small sample size may not provide enough data in one trial. This is the reason for repeating the experiment several times and using the average number of "infected" students per day for data analysis. Discuss with students the importance of having a large sample group in order to verify the math model in the experiment.

Data Analysis Notes

1. Students should plot the average number of "infected" students as a function of time and use logistic regression to compare the experimental data with the restricted growth function. They should use residuals to evaluate the best-fitting curve they calculated.

2. Students should be able to describe the function as approaching a horizontal asymptote equal to the number of students and compare the asymptote of the logistic regression equation with the actual number of students in the class.

3. Students should consider the function at infinity and at zero to determine the meaning of the coefficients A and B in the equation for the logistic curve.

4. Students should analyze and explain changes in the growth rate of the number of "infected" students. Students can analyze the number of people added to the group of "infected" people over time and notice the behavior

of this function (this is equivalent to calculating $\frac{\Delta N}{\Delta t}$). I suggest half-day values for time values in this case.

5. Most data sets obtained for a class size of 15–20 students will display the properties of the logistic function and will provide the qualitative features of the logistic model. However, numeric analysis of the growth rate function may not provide enough data for some experimental data sets. This is another reason to repeat the experiment several times and to use the average values of the number of "infected" students in calculations of the growth rate.

6. Because the derivative of the function $\frac{dN}{dt}$ is proportional to the product $N(A - N)$, students are asked to find linear regression between these two data sets. Because the derivative is calculated at the midpoint of each interval, this list has one data point less than the list containing the product $N(A - N)$. So students should delete the last data point from the list containing $N(A - N)$ before they run the linear regression.

7. Students derive the differential equation based on the linear regression. Theoretically, the linear regression equation should have the form $y = kx$, and the value of the slope k is needed to set up the differential equation $\frac{dN}{dt} = kN(A - N)$. Because of experimental error, students may get an equation of the form $y = kx + b$. In that case, they should use the value of the slope and disregard the value of the y-intercept.

8. For quantitative comparison between experimental data and the solution of the differential equation, students can find the percentage error between the coefficients A, B, and k in the logistic regression equation and in the solution of the differential equation.

Sample Data

The simulation was performed in a class of 20 students. A single student was selected to be "infected," so initially there was one "infected" person. This student used the random integer generator to choose the next "infected" person.

		Days										
		0	**1**	**2**	**3**	**4**	**5**	**6**	**7**	**8**	**9**
Number of "infected" people	Trial #1	1	2	4	8	13	17	19	20	20	20
	Trial #2	1	2	4	6	10	14	16	19	20	20
	Trial #3	1	2	4	7	10	15	19	20	20	20
	Trial #4	1	2	4	7	12	17	18	20	20	20
	Trial #5	1	2	4	7	12	16	19	20	20	20
	Average number of "infected" people	1	2	4	7	11.4	15.8	18.2	19.8	20	20

Sample Graphs

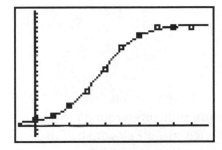

Experimental data along with the logistic regression curve

The residuals show no pattern, which supports the logistic curve regression.

Using logistic regression on the data yields

$$N(t) = \frac{20.5}{1 + 25.3e^{-0.87t}}$$

The horizontal asymptote of this function is $N = 20.5$. The percentage error between this number and population size is $\frac{(20.5 - 20)}{20} \cdot 100\% = 2.5\%$. Initially at $t = 0$, $N_0 = \frac{20.5}{25.3} = 0.81$. The percentage error between this value and the actual value of 1 is $(1 - 0.81) \cdot 100\% = 19\%$. The fit seems to be very good.

At the beginning, the function $N(t)$ is increasing exponentially because more people become infected and can infect others. When the number of the "infected" people is about half the population, the growth rate is the largest. After that, the function does not grow as fast because there are fewer people who can be "infected." The function reaches its upper boundary at the number of students in the class.

Theoretically, the whole population becomes "infected" after a very long time, so $\lim\limits_{t \to \infty} N(t) = \lim\limits_{t \to \infty} \dfrac{A}{1 + Be^{-kAt}} = A$. Then the coefficient A represents the size of the population. Initially, we have $N(0) = N_0 = \dfrac{A}{1 + B}$. Solving for B, we get $B = \dfrac{A - N_0}{N_0}$. This represents the fraction of uninfected people to infected people initially.

Analyze the growth rate of the function $N(t)$:

Days	0.5	1.5	2.5	3.5	4.5	5.5	6.5	7.5	8.5
Growth rate	1	2	3	4.4	4.4	2.4	1.6	0.2	0

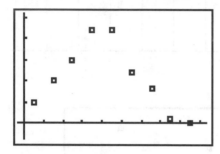

The StatPlot of the growth rate as a function of time

As expected, the growth rate reaches its maximum sometime around $t = 4$ days, which corresponds to 11.3, the number of "infected" people close to half the population, or 10. The growth rate of the function is increasing at first. When the number of "infected" people reaches half the population, the growth rate achieves its maximum value and starts decreasing. When all the people have been "infected," the growth rate decreases to zero.

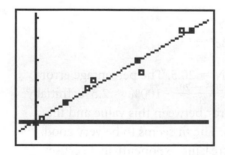

The StatPlot of the growth rate as a function of $N(A - N)$ with the linear regression curve

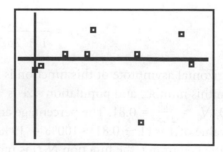

The residuals for the linear regression show no pattern.

$y = 0.044x + 0.086$
  $r^2 = 0.97$

Neglecting the y-intercept, we get the differential equation $\frac{dN}{dt} = 0.044N(20 - N)$ with the initial condition $N_0 = 1$. Here $k = 0.044$, and $A = 20$.

Solution of the differential equation:

$$\frac{dN}{N(A - N)} = k\,dt$$

$$\int_{N_0}^{N} \frac{dN}{N(A - N)} = \int_{0}^{t} k\,dt$$

$$\frac{1}{A}\int_{N_0}^{N}\left(\frac{1}{N} + \frac{1}{A - N}\right) dN = kt$$

$$(\ln N - \ln (A - N))\Big|_{N_0}^{N} = k\,At$$

$$\ln \frac{N}{A - N} - \ln \frac{N_0}{A - N_0} = k\,At$$

$$\ln \frac{N}{A - N} \cdot \frac{A - N_0}{N_0} = k\,At$$

$$\frac{N}{A - N} = \frac{N_0}{A - N_0}\,e^{kAt}$$

$$N\left(1 + \frac{N_0}{A - N_0}e^{kAt}\right) = A\frac{N_0}{A - N_0}e^{kAt}$$

$$N = \frac{A}{1 + \dfrac{A - N_0}{N_0}e^{-kAt}}$$

Substituting all the given information—$A = 20$, $N_0 = 1$, $k = 0.044$—into the equation, we get

$$N = \frac{20}{1 + 19e^{-0.88t}}$$

The following graph shows a plot of this function along with the experimental data:

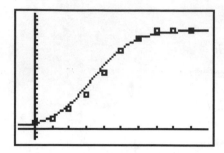

TABLE 1 *Comparison of the Logistic Regression Curve and the Solution of the Differential Equation*

Logistic regression curve	Solution of the differential equation	Percentage error
$N(t) = \dfrac{20.5}{1 + 25.3e^{-0.87t}}$	$N = \dfrac{20}{1 + 19e^{-0.88t}}$	
$A = 20.5$	$A = 20$	$\dfrac{(20.5 - 20)}{20} \cdot 100\% = 2.5\%$
$B = 25.3$	$B = 19$	$\dfrac{(25.3 - 19)}{19} \cdot 100\% = 33\%$
$k = \dfrac{0.87}{20.5} = 0.0424$	$k = 0.044$	$\dfrac{(0.044 - 0.0424)}{0.044} \cdot 100\% = 3.6\%$

With more trials or a larger sample group, the experimental coefficient B could also be brought much closer to the theoretical.

FURTHER EXPLORATIONS

1. What if two students were initially "infected"? Would the differential equation remain the same? How does the initial condition affect the solution of the differential equation?

2. Based on your analysis of the logistic model, describe how to find the function that satisfies the given differential equation with the given initial condition without actually integrating the differential equation.